Signature Series
Comic Bags

Revolutionary comic sleeve designed for obtaining autographs

The choice of the top comic professionals

WIZARD WORLD SUPPLIES
Ultra•PRO®

- Minimizes handling while in process of having comic books signed

- Tinted material to easily identify the signature area

- Fully wraps around and protects the comic book to keep it in ideal condition for grading

- Made from archival quality polypropylene film

1 BOOK PLACED INTO POCKET

2 TURN REMAINING TWO (2) PANELS AS SHOWN

3 READY FOR SIGNATURE

4 PULL PAPER BACKING FROM ADHESIVE STRIP

5 FOLD REMAINING PANEL AS SHOWN

6 PRESS PANEL ONTO ADHESIVE STRIP IN MULTPLE PLACES

ONCE SEALED, THE COMIC IS READY TO SUBMIT FOR GRADING

Ultra•PRO®

Stay connected with us:

 ultrapro.com @UltraProIntl facebook.com/UltraProInternational

For a list of stores carrying Ultra PRO supplies, visit www.findultrapro.com

BECKETT
STAR WARS
COLLECTIBLES PRICE GUIDE

THE HOBBY'S MOST RELIABLE AND RELIED UPON SOURCE™

FOUNDER & ADVISOR: DR. JAMES BECKETT III

EDITED BY MATT BIBLE WITH THE BECKETT PRICE GUIDE STAFF
KYLE DOBBINS - SPECIAL CONTRIBUTOR

BECKETT is a registered trademark of BECKETT MEDIA LLC, DALLAS, TEXAS
Manufactured in the United States of America | Published by Beckett Media LLC

Beckett Media LLC
4635 McEwen Dr., Dallas, TX 75244
(972) 991-6657 • beckett.com

First Printing
ISBN: 978-1-936681-21-1

TOP 10

STAR WARS FUNKO POP VINYL

BY MATT BIBLE

1

#23 DARTH MAUL (HOLOGRAPHIC)/480
(2012 SDCC EXCLUSIVE)

2

#6B CHEWBACCA (FLOCKED)/480
(2011 SDCC EXCLUSIVE)

3

#24 BIGGS DARKLIGHTER/480
(2012 SDCC EXCLUSIVE)

4

#14 SHADOW TROOPER/480
(2011 SDCC EXCLUSIVE)

5

#25 501ST CLONE TROOPER/480
(2012 SDCC EXCLUSIVE)

6

#32 BOBA FETT DROIDS/480
(2013 SDCC EXCLUSIVE)

7

#16 LUKE SKYWALKER STORM-
TROOPER/1000 (2011 ECCC EXCLUSIVE)

8

#15 HAN SOLO STORMTROOPER/1000
(2011 ECCC EXCLUSIVE)

9

#54A PRINCESS LEIA (BOUSSH
UNMASKED)/1008 (2015 SDCC EXCLUSIVE)

10

#33B DARTH VADER
(HOLOGRAPHIC GLOW-IN-THE-DARK)
(2014 PARIS EXPO EXCLUSIVE)

TOP 20

STAR WARS TRADING CARD SETS

BY MATT BIBLE

CHARACTERS '77

LUKE SKYWALKER

[2] 2007 STAR WARS 30TH ANNIVERSARY

WHY THE FORCE IS STRONG:

• Comprehensive in all regards (it even includes cards of the infamous Holiday Special)
• First Harrison Ford autograph
• Huge autograph checklist that includes much of the main cast.
• Signers also include unsung heroes from behind the camera and legendary composer John Williams.
• Stamped buyback box toppers still very popular, particularly the latter series.
• Lots of high quality sketch cards.

• Still popular with a lot of fans who might not otherwise collect trading cards.
• Later series have some interesting behind-the-scenes shots.
• Oh, and that C-3PO card!

STAR WARS
MASTERWORK

QUI-GON JINN

[4] 2015 STAR WARS MASTERWORK

WHY THE FORCE IS STRONG:

• First high-end Star Wars set.
• Large on-card autograph checklist.
• Plenty of other premium inserts including relics.
• Challenging base set.

[1] 2017 STAR WARS STELLAR SIGNATURES

WHY THE FORCE IS STRONG:

• The most premium Star Wars set ever made.
• Only 100 boxes produced.
• Base set limited to 40 copies.
• Contains the most comprehensive mixture of old and new Star Wars performers.
• With the exception of Carrie Fisher and Kenny Baker, all autographs are on-card.
• Ben Mendehlson's first autograph was available via redemption of the Mark Hamill autograph.

STAR WARS™ 121

Han Solo and Chewbacca

[3] 1977 STAR WARS

WHY THE FORCE IS STRONG:

• The set that started it all
• Most recognizable Star Wars set of all-time.

STAR WARS GALAXY

[5] 1993-95 SW GALAXY

WHY THE FORCE IS STRONG:

• Brought Star Wars cards back after a ten-year hiatus.
• Art-based approach laid groundwork for new styles of sets.
• Gorgeous design and artwork.

[6] 2001 STAR WARS EVOLUTION

WHY THE FORCE IS STRONG:

• First set of Star Wars trading cards to include actor autographs
• Strong autograph checklist
• Thematically spawned a sequel in 2006 and another in 2016.

from the Original Trilogy.
• Old-school look and feel.
• First autographs of Mark Hamill and James Earl Jones.
• Retail-only Letter Stickers are tough to find and still popular with set builders.

Contains autographs of new stars Daisy Ridley and Adam Driver (his first in any product).
• Also contains autographs of old-school stars Harrison Ford and Carrie Fisher.
• Eclectic relic cards that feature stamps and medallions.

[7] 1995 STAR WARS WIDEVISION

WHY THE FORCE IS STRONG:

• Introduced oversized Widevision line.
• Presents images as they're showcased on the big screen.
• Backs contain plenty of information and production artwork.
• Extensive promo card checklist.

[8] 2004 STAR WARS HERITAGE

WHY THE FORCE IS STRONG:

• First set to have sketch cards

[9] 1980 STAR WARS EMPIRE STRIKES BACK

WHY THE FORCE IS STRONG:

• Original Trilogy set.
• Three series are not as many as first film but still comprehensive as a whole with larger checklists.
• Ralph McQuarrie artwork included on some cards.

[10] 2016 STAR WARS MASTERWORK

WHY THE FORCE IS STRONG:

• The high-end follow-up effort to the 2015 set.
• Features 80 total autograph signers!

[11] 1996 STAR WARS 3-DI WIDEVISION

WHY THE FORCE IS STRONG:

• One of the smallest print runs of any 1990's Star Wars set.
• First Star Wars cards to use 3-D technology.

[12] 2015 STAR WARS HIGH TEK

WHY THE FORCE IS STRONG:

• Acetate designs and pattern variations make it easy to collect the set several ways.
• All autographs are on-card.

- Deep checklist of signers from seven films plus TV shows.
- First set with a John Boyega auto.

features Harrison Ford, Mark Hamill, Carrie Fisher, Anthony Daniels, Kenny Baker, and Peter Mayhew
- Contains medallion relics and autographed medallion relics, including Millennium Falcon medallion relic signed by Harrison Ford!

outside of inserts.
- Refractors make their franchise debut.
- Takes an all-art approach but each artist did a nine-card group based on a similar theme.

[13] 2013 STAR WARS JEDI LEGACY

WHY THE FORCE IS STRONG:

- First pack-inserted Star Wars memorabilia cards.
- Franchise's first film cell cards.
- Strong autograph checklist.
- Different spin on the stories of Luke Skywalker and Darth Vader.

[14] 2017 STAR WARS 40TH ANNIVERSARY

WHY THE FORCE IS STRONG:

- Commemorates 40 Years of Saga.
- A very full 200-card base set.
- Retro design to pay homage to original.
- 62 different autographs including the elusive Six-Person booklet auto that

[15] 2002 STAR WARS ATTACK OF THE CLONES WIDEVISION

WHY THE FORCE IS STRONG:

- Like other Widevision sets, base cards look excellent.
- Large autograph checklist which includes the only autos of Frank Oz (Yoda) and Ahmed Best (the character everyone loves to hate, Jar Jar Binks).

[16] 1996 STAR WARS FINEST

WHY THE FORCE IS STRONG:

- First full chromium Star Wars set

[17] 2014 STAR WARS RETURN OF THE JEDI 3-D WIDEVISION

WHY THE FORCE IS STRONG:

- Limited print run sold out quickly as an online exclusive.
- Autos randomly inserted as bonus.
- Technology makes for a stunning base set.
- Some of the greatest packaging ever for a trading card product, Star Wars or not.

Millenium Falcon

[18] 2004 STAR WARS CLONE WARS

WHY THE FORCE IS STRONG:
- First Star Wars sketch cards.
- Cool artwork from Genndy Tartakovsky short cartoon anthology.

[19] 1977 STAR WARS WONDER BREAD

WHY THE FORCE IS STRONG:
- Fresh, memorable design.
- Nice alternative and compliment to the original 1977 Topps set.

[20] 1996 STAR WARS SHADOWS OF THE EMPIRE

WHY THE FORCE IS STRONG:
- Most use character images from original 1993 Star Wars Galaxy.
- Popular with set builders.

TOP 20

STAR WARS AUTOGRAPHS

BY MATT BIBLE

1

2016 STAR WARS MASTERWORK
AUTOGRAPHS DAISY RIDLEY

2

2007 STAR WARS 30TH ANNIVERSARY
AUTOGRAPHS HARRISON FORD

3

2004 STAR WARS HERITAGE
AUTOGRAPHS MARK HAMILL

8

2016 STAR WARS ROGUE ONE SERIES ONE
AUTOGRAPHS FELICITY JONES

9

2001 STAR WARS EVOLUTION
AUTOGRAPHS BILLY DEE WILLIAMS

10

2016 STAR WARS MASTERWORK
AUTOGRAPHS ADAM DRIVER

15

2007 STAR WARS 30TH ANNIVERSARY
AUTOGRAPHS JOHN WILLIAMS

16

2010 STAR WARS EMPIRE STRIKES BACK 3-D
WIDEVISION AUTOGRAPHS IRVIN KERSHNER

17

2001 STAR WARS EVOLUTION
AUTOGRAPHS PETER MAYHEW

4

2001 STAR WARS EVOLUTION
AUTOGRAPHS CARRIE FISHER

5

2004 STAR WARS HERITAGE
AUTOGRAPHS JAMES EARL JONES

6

2002 STAR WARS ATTACK OF THE CLONES
WIDEVISION AUTOGRAPHS FRANK OZ

7

2001 STAR WARS EVOLUTION
AUTOGRAPHS IAN MCDIARMID

11

2006 STAR WARS EVOLUTION UPDATE
AUTOGRAPHS HAYDEN CHRISTENSEN

12

2005 STAR WARS REVENGE OF THE SITH
WIDEVISION AUTOGRAPHS SAMUEL L. JACKSON

13

2001 STAR WARS EVOLUTION
AUTOGRAPHS ANTHONY DANIELS

14

2001 STAR WARS EVOLUTION
AUTOGRAPHS KENNY BAKER

18

2010 STAR WARS EMPIRE STRIKES BACK 3-D
WIDEVISION AUTOGRAPHS RALPH MCQUARRIE

19

2015 STAR WARS HIGH TEK
AUTOGRAPHS JOHN BOYEGA

20

2001 STAR WARS EVOLUTION
AUTOGRAPHS JEREMY BULLOCH

TOP 10

VINTAGE STAR WARS ACTION FIGURES

BY KYLE DOBBINS

1

1977-78 STAR WARS BOBA FETT (ROCKET FIRING PROTOTYPE)

2

1977-78 12-BACKS A JAWA (VINYL CAPE)

3

1980-82 STAR WARS EMPIRE STRIKES BACK FX-7 (MEDICAL DROID) PALITOY

4

1983 STAR WARS RETURN OF THE JEDI LUKE SKYWALKER (JEDI KNIGHT OUTFIT) LILY LEDY

5

1985 STAR WARS POWER OF THE FORCE YAK FACE

6

1977-78 STAR WARS 12-BACKS A DARTH VADER (DOUBLE TELESCOPING LIGHTSABER)

7

1977-78 STAR WARS 12-BACKS A BEN (OBI-WAN) KENOBI (DOUBLE TELESCOPING LIGHTSABER)

8

1985 STAR WARS DROIDS VLIX GLASSLITE

9

1977-78 STAR WARS 21-BACKS B BOBA FETT

10

1977-78 STAR WARS 12-BACKS A LUKE SKYWALKER (DOUBLE TELESCOPING LIGHTSABER)

TOP 10

VINTAGE STAR WARS VEHICLES & PLAYSETS

BY KYLE DOBBINS

1

1977-78 STAR WARS VEHICLES MILLENNIUM FALCON

2

1978 STAR WARS PLAYSETS CANTINA ADVENTURE SET (SEARS)

3

1978 STAR WARS PLAYSETS DEATH STAR SPACE STATION (KENNER)

4

1978 STAR WARS VEHICLES X-WING FIGHTER

5

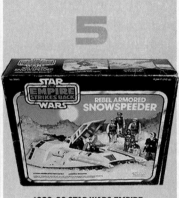

1980-82 STAR WARS EMPIRE STRIKES BACK SNOWSPEEDER

6

1983 STAR WARS RETURN OF THE JEDI VEHICLES TIE INTERCEPTOR

7

1983 STAR WARS RETURN OF THE JEDI VEHICLES IMPERIAL SHUTTLE

8

1980-82 STAR WARS EMPIRE STRIKES BACK AT-AT

9

1978 STAR WARS VEHICLES LAND SPEEDER

10

1983 STAR WARS RETURN OF THE JEDI VEHICLES Y-WING FIGHTER

FROM THE BEG

INNING

A look
at the
Star Wars
Galaxy

EPISODE I
THE PHANTOM MENACE

RELEASED: MAY 1999
BOX OFFICE: $1.027 BILLION

The first of the prequel trilogy launched 22 years after *A New Hope*. The Trade Federation has blocked off routes to the planet Naboo, and Jedi Qui-Gon Jinn and a young Obi-Wan Kenobi are sent to negotiate. Queen Padmé Amidala is rescued, and her ship lands on Tatooine for repairs.

This is where the Jedi meet Anakin Skywalker as a young slave boy. Qui-Gon realizes his potential and similarities to an ancient prophesy of one who would bring balance to the Force.

The Sith—the mortal enemy of the Jedi—return from the shadows in the form of Darth Maul and Darth Sidious, who is pulling strings from both sides under the disguise of Naboo's Senator Palpatine.

It's evident that a war is coming, as tensions between the Republic and the Trade Federation rise. Qui-Gon trains Anakin to be a Jedi.

The Jedi are sent to Naboo to investigate the return of the Sith. Back on her home planet, Queen Amidala recruits the Gungans— underwater creatures on Naboo— to help fight the Trade Federation's invasion of the planet.

Qui-Gon and Obi-Wan battle Darth Maul in a mesmerizing lightsaber duel. Darth Maul kills Qui-Gon, but Obi-Wan cuts Maul in half, ending the Sith's resurgence.

Senator Palpatine rises to become the new Supreme Chancellor of the Senate, where he continues to manipulate the Republic and the coming Separatist movement. Obi-Wan convinces a reluctant Jedi Council to allow him to train Anakin as a Jedi.

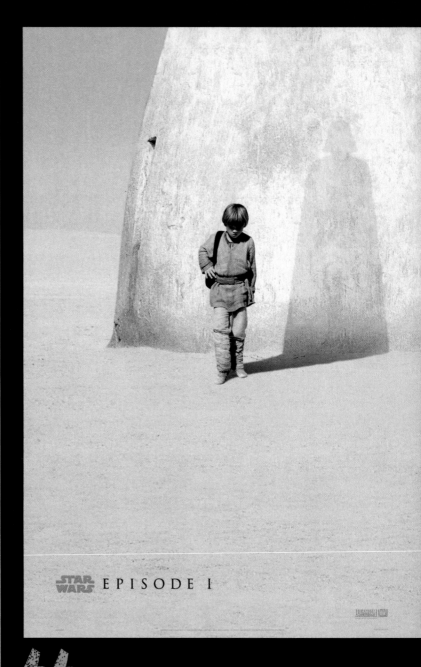

STAR WARS EPISODE I

> **AS SURELY AS ANAKIN SKYWALKER POINTS THE WAY INTO THE FUTURE OF *STAR WARS*, SO DOES *THE PHANTOM MENACE* RAISE THE CURTAIN ON THIS NEW FREEDOM FOR FILMMAKERS. AND IT'S A LOT OF FUN. GIVE ME TRANSPARENT UNDERWATER CITIES AND VAST HOLLOW SENATORIAL SPHERES ANY DAY."**
>
> **– ROGER EBERT**

EPISODE II
ATTACK OF THE CLONES

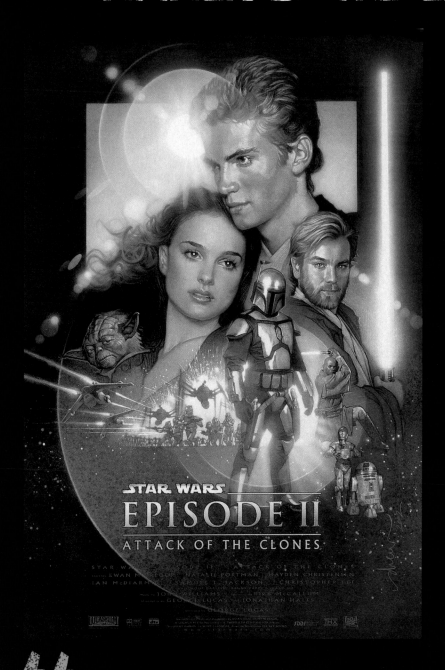

STAR WARS
EPISODE II
ATTACK OF THE CLONES

EWAN McGREGOR · NATALIE PORTMAN · HAYDEN CHRISTENSEN
IAN McDIARMID · SAMUEL L. JACKSON · CHRISTOPHER LEE
JOHN WILLIAMS · RICK McCALLUM
GEORGE LUCAS · JONATHAN HALES
GEORGE LUCAS

> **CLONES** ENDS WITH A WEDDING FOR THE FUTURE PARENTS OF LUKE AND PRINCESS LEIA. BUT IT'S THE GLIMPSE OF DARTH VADER THAT LUCAS GIVES US IN ANAKIN – TRAUMATIZED BY THE MURDER OF HIS MOTHER AND CAPABLE OF KILLING INNOCENTS – THAT REMINDS US OF THE DARK POWER **STAR WARS** EXERTED BEFORE IT BECAME A FRANCHISE."

– PETER TRAVERS, ROLLING STONE

RELEASED: MAY 2002
BOX OFFICE: $649.4 MILLION

Several years removed from the events of *The Phantom Menace*, Anakin has become a talented yet arrogant young Jedi. There is a growing Separatist movement led by former Jedi Master Count Dooku. Anakin and Obi-Wan are assigned to protect Padmé Amidala, as she plans to push for the creation of an army to help the Jedi deal with the Separatists. A bounty hunter tries to kill her, and Obi-Wan investigates the origin of the would-be assassin. This leads him to the planet Kamino where he discovers that a clone army is being produced for the Republic. The bounty hunter Jango Fett serves as the army's DNA origin. Obi-Wan follows him and his young son Boba to Geonosis, where Obi-Wan discovers that Count Dooku is amassing his own army of droids.

Meanwhile, Anakin, who has stayed behind to protect Padmé, has disturbing visions of his mom suffering back on his home planet of Tatooine. He and Padmé go to save her. He discovers that she was taken by Tusken Raiders, and while he finds her, he's unable to save her. He slaughters the Tuskens and vows that he will become the most powerful Jedi ever.

Obi-Wan tells Anakin of the droid army just before he is captured on Geonosis. Supreme Chancellor Palpatine is given emergency powers to send the clones to battle the droids. Anakin and Padmé go to rescue Obi-Wan, but all three are captured. Before they are executed, the trio is rescued by a band of Jedi and clone soldiers. Anakin and Obi-Wan attempt to stop Dooku, but he overpowers them, cutting off Anakin's arm. Yoda comes to their rescue and battles Dooku, but he gets away and delivers blueprints of the Death Star to his master, Darth Sidious. This begins the Clone Wars.

EPISODE III
REVENGE OF THE SITH

RELEASED: MAY 2005
BOX OFFICE: $848.8 MILLION

Revenge of the Sith takes place about three years into the Clone Wars, which have created division across the galaxy. Anakin and Obi-Wan rescue Supreme Chancellor Palpatine, who has been kidnapped by General Grievous, the leader of the droid army. The two Jedi battle Count Dooku again, and Palpatine convinces Anakin to go against the Jedi way and execute Dooku. Anakin returns to Padmé, who is now his wife. She tells him she's pregnant. Anakin begins having visions of Padmé dying in childbirth, much like the visions he had of his mother.

Palpatine, who continues to manipulate Anakin, tells him the story of Darth Sideous, a Sith Lord who learned the power to save people from death. This is a major turning point in Anakin's descent to the Dark Side, as he thinks he can learn the power to save Padmé. He discovers that Palpatine is actually a Sith Lord, which he reports to Jedi Master Mace Windu. Windu confronts Palpatine and nearly kills him, but Anakin saves him in fear of losing the ability to save Padmé.

Anakin vows to serve Palpatine, who dubs him "Darth Vader." Palpatine orders the clone soldiers to murder the Jedi during battle. Anakin leads a group of droids to massacre the rest of the Jedi at the Jedi Temple, as well as the Separatist leaders on the planet Mustafar. It's here where Obi-Wan and Anakin battle after Anakin chokes Padmé unconscious for believing she betrayed him. The battle leaves Anakin dismembered and nearly burnt to death. Palpatine transforms the Republic into the Galatic Empire. He and Yoda fight to a stalemate before Palpatine rescues Anakin and has him placed into the black, menacing Darth Vader suit. They oversee the construction of the Death Star while Obi-Wan, Yoda and Bail Organa agree to hide newborn babies Luke and Leia from the Empire. Padmé dies just after they're born.

> **HAVING SPENT TWO SCATTERSHOT BLOCKBUSTERS WHETTING OUR APPETITE FOR THE FALL OF ANAKIN SKYWALKER, GEORGE LUCAS MAKES IT EASY TO EXPERIENCE *STAR WARS: EPISODE III – REVENGE OF THE SITH* AS A RUSH OF DELIVERANCE."**
>
> **– OWEN GLIEBERMAN, ENTERTAINMENT WEEKLY**

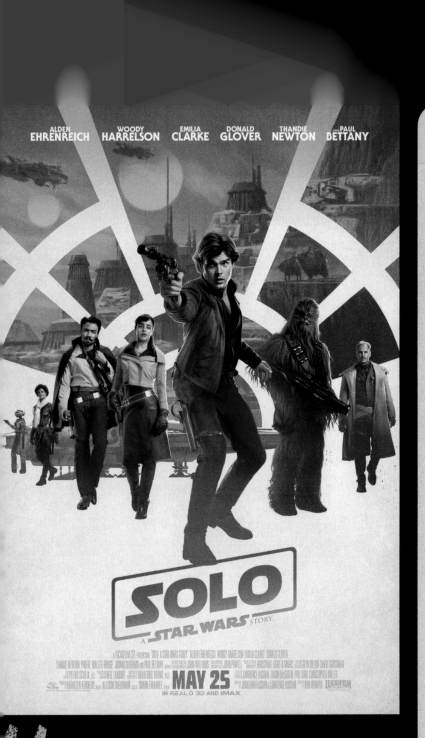

ALDEN **EHRENREICH** · WOODY **HARRELSON** · EMILIA **CLARKE** · DONALD **GLOVER** · THANDIE **NEWTON** · AND PAUL **BETTANY**

SOLO
A STAR WARS STORY

MAY 25
IN REAL D 3D AND IMAX

RELEASED: MAY 2018
BOX OFFICE: $392.9 MILLION

Another spinoff film in the expanded Star Wars storyline, Solo tells a back story of everyone's favorite "scruffy-looking nerf herder." A confident young Han and his lover, Qi'ra, bribe their way onto a transport out of Corellia. Qi'ra is captured by Imperial troopers as they are going through the gate. Han promises to find her and then joins the Imperial Navy.

Three years pass. Han meets Tobias Beckett and his small band of criminals posing as Imperial troopers during a battle. Han is arrested and thrown into a prison with "the beast," who turns out to be Chewbacca. Able to understand the wookie, Han and Chewbacca work together to escape. They convince Beckett to let them join their plan to steal a huge load of coaxium, a powerful hyperspace fuel, from Vandor-1. The plan is faulted by Cloud Riders who also try to steal the coaxium, which explodes in the attempt.

The coaxium was for crime boss Dryden Vos, so Han and Chewbacca vow to help Beckett steal another shipment. The group goes to meet Vos where Han finds Qi'ra, who has become a top lieutenant for Vos. Han reveals his plan to steal unrefined coaxium, then the group seeks help from smuggler and pilot Lando Calrissian. They reach the coaxium mines on Kessel in the Millennium Falcon, Lando's ship. After stealing enough coaxium, Han navigates the ship through the dangerous Kessel Run to avoid an Imperial blockade. Enfys, the leader of the Cloud Riders, tracks the crew and reveals they are actually rebels trying to prevent the crime bosses and the Empire from increasing their power. The two groups join forces, but Beckett betrays them. Qi'ra kills Vos as Beckett takes the coaxium for himself. Qi'ra reveals the failure to Vos' superior, Darth Maul, and takes Vos' place.

Han catches up with Beckett and shoots him before he can do the same to him. Enfys and the rebels end up with the coaxium. Han wins the Millennium Falcon from Lando in a card game. He and Chewbacca head to Tatooine for a job with a "big-shot gangster."

> DIRECTOR RON HOWARD'S SLICK, FUNNY PREQUEL OFFERS A RESPECTABLE LEAD PERFORMANCE THAT CAPTURES HARRISON FORD'S SMIRKY, ROGUISH CHARISMA AND FILLS IN SEVERAL STAR WARS GAPS.

– SANDIE ANGULO CHEN, COMMON SENSE MEDIA, 2018

ROGUE ONE
A STAR WARS STORY

RELEASED: DECEMBER 2016
BOX OFFICE: $1.056 BILLION

A spinoff prequel story to *A New Hope*, *Rogue One* tells the story of the band of Rebels who steal the schematics of the original Death Star. Galen Erso is a scientist and engineer forced by the Empire to construct the Death Star. He's hiding with his family when Imperial weapons developer Orson Krennic finds him, wanting him to complete the Death Star. Galen's young daughter Jyn hides while her father is taken away. Family friend and Rebel leader Saw Gerrera keeps Jyn safe. Fifteen years pass. Pilot Bodhi Rook defects from the Empire and smuggles a message from Galen to Gerrera about a weakness Galen built into the Death Star.

Jyn is in an Imperial labor camp but she's freed by Rebel Cassian Andor and brought to a Rebel base. The Rebels want Jyn to find her father so they can learn more about the Death Star, however, Cassian is ordered to kill Galen. Jyn, Cassian droid K-2SO travel to Jedha and meet Chirrut Îmwe and Baze Malbus. They hook up with Gerrera, who shows Jyn the message from her father. The message instructs them to go to the planet Scarif to retrieve the Death Star schematics. Bodhi leads the group to Galen's research facility, and Cassian decides not to kill him. However, Rebel ships attach the facility, killing Galen. Krennic meets with Darth Vader and seeks his support, but Vader warns him to not allow any more breaches in security.

Jyn leads a secret mission to steal the Death Star plans on Scarif. Jyn, Cassian and K-2SO infiltrate the data tower and steal the plans during a final confrontation with Krennic. More Rebels join the fight when they learn of the mission. Bodhi, Chirrut and Baze are killed in battle, but not before completing their parts of the mission. The plans are transmitted to a Rebel ship before the Death Star destroys the base on Scarif, killing Krennic, Jyn and Cassian. Darth Vader intercepts the Rebel ship with the schematics and slaughters several Rebel soldiers. But the schematics are downloaded and quickly taken to Princess Leia on an escape ship. These events happen just before the beginning of *A New Hope*.

" THE INHERENT PROBLEM IN A STORY ABOUT THE SUICIDE MISSION TO STEAL THE DEATH STAR PLANS USED TO BLOW UP THE SPACE STATION AT THE END OF A NEW HOPE IS THAT WE ALREADY KNOW HOW IT ENDS. THERE'S NO SUSPENSE, NO MOMENTUS, NO STAKES."

— RENE RODRIGUEZ, MIAMI HERALD, 2016

EPISODE IV

A NEW HOPE

A long time ago in a galaxy far, far away...

© 1977 Twentieth Century-Fox

TWENTIETH CENTURY-FOX Presents
A LUCASFILM LTD. PRODUCTION
STAR WARS
Starring MARK HAMILL HARRISON FORD CARRIE FISHER
PETER CUSHING
and
ALEC GUINNESS
Written and Directed by GEORGE LUCAS Produced by GARY KURTZ Music by JOHN WILLIAMS
PANAVISION® PRINTS BY DE LUXE® TECHNICOLOR®
Original Motion Picture Soundtrack on 20th Century Records and Tapes

Making Films Sound Better

DOLBY SYSTEM
Noise Reduction · High Fidelity

STAR WARS

" STRIP *STAR WARS* OF ITS OFTEN STRIKING IMAGES AND ITS HIGH-FA-LUTIN' SCIENTIFIC JARGON, AND YOU GET A STORY, CHARACTERS, AND DIALOGUE OF OVERWHELMING BANALITY, WITHOUT EVEN A 'FUTURE' CAST TO THEM. CERTAINLY THE MENTALITY AND VALUES OF THE MOVIE CAN BE DUPLICATED IN THIRD-RATE NON-SCIENCE FICTION OF ANY PLACE OR PERIOD. OH DULL NEW WORLD!"

– JOHN SIMON, NEW YORK MAGAZINE, 1977

RELEASED: MAY 1977
BOX OFFICE: $775.4 MILLION

From the opening scene of a massive Star Destroyer passing overhead to the crazy characters in Mos Eslie Cantina, this is the film that launched a worldwide empire 40 years ago. Darth Vader captures Princess Leia, who hides the stolen plans to the Empire's Death Star in droid R2-D2. She records a message for former Jedi Obi-Wan Kenobi, who is hidden on the desert planet of Tatooine. A young Luke Skywalker buys R2-D2 and his android buddy C-3PO to work on his uncle's farm. He discovers the message, which triggers a series of events that sends Luke off on an adventure with Obi-Wan to fight the oppressive Galactic Empire and train to become a Jedi Knight.

The two meet up with the smuggler Han Solo and Chewbacca, who agree to take them to Leia's home planet of Alderaan. On the way, the entire planet is destroyed by the Death Star, demonstrating the power the Empire holds over the galaxy. After allowing themselves to be captured, Luke, Han and Chewie rescue Leia. Darth Vader battles Obi-Wan in the first lightsaber duel in the saga while the others escape. Obi-Wan sacrifices himself and becomes one with the Force, allowing him to continue to communicate with Luke.

Later, the Rebel Alliance devises a plan to destroy the Death Star using information from the stolen plans. Luke is part of the attack squadron, and maneuvers a narrow trench to reach the target. He uses the Force to focus when firing torpedoes through a small opening at the end of the trench. The Death Star explodes just as it is about to fire on the Rebel base.

EPISODE V
THE EMPIRE STRIKES BACK

RELEASED: MAY 1980
BOX OFFICE: $538.4 MILLION

The consensus fan favorite of the entire franchise, *The Empire Strikes Back* is also regarded by many as the best in the saga. After being forced from their base, the Rebels operate from the ice planet of Hoth. The Empire discovers their location and mounts an assault using massive AT-AT walkers. Most of the Rebels escape, and Luke goes to train with Jedi Master Yoda on Dagobah.

Han, Leia and Chewie find safety (or so they think) in the Cloud City, run by Han's former friend and fellow smuggler, Lando Calrissian. However, the band of heroes are betrayed and ambushed by Darth Vader.

His ultimate plan is to lure Luke and bring him to the Emperor. Vader freezes Han in carbonite as a test for trapping Luke. He hands Han over to the bounty hunter Boba Fett, who brings Han to the gangster Jabba the Hutt.

Vader's plan works. While training with Yoda, Luke senses his friends are in danger and goes to help, promising Yoda he will return.

Yoda knows he's not ready to face Vader, and urges Luke not to go. At the Cloud City, Luke escapes Vader's trap. After a lightsaber duel where Vader cuts Luke's hand off, Luke has nowhere to go when Vader reveals to Luke that he is his father.

It's one of the most shocking twists in Hollywood history. The family dynamic is a major factor in all the films from this point on. Lando regains control of the city, and the heroes escape in the Millennium Falcon. Luke falls into a chute to flee Vader, and his friends come back to save him.

THE STAR WARS SAGA CONTINUES

THE EMPIRE STRIKES BACK
STAR WARS

Starring
MARK HAMILL · HARRISON FORD · CARRIE FISHER
BILLY DEE WILLIAMS · ANTHONY DANIELS
as C-3PO

Co-starring DAVID PROWSE · KENNY BAKER · PETER MAYHEW · FRANK OZ
as Darth Vader as R2-D2 as Chewbacca as Yoda

Directed by IRVIN KERSHNER Produced by GARY KURTZ
Screenplay by LEIGH BRACKETT and LAWRENCE KASDAN Story by GEORGE LUCAS
Executive Producer GEORGE LUCAS Music by JOHN WILLIAMS

PG PARENTAL GUIDANCE SUGGESTED
SOME MATERIAL MAY NOT BE SUITABLE FOR CHILDREN
DOLBY STEREO
IN SELECTED THEATRES
Filmed in Panavision® · Color by Rank Film Laboratories · Prints by Deluxe®
ORIGINAL SOUNDTRACK ON RSO RECORDS

> **I'M NOT SURE I'M UP FOR SEVEN MORE *STAR WARS* ADVENTURES, BUT I CAN HARDLY WAIT FOR THE NEXT ONE."**
>
> **– PAULINE KAEL, THE NEW YORKER, 1980**

EPISODE VI
RETURN OF THE JEDI

STAR WARS
RETURN OF THE JEDI

Starring
MARK HAMILL · HARRISON FORD · CARRIE FISHER
BILLY DEE WILLIAMS · ANTHONY DANIELS as C-3PO
Co-starring DAVID PROWSE · KENNY BAKER · PETER MAYHEW · FRANK OZ
Directed by RICHARD MARQUAND Produced by HOWARD KAZANJIAN
Story by GEORGE LUCAS Screenplay by LAWRENCE KASDAN and GEORGE LUCAS
Executive Producer GEORGE LUCAS Music by JOHN WILLIAMS

> " THIRD INSTALLMENT IN THE *STAR WARS* SAGA IS A SHEER DELIGHT. SOME ROUTINE PERFORMANCES ARE COMPENSATED FOR BY INGENIOUS NEW CHARACTERS AND SPECIAL EFFECTS."

– LEONARD MALTIN, ENTERTAINMENT WEEKLY, 1983

RELEASED: MAY 1983
BOX OFFICE: $572.7 MILLION

After the defeat in *The Empire Strikes Back*, the heroes plan to rescue Han from Jabba the Hutt. Leia frees Han from the carbonite, but they are captured in the attempt. Jabba plans to execute the group. However, the heroes escape after a thrilling battle. Luke keeps his promise to Yoda, and returns to complete his training. The Jedi Master is dying, and tells Luke that when he is gone, Luke will be the last of the Jedi. Yoda confirms that Darth Vader is Luke's father, and tells Luke there is another Skywalker. Obi-Wan, talking with Luke through the Force, tells him how he hid Luke and his twin sister from Vader. Luke realizes that Leia is his sister.

Meanwhile, the Empire is constructing a new Death Star. The Rebels discover this and plan to destroy its shield generator before attacking the Death Star. Han, Luke, Leia and Chewie lead an attack on the shield generator located on the forest moon of Endor. However, Vader, sensing that Luke is with them, is prepared. The heroes get unexpected help from the Ewoks—the native creatures on the moon. Luke allows himself to be captured so that he can face Darth Vader and the Emperor, who try to turn Luke to the Dark Side.

Luke and Vader have their final battle. Luke defeats his father, cutting his hand off just as Vader had done to Luke. Luke realizes he's turning into his father, and refuses to join the Dark Side. He nearly dies at the hands of the Emperor, but Vader sacrifices himself to save his son, throwing the Emperor down a large shaft. This ultimately turns Vader back to the good side. The Death Star is destroyed and balance returns to the galaxy.

EPISODE VII
THE FORCE AWAKENS

RELEASED: DECEMBER 2015
BOX OFFICE: $2.066 BILLION

Continuing the *Star Wars* storyline for the first time in more than 30 years, *The Force Awakens* mixes old heroes and villains with a new generation. Luke Skywalker is in hiding. The oppressive First Order is rising to power and aims to eradicate The New Republic. They have built a mega-weapon called Starkiller Base capable of destroying an entire system of planets at once. Resistance fighter pilot Poe Dameron obtains a map reveling Luke's location and hides it in the droid BB-8. But Kylo Ren commands a band of stormtroopers that capture Poe. Poe escapes with the help of a defecting stormtrooper he names "Finn." They crash on the planet of Jakku.

Finn meets Rey, a scavenger girl who has found BB-8. The two steal the Millennium Falcon and flee after First Order pilots discover them. They are captured by Han Solo and Chewbacca, who want to take back their lost ship. The crew then sees the map in BB-8, and Han notices that it's incomplete. They find help from Maz Kanata, who assists them in getting BB-8 to the Resistance. While at Maz's cantina, Rey finds Luke's original lightsaber and has visions when she touches it.

Kylo Ren, who was once trained by Luke before turning to the Dark Side, captures Rey after he discovers she has seen the map leading to Luke. But he is unable to overpower her with the Force. Rey, who is just discovering her ability to use the Force, escapes and meets up with Han, Finn and Chewie. Han confronts Kylo Ren, who we learned is actually Han and Leia's son. Han tries to convince him to leave the Dark Side and return to his family, but Kylo Ren murders his father. Rey and Kylo Ren engage in a lightsaber duel after the heroes successfully disable Starkiller Base. Rey defeats and injures Kylo Ren. She then travels to find Luke after the map is pieced together. She hands Luke his lightsaber, indicating that he will begin training Rey as a Jedi.

A LUCASFILM LTD. PRODUCTION A BAD ROBOT PRODUCTION "STAR WARS: THE FORCE AWAKENS" HARRISON FORD MARK HAMILL CARRIE FISHER ADAM DRIVER DAISY RIDLEY JOHN BOYEGA OSCAR ISAAC LUPITA NYONG'O ANDY SERKIS DOMHNALL GLEESON ANTHONY DANIELS PETER MAYHEW AND MAX VON SYDOW MUSIC BY JOHN WILLIAMS VISUAL EFFECTS AND ANIMATION BY INDUSTRIAL LIGHT & MAGIC COSTUME DESIGNER MICHAEL KAPLAN EDITORS MARY JO MARKEY, A.C.E. MARYANN BRANDON, A.C.E. PRODUCTION DESIGNERS RICK CARTER AND DARREN GILFORD DIRECTOR OF PHOTOGRAPHY DAN MINDEL, A.S.C., B.S.C. EXECUTIVE PRODUCERS TOMMY HARPER JASON McGATLIN CO-PRODUCER MICHELLE REJWAN PRODUCED BY KATHLEEN KENNEDY, p.g.a. J.J. ABRAMS, p.g.a. BRYAN BURK, p.g.a. WRITTEN BY LAWRENCE KASDAN & J.J. ABRAMS AND MICHAEL ARNDT DIRECTED BY J.J. ABRAMS

DECEMBER 18
IN 3D, REAL D 3D AND IMAX 3D

> " INCOMING WRITER-DIRECTOR J.J. ABRAMS SEEMS TO HAVE HAD THE ORIGINAL THREE FILMS FIRMLY IN MIND WHEN HE EMBARKED ON THIS MONUMENTAL NEW UNDERTAKING, STRUCTURED AS A SERIES OF CLEVER IF SOMETIMES WOBBLY CALLBACKS TO A TRILOGY THAT CAPTIVATED A GLOBAL AUDIENCE AND HELPED CEMENT HOLLYWOOD'S BLOCKBUSTER PARADIGM.'

EPISODE VIII
THE LAST JEDI

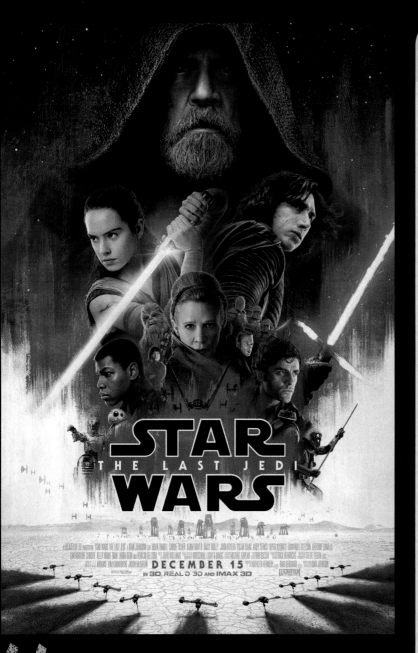

RELEASED: DECEMBER 2017
BOX OFFICE: $1.321 BILLION

The second installment in the Star Wars sequel trilogy brought mixed reviews from critics and fans. After the destruction of Starkiller Base in The Force Awakens, the evil First Order chases Resistance forces from D'Qar. Vice Admiral Holdo reveals a plan of retreat. Defying her order, Poe, Finn, BB-8 and a mechanic named Rose plan to disable the First Order's tracking device on the main ship.

Rey, having found Luke in self-exile on the Jedi temple Ahch-To, tries to convince the Jedi master to train her and join the Resistance. Rey tells Luke of Han Solo's death at the hands of Kylo Ren. Still blaming himself for Kylo's corruption to the Dark Side, Luke refuses to join Rey. Rey and Kylo begin to connect and communicate through the Force, not understanding how it's happening. Rey is determined to convert Kylo away from the First Order and Supreme Leader Snoke.

After acquiring a master hacker to help them deactivate the tracking system, Finn, Rose and BB-8 are captured onboard Snoke's ship. Rey also lands on the ship to confront Snoke and Kylo. Snoke orders Kylo to kill Rey, but he kills Snoke in a surprise twist. He asks Rey to join him so they can rule the galaxy together. Rey refuses, and the two engage in a dramatic lightsaber battle to a draw. Admiral Holdo rams her ship into the First Order feet at light speed, allowing the rest of the Resistance to escape.

Luke finally appears during the final battle as the remnant of Resistance fighters are corned by First Order ground troops. Kylo orders all fire power to concentrate on Luke, who emerges unharmed. Kylo strikes Luke, revealing Luke is a Force projection. Luke is actually still on Ahch-To. Rey helps the rest of the Resistance escape, while Luke dies at peace to become one with the Force.

> **IT'S AS IF RIAN JOHNSON'S ASSIGNMENT WAS TO EXTEND THE FRANCHISE WITHOUT CHANGING ANYTHING FUNDAMENTAL, WHICH IS CLOSER TO THE WAY CLASSIC TELEVISION AND VINTAGE JAMES BOND MOVIES OPERATE.**

– PETER DEBRUGE, VARIETY, 2017

20 GREATEST SCENES

Interesting ... Most Interesting

BY DAVID LEE

Ranking the top 20 greatest scenes in Star Wars film history feels a lot like facing Lord Vader himself. It can be an intimidating task, and there's no one right way to do it. Everyone is going to have different opinions, but that's what makes it fun.

We wanted to include scenes that are not only memorable, quotable and just plain cool, but also impactful and vital to the entire Star Wars saga. We included the eight feature films from the original trilogy, the three prequels, The Force Awakens and Rouge One. A scene is more than just a single moment or quote. It may be great because of the action, dialog, character or plot development, setting or all of the above. Now on to the list ...

YODA VS. COUNT DOOKU

STAR WARS: ATTACK OF THE CLONES

[20] YODA VS. COUNT DOOKU

(ATTACK OF THE CLONES)

Yoda fights! This scene in *Attack of the Clones* isn't his only battle, but it is his first. That alone makes it impactful, and it gave fans a look at Yoda they always wanted to see. It was an awesome surprise to those who hoped they would see the Jedi Master wield his lightsaber (a small green one, of course) in the prequels.

Count Dooku, the leader of the Separatist movement, has just defeated Anakin and Obi-Wan when Yoda comes limping in with the aid of his walking stick. After failing to drop some heavy stuff on Yoda, Dooku results to Force lightning, which Yoda easily handles. Dooku then issues the line, "It is obvious that this contest cannot be decided by our knowledge of the Force, but by our skills with a lightsaber."

OK, that's kind of cheesy, but the two masters engage in a fast-paced lightsaber battle revealing Yoda's unique fighting style. He spins, jumps and flips around in a flurry of movement. We also learn in this scene that Dooku was once Yoda's apprentice.

FAILURE IN THE CAVE

STAR WARS: THE EMPIRE STRIKES BACK

[19] THE FAILURE AT THE CAVE

(THE EMPIRE STRIKES BACK)

A critical failure yet major growing point in Luke's training with Yoda, this scene is as creepy as it is meaningful and deep. Luke senses something not far away. Yoda tells him it's a place strong with the Dark Side of the Force. He tells Luke that he must go, making it obvious that it's a test Luke must face alone. There is a calm and sadness to Yoda's demeanor, as if he knows Luke will fail.

Luke: "What's in there?"

Yoda: "Only what you take with you."

Yoda warns Luke that he will not need his weapons, but he takes them anyway. Luke is caught off guard by Darth Vader (or what appears to be), and cuts his head off after a quick light saber battle. The helmet explodes to reveal Luke's face. This is some deep, creative foreshadowing, hinting at Luke's possible destiny of turning to the Dark Side to take Vader's place. At this point, it hasn't been revealed that Vader is Luke's father, so the scene is bursting with meaning.

THE DESTRUCTION OF SCARIF

[18] THE BATTLE OF SCARIF

(ROUGE ONE)

It's the climax of the mission to steal the layouts of the Empire's Death Star. The plans are protected in a larger data tower on Scarif. It's a beautiful beach setting for a battle. We've seen snow, space, desert and forest battles up to this point.

The battle includes AT-ATs stomping on the beach, tactical diversions from the Rebels, infiltration, and an awesome space battle just outside the planet's atmosphere that includes two star destroyers crashing into each other. Who doesn't want to see that?

The battle turns into a suicide mission for the diverse and unlikely group of heroes. Jyn Erso, Cassian Andor, K-2SO, Chirrut Îmwe, Baze Malbus and Bodhi Rook all die, but not before they each complete their parts of the overall mission against seemingly insurmountable odds.

THE TRASH COMPACTOR

STAR WARS: A NEW HOPE

[17] THE TRASH COMPACTOR

(A NEW HOPE)

Luke, Han and Chewie rescue Princess Leia, but Stormtroopers have them trapped in a corridor. Leia grabs a blaster and shoots open a hole. The group dives in one at a time and ends up in a huge trash compactor with nasty knee-high water.

There's nowhere to go, and some freaky white snake thing takes Luke under the water, releasing him as soon as the compactor is activated. The group's going to be crushed to death, but Luke calls C-3PO and R2-D2 to stop the compactor just in time. This is the first time Luke, Han, Chewie and Leia are together, so we get to see how their personalities interact. The setting of the entire scene, with Luke and Han in Stormtrooper uniforms, is one of the most memorabilia in the entire franchise.

THE EXECUTION OF ORDER 66

[16] ORDER 66

(REVENGE OF THE SITH)

This is an underrated scene but a major turning point in the rise of the Empire. Chancellor Palatine has been playing both sides the whole time, pulling the strings on the side of the Separatists and the side of the Republic under the cloak of Darth Sidious. He flips the switch with Order 66.

The Republic has created an army of clone soldiers (which preclude the Stormtroopers) spread across the galaxy fighting several battles alongside the Jedi. But when Palatine issues "Order 66" the clones, which are engineered to be completely obedient, murder the Jedi during battle. This was the beginning of the Jedi purge and cleared the way for the fast rise of the Galactic Empire.

There's an awesome moment when Yoda senses two clone soldiers about to kill him. He leaps backward and slices their heads off with one move. Also during this takeover, Anakin (now officially Darth Vader) leads an assault on the Jedi temple, which includes murdering younglings.

[15] DARTH PLAGUEIS THE WISE

(REVENGE OF THE SITH)

Another underrated scene, this is the final point that draws Anakin to the Dark Side. He's haunted by vivid visions of Padmé suffering and dying—visions of the future. Anakin had similar visions of his

DARTH PLAGUEIS

SITH LORD

mother, whom he was not able to save.

Chancellor Palatine and Anakin are watching some kind of fancy space bubble ballet when Palatine continues to manipulate Anakin with increasing distrust in the Jedi Council. He asks Anakin if he has heard of the tragedy of Darth Plagueis the Wise, a powerful Sith Lord. Palpatine says that he discovered the power to create life and keep people from dying. "The Dark Side of the Force is a pathway to many abilities some consider to be unnatural," Palpatine says. Of course, Anakin is obsessed with power, so this is Palpatine's final move to pull him to the Dark Side.

After telling Anakin how Darth Plagueis was killed in his sleep by his apprentice, Anakin asks, "Is it possible to learn this power?" Palpatine responds, "Not from a Jedi."

Those last lines are terrific. You just know that Anakin can't resist crossing over to the Dark Side now. He wasn't able to save his mother, but now he thinks he can learn the power to save Padmé.

The end of Alderaan

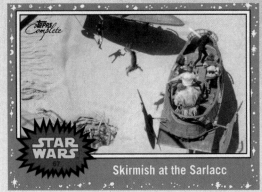

Skirmish at the Sarlacc

[14] THE DESTRUCTION OF ALDERAAN

(A NEW HOPE)

This seems to be one of the more forgotten moments for a lot of Star Wars fans, but that doesn't minimize this scene's impact on the overall story. It's the first time we see the power the Empire has over the galaxy. Grand Moff Tarkin orders the biggest test for the Empire's aptly-named Death Star—destroying Princess Leia's home planet of Alderaan. Leia was just captured by Darth Vader, who is searching for Death Star plans stolen by the Rebel Alliance. She issues a great line when brought to Tarkin that reveals her personality and confidence.

"Governor Tarkin, I should have expected to find you holding Vader's leash. I recognized your foul stench when I was brought on board," she says. (Oddly, this is the only scene where Leia is forcing a British accent.)

Leia is forced to watch her planet be destroyed by one blast of the Death Star. Meanwhile, Obi-Wan and Luke are on the Millennium Falcon headed to Alderaan when Obi-Wan feels the planet's destruction. "I felt a great disturbance in the Force, as if millions of voices suddenly cried out in terror, and were suddenly silenced. I feel something terrible has happened." This illustrates the great imbalance the Empire is creating in the Force.

[13] ESCAPING JABBA'S EXECUTION

(RETURN OF THE JEDI)

This scene involves a lot of characters and action. It's also a major turning point for the Rebel leaders after the defeat in *The Empire Strikes Back*. Luke, Leia, Chewbacca and Lando plan to rescue Han, who has become Jabba's favorite ornament after he was frozen in Carbonite. Leia frees Han but then is taken as Jabba's slave. Jabba plans to execute Luke, Chewie and Han by throwing them into the pit of Sarlacc where they are to be "slowly digested over a thousand years." Not sure how that works, but it doesn't sound good.

However, Luke and Lando have the escape planned. Just as Luke is forced off a plank into the pit, he turns and flips back up onto the ship as R2-D2 shoots Luke's lightsaber to him. During the battle, Leia manages to choke Jabba to death with the chain he's using to enslave her. Lando and Chewie rescue Han from sliding into the pit. Everyone's favorite bounty hunter, Boba Fett, falls into the pit after Han accidently activates his jetpack. It's an odd death for such a fan-favorite character. The band of heroes escapes and picks up R2-D2 and C-3PO on the way out of the Dune Sea.

[12] KYLO REN MURDERS HIS FATHER

(THE FORCE AWAKENS)

This scene is a powerful wave of shock, sadness and intensity. We learn that Kylo Ren is Han and Leia's son, and was once trained by Luke to be a Jedi. But like his grandfather, Darth Vader, Kylo Ren is obsessed with power. This obsession turned him to the Dark Side, but he's still conflicted and feels the "pull to the Light" as he describes it.

Death of Han Solo

As Han, Chewie, Finn and Rey are helping disable Starkiller Base from the inside, Han takes an opportunity to try to convince his son to return to his family.

Alone on a long bridge, Kylo Ren tells Han, "I'm being torn apart. I want to be free of this pain. I know what I have to do, but I don't know if I have the strength to do it. Will you help me?"

He takes his lightsaber as if to hand it over to his father, but suddenly ignites it through Han's body. Looking his father in the eyes, Kylo Ren simply says, "Thank you." It's an evil, cold moment, as he chooses to end his inner conflict by murdering his father. Han falls lifelessly. This could be a major character development for Kylo Ren in the up-coming two sequels.

We love the recreation done via action figures by s.w.kustoms, pictured above.

[11] KYLO REN VS. REY ON STARKILLER BASE

(THE FORCE AWAKENS)

A lightsaber battle in the snow between the new bad guy and the new hero of the Star Wars sequels gave fans what they wanted. The battle was more like the grudge fights we saw in the original trilogy, as opposed to the acrobatic fights in the prequels. Kylo Ren reaches for his grandfather's original lightsaber that's stuck in the show. Struggling to bring it to his hand, it suddenly whips past him into Rey's hand.

It's a cool, dark setting with the glow of the sabers reflecting off the snow and their faces. The planet housing Starkiller Base is collapsing around them. Kylo Ren's anger and insecurities are apparent, but as he backs Rey up to a deep ravine, he tells her that he can show her the ways of the Force. Rey then channels the Force to overcome him, eventually slashing him across the face. This obviously sets up intriguing possibilities for the future sequels, as we later discover that Rey will train with Luke and that Supreme Leader Snoke knows Kylo Ren is ready to complete his training.

[10] ANAKIN/DARTH VADER VS. OBI-WAN

(REVENGE OF THE SITH)

We always knew that Obi-Wan and Darth Vader likely fought when they were younger. All the prequels were building to this long duel. The fight begins with Anakin (who at this point has already been crowned "Darth Vader") force-choking a pregnant Padmé. This confirms to Obi-Wan that he has fully transitioned to the Dark Side.

The fast-paced fight between former best friends and master/student has some mesmerizing swordsmanship. The setting is the fiery, lava-filled planet of Mustafar, which creates its own element of danger. There are some parts that are a little over-the-top, but the ending is one of the best and most intense moments in the entire franchise.

Obi-Wan manages to get back to ground, keeping Anakin floating on a platform above on the lava where they were fighting. Anakin tries to leap onto the ground when his former master slices his legs off at the knees. Anakin is boiling over with pain and hate, which seems to physically change him. The lava burns him almost to a point of non-recognition. Obi-Wan has no choice but to leave his friend to die. Of course this happens just before the Emperor shows up to save Anakin and place him into the ominous life support suit he'll wear for the rest of his life.

[9] "NO. TRY NOT. DO, OR DO NOT. THERE IS NO TRY."

(THE EMPIRE STRIKES BACK)

As Luke's training with Yoda advances, this scene brings some of the most quotable Yodaisms in the entire franchise. During his training, Luke's crashed X-Wing sinks further into the Dagobah swamp, convincing Luke that he'll never get the ship out. Yoda says that the ship is no different than anything else Luke has learned to move and manipulate with the Force.

20 GREATEST SCENES

"NO. TRY NOT. DO, OR DO NOT. THERE IS NO TRY."

Yoda's quick response is one of the most quoted lines in the Star Wars saga ... and is why it landed at No. 9 on our 20 Greatest Scenes list.

STAR WARS: THE EMPIRE STRIKES BACK
PREMIERE DATE: MAY 21, 1980

Luke: "Alright, I'll give it a try."

Yoda: "No. Try not. Do, or do not. There is no try."

Yoda's quick response is one of the most quoted lines in the Star Wars saga. Luke of course fails to get the entire ship out, saying it's too big. "You want the impossible," he says after Yoda gives him a lesson on how the Force works. Yoda then lifts the ship out of the swamp and places it safely on the land.

Luke: "I don't… I don't believe it."

Yoda: "That is why you fail."

Those are powerful words. It's a bit of ironic foreshadowing, too, as Luke becomes an incredibly powerful Jedi with supreme confidence in his ability to wield the Force.

HAN SOLO IS FROZEN IN CARBONITE
STAR WARS: THE EMPIRE STRIKES BACK

[8] FROZEN IN CARBONITE

(THE EMPIRE STRIKES BACK)

There's so much going on in and around this key scene in The Empire Strikes Back. It's pretty much the lowest point for the small band of Rebel leaders. Han, Leia and Chewie are ambushed by Darth Vader in the cloud city. Bounty hunters hired by Jabba the Hutt want Han, and Vader wants to test the carbon-freezing chamber he plans to use on Luke. Han is the guinea pig, being tortured and frozen alive in carbonite.

As he is lowered into the chamber, Leia tells him, "I love you." Han, in very Han-like fashion, calmly

responds, "I know." Han is taken to Jabba, and Vader resets the chamber to trap Luke. The iconic image of Han frozen in the large block is one of the most recognizable in the entire franchise. It's been used to create things such as ice cube trays, refrigerators and wall decals.

[7] HAN SHOOTS FIRST

(A NEW HOPE)

Han Solo™ cornered by Greedo!™
© 1977 20TH CENTURY-FOX FILM CORP. All Rights Reserved.

The Mos Eisley Cantina is loaded with crazy Star Wars characters. As Obi-Wan and Luke enter the cantina, Obi-Wan tells his new pupil, "You'll never find a more wretched hive of scum and villainy." The old and future Jedi find and agree with Han Solo (his first appearance) on a price to take them to Alderaan. Han is stopped by Greedo—one of Jabba the Hutt's bounty hunters looking to bring Han to Jabba, preferably dead. The two are sitting at a table when Han shoots Greedo from underneath the table. The camera twice shows Han slowly going for his blaster, building up tension.

This scene sparked a ton of controversy with the 1997 re-mastered edition when an initial blast from Greedo was added to the scene to try to downplay Han as a "killer." It shows Greedo's shot missing Han's head and Han shooting just a split-second after. It even resulted in popular "Han Shot First" t-shirts. Many fans didn't appreciate the scene-tampering, thinking the original captured Han's personality much better.

[6] THE DUEL OF THE FATES

(THE PHANTOM MENACE)

A *Phantom Menace* scene in the Top 10? Yep. While Episode I is the biggest disappointment in the movie franchise, this scene with the fierce Darth Maul wielding an intimidating double-blade lightsaber against Qui-Gon Jinn and a young Obi-Wan is fantastic. The "Duel of the Fates" music composition provides an intense backdrop throughout the fight. Darth Maul remains a mysterious and evil character in film, but we get to see his full power and ability here. No words are spoken between the combatants during the fight, which further dehumanizes Maul and paints him as relentless devil-like character.

The three meet in a hanger near the end of the movie when Maul ignites his dual-bladed lightsaber. He handles both Jedi until they are separated by an energy shield. Qui-Gon kneels to gather himself while Darth Maul paces back and forth like a caged animal. His face is full of hate. He then kills Qui-Gon while Obi-Wan watches, still trapped behind the energy shield. The young Jedi gets his revenge (not that a Jedi wants such things) when he slices Darth Maul in half.

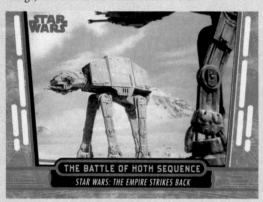

[5] BATTLE ON HOTH

(THE EMPIRE STRIKES BACK)

The opening battle of *The Empire Strikes Back* takes place on the icy planet of Hoth. The Empire discovers the Alliance's Echo Base hidden on Hoth, and Darth Vader is on a personal mission to capture Luke after the Empire's defeat at the Death Star. It's an awesome and unique setting for a battle involving snow speeders, plenty of ground troops, and our first look at the giant AT-AT walkers tasked with destroying the Rebel Alliance's main power generator.

One of the iconic moments is when a Rebel snow speeder wraps a tow cable around the legs of an AT-AT, bringing it down. Luke single-handedly destroys one of the giant walkers after crashing in the snow. He harpoons up to its belly and cuts an opening with his lightsaber. He throws a grenade inside and detached his harpoon cable,

falling to the snow. The Rebels have to abandon their secret base, but manage to get large transports through the Empire blockade just outside Hoth.

[4] VADER ANNIHILATES REBEL SOLDIERS

(ROUGE ONE)

Darth Vader just may be the greatest Hollywood villain of all time. This scene in *Rouge One* gave fans a glimpse of the legendary Sith Lord they always wanted. It also perfectly connects with the beginning of *A New Hope*.

After the Death Star readouts are stolen on Scarif, they're transmitted to a Rebel ship and downloaded on what resembles a floppy disc. Vader catches up to the ship and lays waste to several armed Rebel soldiers. A door jams, trapping some of the soldiers in a corridor. Vader, standing in the dark, ignites his lightsaber. The terrified solders open fire on him. We see Vader's rage and power as he effortlessly slaughters the solders.

We also realize these events happen just before the opening of *A New Hope* when Vader catches up to Princess Leia. She is handed the downloaded readouts at this scene. The Rebels narrowly escape on a smaller cargo ship. It's the same ship being chased by a Star Destroyer in the first scene of *A New Hope*.

[3] THE TRENCH RUN

(A NEW HOPE)

The long-shot attempt to destroy the Death Star ends with a small group of X-Wing fighters maneuvering to the end a narrow trench. Luke is among them, and ends up being the Rebels' last hope. It's a tense scene where every second counts. Meanwhile, the Death Star is moving into position to destroy the Rebel base.

Darth Vader arrives in his specially-designed TIE fighter, knocking off a few X-Wings before focusing on Luke, who is the only pilot left. Luke hears Obi-Wan tell him to

MERIDIAN TRENCH

"Use the Force, Luke" instead of relying on the computer targeting system. Luke turns off his targeting computer. The Death Star is ready to fire on the Rebel base, but Han Solo shows up in the Millennium Falcon just in time to help, which knocks Vader out of the trench.

Using the Force to focus, Luke fires a seemingly impossible torpedo shot into the narrow opening at the end of the trench, setting off the chain reaction that destroys the Death Star.

The final duel

[2] LUKE DEFEATS AND TURNS VADER
(RETURN OF THE JEDI)

It's the final showdown between Luke and Vader. Father and son. The Light and the Dark. This long scene is full of inner and outer conflict. It's Luke's ultimate struggle to see if he will bring balance back to the galaxy or take his father's place. He's determined to bring Vader back to the good side, but also is tempted to kill the Emperor. At first, Luke even refuses to fight.

During the duel, Vader senses Luke's feelings for his twin sister, who was hidden from Vader. "If you will not turn to the Dark Side, perhaps she will," he says. This is when Luke loses control and forcefully strikes his father down. He cuts Vader's hand off in symbolic fashion, just as Vader did to

him. Luke looks at the black glove covering his own robotic right hand, then at Vader's severed mechanical arm. He realizes he's turning into his father. It's a powerful moment.

The Emperor senses Luke's anger, but then Luke gathers himself and throws his lightsaber away as he says, "Never . . . I'll never turn to the Dark Side. You've failed, your Highness. I am a Jedi, like my father before me."

"So be it, Jedi," the Emperor responds as he tries to destroy Luke with Force lightning. Luke is begging his father to save him. In Vader's final act, he sacrifices himself and throws the Emperor down a deep shaft to save his son. Not only does Luke defeat Vader and survive the Emperor's test, he turns his father back to the good side. When Luke removes Vader's helmet, he reveals his father's true face—a mangled, twisted and vulnerable old man.

[1] "NO . . . I AM YOUR FATHER."
(THE EMPIRE STRIKES BACK)

No other scene is more memorable or impactful than the ultimate twist at the end of *The Empire Strikes Back*. Bloodied and defeated, Luke is literally hanging on for his life after Darth Vader slices his hand off. With seemingly no hope left, Vader tries to persuade Luke to join the Dark Side.

Luke: "I'll never join you."

Vader: "If you only knew the power of the Dark Side. Obi-Wan never told you what happened to your father…"

Luke: "He told me enough. He told me you killed him."

Vader: "No… I am your father."

The pain in Luke's face is definite as he's unable to deny this truth. This revelation created a totally different and deeper dynamic for the entire saga. The family dynamic continues to be a core storyline from this point on, even carrying through the most recent films, *The Force Awakens* and *Rogue One*. It's also the central scene that makes *The Empire Strikes Back* a fan-favorite of the film franchise.

THE PEOPLE'S PRINCESS

CARRIE FISHER WAS A LOT OF THINGS TO A LOT OF PEOPLE: AN ACTRESS, A FEMINIST, A PRINCESS AND A SURVIVOR.

ABOVE ALL ELSE, SHE WAS A ROLE MODEL TO MILLIONS.

BY ALLAN MUIR

CARRIE FISHER: THE PEOPLE'S PRINCESS

For the final 40 years of her life, Carrie Fisher struggled to come to terms with the character that made her famous.

But this would have helped.

Fisher, who counted herself a proud feminist, passed away in December, 2016 at age 60, less than a month before she planned to take part in one of the many Women's Marches that took place around the world on Jan. 21. And yet she, or at least her character, was in attendance at all of them. There among the protest signs carried by the millions of marchers was one designed by artist Hayley Gilmore that pictured a defiant Princess Leia Organa with an upraised blaster declaring, "A Woman's Place Is in the Resistance." Others carried placards showing Leia with a brook-no-fools glare, or re-imagined as World War II icon Rosie the Riveter. These were more than just clever tributes from fans still processing the star's death. In fact, the message those signs delivered was clear: In the face of looming oppression, these women viewed Leia as the embodiment of hope.

" She was OUR princess . . . and the actress who played her blurred into one gorgeous, fiercely independent and ferociously funny, take-charge woman who took our collective breath away."

- MARK HAMILL ON CO-STAR CARRIE FISHER

CARRIE FISHER: THE PEOPLE'S PRINCESS

"For me, it meant carrying on Carrie's mission," her brother, Todd Fisher, told Vanity Fair of Fisher's post-humous presence at the marches. "She was a champion of women, no one can deny it...[or the] enormous influence she's had. Women around the world—women who are struggling for their identity, for their position, for equality, whatever the case may be. We started to see how many people idolized her."

It's easy to understand that attachment. The wry and fearless warrior Fisher created over five Star Wars films (six, if you count a computer-generated cameo at the end of *Rogue One*) felt completely familiar and yet was unlike anything we'd seen before. She was strong, com-passionate, daring, vulnerable, charming, thoughtful, reckless, capable and the smartest person in the room. Hardly like we'd expect from a princess.

And yet, thanks to Fisher's soulful performance, she made an indelible mark, earning a place as one of the most revered characters in cinematic history as well as one of the most influential. Leia, the princess-saboteur, was the game changer: the alpha female. Without her, there'd be no Rey or Jyn Erso in the Star Wars universe. Maybe more importantly though, there'd be no Ellen Rip-ley (Alien), no Katniss Everdeen (The Hunger Games), no Merida (Brave), no Captain Janeway (Star Trek: Voyager) and no Buffy Summers (Buffy The Vampire Slayer).

She was the one who made anything seem possible. Even while wearing a gold metal bikini, she came to repre-sent strength and independence to generations of women.

"In 'Star Wars,' she was our great and powerful princess — feisty, wise and full of hope in a role that was more difficult than most people might think," said cre-ator George Lucas during a tribute to Fisher at the 2017 Star Wars Celebration in London. "She played a part that was very smart, and she was having to hold her own against two big lugs, goofballs that were screwing ev-erything up. She was the boss. It was her war, and when I cast it, I said I want somebody young to play the part. I want somebody very young. When Carrie came in, she was that character. She was very strong, very smart, very funny, very bold, very tough, and there really wasn't much of a question. There are not very many people like her. They are one in a billion. For this particular part, it was absolutely perfect. … She wore a dress through the whole thing, but she was the toughest in the group."

"She was OUR Princess, damn it, and the actress who played her blurred into one gorgeous, fiercely indepen-dent and ferociously funny, take-charge woman who took our collective breath away," Mark Hamill added.

> **From the first film, she was just a soldier, front line and center. The only way they knew to make the character strong was to make her angry. In Return of the Jedi, she [finally got] to be more feminine, more supportive, more affectionate."**
>
> - CARRIE FISHER

While others immediately appreciated Leia's impact, Fisher struggled to make peace with the role that changed her life and elevated her as an icon. ("I signed away the rights to my likeness," she joked. "Every time I look in the mirror, I have to send George a check for two bucks.") It caused her great frustration that the ground-breaking nature of her character could only have gained traction under very specific circumstances.

CARRIE FISHER: THE PEOPLE'S PRINCESS

"Movies are dreams," she told Rolling Stone during a 1983 interview promoting the release of Return of the Jedi. "They work on you subliminally. You can play Leia as capable, independent, sensible, a soldier, a fighter, a woman in control – control being, of course, a lesser word than master. But you can [only] portray a woman who's a master and get through all the female prejudice if you have her travel in time, if you add a magical quality, if you're dealing in fairy-tale terms."

Of course, there were some who still preferred females to adhere to the more submissive stereotypes. "There are a lot of people who don't like my character in these movies," Fisher said.

"They think I'm some kind of space bitch."

Nevertheless, Fisher persisted. As did Leia, the cool and defiant princess who became a general in the films and, later, in the Star Wars Extended Universe novels, ended up ruling the entire galaxy as the New Republic Chief of State.

Lucas, to his enduring credit, understood not just the need for a fully-realized, fully independent female lead like Leia, but the dramatic potential as well. As he brought her to life with Fisher (who famously offered re-writes for Episodes V and VI after choking on George's words), they up-ended the heroic paradigm and in the process, created a template that allowed the generations that followed to view gender and heroism through a different lens.

The traditional (male) protagonists in Star Wars needed time and motivation to grow into their roles as heroes. Luke Skywalker was a frustrated farm boy searching for adventure or his purpose or anything else that would get him off the desolate rock that was his home world before he stumbled onto his destiny. Han Solo was a scoundrel who operated in the grey areas, always valuing his own hide, and his own needs, before begrudgingly learning the lesson of sacrifice.

But Leia? She was always a hero.

Raised by her adoptive father, Bail Organa, she served the people of Alderaan in the Senate while leading a clandestine campaign of espionage and sabotage to overthrow the Empire. She was fast with a blaster (we see her dropping a stormtrooper with one shot in her memorable first scene in A New Hope), tough enough to hold on to her secrets while being tortured by Darth Vader and utterly calm as she faced repeated instances of certain death.

And she was quick with the snark, too.

"Governor Tarkin," she sneered upon being brought face to face with the Death Star commander in A New Hope. "I should've expected to find you holding Vader's leash.

I recognized your foul stench when I was brought on board."

But while that cool, fearless personality is part of her appeal, the key is something else entirely: It's that she never slipped into the damsel-in-distress archetype. Sure, she found herself in a few tight spots along the way—imprisoned on the Imperial starship in A New Hope or chained on Jabba's barge in Return of the Jedi—but she never needed to be rescued.

With Leia, it was simply a matter of waiting for an opportunity to extricate herself from a tough spot and then jumping back in to help the boys out of the mess they created. She was always in control, the engine of her own fate. She isn't altered by her surroundings. She forces them to change.

While Fisher admired that strength, she saw an early single-mindedness to the character.

"She has no friends, no family; her planet was blown up in seconds so all she has is a cause," Fisher told Rolling Stone. "From the first film, she was just a soldier, front line and center. The only way they knew to make the character strong was to make her angry. In Return of the Jedi, she [finally got] to be more feminine, more supportive, more affectionate."

But even as Leia grew, she didn't grow soft. In that film she took a laser blast in the arm before wiping out a squadron of Empire troops to save Han during the Battle of Endor. She also offered one of the great turnabouts in film history, responding to Solo's declaration of love with an epic, albeit fatalistic, "I know."

That indomitable spirit carried on through her most recent appearance in The Force Awakens and The Last Jedi, where it was revealed that she had continued to lead the fight against oppression as a general with the Resistance. Older, and deeply scarred after losing her son, Ben Solo, to the dark side, she was focused on "the only thing she was ever good at" – leading the rebel forces against the First Order.

"[She's] solitary," Fisher said of Leia. "Under a lot of pressure. Committed as ever to her cause, but I would imagine feeling somewhat defeated, tired, and pissed."

Although Fisher's family gave Lucasfilm permission to use recent footage of the actress in 2019's Episode IX, company president Kathleen Kennedy said that she will not be in the final film. That means Leia's final appearance was in Star Wars: The Last Jedi. It seems certain that she had regained the spark that defined her in the original trilogy, setting Leia up for a fitting, if sadly premature, conclusion to her uniquely heroic journey.

FOREVER A BOY

WONDER

Forty years ago Mark Hamill landed
the role of a lifetime, and made it his own.
Now in his mid-60s, Hamill's Luke Skywalker is on
the cusp of lighting up the silver screen again.

BY JEFF SULLIVAN

MARK HAMILL: FOREVER A BOY WONDER

There was going to be a Luke Skywalker, that much was certain once 20th Century Fox agreed to back George Lucas' sci-fi project after several other studios passed. And there were going to be hundreds of actors trying out for the lead role. Among them was not Mark Hamill, who at the time was co-starring on the short-lived TV series *Texas Wheelers* with Gary Busey.

When the 24-year old wasn't on set, he usually found his way to Robert Englund's couch. Yes, as in the future Freddy Krueger. That is where he was, his cowboy boots by the door, three Heinekens into a six-pack, watching *The Mary Tyler Moore Show*, when Englund returned from his dual auditions for two movies that were sharing a sound stage, *Apocalypse Now* and yes, *Star Wars*, where he read for Han Solo. However, it was the role of Skywalker that made him think of the ideal fit.

In a recent interview, Englund says, "I told him, 'I think you're right for this, man. This character is like a space prince, and it's George Lucas! Mark, you've got to do this. Wow, what if you got to be in a George Lucas movie … you're the kind of actor he loves!' So, he got on the phone to his agent and the rest is history."

HAMILL AND CARRIE FISHER DURING A BREAK IN FILMING THE ORIGINAL STAR WARS.

> **"** I told him, 'I think you're right for this, man. This character is like a space prince, and it's George Lucas! Mark, you've got to do this. Wow, what if you got to be in a George Lucas movie ... you're the kind of actor he loves!' So, he got on the phone to his agent and the rest is history."
>
> **- ROBERT ENGLUND**

MARK HAMILL: FOREVER A BOY WONDER

There is no debating Luke Skywalker among the most iconic characters in cinema history. Some would even rank him at the top. And that legend is only going to grow more so in the coming years and decades with another two movies remaining in the most recent trilogy. *Star Wars: Episode VIII The Last Jedi* is slated for a Dec. 15 release later this year with Hamill expected to play a significant role after just a cameo at the end of A Force Awakens.

At the time of his original casting, Hamill was a relative unknown, although as he was quick to point out, he did have 148 credits, dating back to *The Bill Cosby Show*, *General Hospital* and *The Partridge Family* as a teenager in the early-1970s. It's also worth noting that Hamill was among the few actors shooting the original *Star Wars* who felt like the film would be a success. Answering a fan's question via his always active Twitter handle, @HamillHimself, he said, "Crew was kind but thought (movie) was 'rubbish.' I kept telling them: 'We're on a winner!'"

Indeed, a winner for the ages, at the time, the highest-grossing movie of all-time. For the gig, Hamill received just $650,000, which was significantly more than his co-stars Harrison Ford and Carrie Fisher, who took in a reported $10,000 a week. However, once the film took off, writer/director Lucas gave each of them a percentage cut of the movie's profits.

By all accounts, Hamill remained grounded when that galaxy from far, far away became the talk of 1977, described by many as a gee-whiz kid. Humble and talkative (his friends at the time called him "Motor-Mouth") by nature, he spent what free time existed at the beach near his then-home in Malibu. His other hobbies included long games of Monopoly and baking cakes. Looking back on this time in 1981, on the cusp of Return of the Jedi, Hamill told People, "In Hollywood, I became an icon, like Mickey Mouse."

Still, he was more in awe than thinking he was all that, even with his own cast.

During what became a worldwide promotion

MARK HAMILL: FOREVER A BOY WONDER

tour in 1977, Hamill spoke in England with childlike exuberance of working with such legendary actors like Alec Guinness and Peter Cushing.

"Unfortunately, I never had a scene with Peter Cushing but he was surprised because I went to work two days just to watch (him) work even though I didn't work with him," Hamill said. "But I'm a fan at heart and I had him sign a couple of posters."

Alas, for Hamill, there was another life-altering event for him in 1977, this one taking place five months before the overwhelming majority would even recognize his name, and almost costing him his life. It would also change the face of the original trilogy, literally.

In his words, to Gossip Magazine in 1978, "What happened was that I was on the wrong freeway. I was way out in the sticks somewhere and there were no cars and no traffic, thank God. I was going about 65-70 mph … I was speeding, going too fast … and what happened, I think, was that I tried to negotiate an off-ramp and lost control, tumbled over, and went off the road. I fractured

my nose and my cheek."

The near-fatal accident required three operations to his face. There have been endless rumors throughout the years on other procedures and plastic surgeries, but Hamill, who seems honest to a fault, has always denied them. In the months following the wreck, many assumed Hamill's acting career was finished, and if not for the success of *Star Wars*, it might have been.

It's also no secret that of the three stars, Ford and Fisher went on to infinitely more success post-trilogy, with the former becoming arguably the biggest star of his generation. There are probably multiple reasons for this but more times than not, the accident is cited as the primary explanation.

"Of the three of us," Hamill told People in 1978. "I've probably been most affected by the movie."

Speaking about the accident, he said, "It was the lowest point of my life. In one year I'd had the biggest breaks I'd ever had, then that. I started thinking I'd never work again."

His scars were written into *The Empire Strikes Back*

WORKING WITH SIR ALEC GUINNESS REMAINS ONE OF HAMILL'S GREATEST ACHIEVEMENTS.

script, with Skywalker having his face scratched in the first scene by a Wampa, although Lucas has said that wasn't the lone reason for the storyline. Still, everyone noticed Hamill looked different in the latter two movies, and no longer had that boyish look.

However, he never stopped acting, even migrating to Broadway to star in *The Elephant Man* in between the last two movies of the trilogy. Hamill also accomplished all of the goals he set for himself before turning 30 years old: star in a movie, appear in a movie nominated for an Oscar, make a million dollars and appear in a Broadway play.

Still, by the time *Return of the Jedi* released in 1983, Hamill was the first to joke about his non-star/star status. He would ask friends and family a trivia question: Name the top-billed actor in the first and third highest-grossing movies of all time.

"It's me, but even my family guesses wrong," Hamill told People in 1981. "My cousin said Richard Dreyfuss.

"I feel I haven't earned celebrity. So much of life is what you roll and where you land. I'm so much like Luke Skywalker. I guess I always will be."

Hamill stayed busy in the 32 years between

appearing as Luke Skywalker, raising his three children with his wife Marilou, who he met before the release of *Star Wars* and married in December 1978 after a brief stretch of, let's call it testing out his new-found recognition.

"I had to taste groupies and fame," he said of the months after *Star Wars*. "I went to Las Vegas to date 38-year old showgirls. That was exciting for about the first 10 minutes."

There were also numerous Broadway shows, including a critically acclaimed performance in *Harrigan 'N Hart* in 1985, simulation video games, mostly sci-fi, and a bevy of voiceovers, most notably the Joker from the *Batman* animated series.

Then came the unexpected return, another trilogy, this one taking place after the original, and director J.J. Abrams most certainly, like fans around the world, wanted Han Solo, Princess Leia and Luke Skywalker to return to the Big Screen. And while Ford took some convincing, it took Hamill all of a few seconds to say yes.

"You know, we (were) all in a great place and we've all done it before, there was a beginning, a middle and end," Hamill told Rolling Stone in 2015

BELOW: IT DIDN'T TAKE LONG FOR THE LUKE SKYWALKER FROM A FORCE AWAKENS TO FIND HIS WAY ONTO A TOY LINE SUCH AS THIS FIGURE PRODUCED BY HOT TOYS.

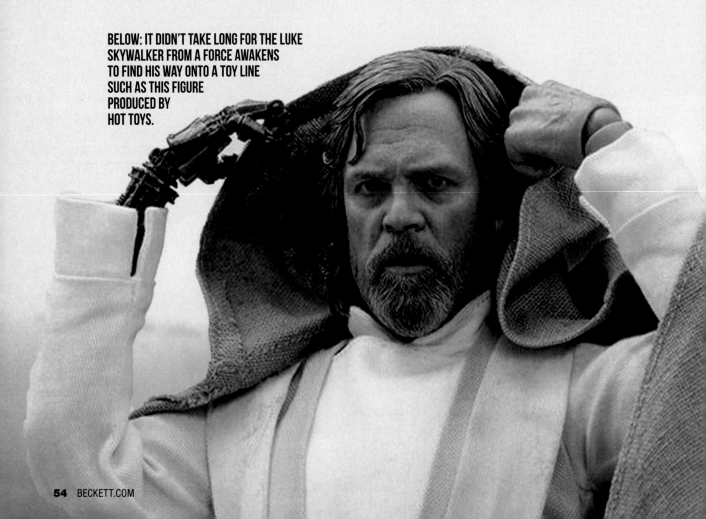

MARK HAMILL: FOREVER A BOY WONDER

STAR WARS CELEBRITY MEANS HAMILL IS A WELCOME GUEST OF MANY, INCLUDING PRINCE CHARLES.

just before the release of *A Force Awakens*. "You have to think about all the aspects of it because, you know, if you want to maintain a low profile, this isn't the best way to do it. [Laughs] And I sort of got into a niche where I did my voiceovers and I could do theater when I wanted to. I mean, all along the way I've been having a really great time and doing a lot of interesting stuff. It's just that people don't really pay a lot of attention."

In another interview from 2015, he added, "I spent a large part of my life putting *Star Wars* behind me so I could move on. (Returning for more films) is like taking out a pair of trousers from the back of the closet and discovering a $20 bill in the pocket."

While fans have only seen a trailer as of the spring, if nothing else, Hamill has a speaking role in The Last Jedi and more than likely, a significant role.

He has been outspoken in his disagreement of his character's direction in the movie, telling ABC News of writer-director Rian Johnson, "When I read (the screenplay), I told Rian, 'I fundamentally disagree with virtually everything you've decided about my character.' It was as shocking for me to read what Rian had written as I'm sure it will be for the audience."

Hamill also acknowledged the possibility of Skywalker going to the dark side, much like his father, Anakin/ Darth Vader, and nephew, Kylo Ren.

The world awaits the answer to that question and many more this December, some 40 years after it all began, a long time ago in a galaxy far, far away, a story which has captivated the world and changed the lives of just about all involved.

Few more so than Hamill, who happened to be sitting on the right couch at the right time.

> **I spent a large part of my life putting Star Wars behind me so I could move on. (Returning for more films) is like taking out a pair of trousers from the back of the closet and discovering a $20 bill in the pocket."**
>
> **- MARK HAMILL, IN A 2015 INTERVIEW**

BELOVED IS YOU

He's old (900 years!), green, short and speaks in bizarre, backward fashion. Even so, Yoda is one of the most admired and quoted species in the galaxy.

BY BRYAN PETRAY

One of the most captivating aspects of the Star Wars saga is the vast collection of species, from a two-foot green omnipotent humanoid to a 16-foot, man-eating reptilian predator called "Rancor." The immeasurable imagination of George Lucas and his ability to create and bring to life so many creatures, races and personalities makes his world an irresistible attraction that has entertained generations for four decades while becoming a worldwide cultural phenomenon.

Among the nucleus of Lucas' prodigious universe is its Grand Master Jedi, Yoda, the essence of the tangible force throughout the plot. His part in the saga is paramount, yet Lucas surrenders few clues when it comes to Yoda's origin and species.

We know that Darth Sidious' early apprentice, the Sith Lord Darth Maul, with his distinctive horns, was of the Zabrak species and came from the planet Dathomir. We also know that Anakin Skywalker's young Padawan learner, Ahsoka Tano, with her elongated striped head tails, was of the Togruta order and came from the planet Shili. And Lucas so ordained that the species of the villainous Jabba the Hutt was so important that it should be included in his title.

There are more than 100 different known species and hundreds of named planets in Lucas' realm, but for his own reasons, the mastermind of the universe chose to keep us in suspense on both when it came to Grand Master Yoda.

When inquired, Lucas hasn't budged. He's been known to use the term "Yoda's species" when asked. "He's the illegitimate child of Kermit and Miss Piggy," Lucas joked in the 2002 documentary *From Puppets to Pixels: Digital Characters in 'Episode II.'*

Whatever his background, Yoda is just cool. And wise. And all-knowing. And did we mention cool?

There is no shortage of theories on Yoda's place of origin. One of the more obvious is to look to his end to perhaps find his beginning. Yoda's chosen destination for his notorious self-imposed exile was at the Outer Rim on the planet Dagobah. There he watched Luke from afar, using the force to discern that he would eventually take on his final student.

Yoda's final destination for his exile and eventual end certainly wasn't as desirable as Luke's choice on the scenic aquatic planet of Ahch-To decades later, or even Obi-Wan's exile excursion on the desolate planet Tatooine. As miserable as it seemed for Luke, Yoda seemed right at home on the snake- and swamp-ridden planet. Which might explain how Dagobah could be Yoda's home. The guess is as good as any, but alas, it's merely a guess.

What we do know is that Yoda was the most accomplished Jedi in the galaxy. Born 900 years before the Battle of Endor, he was trained by Jedi Master N'Kata Del Gormo. He went on to achieve the rank of Master Jedi at around 100 years of age and trained more than 20,000 younglings and Padawan learners over eight centuries in service to the Jedi Order.

Even the mightiest can face overbearing adversity and fail. Yoda's flaws and failures make fans identify with him. In a way, they see themselves in Yoda. Someone who wields great power, but carries a heavy burden against a formidable foe. His fallacy makes him relatable.

His powers were extraordinary and numerous. And his wisdom and precognition skills only scratch the surface to his full arsenal. In addition to his mastery of force acrobatics and lightsaber combat, the three-fingered Jedi legend also wielded a force shockwave, a force push as well as force absorption abilities. And under the tutelage of the spirit form of his former student, Qui-Gon Jin, Yoda also harnessed the rare ability to communicate with deceased Jedi in spirit known as the cosmic force.

With extraordinary power and abilities, it's easy to see why so many fans are infatuated with the Grand Master. His popularity is as great as his midi-chlorian count. But there's several layers to this phenomenon.

There's something to be said for a lifeform that lives for 900 years and is able to end on his own terms as Yoda did. And considering the conflict in place that he faced over those nine centuries, it's an even more impressive feat.

While Yoda's wisdom and power is legendary, he

wasn't without miscue. Several of his most talented students, Count Dooku and Anakin Skywalker (to a lesser extent) fell victim to the dark side of the force. He oversaw the almost complete genocide of the Jedi Order after Supreme Chancellor Palpatine ordered the Grand Army of the Republic to execute Order 66 – branding the Jedi as traitorous and to be executed on sight.

Even the mightiest can face overbearing adversity and fail. Yoda's flaws and failures make fans identify with him. In a way, they see themselves in Yoda. Someone who wields great power, but carries a heavy burden against a formidable foe. His fallacy makes him relatable.

His unique manner of speaking, often referred to as "Yodic," using the subject-object-verb format, along with his diminutive features adds to his unfailing charm.

"Size matters not. Look at me. Judge me by my size, do you?" Yoda asked Luke Skywalker in *The Empire Strikes Back*. "And where you should not. For my ally is the force. And a powerful ally, it is." Who among us can't relate to the natural human instinct to root for the underdog?

But perhaps the biggest reason that Yoda became the saga's most beloved character is a combination of Lucas creativity, storytelling and, in his great wisdom, imparting the role to Frank Oz. The award-winning American puppeteer, also known for his work on *Sesame Street* (Cookie Monster, Bert and Grover) and *The Muppet Show* (Fozzie Bear and Miss Piggy), wowed fans as Yoda's voice and performed much of the actual puppetry work of the non-CGI incarnation of the legendary Jedi.

His work in *The Empire Strikes Back* was so widely admired that it presented a strong case to become the first puppeteer in a movie to receive an Academy Award nomination. There was a movement in Hollywood for him being considered for Best Supporting Actor, but the academy ultimately decided that a puppeteer wasn't an actor.

Regardless, Oz's role in bringing Yoda to life was brilliant. And the final product was an immensely popular character with great depth. In 2008, Yoda ranked No. 25 on Empire Magazine's list of the 100 Greatest Movie Characters of All Time, considered among unforgettable silver-screen contemporaries such as James Bond, Forrest Gump, Ferris Bueller and Indiana Jones.

As popular as he is, Yoda is still an enigma to even the most fanatical Star Wars enthusiast. Perhaps Lucas' shroud of mystery cast over one of his favorite characters was all part of a master plan of a future spin-off movie. With nearly 900 years' worth of a blank canvas, there's so much potential that could come with a telling of his full story.

THE WISDOM OF YODA

NINE OF YODA'S GREATEST QUOTES

[9] "Through the Force, things you will see. Other places. The future . . . the past. Old friends long gone."
– THE EMPIRE STRIKES BACK

[8] "Adventure. Excitement. A Jedi craves not these things."
– THE EMPIRE STRIKES BACK

[7] "Judge me by my size do you?"
– THE EMPIRE STRIKES BACK

[6] "Fear is the path to the dark side, fear leads to anger, anger leads to hate, hate leads to suffering."
– EPISODE 1 – THE PHANTOM MENACE

[5] "Not if anything to say about it I have."
– EPISODE III – REVENGE OF THE SITH

[4] "Always two there are, no more, no less. A master and an apprentice."
– EPISODE 1 – THE PHANTOM MENACE

[3] "That is why you fail."
– THE EMPIRE STRIKES BACK, IN RESPONSE TO LUKE SAYING "I DON'T BELIEVE IT."

[2] "When 900 years old you reach, look as good you will not."
– RETURN OF THE JEDI

[1] "Do. Or not do. There is no try."
– THE EMPIRE STRIKES BACK

WICKED GOOD

His taste in color runs black and he's a bit of a heavy breather. It's all part of the Darth Vader aura, the most intimidating – and fascinating - presence in the Star Wars galaxy ... *and Hollywood's greatest villain.*

BY ROGER FERNANDEZ

" I had to make Darth Vader scary without the audience ever seeing his face. His character's got to go beyond that. He's done a lot of horrible things in his life that he isn't particularly proud of. Ultimately, he's just a pathetic guy who's had a very sad life."

- GEORGE LUCAS IN AN
INTERVIEW WITH ROLLING
STONE MAGAZINE

DARTH VADER: WICKED GOOD

ACTORS PETER CUSHING, CARRIE FISHER AND DAVID PROWSE ON THE SET OF THE ORIGINAL STAR WARS FILM.

To loosely borrow a famous line the one-and-only Obi-Wan Kenobi used in the original *Star Wars* movie, this is the villain you're looking for.

Darth Vader, it turns out, is in fact the chosen one, the one you hate, you love, you hate to love and love to hate. No, we're not trying to work an old Jedi mind trick on you.

It's the truth. Hollywood and pop culture have never had it so good and so bad when it comes to villains, and the *Star Wars* franchise can take credit for coming up with a dream of a nightmare bad guy.

When you really think about it, the dark-mask-wearing, heavy-breathing, light-saber-wielding, wanna-conquer-the-galaxy-and-fulfill-his-destiny tough guy may be as popular and beloved as any of the heroes in the enduring saga.

Move over, Luke Skywalker, step aside Princess Leia, out of the way Han Solo, and that goes for you too, Chewbacca and Yoda — Lord Vader may have the inside track on all of them in a *Star Wars* adoration contest.

It takes a special kind of evil to get that much love.

DARTH VADER: WICKED GOOD

THERE IS A VADER SIGHTING ...

The world first laid eyes on this fearsome figure in the opening moments of Episode IV – the original *Star Wars* - when Vader stormed through the hallways of a starship, barking out orders, interrogating a rebel and finishing him off with one of his patented choke holds. Viewers didn't exactly know what to make of Vader, who appeared to be some type of man/robot hybrid with a booming voice and top-dog status.

And that's exactly the way Stars Wars creator George Lucas wanted it. The aim was to make the antihero an incomparable unnerving enigma. Vader proved to be a shock to the senses from the very start. The more we saw him, the more we wanted to know about him — from a safe distance, of course.

"I had to make Darth Vader scary without the audience ever seeing his face," Lucas told Rolling Stone magazine. "Basically, it's just a black mask. I said, 'How do I make that evil and scary?' I mean, he's big and black and he's got a cape and a samurai helmet, but that doesn't necessarily make people afraid of him. His character's got to go beyond that — that's how we get his impersonal way of dealing with things. He's done a lot of horrible things in his life that he isn't particularly proud of. Ultimately, he's just a pathetic guy who's had a very sad life."

ACTOR DAVID PROWSE (SHOWN ABOVE IN AN IMAGE FROM 2013) WAS THE MAN IN THE SUIT FOR DARTH VADER WHILE JAMES EARL JONES (SHOWN BELOW) PROVIDED THE CHARACTER'S IMPOSING VOICE.

Let's start with the character's name, which provided a hidden clue. "Darth" is a variation of dark, and "Vader" is Dutch for father. "So it's basically Dark Father," Lucas added in Rolling Stone. Little could audiences have known that Lucas had provided a sneaky hint to a planet-shaking plot twist that would rattle viewers down the line.

Now let's turn to the obvious: the look. It is the foundation for the character's popularity. The film industry had never seen anything like Vader. In Hollywood, villains were simply troublemakers who more or less looked like someone you might bump into at the grocery store, only they went about their daily life concocting sinister plans.

Perhaps, at the worst, they wore black and maybe an eyepatch, spoke with a British or Eastern European accent or sported a perpetual scowl or unsightly scar. With Vader, we didn't know whether he was chewing bubble gum or even awake, for that matter. The expression-less mask, not to mention his height and dark, flowing cape, made him that much more psychologically terrifying.

Can't forget to mention he's an expert with a lightsaber and has mastered the Force, thus he's able to wring the life out of anyone who crosses him without so much laying a finger on them. That nifty weaponry and "Force choke" gives him an aura of invincibility.

HE'S A HEAVY BREATHER

Toss in the breathing. How many movie characters would you recognize on their breathing pattern alone? It's unmistakable, one of the most distinct and menacing sounds the film industry has ever produced. If it takes you more than a split second to identify it, perhaps you've stopped breathing. Admit it — as a *Star Wars* fan, you've tried to copy that sound, just as you've tried to emulate Vader's voice.

That voice. That sweet, full-toned, authoritative and ominous sound provided by James Earl Jones. He's the man who told us "This is CNN" and later gave sports fans goosebumps talking about baseball in a middle-of-nowhere Iowa cornfield in *Field of Dreams*. Never mind those other roles. His voice is the one that will speak for the Dark Side for eternity.

Jones admitted to The New York Times Magazine to having a little fun putting Darth Vader's voice to use off the set. Who wouldn't?

"I did that once when I was traveling cross-country," he said. "I used Darth as my handle on the CB radio.

DARTH VADER: WICKED GOOD

The truck drivers would really freak out — for them, it was Darth Vader. I had to stop doing that."

We've got the visuals. We've got the sounds. And just to add to the sensory overload, the powers that be asked composer John Williams, the man who created the eerie *Jaws* theme, to whip up a little tune for Vader. "The Imperial March" nailed it. It's intimidating, apocalyptic and perfectly captures the unpleasant tone in all things Vader and the Empire. The song has become the unofficial anthem for anything or anyone with a despicable side.

Episode IV made it clear that Vader was a bad dude, assuming he was human, and downright cold. The more the films peeled his layers, the more we realized there was a glimmer of humanity behind the darkness. Heck, he was even a cute kid at one time and had what it took to be — spoiler alert — a dedicated Skywalker family man.

In later films, created to unveil Vader's backstory, we meet him as a young Anakin Skywalker, a slave boy thought to be the "Chosen One." The young Jedi in training was supposed to bring balance to the Force. Oops. Not quite. He's the classic case of a good kid gone bad, caught up trying to rule an entire galaxy, far, far, away. It could happen to the best of us.

In The *Empire Strikes Back*, Vader reveals himself as Luke Skywalker's father and asks the youngster to join him as the nastiest pop/son duo in the galaxy. While that reunion didn't pan out, Vader, in *Return of the Jedi*, showed compassion and proved that family always comes first when he saved Luke from the Emperor. See, he wasn't such an evildoer after all, and it's not so tough to sympathize with him.

It's impossible not to jump on the Team Vader bandwagon when he tosses the Emperor into oblivion. For all that venom and rancor early on, Vader rebounds and totally redeems himself. That's part of the attraction to the character, his transformation from a monster into a human. It's like *Beauty and the Beast* in space, only with less fur (outside of Chewie and the Ewoks), less ballroom dancing and a lot more lightsaber battles.

Few are the movie villains who can stand up to that kind of range, which is why Vader is one of best you'll ever see. An impeccable mix of visual awe and character development thrust him into the pop culture pantheon.

Vader pulled off the improbable as the poster boy for both right and wrong. No one wants to be him, yet, at the same time, everyone wants to be him. Look around the neighborhood come Halloween. His is a costume that's been in style since 1977, and it's still as hip as ever.

You'll catch him at sporting events. At Oakland Raiders home games, take a glance at the team's famed "Black Hole" section and you're sure to spot a Darth-Vader-clad fan cheering on the Silver and Black. Vader's theme song is always a go-to tune at stadiums and arenas whenever the home squad wants to take a jab at "vile" visiting teams.

Even Disneyland, "The Happiest Place on Earth," featured Vader in promotional ads. You've come a long way in popularity, and most certainly anger management, when you can make a seamless transition from aspiring to snatch power at all costs to taking a spin on the Dumbo ride. That, folks, is what you call doing a complete 180.

HOLLYWOOD GOLD

He's such a power player that he's the equivalent of a March Madness No. 1 seed. Since 2013, StarWars.com has run an official NCAA-style bracket tournament, called "This is Madness," to determine the franchise's top character. Vader is practically a dynasty. He has dominated the Dark Side's half of the bracket, reached the final in the first four editions and won it in 2015.

Hollywood obviously has an affinity for him. Run an on-line search for the greatest movie villains of all time. Vader frequently comes up the best of the worst. *The Wizard of Oz*'s wicked witch can't hang with him, and neither can *Halloween*'s Michael Myers.

When was the last time you saw Hannibal Lecter (*The Silence of the Lambs*) on a lunchbox, Norman Bates (*Psycho*) on kids' light-up shoes or Hans Gruber (*Diehard*) featured on a waffle maker? Vader is a merchandiser's dream, and everyone from toddlers to grandparents can't get enough of him. He made it chic to go against the grain in the ceaseless conflict that is good vs. evil.

The thing that makes Vader stand out in a bad bunch on earth, as out of this world as he has always been, is that deep down we can all relate to him on a certain level. That can't be said for most movie meanies.

"The first film, people didn't even know whether there was a person there," Lucas said in Rolling Stone. "They thought he was a person. They thought he was a monster or some kind of a robot. In the second film, it's revealed that he's a human being, and in the third film you find out that, yes, he's a father and a regular person like the rest of us."

Dare tell Vader he's not the most iconic ruffian the world has ever known, and you're likely to get an icy-cold stare and a calculated response that should sound familiar: "I find your lack of faith disturbing." He allowed all of us to believe that sometimes it's good to be a little bad.

40 GREATEST CHARACTERS

BY RYAN CRACKNELL

After a bunch of films, a couple of television series, dozens of books and lots of other stories in other mediums, *Star Wars* has introduced an entire universe of characters. Many are icons to multiple generations. And then there's Jar Jar Binks.

Several factors go into great *Star Wars* characters. Story and personality are the big ones. These bring the emotional core that make us relate and feel a connection.

But let's be honest. Some *Star Wars* characters achieve greatness not because they make us feel but because they look cool. In a visual medium like film, an inspired design can make an impact just like a scene that brings a smile or causes our eyes to water.

With those things in mind, here are 40 of the most unforgettable *Star Wars*

[40] MALAKILI

Malakili has the look of someone who's tough. He's a big guy without much use for shirts. His job is to look after the monstrous Rancor that resides under Jabba the Hutt's throne, gobbling up anyone who wrongs the slimy gangster. It turns out that Malakili's tough exterior is all a facade. When it comes to him and his Rancor, Malakili is all teddy bear.

[39] WICKET

Wicket is the young hero of the Ewoks. The teddy bears with spears may get a bad rap by some who don't want their Star Wars cute and cuddly, but Wicket is different. Between all the yup-nubbing is a tough adventurer who shows little fear and lots of heart. And if your Saturday mornings in the '80s involved the Ewoks cartoon, your respect for Wicket and his adventures is probably even higher.

[38] GREEDO

Greedo's time on the screen may be limited but his legacy is undeniable. He's part of the scum that makes the Star Wars universe so appealing. The Rodian bounty hunter looks as though he's related to the Sleestak's from *Land of the Lost*. It's in his death that Greedo's memorable status is cemented. Originally, Han shot first in their fateful meeting at the Mos Eisley Cantina. But through George Lucas' changing mind, that changed because the creator felt good guys should only protect themselves. With that, the Han Shot First movement was born, rebelling against tinkering with a classic series. And now Greedo is part of an even bigger history.

[37] ADMIRAL ACKBAR

"It's a trap!" It's funny how one line of dialogue can make a character unforgettable. Admiral Ackbar has a lot more going for him, though. He's essentially a humanoid squid

with a uniform that would fit in at a disco. That's hard to pull off. At the center of several key battles, Admiral Ackbar has to be respected for his tactical knowledge and expertise, as well.

[36] PADMÉ AMIDALA

Given her importance in the Star Wars saga, Padmé should rank much higher. However, the way she's introduced in the prequels, it's hard to truly get behind her. Many of her costumes are amazing. But this is Star Wars, a place with strong female leads thrive and inspire. Padmé has a few moments here and there, but many are crippled by the awkward courtship between her and her "Annie."

[35] ASAJJ VENTRESS

Asajj Ventress is not only one of the toughest characters in the Star Wars universe, but she's also one of the scariest. Rising from a slave to apprentice of Count Dooku and bounty hunter, the dark side runs deep in the Dathomirian. Wielding a pair of lightsabers, she participated in several big battles in both the *Clone Wars* micro-series and was a central villain in the later *Clone Wars* series.

[34] CHOPPER

Droids have provided plenty of laughs over the course of all the films and various television shows. For machines, they sometimes offer some heart that makes them endearing. A member of the crew on *Rebels*, the C1-10P droid can be a little bit cranky at times and even do things the way he wants. But Chopper sometimes shows a more playful side. In interviews, Dave Filoni, the executive producer of *Rebels*, has compared Chopper to being like a family cat much like R2-D2 is likened to a dog.

[33] CAPTAIN REX

The story of Captain Rex is an expansive one. It's also fairly complex. He's a central figure in *The Clone Wars*. A clone himself, he's the model trooper. By the time Rebels rolled around, Rex is much older thanks to his accelerated aging. But this simply adds more depth to his personality now that he's grizzled and gone through so much.

It can also be said now that Rex's appearances didn't stop there. Dave Filoni recently acknowledged that Rex may have been fighting for the Rebels once again on Endor during *Return of the Jedi*. Filoni has supported the idea that a noticeably older fighter among the group could indeed be Captain Rex.

[32] SAW GERRERA

Somewhat of a militant extremist, Saw Gerrera's story is filled with personal tragedy. Although best known for his central role in *Rogue One*, he was first introduced on *The Clone Wars*. That's where his tragic origins are laid out. With several years and many battles happening between then and *Rogue One*, Gerrera continued to transform — mentally and physically. In the film, his appearance is somewhat monstrous, adding a bit of a frightening edge to his character.

[31] JABBA THE HUTT

Unless you're one of his prisoners or part of his endless diet, being in the company of Jabba the Hutt means a never-ending party. Pre-Special Edition, Jabba was introduced by name early on as someone Han Solo was running away from. And for good reason as said slug-like creature would later go on to use him as a wall hanging. Jabba, or at least a computer-generated imposter, was later edited back into *A New Hope* but the good one is the original from *Return of the Jedi*. The slime, the laugh, the eyes — he's grotesque and disgusting. But he commands your attention, even if you're not one of his captives.

[30] GRAND ADMIRAL THRAWN

Timothy Zahn's Star Wars novels from the early 1990s helped bring the franchise back into the mainstream. Grand Admiral Thrawn was a big reason why. Heading up the post-Vader Empire, Thrawn led by being a ruthless tactician. He's more of a thinking-person's villain than one who controlled by brute force. As part of the Expanded Universe, Thrawn was no longer part of canon for a period of time. However, he was made official again after being brought back for *Rebels*.

[29] POE DAMERON

Introduced in *The Force Awakens*, there's still a bit to be revealed about Poe. One thing that is obvious about the Resistance X-Wing pilot is his charm. As a character, he's something of an original trilogy hybrid of Luke and Han. It's obvious that Poe has a central role in the new films, but how it plays out is still a bit of a mystery. He has some great moments, particularly alongside Finn. But, there's not quite the same dynamic depth showcased by the former Stormtrooper and Rey.

[28] EZRA BRIDGER

Jedi apprentice with humble beginnings — where have you heard that before? While the parallel to the Skywalker lineage is obvious, Ezra Bridger's journey is a different one. The character that the animated *Rebels* revolves around, Ezra isn't your typical hero. As the show gets ready for its final run, there's a definite darkness about his destiny. That not only makes Rebels more interesting, but Ezra as well.

[27] K-2SO

Droids aren't generally known for their emotion. They know right from wrong, black from white. K-2SO brings a level of sarcasm and feeling not normally

40 GREATEST CHARACTERS

reserved for robots. The result is several laughs and a surprising amount of tender moments with Jynn Erso, Cassian Andor and the Rebel spies. K-2SO's imposing size and spindly arms make for a memorable look that further adds to the characterization. It's almost like the reprogrammed Imperial droid is a confused teenager or young adult coming to grips with what the future holds.

[26] QUI-GON JINN

Make no mistake about it, Qui-Gon Jinn takes up the wise Obi Wan Kenobi role of *The Phantom Menace*. His apprentice? A young, less gray-haired version of Obi Wan. A bit of an outsider among the Jedi, he's still extremely powerful with the Force and swings a strong lightsaber. Without a lot of backstory enjoyed by so many other characters, Qui-Gon can be seen as a little too similar to the older version of Kenobi introduced in *Star Wars*.

[25] BAZE MALBUS

Baze Malbus has a cool factor about him just for the massive gun that he carries. His appeal goes deeper, though. A member of the Guardians of the Whills, it's Baze's friendship with Chirrut Îmwe that makes him memorable. Despite not being seen on screen for long, the two have a deep connection that is both authentic and unique to the saga. Star Wars has its share of pairs, but few feel as genuine as Baze and Chirrut.

[24] SABINE WREN

When we think of Mandalorians in Star Wars, usually the attention shifts to Boba Fett's armor. Over the course of Rebels, Sabine has made a case. She's edgy, she's tough and her role with the Mandalorian people is one of destiny. Sabine isn't the lead in *Rebels* but she's the type of character that a lot people have gravitated towards because of her strength. But as the show has progressed, her importance has grown in key storylines. Her strength as a leader brings a sense of destiny and promise, which only makes her more interesting to watch and follow.

[23] LANDO CALRISSIAN

Lando's a suave, cape wearer who seems like the coolest guy ever — until he sells out his friend and becomes the Judas of the original trilogy. But Star Wars has plenty of redemption points with Lando being one of the swiftest. Bits and pieces of Lando's backstory have been worked into the films, books and comics, but perhaps his biggest claim to fame is losing the Millennium Falcon to Han Solo in a game of Sabaac.

[22] MARA JADE

Perhaps the most prominent member of the Expanded Universe, Mara Jade was first introduced in Timothy Zahn's "Heir to the Empire." Trained by Emperor Palpatine, she shared a connection that went beyond his death. Over the course of Zahn's novels, she undergoes a major transformation in attitude. Mara Jade became a focal point of several more Star Wars books in the years that followed. Whether villain or hero, she's one of the strongest females in all of Star Wars. At least she was. With the elimination of the Expanded Universe, Mara Jade is currently not part of canon. However, like Thrawn, that could change as the revised canon grows.

[21] KANAN JARRUS

The rugged leader of the Ghost on *Rebels,* Kanan is a Jedi who never finished his training. It could be argued that he never reached his full potential. As *Rebels* has progressed, Kanan continues to change and evolve, both physically and with his powers. Watching over and guiding Ezra, the relationship has some similarities to Obi-Wan with Anakin and later Luke. At the same time, it's different. Kanan is on his own journey of self-discovery.

[20] JYN ERSO

Jyn Erso isn't the typical Star Wars hero. She's strong, but she's part of a team. Jyn is the central figure in *Rogue One*, but she's one in a group. She's one of many. And that's what makes her role in the franchise interesting. We learn about her backstory quickly and in a straightforward manner. Jyn is a reluctant soldier, but one nonetheless. Ultimately selfless and dedicated to the important job she has no choice but completing, she gets her big moment and a somewhat surprising sendoff.

[19] FINN

Despite all the Stormtroopers shown on screen over the decades, few glimpses have been offered under the helmet. Because they act as a collective force, it makes it all the more impactful when FN-2187 removes his blood-marked mask to reveal the person we now know as Finn. Brave, funny, dedicated and a risk-taker, Finn is the consummate hero. And yet, there's still plenty we don't know about him — what he doesn't know about himself. A journey awaits, which should make him even more interesting by the time it's done.

[18] DARTH MAUL

When *The Phantom Menace* arrived, Darth Maul was everywhere. And for good reason. His stare was piercing and nightmare-inducing. His skin and horns were devilish. Let's not discount the fact that he swung a double-sided lightsaber. Unfortunately, his appearance in the film was limited. The scenes were memorable, but more from Maul was needed. He was brought back for both the animated *Clone*

Wars and *Rebels*, which helped flesh out his character more and create a character that was interesting for more than just his look.

[17] CHIRRUT ÎMWE

Sometimes you just have to believe. Chirrut Îmwe believed in the Force but he was no Jedi. That didn't stop him from trying to tap into its mystical powers. It'd be easy to overlook the heavily spiritual Chirrut Îmwe. He's an old, blind man who mutters to himself. What could he accomplish? Plenty. Even without Force powers, Chirrut knows how to take care of himself, even when surrounded by a mob of aggressive troopers. On top of all that, there's a quick wit, lots of humor, loyalty and caring demeanor. It's hard not to feel anything but warmth towards him.

[16] R2-D2

Sometimes "beeps" and "boops" can go a long way in establishing a character. R2-D2 may not be a droid of many words, but he has a way of being heard. Whether he's hacking into the Death Star computers, fixing spaceships in mid-flight, carrying messages to or cutting open an Ewok net, Artoo is a resourceful little robot who brings companionship, humor and plenty of heart — even if he doesn't have one.

[15] AHSOKA TANO

Introduced in *The Clone Wars*, Ahsoka was a Jedi Padawan working alongside Anakin. Her training paralleled her personal growth as a teenager. It was a little scary, sometimes frustrating adventure with several turning points along the way. Because we watch knowing Anakin's fate, it's also heartbreaking to see their bond form and know at some point there's going to be a breaking point.

[14] BB-8

When the first clips of BB-8 surfaced, there was a sense

that the robot could be the next Jar-Jar Binks — a character that panders to the youngest of viewers and is nothing but obnoxious. It turns out BB-8 was all right. In fact, he was more than all right. The parallels to Artoo are obvious but they're far from identical. The spherical build of BB-8 adds a sense of innovation. His part in adventures is exciting. And his "flaming thumb" provides one of the biggest laughs of all the films.

[13] EMPEROR PALPATINE

Many layers exist to this evil puppet master. Like any good villain, he plays the long game. Palpatine hides in plain sight as a Senator of the Galactic Republic. In the shadows, he's something much darker. It's Palpatine who is responsible for luring Anakin to the Dark Side and creating the monster known as Darth Vader. But much of this depth comes to light in the prequels.

Even in the original trilogy, when he's simply the Emperor, there's plenty that's frightening about him. He's old and shrivelled. He hides behind a cloak and remains largely mysterious. He shoots lightning bolts from his fingertips. And that voice, a croak that induced many a nightmare to a generation of young viewers.

[12] KYLO REN

Looking to emulate the dark path of his grandfather, Darth Vader, Kylo Ren has the dark outfit and mask that makes him memorable simply by sight. For reasons not fully revealed as of yet, there is a deep-seated rage within him. Even if there is some sort of eventual redemption, it may be hard to forgive him for putting the Dark Side before family.

[11] GRAND MOFF TARKIN

No matter how you look at it, you can't not have strong feelings towards someone who blows up an entire planet and everyone on it. When that planet happens to belong to a beloved character like Princess Leia, clench fists are bound to happen. When it comes to film, that's a good thing. Someone's doing something right if you feel emotion, no matter if it's positive or negative.

Grand Moff Tarkin is the essence of cold and calculating. He always seems to be in deep thought, treating every breath as though it were part of a massive game of chess. He's an intelligent villain who operates on logic over emotion, bring balance to Darth Vader and terror to the Rebel Alliance.

CINDY ORD/GETTY IMAGES

40 GREATEST CHARACTERS

[10] BOBA FETT

Boba Fett was at his coolest when the least was known about him. When he was introduced, he was something of a mystery man who had a cool outfit, awesome blaster and killer spaceship. He had a rocket pack to boot. And the job of bounty hunter? Boba Fett has that aura of cool surrounding him like an intergalactic James Dean. For the first couple of decades of Star Wars, Boba Fett was probably the coolest character in the saga. But through the Special Editions and prequels, we learned a little more about him and his origins. He can't be seen with the same mystery anymore. A less is more approach would have worked just fine for Boba Fett.

[9] C-3PO

C-3PO isn't the most likeable character. Sometimes, the droid can be a little irritating. If he were a kid in class, he'd be the one at the front of the room with his hand up. He's the one who always tells you when you're wrong. But that's by design. Although things may revolve around the Skywalker family, C-3PO is our guide. Precision is in his programming. And sometimes, the golden robot's takes offer up some refreshing honesty the heroes might not want to hear. But it's a reflection of the danger at hand and the excitement of the stories. As far as design goes, C-3PO is impeccable. The classic golden version harkens back to Fritz Lang's black-and-white classic *Metropolis*. It adds a level of iconography for a franchise that is filled with instantly recognizable costumes and designs.

[8] CHEWBACCA

Chewbacca is more a Wookiee of action rather than words — or growls. Primarily working as Han Solo's partner, Chewbacca is a symbol of bravery, companionship and loyalty. He may look imposing and tough (because he is), but there's a warm, cuddly side to Chewie as well that goes beyond his fur. He's a family man, one of the lone takeaways from the infamous Holiday Special.

[7] YODA

For a small, green creature, Yoda carries quite the lightsaber. Throughout the Star Wars saga, whether it's on the big screen, TV or on the page, he's a gatekeeper of sorts for the Force. And while his power and position make him notable, it's his characterization that makes him so memorable. Most of his lines have a Yogi Berra-type of nonsense to them that actually bring forth a sense of wisdom. Yoda is funny, he's cute and, perhaps most of all, he believes in the good of life even when things are at their darkest.

[6] REY

Who is Rey? We still don't fully know. But the glimpse that we've been given is that she's something special. Sometimes mystery works against you. In this online age, the mystery surrounding Rey, which will be fleshed out in *The Last Jedi* and Episode IX, makes for endless discussion and theories. It works to add to the mystique surrounding her. What we do know is that she's strong and resourceful. She's both serious and lends an element of humor. Even she doesn't fully grasp the power that she holds. That's a big part of her intrigue. *The Force Awakens* gave us a taste to show that she fits in with the Star Wars greats and it's exciting to root along with her.

[5] OBI-WAN KENOBI

Introduced as the wise wizard, Ben Kenobi turned out to be so much more. His place in the saga shows the biggest change. When things start out, he's a young jedi. He's learning and still prone to mistakes. Battle after battle, big and small, there's no character that grows more over the course of the saga than Ben Kenobi, except for maybe Anakin. The dynamic with Obi-Wan is different, though. Anakin may share a similar level of loss, but Ben deals with it differently. His place on the Light Side of the Force is never in doubt. He may not be perfect, but he's a hero at every stage.

40 GREATEST CHARACTERS

[4] PRINCESS LEIA ORGANA

Sometimes the term "princess" brings a negative connotation in movies. Princesses have a long history of being portrayed as needing to be saved by a knight in shining armor and a perfect smile. Leia Organa is not your typical princess. Yes, Star Wars sees her getting saved by not one but two handsome gents, but over the course of the rest of the original trilogy and *The Force Awakens*, she's the one giving the orders. Leia is strong. She's comfortable giving orders, making tough decisions and getting into the thick of things. Whether that's as a diplomat, a battlefield warrior, a friend, lover or family member, it doesn't matter.

[3] HAN SOLO

Han Solo is the kind of person many people imagine being in some sort of alternate reality. Free-spirited scoundrel, he does what he wants, when he wants. Han is handsome, funny, speaks his mind and usually gets his way. He's funny, he goes on adventures and he knows how to talk his way out of almost any tough situation. And those that he can't — he has a blaster in his holster and a Wookiee at his side. Even with the tough exterior, Han Solo has heart. He's loyal to his friends, even when it's inconvenient. Of the major Star Wars characters, Han is the closest thing we have to an everyman. He has no special powers, just skills. Flaws and all, it makes him rounded and relatable.

[2] LUKE SKYWALKER

From a whiny desert farm boy to wise, old wizard-type, Luke Skywalker's gone through a lot of changes. A prototypical hero, he answers the call of adventure, making many important stops and discoveries along the way — including discovering that princess he kissed was actually his sister. Luke is our guidepost through the original trilogy. Early on, it looked like he was going to be one of those unbearable leads and kill everything before the Empire got the chance. In particular, it's hard not to cringe (or laugh) when we first meet him. Just listen to him sound like a three-year-old complaining to his Uncle Owen. But then things change. Destiny takes over and a champion emerges. It goes far beyond the first Death Star. In the films and adventures that follow, Luke continues to discover more about himself, his powers and responsibility — not to mention the potential dangers those bring as Light and Dark battle on inside him.

[1] DARTH VADER/ ANAKIN SKYWALKER

Star Wars is formed around Anakin Skywalker and his descent into Darth Vader. It's a story of tragedy, rage, sadness and hope. It's the eternal struggle of good and evil played out in epic battles, iconic costumes and big moments. Because we met Anakin after we knew what he became, there's always a certain edge about his younger self. But all that lays the groundwork for the infamous villain that he would become. Even in death, he continues to influences the Dark Side through Kylo Ren. Darth Vader's menacing look matches his actions. He's a figure of strength, danger and evil — a recipe for nightmares. The movies give him several big moments, particularly when it comes to turning point battles. But Darth Vader isn't just about lightsabers and heavy breathing. He's a fleshed out and fully realized character. Between the films, TV shows, spinoff books, comics and other stories, we know who he is and how he got there. Despite all the horrible things he does, there's a certain part of us that cheers for him. So even in a universe filled with memorable characters, Vader reigns supreme.

WHAT'S LISTED?

Products in the price guide typically:

- Are produced by licensed manufacturers
- Are widely available
- Have market activity on single items

WHAT THE COLUMNS MEAN

The LO and HI columns reflect current retail selling ranges. The HI column on the right generally represents the full retail selling price. The LO column on the left generally represents the lowest price one would expect to find with extensive shopping.

CONDITION

Prices in this issue reflect the highest raw condition (i.e. not professionally graded by a third party) of the card commonly found at shows, shops, online, and right out of the pack for brand new releases. This generally means NrMint to Mint condition. Action figure prices are based on Mint condition. Action figures that are loose (out-of-package) are generally sold for 50 percent of the listed price, but may list for less/more depending on popularity, condition, completeness, and market sales.

CURRENCY

This price guide is intended to reflect the entire North American market. While not all the cards/figures are produced in the United States, they will reflect the market value in U.S. dollars.

GLOSSARY/LEGEND

Our glossary defines terms most frequently used in the action figure/non-sports card collecting hobby. Some of these terms are common to other types of collecting. Some terms may have several meanings depending on the use and context.

ALB	Album exclusive card. This indicates that a card was only available in a collector album or binder that was devoted to a certain product.
AU	Certified autograph
BB	Box bottom - A card or panel of cards on the bottom of a trading card box.
BI	Box incentive
BN	Barnes & Noble exclusive
BT	Box topper - A card, either regulation or jumbo-sized, that is inserted in the top of a box of trading cards.
C	Common card
CI	Case-Incentive or Case Insert - A unique card that is offered as an incentive to purchase a case (or cases) of trading cards.
COA	Certificate of Authenticity - A certificate issued by the manufacturer to insure a product's authenticity.
COR	Corrected version of an error (ERR) card
CT	Case-topper exclusive card
D23	Disney D23 Convention
ECCC	Emerald City Comic Con
EE	Entertainment Earth exclusive - An exclusive that was offered for sale on Entertainment Earth's website.
EL	Extremely limited
ERR	Error card - A card with erroneous information, spelling, or depiction on either side of the card, most of which are not corrected by the manufacturer.
EXCH	Exchange card
FACT	Factory set exclusive
FLK	Flocked variant - This description applies exclusively to Funko products.
FOIL	holofoil
GCE	Galactic Convention Exclusive - This description applies specifically to Funko products.
GEN	General distribution - This term most usually applies to promotional cards.
GITD	Glow-in-the-Dark variant - This description usually applies to Funko products.
GS	GameStop exclusive
HOLO	hologram

HT	Hot Topic exclusive
L	Limited
LE	Limited Edition
LS	Limited Series
MEM	Memorabilia card
MET	Metallic variant - This describes a metallic version of a Funko product.
NNO	Unnumbered card
NSU	Non-Sports Update exclusive card
NYCC	New York Comic Con
OPC	O-Pee-Chee (a Canadian subsidiary of Topps)
R	Rare card
RED	Redemption card
SDCC	San Diego Comic Con
SI	Set-Incentive
SP	Single or Short Print - A short print is a card that was printed in less quantity compared to the other cards in the same series.
SR	Super Rare card
SWC	Star Wars Celebration
TW	Toy Wars exclusive
U	Uncommon card
UER	Uncorrected error
UNC	Uncut sheet or panel
UR	Ultra Rare card
VAR	Variation card - One of two or more cards from the same series, with the same card number, that differ from one another in some way. This sometimes occurs when the manufacturer notices an error in one or more of the cards, corrects the mistake, and then resumes the printing process. In some cases, one of the variations may be relatively scarce.
VAULT	This description applies specifically to Funko products and indicates a figurine that has been re-released by the company.
VL	Very Limited
VR	Very Rare card
WG	Walgreen's exclusive
WM	Walmart exclusive

As with any publication, we appreciate reader feedback. While there are many listings, not all collectibles may be priced due to market constraints. If you have any questions, concerns, or suggestions, please contact us at: **nonsports@beckett.com**

Action Figures and Figurines

PRICE GUIDE

VINTAGE

1977-78 Star Wars 12-Backs A

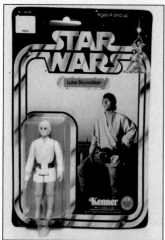

1	Ben Kenobi grey hair	1250.00	2500.00
2	Ben Kenobi white hair	1250.00	2500.00
3	Ben Kenobi (w/double telescoping lightsaber)	4000.00	8000.00
4	C-3PO	500.00	1000.00
5	Chewbacca	1000.00	2000.00
6	Darth Vader	1750.00	3500.00
7	Darth Vader (w/double telescoping lightsaber)	5000.00	8500.00
8	Death Squad Commander	450.00	900.00
10	Han Solo (small head)	1500.00	3000.00
12	Jawa (plastic cape)	5000.00	8500.00
13	Luke Skywalker (blond hair)	1500.00	3000.00
14	Luke Skywalker/telescoping lightsaber	6000.00	10000.00
15	Princess Leia	1500.00	3000.00
16	R2-D2	1000.00	2000.00
17	Stormtrooper	500.00	1000.00

1977-78 Star Wars 12-Backs B

1	Ben Kenobi (grey hair)	1000.00	2000.00
2	Ben Kenobi (white hair)	1000.00	2000.00
4	C-3PO	400.00	750.00
5	Chewbacca	800.00	1500.00
6	Darth Vader	1400.00	2800.00
10	Han Solo (small head)	1200.00	2250.00
11	Jawa	625.00	1250.00
13	Luke Skywalker (w/blond hair)	1000.00	2000.00
16	R2-D2	625.00	1250.00
17	Stormtrooper	500.00	850.00
18	Tusken Raider	500.00	850.00

1977-78 Star Wars 12-Backs C

4	C-3PO	400.00	750.00
5	Chewbacca	625.00	1250.00
6	Darth Vader	1000.00	2000.00
8	Death Squad Commander	450.00	850.00
9	Han Solo (large head)	850.00	1700.00
11	Jawa	600.00	1200.00

13	Luke Skywalker (blond hair)	750.00	1500.00
14	Luke Skywalker (w/telescoping lightsaber)	4000.00	8000.00
15	Princess Leia	500.00	1000.00
16	R2-D2	500.00	1000.00
17	Stormtrooper	400.00	750.00
18	Tusken Raider	400.00	750.00

1977-78 Star Wars 12-Backs D

4	C-3PO	400.00	750.00
5	Chewbacca	500.00	1000.00
13	Luke Skywalker (blond hair)	500.00	1000.00
15	Princess Leia	500.00	1000.00
16	R2-D2	500.00	1000.00

1977-78 Star Wars 12-Backs E

16	R2-D2	350.00	850.00

1977-78 Star Wars 20-Backs A

1	Ben Kenobi (white hair)	75.00	150.00
2	C-3PO	50.00	100.00
3	Chewbacca	60.00	120.00
5	Death Squad Commander	60.00	120.00
9	Han Solo (large head)	200.00	350.00
10	Jawa	75.00	150.00
13	Princess Leia	125.00	225.00
18	Stormtrooper	50.00	100.00
19	Tusken Raider	60.00	120.00

1977-78 Star Wars 20-Backs B

5	Chewbacca	60.00	120.00
17	Stormtrooper.	50.00	100.00
19	Death Star Droid	75.00	150.00
20	Greedo	60.00	120.00
21	Hammerhead	100.00	200.00
22	Luke X-Wing Pilot	125.00	250.00
23	Power Droid	50.00	100.00
24	R5-D4	75.00	150.00

25	Snaggletooth (red)	60.00	120.00
26	Walrus Man	60.00	120.00

1977-78 Star Wars 20-Backs C

5	Chewbacca	60.00	120.00
8	Death Squad Commander	60.00	120.00
11	Jawa	75.00	150.00
17	Stormtrooper	50.00	100.00
21	Hammerhead	100.00	200.00
22	Luke X-Wing Pilot	125.00	250.00

1977-78 Star Wars 20-Backs D

11	Jawa	75.00	150.00
19	Death Star Droid	75.00	150.00
22	Luke X-Wing Pilot	125.00	250.00
24	R5-D4	75.00	150.00

1977-78 Star Wars 20-Backs E

2	Ben Kenobi (white hair)	75.00	150.00
5	Chewbacca	60.00	120.00
6	Darth Vader	100.00	200.00
8	Death Squad Commander	60.00	120.00
11	Jawa	75.00	150.00
13	Luke Skywalker (blond hair)	150.00	300.00
15	Princess Leia	125.00	225.00
17	Stormtrooper	50.00	100.00
18	Tusken Raider	60.00	120.00
20	Greedo	60.00	120.00
21	Hammerhead	100.00	200.00
22	Luke X-Wing Pilot	125.00	250.00
23	Power Droid	50.00	100.00
24	R5-D4	75.00	150.00
25	Snaggletooth (red)	60.00	120.00
26	Walrus Man	60.00	120.00

1977-78 Star Wars 20-Backs F

6	Darth Vader	100.00	200.00
15	Princess Leia	125.00	225.00

1977-78 Star Wars 20-Backs G

8	Death Squad Commander	60.00	120.00
9	Han Solo (large head)	200.00	350.00
11	Jawa	75.00	150.00
13	Luke Skywalker (blond hair)	150.00	300.00
18	Tusken Raider	60.00	120.00

1977-78 Star Wars 20-Backs H

18	Tusken Raider	60.00	120.00

1977-78 Star Wars 20-Backs I

11	Jawa	80.00	150.00

1977-78 Star Wars 20-Backs J

11	Jawa	80.00	150.00
17	Stormtrooper	50.00	100.00
26	Walrus Man	60.00	120.00

1977-78 Star Wars 20-Backs K

11	Jawa	75.00	150.00
17	Stormtrooper	50.00	100.00
18	Tusken Raider	60.00	120.00

1977-78 Star Wars 21-Backs A1

2	Ben Kenobi (white hair)	75.00	150.00
6	Darth Vader	100.00	200.00
9	Han Solo (large head)	350.00	350.00
11	Jawa	75.00	150.00

1977-78 Star Wars 21-Backs A2

13	Luke Skywalker (blond hair)	150.00	300.00
16	R2-D2	50.00	100.00
20	Greedo	60.00	120.00
21	Hammerhead	100.00	200.00
22	Luke X-Wing Pilot	125.00	250.00
23	Power Droid	50.00	100.00
24	R5-D4	75.00	150.00
25	Snaggletooth (red)	60.00	120.00
26	Walrus Man	60.00	120.00

1977-78 Star Wars 21-Backs B

4	C-3PO	50.00	100.00
6	Darth Vader	100.00	200.00
8	Death Squad Commander	60.00	120.00
9	Han Solo (large head)	200.00	350.00
13	Luke Skywalker (blond hair)	150.00	300.00
15	Princess Leia	125.00	225.00
16	R2-D2	50.00	100.00
18	Tusken Raider	60.00	120.00
20	Greedo	60.00	120.00
21	Hammerhead	100.00	200.00
22	Luke X-Wing Pilot	125.00	250.00
23	Power Droid	50.00	100.00
24	R5-D4	75.00	150.00
25	Snaggletooth (red)	60.00	120.00
26	Walrus Man	60.00	120.00
27	Boba Fett	3000.00	5000.00

1977-78 Star Wars 21-Backs C

2	Ben Kenobi (white hair)	75.00	150.00
4	C-3PO	50.00	100.00
5	Chewbacca	60.00	120.00
6	Darth Vader	100.00	200.00
8	Death Squad Commander	60.00	120.00
9	Han Solo (large head)	200.00	350.00
13	Luke Skywalker (blond hair)	150.00	300.00
15	Princess Leia	125.00	225.00
16	R2-D2	50.00	100.00
20	Greedo	60.00	120.00
22	Luke X-Wing Pilot	125.00	250.00

23	Power Droid	50.00	100.00
25	Snaggletooth (red)	60.00	120.00
26	Walrus Man	60.00	120.00

1977-78 Star Wars 21-Backs D

13	Luke Skywalker (blond hair)	60.00	300.00

1977-78 Star Wars 21-Backs E4

26	Walrus Man	60.00	120.00

1977-78 Star Wars 21-Backs E5

26	Walrus Man	60.00	120.00

1977-78 Star Wars 21-Backs F

26	Walrus Man	60.00	120.00

1977-78 Star Wars (loose)

1a	Ben Kenobi (grey hair)	20.00	50.00
1b	Ben Kenobi (white hair)	20.00	50.00
2	Boba Fett	25.00	60.00
3	C-3PO	12.00	30.00
4	Chewbacca	12.00	30.00
5	Darth Vader	20.00	50.00
6	Death Squad Commander	10.00	25.00
7	Death Star Droid	10.00	25.00
8	Greedo	12.00	30.00
9	Hammerhead	12.00	30.00
10a	Han Solo (large head)	20.00	50.00
10b	Han Solo (small head)	20.00	50.00
11	Jawa	15.00	40.00
12a	Luke Skywalker (blond hair)	20.00	50.00
12b	Luke Skywalker (brown hair)	20.00	50.00
13	Luke Skywalker X-wing	15.00	40.00
14	Power Droid	10.00	25.00
15	Princess Leia	15.00	40.00
16	R2-D2	12.00	30.00
17	R5-D4	10.00	25.00
18a	Snaggletooth blue	75.00	350.00
	(found in cantina playset)		
18b	Snaggletooth (red)	10.00	25.00
19	Stormtrooper	10.00	25.00
20	Tusken Raider	10.00	25.00
21	Walrus Man	10.00	25.00

1978 Star Wars Accessories

1	1977 Early Bird Package w/figures Chewbacca, Leia, Luke, R2-D2	1750.00	3000.00
2	Mini Collector's Case	120.00	250.00

1978 Star Wars Accessories (loose)

10	Mini Collector's Case	15.00	30.00

1978 Star Wars Playsets

1	Cantina Adventure Set/Greedo Snaggletooth blue/Hammerhead/Walrusman	400.00	800.00
2	Creature Cantina Action	300.00	600.00
3	Death Star Space Station	600.00	1200.00
4	Droid Factory	200.00	400.00
5	Jawa Sandcrawler (radio controlled)	1200.00	3000.00
6	Land of the Jawas	150.00	300.00

1978 Star Wars Playsets (loose)

1	Cantina Adventure Set/Greedo Snaggletooth blue/Hammerhead/Walrusman	50.00	100.00
2	Creature Cantina Action		
3	Death Star Space Station	75.00	150.00
4	Droid Factory	30.00	60.00
5	Jawa Sandcrawler (radio controlled)		
6	Land of the Jawas	30.00	60.00

1978 Star Wars Vehicles

1	Imperial Troop Transporter	200.00	400.00
2	Land Speeder	125.00	250.00
3	Millenium Falcon	700.00	1200.00
4	Patrol Dewback	125.00	250.00
5	Sonic Controlled Land Speeder		600.00
6	TIE Fighter	75.00	150.00
7	TIE Fighter Darth Vader	150.00	300.00
8	X-Wing Fighter	100.00	200.00

1978 Star Wars Vehicles (loose)

1	Imperial Troop Transporter	15.00	30.00
2	Land Speeder	15.00	30.00
3	Millenium Falcon	75.00	150.00
4	Patrol Dewback	25.00	50.00
5	Sonic Controlled Land Speeder	100.00	200.00
6	TIE Fighter	25.00	50.00
7	TIE Fighter Darth Vader	30.00	60.00
8	X-Wing Fighter	30.00	60.00

1979-80 Star Wars 12-inch

1	Ben Kenobi	125.00	225.00
2	Boba Fett	300.00	600.00
3	C-3PO	125.00	250.00
4	Chewbacca	100.00	200.00
5	Darth Vader	150.00	300.00
6	Han Solo	125.00	250.00
7	IG-88	600.00	1200.00
8	Jawa	100.00	200.00
9	Luke Skywalker	125.00	250.00
10	Princess Leia	125.00	250.00
11	R2-D2	100.00	200.00
12	Stormtrooper	200.00	350.00

1979-80 Star Wars 12-inch (loose)

1	Ben Kenobi	50.00	100.00
2	Boba Fett	150.00	300.00
3	C-3PO	20.00	40.00

4 Chewbacca	30.00	60.00
5 Darth Vader	50.00	100.00
6 Han Solo	60.00	120.00
7 IG-88	150.00	300.00
8 Jawa	25.00	50.00
9 Luke Skywalker	30.00	60.00
10 Princess Leia	30.00	60.00
11 R2-D2	25.00	50.00
12 Stormtrooper	25.00	50.00

1980-82 Star Wars Empire Strikes Back 21-Backs
G

5 Ben Kenobi	50.00	100.00
8 Boba Fett	2750.00	5500.00
10 C-3PO	60.00	120.00
12 Chewbacca	50.00	100.00
14 Darth Vader	100.00	200.00
15 Death Squad Commander	150.00	300.00
16 Death Star Droid	50.00	100.00
19 Greedo	50.00	100.00
20 Hammerhead	50.00	100.00
21 Han Solo (Large Head)	60.00	120.00
29 Jawa	40.00	80.00
37 Luke Skywalker (Blond Hair)	100.00	200.00
39 Luke X-Wing Pilot	50.00	100.00
40 Power Droid	60.00	120.00
41 Princess Leia	60.00	120.00
46 R2-D2	60.00	120.00
48 R5-D4		
51 Sand People	50.00	100.00
52 Snaggletooth (Red)	40.00	80.00
54 Stormtrooper	50.00	100.00
56 Walrus Man	50.00	100.00

1980-82 Star Wars Empire Strikes Back 21-Backs
H1

| 5 Ben Kenobi | 50.00 | 100.00 |
| 39 Luke X-Wing Pilot | 50.00 | 100.00 |

1980-82 Star Wars Empire Strikes Back 21-Backs
H2

| 56 Walrus Man | 50.00 | 100.00 |

1980-82 Star Wars Empire Strikes Back 21-Backs
I

8 Boba Fett	2250.00	4500.00
19 Greedo	50.00	100.00
20 Hammerhead	50.00	100.00

1980-82 Star Wars Empire Strikes Back 31-Backs
A

5 Ben Kenobi	225.00	450.00
7 Bespin Security Guard (White)	150.00	300.00
8 Boba Fett	1500.00	3000.00
9 Bossk	350.00	675.00
12 Chewbacca	350.00	675.00
18 FX-7	300.00	575.00
19 Greedo	275.00	550.00
21 Han Solo (Large Head)	325.00	650.00
22 Han Solo (Small Head)	325.00	650.00
24 Han Solo Hoth	275.00	550.00
25 IG-88	300.00	600.00
27 Imperial Stormtrooper Hoth	225.00	450.00
29 Jawa	225.00	450.00
39 Luke X-Wing Pilot	250.00	475.00
40 Power Droid	225.00	450.00
46 R2-D2	225.00	450.00
48 R5-D4	225.00	450.00
52 Snaggletooth (Red)	200.00	400.00
53 Star Destroyer Commander	200.00	400.00
54 Stormtrooper	175.00	375.00

1980-82 Star Wars Empire Strikes Back 31-Backs
B

10 C-3PO	60.00	120.00
14 Darth Vader	100.00	200.00
16 Death Star Droid	50.00	100.00
20 Hammerhead	50.00	100.00
31 Lando Calrissian (Without Teeth)	40.00	80.00
34 Luke Bespin (Blond Hair/Walking)	100.00	200.00
37 Luke Skywalker (Blond Hair)	100.00	200.00
41 Princess Leia	60.00	120.00
42 Princess Leia Bespin (Flesh Neck)	60.00	120.00
50 Rebel Soldier Hoth	30.00	60.00
51 Sand People	50.00	100.00
54 Stormtrooper	50.00	100.00
56 Walrus Man	50.00	100.00

1980-82 Star Wars Empire Strikes Back 31-Backs
C

| 48 R5-D4 | 125.00 | 300.00 |

1980-82 Star Wars Empire Strikes Back 32-Backs
A

7 Bespin Security Guard (White)	30.00	60.00
8 Boba Fett	1500.00	3000.00
10 C-3PO	60.00	120.00
12 Chewbacca	50.00	100.00
18 FX-7	50.00	100.00
24 Han Solo Hoth	50.00	100.00
25 IG-88	60.00	120.00

37 Luke Skywalker (Blond Hair)	100.00	200.00
41 Princess Leia	60.00	120.00
50 Rebel Soldier Hoth	30.00	60.00
54 Stormtrooper	50.00	100.00
56 Walrus Man	50.00	100.00

1980-82 Star Wars Empire Strikes Back 32-Backs
B

5 Ben Kenobi	50.00	100.00
9 Bossk	200.00	350.00
14 Darth Vader	100.00	200.00
19 Greedo	50.00	100.00
21 Han Solo (Large Head)	60.00	120.00
27 Imperial Stormtrooper Hoth	60.00	120.00
31 Lando Calrissian (Without Teeth)	40.00	80.00
33 Luke Bespin (Blond Hair/Gun Drawn)	100.00	200.00
39 Luke X-Wing Pilot	50.00	100.00
42 Princess Leia Bespin (Flesh Neck)	60.00	120.00
46 R2-D2	60.00	120.00
53 Star Destroyer Commander	150.00	300.00
58 Yoda (Orange Snake)	75.00	150.00

1980-82 Star Wars Empire Strikes Back 32-Backs
C

| 7 Bespin Security Guard (White) | 30.00 | 60.00 |
| 27 Imperial Stormtrooper Hoth | 60.00 | 120.00 |

1980-82 Star Wars Empire Strikes Back 41-Backs
A

1 2-1B	30.00	60.00
2 4-LOM	75.00	150.00
3 AT-AT Commander	30.00	60.00
4 AT-AT Driver	40.00	80.00
5 Ben Kenobi	50.00	100.00

6 Bespin Security Guard (Black)	30.00	60.00
7 Bespin Security Guard (White)	30.00	60.00
8 Boba Fett	800.00	1700.00
9 Bossk	50.00	100.00
10 C-3PO	60.00	120.00
11 C-3PO (Removable Limbs)	60.00	120.00
12 Chewbacca	50.00	100.00
13 Cloud Car Pilot	40.00	80.00
14 Darth Vader	100.00	200.00
16 Death Star Droid	50.00	100.00
17 Dengar	60.00	120.00
18 FX-7	50.00	100.00
19 Greedo	50.00	100.00
20 Hammerhead	50.00	100.00
21 Han Solo (Large Head)	60.00	120.00
22 Han Solo (Small Head)	60.00	120.00
23 Han Solo Bespin	60.00	120.00
24 Han Solo Hoth	50.00	100.00
25 IG-88	60.00	120.00
26 Imperial Commander	30.00	60.00
27 Imperial Stormtrooper Hoth	60.00	120.00
28 Imperial TIE Fighter Pilot	50.00	100.00
29 Jawa	40.00	80.00
30 Lando Calrissian (With Teeth)	40.00	80.00
31 Lando Calrissian (Without Teeth)	40.00	80.00
32 Lobot	40.00	80.00
33 Luke Bespin (Blond Hair/Gun Drawn)	100.00	200.00
35 Luke Bespin (Brown Hair/Gun Drawn)	100.00	200.00
36 Luke Hoth	50.00	100.00
37 Luke Skywalker (Blond Hair)	50.00	100.00
39 Luke X-Wing Pilot	50.00	100.00
40 Power Droid	60.00	120.00
41 Princess Leia	60.00	120.00
45 Princess Leia Hoth	60.00	120.00
46 R2-D2	60.00	120.00
47 R2-D2 (Sensorscope)	75.00	150.00
48 R5-D4		
49 Rebel Commander	40.00	80.00
50 Rebel Soldier Hoth	30.00	60.00
51 Sand People	50.00	100.00
52 Snaggletooth (Red)	40.00	80.00
53 Star Destroyer Commander	150.00	300.00
54 Stormtrooper	50.00	100.00
56 Walrus Man	50.00	100.00
58 Yoda (Orange Snake)	75.00	150.00
59 Zuckuss	50.00	100.00

1980-82 Star Wars Empire Strikes Back 41-Backs
B

1 2-1B	30.00	60.00
8 Boba Fett	500.00	1000.00
9 Bossk	50.00	100.00
10 C-3PO	60.00	120.00
18 FX-7	50.00	100.00
21 Han Solo (Large Head)	60.00	120.00
32 Lobot	40.00	80.00
33 Luke Bespin (Blond Hair/Gun Drawn)	100.00	200.00
39 Luke X-Wing Pilot	50.00	100.00
50 Rebel Soldier Hoth	30.00	60.00
54 Stormtrooper	50.00	100.00
57 Yoda (Brown Snake)	300.00	600.00
58 Yoda (Orange Snake)	75.00	150.00

1980-82 Star Wars Empire Strikes Back 41-Backs
C

4 AT-AT Driver	40.00	80.00
7 Bespin Security Guard (White)	30.00	60.00
12 Chewbacca	50.00	100.00
24 Han Solo Hoth	50.00	100.00
25 IG-88	60.00	120.00
26 Imperial Commander	30.00	60.00
29 Jawa	40.00	80.00

37 Luke Skywalker (Blond Hair)	100.00	200.00
41 Princess Leia	60.00	120.00
49 Rebel Commander	40.00	80.00
55 Ugnaught	30.00	60.00
56 Walrus Man	50.00	100.00

1980-82 Star Wars Empire Strikes Back 41-Backs
D

1 2-1B	30.00	60.00
8 Boba Fett	900.00	1800.00
18 FX-7	50.00	100.00
21 Han Solo (Large Head)	60.00	120.00
23 Han Solo Bespin	60.00	120.00
27 Imperial Stormtrooper Hoth	60.00	120.00
30 Lando Calrissian (With Teeth)	40.00	80.00
32 Lobot	40.00	80.00
35 Luke Bespin (Brown Hair/Gun Drawn)	100.00	200.00
39 Luke X-Wing Pilot	50.00	100.00
44 Princess Leia Bespin (Neck Painted/Front)	60.00	120.00
45 Princess Leia Hoth	60.00	120.00
50 Rebel Soldier Hoth	30.00	60.00
54 Stormtrooper	50.00	100.00
57 Yoda (Brown Snake)	100.00	200.00
58 Yoda (Orange Snake)	75.00	150.00

1980-82 Star Wars Empire Strikes Back 41-Backs
E

4 AT-AT Driver	40.00	80.00
7 Bespin Security Guard (White)	30.00	60.00
10 C-3PO	60.00	120.00
12 Chewbacca	50.00	100.00
17 Dengar	60.00	120.00
19 Greedo	50.00	100.00
24 Han Solo Hoth	50.00	100.00
25 IG-88	60.00	120.00
26 Imperial Commander	30.00	60.00
27 Imperial Stormtrooper Hoth	60.00	120.00
29 Jawa	40.00	80.00
37 Luke Skywalker (Blond Hair)	100.00	200.00
38 Luke Skywalker (Brown Hair)	125.00	250.00
41 Princess Leia	60.00	120.00
49 Rebel Commander	40.00	80.00
50 Rebel Soldier Hoth	30.00	60.00
51 Sand People	50.00	100.00
52 Snaggletooth (Red)	40.00	80.00
53 Star Destroyer Commander	150.00	300.00
55 Ugnaught	30.00	60.00
56 Walrus Man	50.00	100.00

1980-82 Star Wars Empire Strikes Back 45-Backs
A

1980-82 Star Wars Empire Strikes Back 45-Backs

1 2-1B	30.00	60.00
2 4-LOM	75.00	150.00
3 AT-AT Commander	30.00	60.00
5 Ben Kenobi	50.00	100.00
6 Bespin Security Guard (Black)	30.00	60.00
7 Bespin Security Guard (White)	30.00	60.00
9 Bossk	50.00	100.00
10 C-3PO	60.00	120.00
12 Chewbacca	50.00	100.00
13 Cloud Car Pilot	40.00	80.00
14 Darth Vader	100.00	200.00
15 Death Squad Commander	150.00	300.00
16 Death Star Droid	50.00	100.00
19 Greedo	50.00	100.00
20 Hammerhead	50.00	100.00
21 Han Solo (Large Head)	60.00	120.00
22 Han Solo (Small Head)	60.00	120.00
23 Han Solo Bespin	60.00	120.00
24 Han Solo Hoth	50.00	100.00
26 Imperial Commander	30.00	60.00
27 Imperial Stormtrooper Hoth	60.00	120.00
28 Imperial TIE Fighter Pilot	50.00	100.00
29 Jawa	40.00	80.00
30 Lando Calrissian (With Teeth)	40.00	80.00
32 Lobot	40.00	80.00
34 Luke Bespin (Blond Hair/Walking)	100.00	200.00
35 Luke Bespin (Brown Hair/Gun Drawn)	100.00	200.00
36 Luke Hoth	50.00	100.00
38 Luke Skywalker (Brown Hair)	100.00	200.00
39 Luke X-Wing Pilot	50.00	100.00
41 Princess Leia	60.00	120.00
42 Princess Leia Bespin (Flesh Neck)	200.00	350.00
44 Princess Leia Bespin (Neck Painted/Front)	200.00	350.00
45 Princess Leia Hoth	60.00	120.00
46 R2-D2	60.00	120.00
47 R2-D2 (Sensorscope)	75.00	150.00
48 R5-D4		
49 Rebel Commander	40.00	80.00
50 Rebel Soldier Hoth	30.00	60.00
51 Sand People	50.00	100.00
52 Snaggletooth (Red)	40.00	80.00
53 Star Destroyer Commander	150.00	300.00
54 Stormtrooper	50.00	100.00
55 Ugnaught	30.00	60.00
56 Walrus Man	50.00	100.00
57 Yoda (Brown Snake)	100.00	200.00
59 Zuckuss	50.00	100.00

1980-82 Star Wars Empire Strikes Back 45-Backs
B

3 AT-AT Commander	30.00	60.00
6 Bespin Security Guard (Black)	30.00	60.00
14 Darth Vader	100.00	200.00
27 Imperial Stormtrooper Hoth	60.00	120.00
50 Rebel Soldier Hoth	30.00	60.00

1980-82 Star Wars Empire Strikes Back 47-Backs
A

1 2-1B	30.00	60.00
2 4-LOM	75.00	150.00
3 AT-AT Commander	30.00	60.00
4 AT-AT Driver	40.00	80.00
5 Ben Kenobi	50.00	100.00
6 Bespin Security Guard (Black)	30.00	60.00
7 Bespin Security Guard (White)	30.00	60.00
8 Boba Fett	600.00	1200.00
9 Bossk	50.00	100.00
11 C-3PO (Removable Limbs)	60.00	120.00
12 Chewbacca	50.00	100.00
13 Cloud Car Pilot	40.00	80.00
14 Darth Vader	100.00	200.00
15 Death Squad Commander	150.00	300.00
16 Death Star Droid	50.00	100.00
17 Dengar	60.00	120.00
18 FX-7	50.00	100.00
19 Greedo	50.00	100.00
20 Hammerhead	50.00	100.00
21 Han Solo (Large Head)	60.00	120.00
23 Han Solo Bespin	60.00	120.00
24 Han Solo Hoth	50.00	100.00
25 IG-88	60.00	120.00
26 Imperial Commander	30.00	60.00
27 Imperial Stormtrooper Hoth	60.00	120.00
28 Imperial TIE Fighter Pilot	50.00	100.00
29 Jawa	40.00	80.00
30 Lando Calrissian (With Teeth)	40.00	80.00
32 Lobot	40.00	80.00
35 Luke Bespin (Brown Hair/Gun Drawn)	125.00	250.00
36 Luke Hoth	50.00	100.00
37 Luke Skywalker (Blond Hair)	100.00	200.00
38 Luke Skywalker (Brown Hair)	125.00	250.00
39 Luke X-Wing Pilot	50.00	100.00
40 Power Droid	60.00	120.00
41 Princess Leia	60.00	120.00
44 Princess Leia Bespin (Neck Painted/Front)		
45 Princess Leia Hoth	60.00	120.00
47 R2-D2 (Sensorscope)	75.00	150.00
48 R5-D4		
49 Rebel Commander	40.00	80.00
50 Rebel Soldier Hoth	30.00	60.00
51 Sand People	50.00	100.00
52 Snaggletooth (Red)	40.00	80.00
53 Star Destroyer Commander	150.00	300.00
54 Stormtrooper	50.00	100.00
55 Ugnaught	30.00	60.00
56 Walrus Man	50.00	100.00
57 Yoda (Brown Snake)	100.00	200.00
58 Yoda (Orange Snake)	75.00	150.00

1980-82 Star Wars Empire Strikes Back 48-Backs
A

1 2-1B	30.00	60.00
3 AT-AT Commander	30.00	60.00
5 Ben Kenobi	50.00	100.00
6 Bespin Security Guard (Black)	30.00	60.00
7 Bespin Security Guard (White)	30.00	60.00
11 C-3PO (Removable Limbs)	60.00	120.00
12 Chewbacca	50.00	100.00
13 Cloud Car Pilot	40.00	80.00
24 Han Solo Hoth	50.00	100.00
26 Imperial Commander	30.00	60.00
27 Imperial Stormtrooper Hoth	60.00	120.00
28 Imperial TIE Fighter Pilot	50.00	100.00
36 Luke Hoth	50.00	100.00
39 Luke X-Wing Pilot	50.00	100.00
45 Princess Leia Hoth	60.00	120.00
47 R2-D2 (Sensorscope)	75.00	150.00
49 Rebel Commander	40.00	80.00
51 Sand People	50.00	100.00
52 Snaggletooth (Red)	40.00	80.00
54 Stormtrooper	50.00	100.00
59 Zuckuss	50.00	100.00

1980-82 Star Wars Empire Strikes Back 48-Backs
B

2 4-LOM	75.00	150.00
5 Ben Kenobi	50.00	100.00
6 Bespin Security Guard (Black)	30.00	60.00
7 Bespin Security Guard (White)	30.00	60.00
9 Bossk	50.00	100.00
11 C-3PO (Removable Limbs)	60.00	120.00
14 Darth Vader	100.00	200.00
17 Dengar	60.00	120.00
18 FX-7	50.00	100.00
26 Imperial Commander	30.00	60.00
27 Imperial Stormtrooper Hoth	60.00	120.00
28 Imperial TIE Fighter Pilot	50.00	100.00
30 Lando Calrissian (With Teeth)	40.00	80.00
33 Luke Bespin (Blond Hair/Gun Drawn)	100.00	200.00
35 Luke Bespin (Brown Hair/Gun Drawn)	125.00	250.00
39 Luke X-Wing Pilot	50.00	100.00
49 Rebel Commander	40.00	80.00
50 Rebel Soldier Hoth	40.00	80.00
54 Stormtrooper	50.00	100.00
55 Ugnaught	30.00	60.00
57 Yoda (Brown Snake)	100.00	200.00
59 Zuckuss	50.00	100.00

1980-82 Star Wars Empire Strikes Back 48-Backs
C

1 2-1B	25.00	60.00
2 4-LOM	80.00	150.00
3 AT-AT Commander	25.00	60.00
4 AT-AT Driver	30.00	80.00
5 Ben Kenobi	50.00	100.00
6 Bespin Security Guard (Black)	25.00	60.00
8 Boba Fett	225.00	450.00
9 Bossk	50.00	100.00
11 C-3PO (Removable Limbs)	60.00	120.00
12 Chewbacca	50.00	100.00
13 Cloud Car Pilot	40.00	80.00
14 Darth Vader	100.00	200.00
18 FX-7	50.00	100.00
23 Han Solo Bespin	60.00	120.00
24 Han Solo Hoth	50.00	100.00
25 IG-88	60.00	120.00
26 Imperial Commander	30.00	60.00
28 Imperial TIE Fighter Pilot	50.00	100.00
29 Jawa	40.00	80.00
30 Lando Calrissian (With Teeth)	40.00	80.00
32 Lobot	40.00	80.00

35 Luke Bespin (Brown Hair/Gun Drawn)	100.00	200.00
36 Luke Hoth	50.00	100.00
39 Luke X-Wing Pilot	50.00	100.00
49 Rebel Commander	40.00	80.00
50 Rebel Soldier Hoth	30.00	60.00
51 Sand People	50.00	100.00
52 Snaggletooth (Red)	40.00	80.00
53 Star Destroyer Commander	150.00	300.00
54 Stormtrooper	50.00	100.00
55 Ugnaught	30.00	60.00
57 Yoda (Brown Snake)	100.00	200.00
59 Zuckuss	50.00	100.00

1980-82 Star Wars Empire Strikes Back (loose)

1 2-1B	6.00	12.00
2 4-LOM	12.50	25.00
3 AT-AT Commander	6.00	12.00
4 AT-AT Driver	7.50	15.00
5a Ben Kenobi (grey hair)	10.00	20.00
5b Ben Kenobi (white hair)	10.00	20.00
6a Bespin guard (black)	6.00	12.00
6b Bespin guard (white)	6.00	12.00
7 Boba Fett	25.00	50.00
8 Bossk	7.50	15.00
9 C-3PO	7.50	15.00
10 C-3PO (removable limbs)	7.50	15.00
11 Chewbacca	6.00	12.00
12 Cloud Car Pilot	6.00	12.00
13 Darth Vader	10.00	20.00
14 Death Squad Commander	10.00	20.00
15 Death Star Droid	6.00	12.00
16 Dengar	6.00	12.00
17 FX-7	6.00	12.00
18 Greedo	6.00	12.00
19 Hammerhead	6.00	12.00
20 Han Solo (Bespin)	7.50	15.00
21 Han Solo (Hoth gear)	6.00	12.00
22 Han Solo (large head)	6.00	12.00
23 Han Solo (small head)	6.00	12.00
24 IG-88	7.50	15.00
25 Imperial Commander	6.00	12.00
26 Imperial Stormtrooper	7.50	15.00
27 Jawa	6.00	12.00
28 Lando Calrissian	6.00	12.00
29 Lando Calrrissian (no teeth)	6.00	12.00
30 Lobot	7.50	15.00
31a Luke Skywalker	10.00	20.00
(Bespin yellow hair tan legs)		
31b Luke Skywalker		
(Bespin yellow hair brown legs)		
31c Luke Skywalker	10.00	20.00
(Bespin brown hair)		
31d Luke Skywalker	12.50	20.00
(Bespin white shirt blond hair)		
31e Luke Skywalker	12.50	25.00
(Bespin white shirt brown hair)		
32 Luke Skywalker (Hoth gear)	6.00	12.00
33 Luke Skywalker X-wing	6.00	12.00
34 Power Droid	7.50	15.00
35a Princess Leia Organa	7.50	15.00
(Bespin flesh neck)		
35b Princess Leia Organa	7.50	15.00
(Bespin turtle neck)		
35c Princess Leia Organa		
(Bespin gold/green neck)		
36 Leia Organa (Hoth gear)	7.50	15.00
37a R2-D2	7.50	15.00
37b R2-D2 (sensorscope)	7.50	15.00
38 R5-D4		
39 Rebel Commander	6.00	12.00
40 Rebel Soldier (Hoth gear)	6.00	12.00
41 Snaggletooth (red)	6.00	12.00
42 Stormtrooper	6.00	12.00

ACTION FIGURES AND FIGURINES

43 TIE Fighter Pilot	6.00	12.00
44 Tusken Raider	6.00	12.00
45 Ugnaught		12.00
46 Walrusman	6.00	12.00
48a Yoda (brown snake)	7.50	15.00
48b Yoda (orange snake)	7.50	15.00
49 Zuckuss	6.00	12.00

1980-82 Star Wars Empire Strikes Back Accessories

1 Darth Vader Case	200.00	350.00
2 Darth Vader Case/Boba Fett/IG88	200.00	400.00
3 Mini Collector's Case	125.00	225.00

1980-82 Star Wars Empire Strikes Back Accessories (loose)

1 Darth Vader Case	15.00	30.00
2 Mini Collector's Case	15.00	30.00

1980-82 Star Wars Empire Strikes Back Playsets

1 Cloud City	200.00	400.00
2 Dagobah	125.00	250.00
3 Darth Vader/ Star Destroyer	125.00	250.00
4 Droid Factory	200.00	350.00
5 Hoth Ice Planet	75.00	150.00
6 Imperial Attack Base	125.00	225.00
7 Land of the Jawas	100.00	200.00
8 Rebel Command Center	100.00	200.00
9 Turret and Probot	40.00	80.00

1980-82 Star Wars Empire Strikes Back Playsets (loose)

1 Cloud City	30.00	60.00
2 Dagobah	25.00	50.00
3 Darth Vader/ Star Destroyer	25.00	50.00
4 Droid Factory	30.00	60.00
5 Hoth Ice Planet	20.00	40.00
6 Imperial Attack Base	30.00	60.00
7 Land of the Jawas	30.00	60.00
8 Rebel Command Center	30.00	60.00
9 Turret and Probot	12.50	25.00

1980-82 Star Wars Empire Strikes Back Vehicles

1 AT-AT	150.00	300.00
2 Imperial Cruiser	100.00	200.00
3 Imperial Transport	100.00	200.00
4 Millenium Falcon	250.00	500.00
5 Patrol Dewback	100.00	200.00
6 Rebel Transport	100.00	200.00
7 Scout Walker	75.00	150.00
8 Slave 1	100.00	200.00
9a Snowspeeder (blue box)	60.00	120.00
9b Snowspeeder (pink box)	75.00	150.00
10 Tauntaun	50.00	100.00
11 Tauntaun (split belly)	60.00	120.00
12 TIE Fighter	75.00	150.00
13 Twin Pod Cloud Car	40.00	80.00
14 Wampa	150.00	300.00
15a X-Wing Fighter (battle damage red photo background box)	100.00	200.00
15b X-Wing Fighter (battle damage landscape photo background box)	100.00	200.00

1980-82 Star Wars Empire Strikes Back Vehicles (loose)

1 AT-AT	40.00	80.00
2 Imperial Cruiser	15.00	30.00
3 Imperial Transport	15.00	30.00
4 Millenium Falcon	50.00	100.00
5 Patrol Dewback	25.00	50.00
6 Rebel Transport	15.00	30.00
7 Scout Walker	15.00	30.00
8 Slave 1	60.00	125.00
9 Snowspeeder	15.00	30.00
10 Tauntaun	20.00	40.00
11 Tauntaun split belly	25.00	50.00
12 TIE Fighter	25.00	50.00
13 Twin Pod Cloud Car	20.00	40.00
14 Wampa	25.00	60.00
15 X-Wing Fighter	30.00	60.00

1980 Star Wars Empire Strikes Back Micro Set

1 Bespin Control Room/Darth Vader Darth Vader lightsaber/Luke Skywalker	30.00	60.00
2 Bespin Freeze Chamber/Boba Fett Darth Vader/Han Solo in cuffs/Han Solo	75.00	150.00
3 Bespin Gantry/Darth Vader Darth Vader lightsaber/Luke Skywalker	40.00	80.00
4 Bespin World/Boba Fett/Darth Vader Darth Vader lightsaber/Han Solo carbonite	100.00	200.00
5 Death Star Compactor/Ben Kenobi Darth Vader lightsaber/Han Solo stormtrooper	125.00	225.00
6 Death Star Escape/Chewbacca	40.00	80.00

Darth Vader/Luke Skywalker/Princess Leia		
7 Death Star World/Ben Kenobi	125.00	225.00
Chewbacca/Darth Vader/Darth Vader lightsaber/Han Solo/Luke Skywalker/Luke Skywalker stormtrooper/Princess Leia/Princess Leia holding gun/Stormtrooper kneeling/Stormtrooper walking/Stormtrooper firing/Stormtrooper firing u		
8 Hoth Generator Attack/AT-AT	30.00	60.00
AT-AT Operator/Darth Vader unpainted/Rebel		
9 Hoth Ion Cannon/Rebel on Tauntaun	50.00	100.00
Rebel crouching/Rebel laying		
10 Hoth Turret Defense	40.00	80.00
Rebel on Tauntaun blaster/Rebel crouching		
11 Hoth Wampa Cave/Chewbacca	30.00	60.00
Han Solo/Luke Skywalker hanging/Probot/Wampa		
12 Hoth World/Hot Wampa Cave	100.00	200.00
Hoth Ion Cannon/Hoth Generator Attack		
13 Imperial TIE Fighter	50.00	100.00
TIE Fighter Pilot		
14 Millenium Falcon/C-3PO	150.00	300.00
Chewbacca with wrench/Lando Calrissian/Luke Skywalker		
15 Snowspeeder	75.00	150.00
X-Wing Pilot sitting/X-Wing Pilot crouching		
16 X-Wing/X-Wing Pilot	75.00	150.00

1980 Star Wars Empire Strikes Back Micro Set (loose)

1 Bespin Control Room	7.50	15.00
2 Bespin Freeze Chamber	12.50	25.00
3 Bespin Gantry	7.50	15.00
4 Bespin World	12.50	25.00
5 Death Star Compactor	12.50	25.00
6 Death Star Escape	7.50	15.00
7 Death Star World	12.50	25.00
8 Hoth Generator Attack	7.50	15.00
9 Hoth Ion Cannon	10.00	20.00
10 Hoth Turret Defense	6.00	12.00
11 Hoth Wampa Cave	7.50	15.00
12 Hoth World	12.50	25.00
13 Imperial Tie Fighter	6.00	12.00
14 Millenium Falcon	12.50	25.00
15 Snowspeeder	6.00	12.00
16 X-Wing	7.50	15.00
17 AT-AT	6.00	12.00
18 AT-AT Operator	.75	2.00
19 Ben Kenobi	1.50	4.00
20 Boba Fett	.75	2.00
21 C-3PO	.75	2.00
22 Chewbacca	.75	2.00
23 Chewbacca (with wrench)	.75	2.00
24 Darth Vader	1.25	3.00
25 Darth Vader (lightsaber)	1.25	3.00
26 Darth Vader (unpainted)	1.25	3.00
27 Han Solo	1.25	3.00
28 Han Solo (carbonite)	1.25	3.00
29 Han Solo (in cuffs)	1.25	3.00
30 Han Solo (stormtrooper)	1.25	3.00
31 Lando Calrissian	.75	2.00
32 Lobot	.75	2.00
33 Luke Skywalker	1.25	3.00
34 Luke Skywalker (hanging)	1.25	3.00
35 Luke Skywalker (lightsaber)	1.25	3.00
36 Luke Skywalker (stormtrooper)	1.25	3.00
37 Princess Leia	1.25	3.00
38 Princess Leia (holding gun)	1.25	3.00
39 Probot	.75	2.00
40 Rebel (crouching)	.75	2.00
41 Rebel (gun at side/unpainted)	.75	2.00
42 Rebel (gun on hip/unpainted)	.75	2.00
43 Rebel (gun on sholder/unpainted)	.75	2.00
44 Rebel (gun on shoulder)	.75	2.00
45 Rebel (laying)	.75	2.00
46 Rebel (laying unpainted)	.75	2.00
47 Rebel (on Tauntaun)	.75	2.00
48 Rebel (on Tauntaun w/blaster)	.75	2.00

49 Rebel (w/blaster at side)	.75	2.00
50 Rebel (w/blaster brown)	.75	2.00
51 Rebel (w/blaster white)	.75	2.00
52 Stormtrooper	.75	2.00
53 Stormtrooper (firing)	.75	2.00
54 Stormtrooper (kneeling)	.75	2.00
55 Stormtrooper (on gun)	.75	2.00
56 Stormtrooper (walking)	.75	2.00
57 TIE Fighter Pilot	.75	2.00
58 Turret Operator	.75	2.00
59 Wampa	1.00	2.50
60 X-Wing Pilot	.75	2.00
61 X-Wing Pilot (crouching)	.75	2.00
62 X-Wing Pilot (sitting)	.75	2.00

1980 Star Wars Empire Strikes Back Mini Rigs

1 CAP-2	10.00	20.00
2 INT-4	20.00	40.00
3 MLC-3	12.50	25.00
4 MTV-7	20.00	40.00
5 PDT-8	15.00	30.00
6 Tripod Laser Canon	20.00	40.00

1980 Star Wars Empire Strikes Back Mini Rigs (loose)

1 CAP-2	5.00	10.00
2 INT-4	7.50	15.00
3 MLC-3	5.00	10.00
4 MTV-7	6.00	12.00
5 PDT-8	7.50	15.00
6 Tripod Laser Canon	7.50	15.00

1983 Star Wars Return of the Jedi 48-Backs D

1 2-1B	40.00	80.00
2 4-LOM	40.00	80.00
5 AT-AT Commander	25.00	50.00
6 AT-AT Driver	40.00	80.00
8 Ben Kenobi	30.00	60.00
10 Bespin Security Guard (black)	30.00	60.00
11 Bespin Security Guard (white)	30.00	60.00
14 Boba Fett	300.00	700.00
16 Bossk	40.00	80.00
18 C-3PO (removable limbs)	40.00	80.00
19 Chewbacca	40.00	80.00
22 Cloud Car Pilot	30.00	60.00
23 Darth Vader	60.00	120.00
25 Death Star Droid	30.00	60.00
26 Dengar	30.00	60.00
28 FX-7	30.00	60.00
31 Greedo	40.00	80.00
32 Hammerhead	25.00	50.00
33 Han Solo (large head)	100.00	200.00
35 Han Solo (Bespin)	60.00	120.00
36 Han Solo (Hoth gear)	60.00	120.00
38 IG-88	20.00	40.00
39 Imperial Commander	40.00	80.00
40 Imperial Stormtrooper Hoth	40.00	80.00
41 Imperial TIE Fighter Pilot	50.00	100.00
42 Jawa	50.00	100.00
46 Lando Calrissian (with teeth)	30.00	60.00
47 Lobot	30.00	60.00
49 Luke Bespin (brown hair gun drawn)	150.00	300.00
50 Luke Hoth	60.00	120.00
55 Luke Skywalker (brown hair)		
56 Luke X-Wing Pilot	100.00	200.00
61 Power Droid	50.00	100.00
62 Princess Leia	450.00	800.00
63 Princess Leia (Bespin neck painted front)		

66 Princess Leia (Hoth)	125.00	250.00
68 R2-D2 (sensorscope)	40.00	80.00
69 R5-D4	50.00	100.00
71 Rebel Commander	40.00	80.00
75 Sand People	40.00	80.00
76 Snaggletooth (red)	50.00	100.00
78 Star Destroyer Commander		
79 Stormtrooper	50.00	100.00
82 Ugnaught	40.00	80.00
83 Walrus Man	30.00	60.00
86 Yoda (brown snake)	60.00	120.00
88 Zuckuss	20.00	40.00

1983 Star Wars Return of the Jedi 65-Backs A

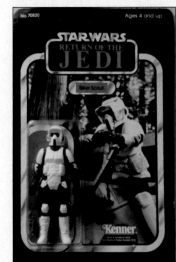

2 4-LOM	40.00	80.00
4 Admiral Ackbar	25.00	50.00
6 AT-AT Driver	40.00	80.00
8 Ben Kenobi	30.00	60.00
10 Bespin Security Guard (black)	30.00	60.00
12 Bib Fortuna	25.00	50.00
13 Biker Scout	30.00	60.00
14 Boba Fett	250.00	500.00
18 C-3PO (removable limbs)	40.00	80.00
19 Chewbacca	40.00	80.00
21 Chief Chirpa	20.00	40.00
22 Cloud Car Pilot	30.00	60.00
23 Darth Vader	60.00	120.00
25 Death Star Droid	30.00	60.00
26 Dengar	30.00	60.00
27 Emperor's Royal Guard	40.00	80.00
29 Gamorrean Guard	25.00	50.00
30 General Madine	20.00	40.00
33 Han Solo (large head)	100.00	200.00
41 Imperial TIE Fighter Pilot	50.00	100.00
42 Jawa	50.00	100.00
43 Klaatu	20.00	40.00
45 Lando Calrisian (skiff)	25.00	50.00
48 Logray	20.00	40.00
50 Luke Hoth	60.00	120.00
51 Luke Jedi Knight (blue lightsaber)	75.00	150.00
52 Luke Jedi Knight (green lightsaber)	75.00	150.00
56 Luke X-Wing Pilot	100.00	200.00
58 Nien Nunb	25.00	50.00
64 Princess Leia (Boushh)	40.00	80.00
68 R2-D2 (sensorscope)	40.00	80.00
72 Rebel Commando	20.00	40.00
74 Ree-Yees	20.00	40.00

77 Squid Head	20.00	40.00
79 Stormtrooper	50.00	100.00
84 Weequay	20.00	40.00
86 Yoda (brown snake)	60.00	120.00
87 Yoda (brown snake/new image)	60.00	120.00
88 Zuckuss	20.00	40.00

1983 Star Wars Return of the Jedi 65-Backs B

1 2-1B	40.00	80.00
2 4-LOM	40.00	80.00
4 Admiral Ackbar	25.00	50.00
5 AT-AT Commander	25.00	50.00
6 AT-AT Driver	40.00	80.00
8 Ben Kenobi	30.00	60.00
10 Bespin Security Guard (black)	30.00	60.00
12 Bib Fortuna	25.00	50.00
13 Biker Scout	30.00	60.00
16 Bossk	40.00	80.00
18 C-3PO (removable limbs)	40.00	80.00
19 Chewbacca	40.00	80.00
21 Chief Chirpa	20.00	40.00
22 Cloud Car Pilot	30.00	60.00
23 Darth Vader	60.00	120.00
24 Darth Vader (new image)	60.00	120.00
25 Death Star Droid	30.00	60.00
27 Emperor's Royal Guard	40.00	80.00
29 Gamorrean Guard	25.00	50.00
30 General Madine	20.00	40.00
33 Han Solo (large head)	100.00	200.00
35 Han Solo (Bespin)	60.00	120.00
36 Han Solo (Hoth gear)	60.00	120.00
38 IG-88	20.00	40.00
39 Imperial Commander	40.00	80.00
40 Imperial Stormtrooper Hoth	40.00	80.00
41 Imperial TIE Fighter Pilot	50.00	100.00
42 Jawa		
43 Klaatu	20.00	40.00
45 Lando Calrisian (skiff)	25.00	50.00
46 Lando Calrisian (with teeth)	30.00	60.00
48 Logray	20.00	40.00
51 Luke Jedi Knight (blue lightsaber)	75.00	150.00
53 Luke Skywalker (blond hair)	100.00	200.00
56 Luke X-Wing Pilot	100.00	200.00
58 Nien Nunb	25.00	50.00
61 Power Droid	50.00	100.00
63 Princess Leia (Bespin neck painted/front picture)		
64 Princess Leia (Boushh)	40.00	80.00
66 Princess Leia (Hoth gear)	125.00	250.00
68 R2-D2 (sensorscope)	40.00	80.00
69 R5-D4	50.00	100.00
71 Rebel Commander	30.00	60.00
72 Rebel Commando	20.00	40.00
73 Rebel Soldier Hoth	50.00	100.00
74 Ree-Yees	20.00	40.00
75 Sand People	40.00	80.00
77 Squid Head	20.00	40.00
78 Star Destroyer Commander		
79 Stormtrooper	50.00	100.00
82 Ugnaught	40.00	80.00
84 Weequay	20.00	40.00
86 Yoda (brown snake)	60.00	120.00
88 Zuckuss	20.00	40.00

1983 Star Wars Return of the Jedi 65-Backs C

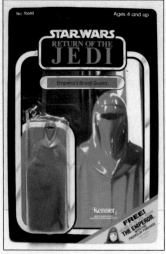

1983 Star Wars Return of the Jedi 77-Backs A

2 4-LOM	40.00	80.00
4 Admiral Ackbar	25.00	50.00
9 Ben Kenobi (new image)	30.00	60.00
12 Bib Fortuna	25.00	50.00
13 Biker Scout	40.00	80.00
15 Boba Fett (new image)	350.00	700.00
18 C-3PO (removable limbs)	40.00	80.00
20 Chewbacca (new image)	40.00	80.00
21 Chief Chirpa	20.00	40.00
23 Darth Vader	60.00	120.00
24 Darth Vader (new image)	60.00	120.00
27 Emperor's Royal Guard	40.00	80.00
29 Gamorrean Guard	25.00	50.00
30 General Madine	20.00	40.00
34 Han Solo (large head/new image)	100.00	200.00
41 Imperial TIE Fighter Pilot	40.00	80.00
42 Jawa	50.00	100.00
43 Klaatu	20.00	40.00
44 Klaatu (skiff)		
45 Lando Calrisian (skiff)	25.00	50.00
48 Logray	20.00	40.00
51 Luke Jedi Knight (blue lightsaber)	75.00	150.00
52 Luke Jedi Knight (green lightsaber)	75.00	150.00
58 Nien Nunb	25.00	50.00
64 Princess Leia (Boushh)	40.00	80.00
68 R2-D2 (sensorscope)	40.00	80.00
72 Rebel Commando	20.00	40.00
74 Ree-Yees	20.00	40.00
77 Squid Head	20.00	40.00
79 Stormtrooper	50.00	100.00
84 Weequay	20.00	40.00
87 Yoda (brown snake/new image)	60.00	120.00
88 Zuckuss	20.00	40.00

1983 Star Wars Return of the Jedi 65-Backs D

1 2-1B	40.00	80.00
4 Admiral Ackbar	25.00	50.00
13 Biker Scout	40.00	80.00
19 Chewbacca	40.00	80.00
21 Chief Chirpa	20.00	40.00
24 Darth Vader (new image)	60.00	120.00
29 Gamorrean Guard	25.00	50.00

1983 Star Wars Return of the Jedi 65-Backs E

30 General Madine	20.00	40.00

1 2-1B	40.00	80.00
2 4-LOM	40.00	80.00
3 8D8	25.00	50.00
4 Admiral Ackbar	25.00	50.00
5 AT-AT Commander	25.00	50.00
6 AT-AT Driver	40.00	80.00
7 AT-ST Driver	20.00	40.00
9 Ben Kenobi (new image)	30.00	60.00
10 Bespin Security Guard (black)	30.00	60.00
11 Bespin Security Guard (white)	30.00	60.00
12 Bib Fortuna	25.00	50.00
13 Biker Scout	40.00	80.00
15 Boba Fett (new image)	350.00	700.00
16 Bossk	40.00	80.00
17 B-Wing Pilot	20.00	40.00
18 C-3PO (removable limbs)	40.00	80.00
20 Chewbacca (new image)	40.00	80.00
21 Chief Chirpa	20.00	40.00
22 Cloud Car Pilot	30.00	60.00
24 Darth Vader (new image)	60.00	120.00
25 Death Star Droid	30.00	60.00
26 Dengar	30.00	60.00
27 Emperor's Royal Guard	40.00	80.00
28 FX-7	30.00	60.00
29 Gamorrean Guard	25.00	50.00
30 General Madine	20.00	40.00
31 Greedo	40.00	80.00
32 Hammerhead	25.00	50.00
34 Han Solo (large head/new image)	100.00	200.00
35 Han Solo (Bespin)	60.00	120.00
36 Han Solo (Hoth gear)	60.00	120.00
37 Han Solo (trench coat)	30.00	60.00
38 IG-88	20.00	40.00
39 Imperial Commander	40.00	80.00
40 Imperial Stormtrooper Hoth	40.00	80.00
41 Imperial TIE Fighter Pilot	50.00	100.00
42 Jawa	50.00	100.00
43 Klaatu	20.00	40.00
44 Klaatu (skiff)	20.00	40.00
45 Lando Calrisian (skiff)	25.00	50.00
46 Lando Calrissian (with teeth)	30.00	60.00
47 Lobot	30.00	60.00
48 Logray	20.00	40.00
49 Luke Bespin (brown hair gun drawn)	150.00	300.00
50 Luke Hoth	60.00	120.00
52 Luke Jedi Knight (green lightsaber)	75.00	150.00
54 Luke Skywalker (blond hair gunner	350.00	600.00
56 Luke X-Wing Pilot	100.00	200.00
58 Nien Nunb	25.00	50.00
59 Nikto	20.00	40.00
61 Power Droid	50.00	100.00
62 Princess Leia	450.00	800.00

63 Princess Leia (Bespin neck painted/front picture)		
64 Princess Leia (Boushh)	40.00	80.00
65 Princess Leia (poncho)	40.00	80.00
66 Princess Leia (Hoth gear)	125.00	250.00
67 Prune Face	20.00	40.00
68 R2-D2 (sensorscope)	40.00	80.00
69 R5-D4	50.00	100.00
70 Rancor Keeper	20.00	40.00
71 Rebel Commander	30.00	60.00
72 Rebel Commando	20.00	40.00
73 Rebel Soldier Hoth	50.00	100.00
74 Ree-Yees	20.00	40.00
75 Sand People	40.00	80.00
76 Snaggletooth (red)	50.00	100.00
77 Squid Head	20.00	40.00
78 Star Destroyer Commander		
79 Stormtrooper	50.00	100.00
80 Teebo	20.00	40.00
81 The Emperor	40.00	80.00
82 Ugnaught	40.00	80.00
83 Walrus Man	30.00	60.00
84 Weequay	20.00	40.00
85 Wicket	40.00	80.00
87 Yoda (brown snake/new image)	60.00	120.00
88 Zuckuss	20.00	40.00

1983 Star Wars Return of the Jedi 77-Backs B

1 2-1B	25.00	50.00
5 AT-AT Commander		
7 AT-ST Driver	20.00	40.00
10 Bespin Security Guard (black)	30.00	60.00
11 Bespin Security Guard (white)	30.00	60.00
13 Biker Scout	30.00	60.00
21 Chief Chirpa	20.00	40.00
24 Darth Vader (new image)	60.00	120.00
26 Dengar	30.00	60.00
28 FX-7	30.00	60.00
29 Gamorrean Guard	25.00	50.00
30 General Madine	20.00	40.00
32 Hammerhead	25.00	50.00
34 Han Solo (large head/new image)	100.00	200.00
37 Han Solo (trench coat)	30.00	60.00
41 Imperial TIE Fighter Pilot	40.00	80.00
43 Klaatu	20.00	40.00
49 Luke Bespin (brown hair/gun drawn)	150.00	300.00
56 Luke X-Wing Pilot	100.00	200.00
59 Nikto	20.00	40.00
61 Power Droid	50.00	100.00
65 Princess Leia (poncho)	40.00	80.00
66 Princess Leia (Hoth gear)	125.00	250.00
67 Prune Face	20.00	40.00
70 Rancor Keeper	20.00	40.00
73 Rebel Soldier Hoth	50.00	100.00
74 Ree-Yees	20.00	40.00
76 Snaggletooth (red)		
77 Squid Head	20.00	40.00
79 Stormtrooper	50.00	100.00
80 Teebo	20.00	40.00
82 Ugnaught	40.00	80.00
84 Weequay	20.00	40.00

1983 Star Wars Return of the Jedi 79-Backs A

3 8D8	25.00	50.00
6 AT-AT Driver	40.00	80.00
7 AT-ST Driver	20.00	40.00
9 Ben Kenobi (new image)	30.00	60.00
15 Boba Fett (new image)	275.00	500.00
17 B-Wing Pilot	20.00	40.00
18 C-3PO (removable limbs)	40.00	80.00
24 Darth Vader (new image)	60.00	120.00
27 Emperor's Royal Guard	40.00	80.00
29 Gamorrean Guard	25.00	50.00

31 Greedo	40.00	80.00
37 Han Solo Trench Coat	30.00	60.00
41 Imperial TIE Fighter Pilot	40.00	80.00
42 Jawa	50.00	100.00
43 Klaatu	20.00	40.00
44 Klaatu (skiff)	20.00	40.00
45 Lando Calrisian (skiff)	25.00	50.00
46 Lando Calrissian (with teeth)	30.00	60.00
52 Luke Jedi Knight (green lightsaber)	75.00	150.00
59 Nikto	20.00	40.00
64 Princess Leia (Boushh)	40.00	80.00
65 Princess Leia (poncho)	40.00	80.00
67 Prune Face	20.00	40.00
70 Rancor Keeper	20.00	40.00
74 Ree-Yees	20.00	40.00
76 Snaggletooth (red)	50.00	100.00
79 Stormtrooper	50.00	100.00
80 Teebo	20.00	40.00
81 The Emperor	40.00	80.00
82 Ugnaught	40.00	80.00
83 Walrus Man	30.00	60.00
85 Wicket	40.00	80.00
87 Yoda (brown snake/new image)	60.00	120.00
88 Zuckuss	20.00	40.00

1983 Star Wars Return of the Jedi 79-Backs B

3 8D8	25.00	50.00
7 AT-ST Driver	20.00	40.00
12 Bib Fortuna	25.00	50.00
17 B-Wing Pilot	20.00	40.00
20 Chewbacca (new image)	40.00	80.00
21 Chief Chirpa	20.00	40.00
24 Darth Vader (new image)	60.00	120.00
27 Emperor's Royal Guard	40.00	80.00
29 Gamorrean Guard	25.00	50.00
35 Han Solo Bespin	60.00	120.00
43 Klaatu	20.00	40.00
44 Klaatu (skiff)		
45 Lando Calrisian (skiff)	25.00	50.00
48 Logray	20.00	40.00
52 Luke Jedi Knight (green lightsaber)	75.00	150.00
56 Luke X-Wing Pilot	100.00	200.00
64 Princess Leia (Boushh)	40.00	80.00
65 Princess Leia (poncho)	40.00	80.00
69 R5-D4	50.00	100.00
70 Rancor Keeper	20.00	40.00
72 Rebel Commando	20.00	40.00
74 Ree-Yees	20.00	40.00
80 Teebo	20.00	40.00
81 The Emperor	40.00	80.00
84 Weequay	20.00	40.00
85 Wicket	40.00	80.00

1983 Star Wars Return of the Jedi 79-Backs C

57 Lumat	40.00	80.00
60 Paploo	40.00	80.00

1983 Star Wars Return of the Jedi (loose)

1 2-1B	6.00	12.00
2 4-LOM	12.50	25.00
3 8D8	6.00	12.00
4 Admiral Ackbar	6.00	12.00
5 Amanaman	60.00	125.00
6 AT-AT Commander	6.00	12.00
7 AT-AT Driver	7.50	15.00
8 AT-ST Driver	6.00	12.00
9 Barada	25.00	60.00
10 Ben Kenobi (blue saber)	10.00	20.00
11 Ben Kenobi (gray hair)	10.00	20.00
12 Ben Kenobi (white hair)	10.00	20.00
13 Bespin Guard (black)	6.00	12.00
14 Bespin Guard (white)	6.00	12.00
15 Bib Fortuna	5.00	10.00
16 Biker Scout (long mask)	5.00	10.00
17 Biker Scout (short mask)	7.50	15.00
18 Boba Fett	25.00	50.00
19 Bossk	7.50	15.00
20 B-Wing Pilot	5.00	10.00
21 C-3PO (removable limbs)	7.50	15.00
22 Chewbacca	6.00	12.00
23 Chief Chirpa	5.00	10.00
24 Cloud Car Pilot	6.00	12.00
25 Darth Vader	10.00	20.00
26 Death Squad Commander	10.00	20.00
27 Death Star Droid	6.00	12.00
28 Dengar	6.00	12.00
29 Dengar (white face)	7.50	15.00
30 Droopy McCool	5.00	10.00
31 Emperor	7.50	
32 Emperors Royal Guard	6.00	12.00
33 FX-7	6.00	12.00
34 Gamorrean Guard	5.00	10.00
35 General Madine	5.00	10.00
36 Greedo	6.00	12.00
37 Hammerhead	6.00	12.00
38 Han Solo	7.50	15.00
39 Han Solo (Bespin)	6.00	12.00
40 Han Solo (carbonite)	80.00	150.00
41 Han Solo (Hoth gear)	6.00	12.00
42 Han Solo (trench coat)	6.00	12.00
43 IG-88	7.50	15.00
44 Imperial Commander	6.00	12.00
45 Imperial Dignitary	20.00	40.00
46 Imperial Gunner	20.00	40.00
47 Imperial Stormtrooper	7.50	15.00
48 Imperial TIE Fighter Pilot	6.00	12.00
49 Jawa	6.00	12.00
50 Klaatu	5.00	10.00
51 Klaatu (skiff)	5.00	10.00
52 Lando Calrissian	6.00	12.00
53 Lando Calrissian (skiff)	6.00	12.00
54 Lobot	7.50	15.00
55 Logray	5.00	10.00
56 Luke Skywalker	10.00	20.00
57 Luke Skywalker bespin	10.00	20.00
brown hair		
58 Luke Skywalker bespin	10.00	20.00
white shirt blond hair		
59 Luke Skywalker bespin	12.50	25.00
white shirt brown hair		
60 Luke Skywalker bespin		

yellow hair brown legs		
61 Luke Skywalker bespin	10.00	20.00
yellow hair tan legs		
62 Luke Skywalker (Hoth gear)	6.00	12.00
63 Luke Skywalker (stormtrooper)	5.00	10.00
64 Luke Skywalker Jedi Knight (blue lightsaber)	6.00	12.00
65 Luke Skywalker Jedi Knight(green lightsaber)	10.00	20.00
66 Luke Skywalker X-wing	50.00	100.00
67 Lumat	10.00	20.00
68 Max Rebo	5.00	10.00
69 Nien Nunb	5.00	10.00
70 Nikto	5.00	10.00
71 Paploo	5.00	10.00
72 Power Droid	5.00	10.00
73 Princess Leia Organa	5.00	10.00
74 Princess Leia Organa	10.00	20.00
bespin flesh neck		
75 Princess Leia Organa bespin	7.50	15.00
gold neck sometimes looks green		
76 Princess Leia Organa	7.50	15.00
bespin turtle neck		
77 Princess Leia Organa (Boushh)		
78 Princess Leia Organa (Hoth gear)	7.50	15.00
79 Princess Leia Organa (poncho)	7.50	15.00
80 Prune Face	7.50	15.00
81 R2-D2 sensorscope	5.00	10.00
82 R5-D4	7.50	15.00
83 Rancor	7.50	15.00
84 Rancor Keeper	20.00	40.00
85 Rebel Commander	5.00	10.00
86 Rebel Commando	5.00	10.00
87 Rebel Soldier (Hoth gear)	5.00	10.00
88 Ree-Yees	6.00	12.00
89 Romba	5.00	10.00
90 Sand People		
91 Snaggletooth (red)	6.00	12.00
92 Snowtrooper	6.00	12.00
93 Squid Head	15.00	30.00
94 Stormtrooper	5.00	10.00
95 Sy Snootles	6.00	12.00
96 Teebo	5.00	10.00
97 Ugnaught	5.00	10.00
98 Walrusman	5.00	10.00
99 Weequay	6.00	12.00
100 Wicket	5.00	10.00
101 Yoda (brown snake)	7.50	15.00
102 Zuckuss	6.00	12.00

1983 Star Wars Return of the Jedi Accessories

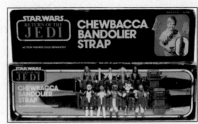

1 C-3PO Case	30.00	60.00
2 Chewy Strap	25.00	50.00
3 Darth Vader Case	75.00	150.00
4 Jedi Vinyl Case	100.00	200.00
5 Laser Rifle Case	40.00	80.00

1983 Star Wars Return of the Jedi Accessories (loose)

1 C-3PO Case	15.00	30.00
2 Chewy Strap	15.00	30.00
3 Darth Vader Case	15.00	30.00

4 Jedi Vinyl Case		15.00	30.00
5 Laser Rifle Case		15.00	30.00

1983 Star Wars Return of the Jedi Playsets

1 Ewok Village		100.00	200.00
2 Jabba The Hutt		30.00	60.00
Salacious Crumb			
3 Jabba The Hutt Dungeon		75.00	150.00
Klaatu/Nikto/8D8			
4 Jabba The Hutt Dungeon		300.00	650.00
EV-9D9/Amanaman/Barada			

1983 Star Wars Return of the Jedi Playsets (loose)

1 Ewok Village		30.00	60.00
2 Jabba The Hutt		15.00	30.00
3 Jabba The Hutt Dungeon		20.00	40.00

1983 Star Wars Return of the Jedi Vehicles

1 AT-AT		150.00	300.00
2 B-Wing Fighter		75.00	150.00
3 Ewok Assault Catapult		25.00	50.00
4 Ewok Glider		30.00	60.00
5 Imperial Shuttle		250.00	500.00
6 Millenium Falcon		125.00	250.00
7 Rancor		150.00	300.00
8 Scout Walker		50.00	100.00
9 Speeder Bike		20.00	40.00
10 Sy Snootles and the Rebo Band		120.00	250.00
(w/Sy Snootles/Droopy McCool/Max Rebo)			
11 TIE Fighter (battle damage)		40.00	80.00
12 TIE Interceptor		60.00	120.00
13 X-Wing (battle damage)		75.00	150.00
14 Y-Wing		75.00	150.00

1983 Star Wars Return of the Jedi Vehicles (loose)

1 AT-AT		40.00	80.00
2 B-Wing Fighter		30.00	60.00
3 Droopy McCool		12.00	30.00
4 Ewok Assault Catapult		15.00	30.00
5 Ewok Glider		15.00	30.00
6 Imperial Shuttle		30.00	60.00
7 Max Rebo		8.00	20.00
8 Millenium Falcon		50.00	100.00
9 Rancor		30.00	80.00
10 Scout Walker		15.00	30.00
11 Speeder Bike		7.50	15.00
12 Sy Snootles		10.00	25.00
13 TIE Fighter (battle damage)		20.00	40.00
14 TIE Interceptor		20.00	40.00
15 X-Wing (battle damage)		30.00	60.00
16 Y-Wing		30.00	60.00

1983 Star Wars Return of the Jedi Tri-Logo

1 2-1B		30.00	60.00
2 8D8		30.00	60.00
3 A-Wing Pilot		40.00	80.00
4 Admiral Ackbar		20.00	40.00
5 Amanaman		100.00	200.00
6 Anakin Skywalker		25.00	50.00
7 AT-AT Commander		20.00	40.00
8 AT-ST Driver		30.00	60.00
9 B-Wing Pilot		20.00	40.00
10 Barada		40.00	80.00
11 Ben Kenobi (blue lightsaber)		60.00	120.00
12 Bespin Guard (black/ tri-logo back only)		150.00	300.00
13 Bespin Guard (white/ tri-logo back only)		250.00	500.00
14 Bib Fortuna		15.00	30.00
15 Biker Scout (long mask)		30.00	60.00
16 Boba Fett		350.00	700.00
17 Bossk		40.00	80.00
18 C-3PO (removable limbs)		40.00	80.00
19 Chewbacca		40.00	80.00
20 Darth Vader		75.00	150.00
21 Death Star Droid		40.00	80.00
22 Dengar		25.00	50.00
23 Emperor		30.00	60.00
24 Emperors Royal Guard		150.00	300.00
25 FX-7		30.00	60.00
26 Gamorrean Guard		30.00	60.00
27 General Madine		60.00	120.00
28 Greedo (tri-logo back only)		60.00	120.00
29 Hammerhead (tri-logo back only)		40.00	80.00
30 Han Solo		75.00	150.00
31 Han Solo (carbonite)		250.00	500.00
32 IG-88		100.00	200.00
33 Imperial Commander		50.00	100.00
34 Imperial Dignitary		125.00	250.00
35 Imperial Gunner		125.00	250.00
36 Jawa		500.00	1000.00
37 Klaatu		15.00	30.00
38 Klaatu (skiff)		25.00	50.00
39 Lando Calrissian		40.00	80.00
40 Lando Calrissian (skiff)		30.00	60.00
41 Lobot		30.00	60.00
42 Luke Skywalker (Bespin)		200.00	400.00
43 Luke Skywalker (gunner card)		125.00	250.00
44 Luke Skywalker (Hoth gear)		200.00	400.00
45 Luke Skywalker Jedi Knight		40.00	80.00
46 Luke Skywalker (stormtrooper)		150.00	300.00
47 Luke Skywalker (poncho)		30.00	60.00
48 Luke Skywalker X-wing		100.00	200.00
49 Lumat		30.00	60.00
50 Nien Nunb		50.00	100.00
51 Nikto		15.00	30.00
52 Paploo		15.00	30.00
53 Princess Leia Organa		60.00	120.00
54 Princess Leia Organa (Bespin turtle neck)		60.00	120.00
55 Princess Leia Organa (Boushh)		75.00	150.00
56 Princess Leia Organa (poncho)		50.00	100.00
57 Prune Face		25.00	50.00
58a R2-D2 (sensorscope/blue background card)		20.00	40.00
58b R2-D2 (sensorscope/sparks card)		75.00	120.00
59 R5-D4		30.00	60.00
60 Rancor		20.00	40.00
61 Rebel Soldier (Hoth gear)		40.00	80.00
62 Ree-Yees		20.00	40.00
63 Romba		30.00	60.00
64 Snowtrooper		30.00	60.00
65 Squid Head		25.00	50.00
66 Stormtrooper		100.00	200.00
67 TIE Fighter Pilot		30.00	60.00
68 Ugnaught		30.00	60.00
69 Warok		50.00	100.00
70 Wicket		40.00	80.00
71 Yak Face		1200.00	2500.00
72a Yoda (brown snake)		50.00	100.00
72b Yoda (orange snake)		500.00	900.00

1985 Star Wars Droids Cartoon

1 A-Wing Pilot		250.00	500.00
2 Boba Fett		1200.00	2500.00
3 C-3PO		250.00	500.00
4 Jann Tosh		30.00	60.00
5 Jord Dusat		30.00	60.00
6 Kea Moll		30.00	60.00
7 Kez-Iban		30.00	60.00
8 R2-D2		250.00	500.00
9 Sise Fromm		150.00	300.00
10 Thall Joben		30.00	60.00
11 Tig Fromm		75.00	150.00
12 Uncle Gundy		30.00	60.00

1985 Star Wars Droids Cartoon (loose)

1 A-Wing Pilot		40.00	80.00
2 Boba Fett		125.00	225.00
3 C-3PO		40.00	80.00
4 Jann Tosh		15.00	30.00
5 Jord Dusat		15.00	30.00
6 Kea Moll		15.00	30.00
7 Kez-Iban		15.00	30.00
8 R2-D2		40.00	80.00
9 Sise Fromm		60.00	120.00
10 Thall Joben		15.00	30.00
11 Tig Fromm		40.00	80.00
12 Uncle Gundy		15.00	30.00

1985 Star Wars Droids Cartoon Coins (loose)

1 A-Wing Pilot		4.00	10.00
2 Boba Fett		12.50	25.00
3 C-3PO		4.00	10.00
4 Jann Tosh		4.00	10.00
5 Jord Dusat		4.00	10.00
6 Kea Moll		4.00	10.00
7 Kez-Iban		4.00	10.00
8 R2-D2		5.00	12.00
9 Sise Fromm		4.00	10.00
10 Thall Joben		4.00	10.00
11 Tig Fromm		4.00	10.00
12 Uncle Gundy		4.00	10.00

ACTION FIGURES AND FIGURINES

1985 Star Wars Droids Cartoon Vehicles

1 A-Wing Fighter	50.00	100.00
2 ATL Interceptor	50.00	100.00
3 Sidegunner	30.00	60.00

1985 Star Wars Droids Cartoon Vehicles (loose)

1 A-Wing Fighter	25.00	50.00
2 ATL Interceptor	25.00	50.00
3 Sidegunner	15.00	30.00

1985 Star Wars Ewoks Cartoons

1 Dulok Scout	25.00	50.00
2 Dulok Shaman	30.00	60.00
3 King Gorneesh	20.00	40.00
4 Lady Gorneesh	25.00	50.00
5 Logray	40.00	80.00
6 Wicket	50.00	100.00

1985 Star Wars Ewoks Cartoons (loose)

1 Dulok Scout	12.50	25.00
2 Dulok Shaman	15.00	30.00
3 King Gorneesh	10.00	20.00
4 Lady Gorneesh	12.50	25.00
5 Logray	20.00	40.00
6 Wicket	25.00	50.00

1985 Star Wars Ewoks Cartoons Coins (loose)

1 Dulok Scout	4.00	10.00
2 Dulok Shaman	4.00	10.00
3 King Gorneesh	4.00	10.00
4 Lady Gorneesh	4.00	10.00
5 Logray	5.00	12.00
60 Wicket	5.00	12.00

1985 Star Wars Power of the Force

1 A-Wing Pilot	50.00	100.00
2 Amanaman	150.00	300.00
3 Anakin Skywalker		
4 AT-AT Driver		
5 AT-ST Driver	50.00	100.00
6 B-Wing Pilot	25.00	50.00
7 Barada	100.00	250.00
8 Ben Kenobi (blue saber)	60.00	120.00
9 Biker Scout	75.00	150.00
10 C-3PO (removable limbs)	50.00	100.00
11 Chewbacca	50.00	100.00
12 Darth Vader	100.00	200.00
13 Emperor	40.00	80.00
14 EV-9D9	175.00	350.00
15 Gamorrean Guard	200.00	400.00
16 Han Solo (carbonite)	150.00	400.00
17 Han Solo (trench coat)	400.00	700.00
18 Imperial Dignitary	50.00	100.00
19 Imperial Gunner	50.00	100.00
20 Jawa	50.00	100.00
21 Lando Calrissian	60.00	120.00
22 Luke Skywalker (Hoth gear)		
23 Luke Skywalker (Jedi)	75.00	150.00
24 Luke Skywalker (poncho)	60.00	120.00
25 Luke Skywalker (stormtrooper)	125.00	250.00
26 Luke Skywalker X-wing	60.00	120.00
27 Lumat	40.00	80.00
28 Nikto	1000.00	1500.00
29 Paploo	40.00	80.00
30 Princess Leia (poncho)	40.00	80.00
31 R2-D2 (lightsaber)	200.00	400.00
32 Romba	40.00	80.00
33 Stormtrooper	100.00	200.00
34 Teebo	60.00	120.00
35 TIE Fighter Pilot		
36 Ugnaught		
37 Warok	50.00	100.00
38 Wicket	40.00	80.00
39 Yak Face	3000.00	7000.00
40 Yoda (brown snake)	300.00	600.00

1985 Star Wars Power of the Force (loose)

1 A-Wing Pilot	25.00	50.00
2 Amanaman	40.00	80.00
3 Anakin Skywalker	15.00	30.00
4 AT-AT Driver		
5 AT-ST Driver	10.00	20.00
6 B-Wing Pilot	10.00	20.00
7 Barada	20.00	40.00
8 Ben Kenobi (blue saber)	20.00	40.00
9 Biker Scout	20.00	40.00
10 C-3PO (removable limbs)	10.00	20.00
11 Chewbacca	20.00	40.00
12 Darth Vader	20.00	40.00
13 Emperor	15.00	30.00
14 EV-9D9	25.00	50.00
15 Gamorrean Guard	50.00	100.00
16 Han Solo (carbonite)	100.00	200.00
17 Han Solo (trench coat)	125.00	225.00
18 Imperial Dignitary	30.00	60.00
19 Imperial Gunner	50.00	100.00
20 Jawa	20.00	40.00
21 Lando Calrissian	25.00	50.00
22 Luke Skywalker (Hoth gear)	25.00	50.00
23 Luke Skywalker (Jedi)	25.00	50.00
24 Luke Skywalker (poncho)	25.00	50.00
25 Luke Skywalker (stormtrooper)	40.00	80.00
26 Luke Skywalker X-wing	25.00	50.00
27 Lumat	15.00	30.00
28 Nikto		
29 Paploo	12.50	25.00
30 Princess Leia (poncho)	20.00	40.00
31 R2-D2 (lightsaber)	100.00	200.00
32 Romba	15.00	30.00
33 Stormtrooper	30.00	60.00
34 Teebo	12.50	25.00
35 TIE Fighter Pilot		
36 Ugnaught		

37 Warok	20.00	40.00
38 Wicket	20.00	40.00
39 Yak Face	350.00	700.00
40 Yoda (brown snake)	75.00	150.00

1985 Star Wars Power of the Force Coins (loose)

1 A-Wing Pilot	6.00	12.00
2 Amanaman	6.00	12.00
3 Anakin Skywalker	20.00	40.00
4 AT-AT Driver		
5 AT-ST Driver	5.00	10.00
6 B-Wing Pilot	5.00	10.00
7 Barada	7.50	15.00
8 Ben Kenobi (blue saber)	7.50	15.00
9 Biker Scout	7.50	15.00
10 C-3PO (removable limbs)	6.00	12.00
11 Chewbacca	7.50	15.00
12 Darth Vader	10.00	20.00
13 Emperor	7.50	15.00
14 EV-9D9	7.50	15.00
15 Gamorrean Guard	10.00	20.00
16 Han Solo (carbonite)	10.00	20.00
17 Han Solo (trench coat)	15.00	30.00
18 Imperial Dignitary	7.50	15.00
19 Imperial Gunner	5.00	10.00
20 Jawa	10.00	20.00
21 Lando Calrissian	6.00	12.00
22 Luke Skywalker (Hoth gear)	10.00	20.00
23 Luke Skywalker (Jedi)	10.00	20.00
24 Luke Skywalker (poncho)	10.00	20.00
25 Luke Skywalker (stormtrooper)	15.00	30.00
26 Luke Skywalker X-wing	10.00	20.00
27 Lumat	5.00	10.00
28 Nikto		
29 Paploo	5.00	10.00
30 Princess Leia (poncho)	7.50	15.00
31 R2-D2 (lightsaber)	7.50	15.00
32 Romba	5.00	10.00
33 Stormtrooper	10.00	20.00
34 Teebo	5.00	10.00
35 TIE Fighter Pilot		
36 Ugnaught		
37 Warok	6.00	12.00
38 Wicket	10.00	20.00
39 Yak Face	150.00	300.00
40 Yoda (brown snake)	20.00	40.00

1985 Star Wars Power of the Force Vehicles

1 Ewok Battle Wagon	125.00	250.00
2 Imperial Sniper Vehicle	75.00	150.00
3 Sand Skimmer	75.00	150.00
4 Security Scout	75.00	150.00
5 Tattoine Skiff	200.00	400.00

1985 Star Wars Power of the Force Vehicles (loose)

1 Ewok Battle Wagon	50.00	100.00
2 Imperial Sniper Vehicle	30.00	60.00
3 Sand Skimmer	30.00	60.00
4 Security Scout	30.00	60.00
5 Tattoine Skiff	100.00	200.00

ACTION FIGURES AND FIGURINES

ACTION FIGURES AND FIGURINES

2018 Solo A Star Wars Story Force Link 2.0

NNO	Chewbacca	6.00	12.00
NNO	Darth Vader	10.00	20.00
NNO	Emperor's Royal Guard		
NNO	Han Solo		
NNO	K-2SO		
NNO	Kylo Ren		
NNO	L3-37		
NNO	Luke Skywalker Jedi Knight		
NNO	Luke Skywalker Jedi Master		
NNO	Maz Kanata		
NNO	Moloch		
NNO	Princess Leia Organa		
NNO	Qi'Ra		
NNO	Quay Tolsite		
NNO	Range Trooper		
NNO	Rey		
NNO	Rio Durant		
NNO	Stormtrooper		
NNO	Stormtrooper Officer		
NNO	Supreme Leader Snoke		
NNO	Tobias Beckett		
NNO	Val		

2018 Solo A Star Wars Story Force Link 2.0 2-Packs

NNO	Han Solo/Chewbacca	15.00	30.00
NNO	Lando Calrissian/Kessel Guard	10.00	20.00
NNO	Qui-Gon Jinn/Darth Maul (w/probe droid)	7.50	15.00
NNO	Rebolt/Corellian Hound	20.00	40.00
NNO	Rose Tico (w/BB-8)/BB-9E	7.50	15.00

2018 Solo A Star Wars Story Force Link 2.0 Creatures

NNO	Rathtar (w/Bala-Tik)	10.00	20.00
NNO	Wampa (w/Luke Skywalker)	15.00	30.00

2018 Solo A Star Wars Story Force Link 2.0 Multi-Packs

NNO	Starter Set (w/Han Solo)	12.50	25.00
NNO	Han Solo/Qi'Ra/Range Trooper/Weazel	30.00	60.00
	(Mission on Vandor 4-Pack)		
NNO	Kylo Ren/Maz Kanata/Poe Dameron/Rey/Snowtrooper		
	(Last Jedi 5-Pack Entertainment Earth Exclusive)		

2018 Solo A Star Wars Story Force Link 2.0 Vehicles

NNO	A-Wing Fighter (w/Tallie)		
NNO	Imperial AT-DT Walker (w/Stormtrooper)	40.00	80.00
NNO	Kessel Run Millennium Falcon (w/Han Solo)	50.00	100.00
NNO	M-68 Landspeeder (w/Han Solo)	15.00	30.00
NNO	Swoop Bike (w/Enfys Nest)	25.00	50.00
NNO	TIE Fighter (w/TIE Fighter Pilot)	30.00	60.00

2007-08 Star Wars 30th Anniversary Collection

1	Darth Vader (w/30th Anniversary coin album)	10.00	25.00
2	Galactic Marine	4.00	8.00
3	Mustafar Lava Miner	4.00	8.00
4	R2-D2	4.00	8.00
5	Obi-Wan Kenobi	4.00	8.00
6	Mace Windu	6.00	12.00
7	Airborne Trooper	4.00	8.00
8	Super Battle Droid	4.00	8.00
9	Concept Stormtrooper	4.00	8.00
	(McQuarrie Signature Series)		
10	Rebel Honor Guard (Yavin)	4.00	8.00
11	Han Solo (smuggler)	4.00	8.00
12	Luke Skywalker (Yavin ceremony)	4.00	8.00
13	Death Star Trooper	5.00	10.00
14	Biggs Darklighter (Rebel pilot)	4.00	8.00
15	Concept Boba Fett (McQuarrie Signature Series)	12.00	25.00
16	Darth Vader (removable helmet)	4.00	8.00
17	Biggs Darklighter (academy gear)	4.00	8.00
18	Luke Skywalker (moisture farmer)	8.00	15.00
19	Jawa & LIN Droid (Tatooine scavenger)	4.00	8.00
20	Imperial Stormtrooper (Galactic Empire)	4.00	8.00
21	Concept Chewbacca	6.00	12.00
	(McQuarrie Signature Series)		
22	M'liyoom Onith (Hementhe)	5.00	10.00
23	Elis Helrot (Givin)	5.00	10.00
24	Boba Fett (animated debut)	6.00	12.00
25	Luke Skywalker (Jedi Knight)	4.00	8.00
26	CZ-4 (CZ-Series droid)	4.00	8.00
27	Umpass-Stay (Klatooinian)	4.00	8.00
28	Concept Darth Vader	8.00	15.00
	(McQuarrie Signature Series)		
29	Hermi Odle (Baragwin)	12.00	25.00
30	C-3PO & Salacious Crumb (Jabba's Servants)	10.00	20.00
31	Roron Corobb (Jedi Knight)	6.00	12.00
32	Yoda & Kybuck (Jedi Master)	4.00	8.00
33	Anakin Skywalker (Jedi Knight)	4.00	8.00
34	Darth Revan (Sith Lord)	30.00	60.00
35	Darth Malak (Sith Lord)	15.00	30.00
36	Pre-Cyborg Grievous	20.00	40.00
	(Kaleesh warlord Qymaen jai Sheelal)		
37	Concept Starkiller Hero	4.00	8.00
	(McQuarrie Signature Series)		
38	Han Solo (w/torture rack)	10.00	20.00
39	Lando Calrissian (smuggler)	4.00	8.00
40	General McQuarrie (Rebel officer)	4.00	8.00
41	4-LOM (bounty hunter)	4.00	8.00
42	Concept Snowtrooper	4.00	8.00
	(McQuarrie Signature Series)		
43	Romba & Graak (Ewok warriors)	12.00	25.00
44	Tycho Celchu (A-Wing pilot)	4.00	8.00
45	Anakin Skywalker (Jedi Spirit)	10.00	20.00
46	R2-D2 (w/cargo net)	4.00	8.00
47	Concept Han Solo (McQuarrie Signature Series)	12.00	25.00
48	Darth Vader (hologram)	4.00	8.00
49a	Clone Trooper (7th Legion Trooper)	4.00	8.00
49b	Clone Trooper	4.00	8.00
	(Revenge of the Sith stand/no coin)		
50a	Clone Trooper (Hawkbat Batallion)	8.00	15.00
50b	Clone Trooper (Hawkbat Batallion)	4.00	8.00
	Revenge of the Sith stand/no coin)		
51a	R2-B1 (astromech droid)	4.00	8.00
51b	R2-B1 (Revenge of the Sith stand/no coin)	4.00	8.00
52	Naboo Soldier (Royal Naboo Army)	6.00	12.00
53a	Rebel Vanguard Trooper (Star Wars: Battlefront)	4.00	8.00
53b	Rebel Vanguard Trooper	4.00	8.00
	(Expanded Universe stand/no coin)		
54	Pax Bonkik (Rodian podracer mechanic)	4.00	8.00
55	Clone Trooper (training fatigues)	8.00	15.00
56a	Padme Amidala (Naboo Senator)	4.00	8.00
56b	Padme Amidala	4.00	8.00
	(Attack of the Clones stand/no coin)		
57a	Jango Fett (bounty hunter)	4.00	8.00
57b	Jango Fett (Attack of the Clones stand/no coin)	10.00	20.00
58a	Voolvif Monn (Jedi Master)	4.00	8.00
58b	Voolvif Monn	4.00	8.00
	(Expanded Universe stand/no coin)		
59	Destroyer Droid (droideka)	4.00	8.00
60	Concept Rebel Trooper	4.00	8.00
	(McQuarrie Signature Series)		

2007-08 Star Wars 30th Anniversary Collection Battle Packs

1	Battle of Geonosis (Jango Fett/Obi-Wan Kenobi/Count Dooku/Aayla Secura)	20.00	40.00
2	Battle on Mygeeto (Galactic Marine/Ki-Adi Mundi Clone Commander Bacara/Super Battle Droid/Tri-Droid)	30.00	60.00
3	Betrayal at Bespin (Boba Fett/Chewbacca Darth Vader/Han Solo/Princess Leia)	20.00	40.00
4	Capture of Tantive IV (Darth Vader 2 Rebel Troopers/2 Stormtroopers)	20.00	40.00
5	Clone Attack on Coruscant (Clone Trooper Commander/4 Clone Troopers)	25.00	50.00
6	Droid Factory Capture (C-3PO with droid head R2-D2/Jango Fett/Anakin/Destroyer Droid)	20.00	40.00
7	Hoth Patrol (Luke Skywalker/Tauntaun/Wampa)	20.00	40.00
8	Jedi vs. Sith (Yoda/Anakin Skywalker	10.00	20.00

Asajj Ventress/General Grievous/Obi-Wan)

9 Jedi vs. Sidious (Darth Sidious/Kit Fisto	10.00	20.00
Mace Windu/Saesee-Tiin/Agen Kolar)		
10 Jedi Training on Dagobah (Yoda/R2-D2	10.00	20.00
Luke Skywalker/Spirit of Obi-Wan/Darth Vader)		
11 The Hunt for Grievous (Captain Fordo	30.00	60.00
Clone Trooper Gunner/3 Clone Troopers)		

2007-08 Star Wars 30th Anniversary Collection
Battle Packs Exclusives

1 Ambush on Ilum	30.00	60.00
(R2-D2/C-3PO/Padme/Chameleon Droids)/(2007 Target Exclusive)		
2 ARC-170 Elite Squad	50.00	100.00
(Astromech Droid/2 Clone pilots/2 Clone Troopers)/(2007 Target Exclusive)		
3 Arena Encounter	100.00	200.00
(Anakin Skywalker/Padme Amidala/Obi-Wan/Creatures)/(2007 Toys R Us Exclusive)		
4 AT-RT Assault Squad	25.00	50.00
(2 AT-RT's/2 AT-RT Drivers/Clone Commander)/(2007 Target Exclusive)		
5 Attack on Kashyyyk	20.00	40.00
(Darth Vader/2 Stormtroopers/2 Wookiee warriors)/(2008 Target Exclusive)		
6 Bantha with Tusken Raiders	30.00	60.00
(brown - Bantha/2 Tusken Raiders/Tusken female)/(2007 Toys R Us Exclusive)		
7 Bantha with Tusken Raiders	50.00	100.00
(tan - Bantha/2 Tusken Raiders/Tusken female)/(2007 Toys R Us Exclusive)		
8 Battle Rancor	60.00	120.00
(w/Felucian warrior)/(2008 Target Exclusive)		
9 Betrayal on Felucia	20.00	40.00
(Aayla Secura/4 Clone Troopers yellow)/(2007 Target Exclusive)		
10 STAP Attack	25.00	50.00
(2 Battle Droids/Super Battle Droid/2 STAP's)/(2008 Toys R Us Exclusive)		
11 Treachery on Saleucami	30.00	60.00
(Commander Neyo/Clone Trooper red/2 BARC Speeder Bikes)/(2007 Walmart Exclusive)		

2007-08 Star Wars 30th Anniversary Collection
Comic Packs

1 Carnor Jax & Kir Kanos		
(2006 Internet Exclusive)		
2 Darth Vader & Rebel Officer		
3 Governor Tarkin & Stormtrooper		
4 Chewbacca & Han Solo		
5 Quinlan Vos & Vilmarh Grahrk		
6 Luke Skywalker & R2-D2		
7 Obi-Wan Kenobi & ARC Trooper		
8 A'sharad Hett & The Dark Woman	20.00	40.00
9 Leia Organa & Darth Vader		
10 Mara Jade & Luke Skywalker	20.00	40.00
11 Anakin Skywalker & Assassin Droid		
12 Baron Soontir Fel & Derek Hobbie Klivian		
13 Koffi Arana & Bultar Swan		
14 Lt. Jundland & Deena Shan		
15 Mouse & Basso		
16 Clone Commando & Super Battle Droid	30.00	60.00
NNO Obi-Wan Kenobi & Bail Organa		

(2007 Walmart Exclusive)

NNO Boba Fett & RA-7 Droid (Wal-Mart Exclusive)	12.00	25.00
NNO Commander Keller & Galactic Marine		
(2007 Walmart Exclusive)		
NNO Count Dooku & Anakin Skywalker		
NNO Kashyyyk Trooper & Wookiee Warrior		
NNO Lando Calrissian & Stormtrooper		

2007-08 Star Wars 30th Anniversary Collection
Commemorative Tins

1 Episode I (Darth Maul/Anakin Skywalker	50.00	100.00
Qui-Gon Ginn/R2-D9)		
2 Episode II (Clone Trooper blue	20.00	40.00
Anakin Skywalker/Count Dooku/Boba Fett)		
3 Episode III (Yoda/Mace Windu		
Anakin Skywalker/Clone Trooper yellow shins)		
4 Episode IV (Stormtrooper black shoulders	20.00	40.00
Princess Leia/Darth Vader/C-3PO)		
5 Episode V (Snowtrooper/Luke Skywalker hoth		
Han Solo hoth/Chewbacca hoth)		
6 Episode VI (Bike Trooper/Darth Vader	20.00	40.00
Princess Leia endor/Rebel Trooper)		
7 The Modal Nodes Cantina Band	30.00	60.00
8 Episode II		
(Mace Windu/Sora Bulq/Oppo Rancisis/Zam Wesell)/(2007 K-Mart Exclusive)		
9 Episode III		
(Commander Cody/Anakin/General Grievous/Clone Pilot)/(2007 K-Mart Exclusive)		
10 Episode VI		
(Darth Vader/R5-J2/Biker Scout/Death Star Gunner)/(2007 K-Mart Exclusive)		

2007-08 Star Wars 30th Anniversary Collection
Evolutions

1 Anakin Skywalker to Darth Vader	20.00	40.00
2 Clone Trooper to Stormtrooper	20.00	40.00
3 The Sith		
4 The Fett Legacy	25.00	50.00
5 The Jedi Legacy	20.00	40.00
6 The Sith Legacy		
7 Vader's Secret Apprentice	30.00	75.00
Secret Apprentice/Sith Lord/Jedi Knight		

2007-08 Star Wars 30th Anniversary Collection
Exclusives

1 Cantina Band Member	20.00	40.00
(2007 Disney Weekends Exclusive)		
2 Concept General Grievous	15.00	30.00
(2007 SWS Exclusive)		
3 Concept Luke Skywalker	15.00	30.00
(McQuarrie Signature Series)		
(2007 C4 & CE Exclusive)		
4 Concept Obi-Wan & Yoda	20.00	40.00
(McQuarrie Signature Series)		
(2007 SDCC Exclusive)		
5 Concept R2-D2 & C-3PO	12.00	25.00
(McQuarrie Signature Series)		
(2007 C4 & CE Exclusive)		
6 Darth Vader & Incinerator Troopers	25.00	50.00
(The Force Unleashed)		
(2008 Walmart Exclusive)		
7 Emperor Palpatine & Shadow Stormtroopers (The Force Unleashed)		
(2008 Walmart Exclusive)		
8 R2-KT	30.00	60.00
(2007 Shared Exclusive)		
9 Shadow Scout Trooper & Speeder Bike	15.00	30.00
(2007 SDCC Exclusive)		
10 Shadow Troopers 2-Pack		
(2008 Jedi-Con Exclusive)		
11 Star Wars Collector Coin		
(2007 Toy Fair Exclusive)		
12 Stormtrooper Commander	25.00	50.00
(2008 GameStop Exclusive)		

2007-08 Star Wars 30th Anniversary Collection
Force Unleashed

9 Imperial EVO Trooper	8.00	15.00
10 Imperial Jumptrooper	10.00	20.00
11a Maris Brood (flesh)	15.00	30.00
11b Maris Brood (white)	10.00	20.00
12 Darth Vader (battle-damaged)	10.00	20.00
13 Rahm Kota	20.00	40.00
14 Emperor's Shadow Guard	20.00	40.00
15 Juno Eclipse	10.00	20.00

2007-08 Star Wars 30th Anniversary Collection
Multi-Packs

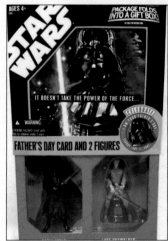

1 Clone Pack (Battlefront II)		
(2007 Shared Exclusive)		
2 Droid Pack (Battlefront II)	25.00	50.00
(2007 Shared Exclusive)		
3 Clones & Commanders Gift Pack	20.00	40.00
(Toys R Us Exclusive)		
4 I Am Your Father's Day Gift Pack (2007 Walmart Exclusive)		
5 The Max Rebo Band Jabba's Palace Entertainers	30.00	60.00
(2007 Walmart Exclusive)		
6 The Max Rebo Band Jabba's Palace Musicians	40.00	80.00
(2007 Walmart Exclusive)		
7 Republic Elite Forces Mandalorians & Clone Troopers		
(2007 Entertainment Earth Exclusive)		
8 Republic Elite Forces Mandalorians	75.00	150.00
& Omega Squad		
(2007 Entertainment Earth Exclusive)		

2007-08 Star Wars 30th Anniversary Collection
Revenge of the Sith

1 Obi-Wan Kenobi	6.00	12.00
2 Darth Vader	10.00	20.00
3 Clone Commander (green)	5.00	10.00
4 Kashyyyk Trooper	8.00	15.00
5 Tri-Droid	8.00	15.00
6 2-1B Surgical Droid	6.00	12.00
7 Po Nudo	8.00	15.00
8 Mustafar Panning Droid	6.00	12.00

2007-08 Star Wars 30th Anniversary Collection
Saga Legends

1 501st Legion Trooper	8.00	15.00
2 Boba Fett	15.00	30.00
3 C-3PO (w/battle droid head)	6.00	12.00
4 Chewbacca	6.00	12.00
5 Clone Trooper (AOTC)	8.00	15.00
6 Clone Trooper (ROTS)	6.00	12.00
7 Darth Maul	8.00	15.00
8 Darth Vader	8.00	15.00
9 Darth Vader (as Anakin Skywalker)	8.00	15.00

10	Destroyer Droid	6.00	12.00
11	General Grievous	12.00	25.00
12	Obi-Wan Kenobi	6.00	12.00
13	Princess Leia (Boushh disguise)	8.00	15.00
14	R2-D2 (electronic)	10.00	20.00
15	Saesee Tiin	8.00	15.00
16	Shock Trooper	10.00	20.00
17	Yoda	8.00	15.00

2007-08 Star Wars 30th Anniversary Collection
Saga Legends Battle Droid 2-Packs

1	Battle Droids 2-Pack I (tan infantry & commander)	8.00	15.00
2	Battle Droids 2-Pack II (maroon blaster and lightsaber damage)	8.00	15.00
3	Battle Droids 2-Pack III (tan blaster and lightsaber damage)	8.00	15.00
4	Battle Droids 2-Pack IV (tan dirty & clean)	8.00	15.00

2007-08 Star Wars 30th Anniversary Collection
Saga Legends Fan's Choice (2007)

1	Biker Scout	8.00	15.00
2	Biker Scout (w/Clone Wars sticker)		
3	Clone Commander (Coruscant)	12.00	25.00
4	Clone Trooper Officer (red)	8.00	15.00
5	Clone Trooper Officer (yellow)	8.00	15.00
6	Clone Trooper Officer (green)	10.00	20.00
7	Clone Trooper Officer (blue)	6.00	12.00
8	Dark Trooper (Fan's Choice Figure #1)	12.00	25.00
9	Imperial Officer (brown hair)	6.00	12.00
10	Imperial Officer (blonde hair)	8.00	15.00
11	Imperial Officer (red hair)		
12	Pit Droids 2-Pack (white)		
13	Pit Droids 2-Pack (brown)		
14	Pit Droids 2-Pack (orange)	12.00	25.00
15	R4-I9	10.00	20.00
16	RA-7	6.00	12.00
17	Sandtrooper (dirty; tan shoulder)	8.00	15.00
18	Sandtrooper (dirty; orange shoulder)	10.00	20.00
19	Sandtrooper (clean; black shoulder)	25.00	50.00
20	Sandtrooper (clean; white shoulder)	12.00	25.00
21	Sandtrooper (dirty; red shoulder)		
22	TC-14	10.00	20.00

2007-08 Star Wars 30th Anniversary Collection
Saga Legends Fan's Choice (2008)

1	501st Legion Trooper		
2	Commander Neyo	10.00	20.00
3	Covert Ops Clone Trooper (gold coin)	10.00	20.00
4	Pit Droids 2-Pack (white)	8.00	15.00
5	Pit Droids 2-Pack (maroon)	8.00	15.00
6	Pit Droids 2-Pack (orange)	8.00	15.00
7	Shadow Stormtrooper	12.00	25.00
8	Utapau Shadow Trooper	12.00	25.00
9	Zev Senesca	8.00	15.00

2007-08 Star Wars 30th Anniversary Collection
Ultimate Galactic Hunt

1	Airborne Trooper	12.00	25.00
2	Biggs Darklighter (Rebel pilot)	7.50	15.00
3	Boba Fett (animated debut)	12.00	25.00
4	Concept Boba Fett (McQuarrie Signature Series)	20.00	40.00
5	Concept Chewbacca (McQuarrie Signature Series)	15.00	30.00
6	Concept Stormtrooper (McQuarrie Signature Series)	12.00	25.00
7	Darth Vader (Sith Lord)	10.00	20.00
8	Galactic Marine	10.00	20.00
9	Han Solo (smuggler)	7.50	15.00

10	Luke Skywalker (Yavin ceremony)	6.00	12.00
11	Mace Windu	7.50	15.00
12	R2-D2	6.00	12.00

2007-08 Star Wars 30th Anniversary Collection
Ultimate Galactic Hunt Gold Coins

1	Airborne Trooper	6.00	12.00
2	Biggs Darklighter	4.00	8.00
3	Boba Fett	6.00	12.00
4	Concept Boba Fett (McQuarrie Signature Series)	10.00	20.00
5	Concept Chewbacca (McQuarrie Signature Series)	7.50	15.00
6	Concept Stormtrooper (McQuarrie Signature Series)	6.00	12.00
7	Darth Vader	5.00	10.00
8	Galactic Marine	5.00	10.00
9	Han Solo	4.00	8.00
10	Luke Skywalker	3.00	6.00
11	Mace Windu	4.00	8.00
12	R2-D2	3.00	6.00

2007-08 Star Wars 30th Anniversary Collection
Vehicles

1	Aayla Secura's Jedi Starfighter	20.00	40.00
2	ARC-170 Fighter (Clone Wars)	50.00	100.00
3	AT-AP Walker	20.00	40.00
4	Anakin Skywalker's Jedi Starfighter (Coruscant)	20.00	40.00
5	Anakin Skywalker's Jedi Starfighter (Mustafar)	20.00	40.00
6	Darth Vader's Sith Starfighter	40.00	80.00
7	Darth Vader's TIE Advanced Starfighter	30.00	60.00
8	General Grievous' Starfighter	25.00	50.00
9	Hailfire Droid	25.00	50.00
10	Mace Windu's Jedi Starfighter	15.00	30.00
11	Obi-Wan's Jedi Starfighter (Coruscant)	25.00	50.00
12	Obi-Wan's Jedi Starfighter (Utapau)	25.00	50.00
13	Saesee Tiin's Jedi Starfighter	20.00	40.00
14	Sith Infiltrator	25.00	50.00
15	TIE Fighter	15.00	30.00
16	Trade Federation Armored Assault Tank (AAT)	20.00	40.00
17	V-Wing Starfighter/ spring-open wings	50.00	100.00

2007-08 Star Wars 30th Anniversary Collection
Vehicles Exclusives

1	Elite TIE Inteceptor/181st Squadron TIE Pilot (Toys R Us exclusive)	75.00	150.00
2	Obi-Wan's Jedi Starfighter (w/hyperspace ring) (2007 Toys R Us Exclusive)	25.00	50.00
3	TIE Bomber (w/TIE Bomber Pilot) (2007 Target Exclusive)	30.00	75.00
4	TIE Fighter (w/TIE Pilot/opening cockpit and ejecting wing panels) (2007 Toys R Us Exclusive)	25.00	50.00
5	Y-Wing Fighter (w/Lt. Lepira & R5-F7) (2007 Toys R Us Exclusive)	75.00	150.00

2017 Star Wars 40th Anniversary Black Series 6-Inch

NNO	Artoo Detoo	30.00	60.00
NNO	Ben (Obi-Wan) Kenobi	15.00	30.00
NNO	Chewbacca	25.00	50.00
NNO	Darth Vader Legacy Pack	30.00	60.00
NNO	Death Squad Commander	15.00	30.00
NNO	Han Solo	25.00	50.00
NNO	Jawa	20.00	40.00
NNO	Luke Skywalker	20.00	40.00
NNO	Luke Skywalker X-Wing Pilot (Celebration Orlando Exclusive)	120.00	250.00
NNO	Princess Leia Organa	15.00	30.00
NNO	R5-D4 (GameStop Exclusive)	20.00	40.00
NNO	Sand People	30.00	60.00
NNO	See Threepio	25.00	50.00
NNO	Stormtrooper	30.00	60.00

2017 Star Wars 40th Anniversary Black Series
Titanium Series 3.75-Inch

1	Darth Vader	15.00	30.00
2	Obi-Wan Kenobi	12.00	25.00
3	Luke Skywalker	12.00	25.00
4	Princess Leia Organa	12.00	25.00
5	Han Solo	15.00	30.00

1998-99 Star Wars Action Collection

1	AT-AT Driver	15.00	30.00
2	Barquin D'an	10.00	20.00
3	Chewbacca in Chains	15.00	30.00
4	Emperor Palpatine	12.00	25.00
5	Grand Moff Tarkin	12.00	25.00
6	Greedo	15.00	30.00
7	Han Solo (carbonite) (Target Exclusive)	15.00	30.00

8 Han Solo (Hoth)	15.00	30.00
9 Jawa	10.00	20.00
10 Luke Skywalker (ceremonial dress)		
11 Luke Skywalker (Hoth)	15.00	30.00
12 Luke Skywalker (Jedi Knight)	12.00	25.00
13 Princess Leia (Hoth)	12.00	25.00
(Service Merchandise Exclusive)		
14 R2-D2	20.00	40.00
15 R2-D2 (detachable utility arms)	20.00	40.00
16 R5-D4	15.00	30.00
(Walmart Exclusive)		
17 Sandtrooper (w/droid)	8.00	15.00
18 Snowtrooper	12.00	25.00
19 Snowtrooper (blue variant)		
20 Wicket	20.00	40.00
(Walmart Exclusive)		
21 Yoda	20.00	40.00

1998-99 Star Wars Action Collection Electronic

1 Boba Fett	25.00	50.00
(KB Toys Exclusive)		
2 Darth Vader	20.00	40.00

1998-99 Star Wars Action Collection Multi-Packs

1 C-3PO and R2-D2 2-Pack	40.00	80.00
2 Emperor Palpatine and Royal Guard 2-Pack	20.00	40.00
3 Wedge Antilles and Biggs Darklighter 2-Pack	25.00	50.00
(FAO Schwarz Exclusive)		
4 Luke (Tatooine)/Leia (Boushh)	40.00	80.00
Han (Bespin) 3-Pack		
(KB Toys Exclusive)		
5 Luke/Han/Snowtrooper/AT-AT Driver Hoth 4-Pack	60.00	120.00
(JC Penney Exclusive)		

1993 Star Wars Bend Ems

1 Admiral Ackbar	7.50	15.00
2 Ben Kenobi	10.00	20.00
3 Bib Fortuna	7.50	15.00
4 Boba Fett	15.00	30.00
5 C-3PO	10.00	20.00
6 Chewbacca	7.50	15.00
7 Darth Vader	12.50	25.00
8 Emperor	10.00	20.00
9 Emperor's Royal Guard	7.50	15.00
10 Gamorrean Guard	7.50	15.00
11 Han Solo	10.00	20.00
12 Lando Calrissian	7.50	15.00
13 Leia Organa	10.00	20.00
14 Luke Skywalker	10.00	20.00
15 Luke Skywalker X-wing	10.00	20.00
16 R2-D2	7.50	15.00
17 Stormtrooper	7.50	15.00
18 Tusken Raider	7.50	15.00
19 Wicket	7.50	15.00
20 Yoda	7.50	15.00
21 4-Piece A New Hope	20.00	40.00
(Chewbacca/Luke Skywalker/R2-D2/Tusken Raider)		
22 4-Piece Empire Strikes Back	20.00	40.00
(Han Solo/Darth Vader/Yoda/Lando Calrissian)		
23 4-Piece Return of the Jedi	25.00	50.00
(Admiral Ackbar/Boba Fett/Wicket/Bib Fortuna)		
24 4-Piece Gift Set 1	20.00	40.00
(Ben Kenobi/Leia Organa/Han Solo/C-3PO)		
25 4-Piece Gift Set 2	20.00	40.00
(Storm Trooper/Wicket/Yoda/Chewbacca)		
26 4-Piece Gift Set 3	20.00	40.00
(Storm Trooper/R2-D2/C-3PO/Darth Vader)		
27 4-Piece Gift Set 4	20.00	40.00
(Emperor/C-3PO/Luke Skywalker/Darth Vader)		
28 6-Piece Gift Set 1	25.00	50.00
(Darth Vader/Stormtrooper/Luke Skywalker/R2-D2/C-3PO		
29 6-Piece Gift Set 2	25.00	50.00
(Stormtrooper/Darth Vader/Emperor's Royal Guard/Admiral Ackbar/Lando Calrissian/Chewbacca)		
30 8-Piece Gift Set	25.00	50.00
(Darth Vader/Luke Skywalker/C-3PO/Emperor/Stormtrooper/R2-D2/Princess Leia/Ewok)		
31 10-Piece Gift Set	30.00	60.00
(R2-D2/Stormtrooper/Darth Vader/Admiral Ackbar/Chewbacca/Han Solo/Princess Leia/Luke Skywalker/Bib Fortuna/Emperor's Royal Guard)		

2014-15 Star Wars Black Series 3.75-Inch Blue

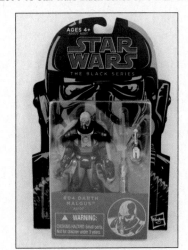

1 R5-G19	10.00	20.00
2A Luke Skywalker Hoth	8.00	15.00
(incorrect elbow pegs)		
2B Luke Skywalker Hoth	8.00	15.00
(correct elbow pegs)		
3 Darth Vader	8.00	15.00
(Revenge Of The Sith)		
4 Darth Malgus	20.00	40.00
5 Starkiller	20.00	40.00
(Galen Marek)		
6 Yoda	12.00	25.00
(pack forward)		
7 Darth Vader	12.00	25.00
(Dagobah Test)		
8 Stormtrooper	10.00	20.00
9 Captain Rex	8.00	15.00
10 Jon Dutch Vander	10.00	20.00
11 Chewbacca	8.00	15.00
12 Clone Commander Wolffe	10.00	20.00
13 Clone Commander Doom	6.00	12.00
14 Imperial Navy Commander	10.00	20.00
15 Commander Thorn	12.00	25.00
16 C-3PO	12.00	25.00

17 Princess Leia Organa	10.00	20.00
(Boushh)		
18 Mosep Binneed	10.00	20.00
19 Han Solo	20.00	40.00
(with Carbonite Block)		
20 Jawas	8.00	15.00

2014-15 Star Wars Black Series 3.75-Inch Blue Exclusives

1 Battle on Endor 8-Pack	80.00	150.00
(Toys R Us Exclusive)		
2 Jabba's Rancor Pit	100.00	200.00
(Toys R Us Exclusive)		

2013-14 Star Wars Black Series 3.75-Inch Orange

1 Padme Amidala	25.00	50.00
2 Clone Trooper Sergeant	6.00	12.00
3A Anakin Skywalker	10.00	20.00
(dark brown hair)		
3B Anakin Skywalker	10.00	20.00
(light brown hair)		
4 Biggs Darklighter	6.00	12.00
5A Luke Skywalker	8.00	15.00
(short medal strap)		
5B Luke Skywalker	8.00	15.00
(long medal strap)		
6 Darth Vader	8.00	15.00
7 Biker Scout	6.00	12.00
8 Clone Pilot	6.00	12.00
9 R2-D2	15.00	30.00
10 Pablo-Jill	20.00	40.00
11 Luminara Unduli	6.00	12.00
12A 41st Elite Corps Clone Trooper		
(incorrect markings)		
12B 41st Elite Corps Clone Trooper	12.50	25.00
(correct markings)		
13 Stormtrooper	8.00	15.00
14 Mara Jade	15.00	30.00
15 Merumeru	10.00	20.00
16 Clone Commander Neyo	10.00	20.00
17 Vizam	8.00	15.00
18 Darth Plageuis	45.00	90.00
19 Mace Windu	12.00	25.00
20 Bastila Shan	20.00	40.00
21 Luke Skywalker	8.00	15.00
22 Yoda	10.00	20.00
23 Toryn Farr	10.00	20.00
24 Snowtrooper Commander	8.00	15.00
25 Dak Ralter	10.00	20.00
26 Darth Vader	15.00	30.00
27 Jabba's Skiff Guard	25.00	50.00
28 Ree-Yees	20.00	40.00
29 Wedge Antilles	8.00	15.00
31 Republic Trooper	25.00	50.00

2013-14 Star Wars Black Series 3.75-Inch Orange Exclusives

1 Luke Skywalker Hoth Battle Gear	6.00	12.00
2 R5-D4		

2015-18 Star Wars Black Series 3.75-Inch Red

NNO Admiral Ackbar	7.50	15.00
NNO Ahsoka Tano	10.00	20.00
NNO AT-ST Driver		
NNO Boba Fett (prototype fatigues)	15.00	30.00
NNO Captain Cassian Andor	6.00	12.00
NNO Captain Phasma	6.00	12.00
NNO Chewbacca	12.50	25.00
NNO Darth Vader	7.50	15.00
NNO Elite Praetorian Guard	15.00	30.00

NNO	Emperor's Royal Guard	6.00	12.00
NNO	Finn (Jakku)	10.00	20.00
NNO	First Order Stormtrooper	6.00	12.00
NNO	First Order Stormtrooper Executioner	6.00	12.00
NNO	Han Solo	7.50	15.00
NNO	Han Solo (Starkiller Base)	7.50	15.00
NNO	Imperial Death Trooper	10.00	20.00
NNO	Kylo Ren	7.50	15.00
NNO	Lando Calrissian	6.00	12.00
NNO	Luke Skywalker	6.00	12.00
NNO	Luke Skywalker (Jedi Master)	6.00	12.00
NNO	Poe Dameron	6.00	12.00
NNO	Ponda Baba	6.00	12.00
NNO	Princess Leia Organa	8.00	15.00
NNO	Princess Leia Organa (D'Qar Gown)	15.00	30.00
NNO	Rey (Jakku)	10.00	20.00
NNO	Rose Tico	6.00	12.00
NNO	Sandtrooper	7.50	15.00
NNO	Scarif Stormtrooper Squad Leader	12.50	25.00
NNO	Sentry Droid Mark IV		
NNO	Sergeant Jyn Erso	6.00	12.00
NNO	Tusken Raider	7.50	15.00

2015-18 Star Wars Black Series 3.75-Inch Red Vehicles

NNO	Special Forces TIE Fighter and Pilot Elite	100.00	200.00

2014-15 Star Wars Black Series 6-Inch Blue

1	Sandtrooper	15.00	30.00
	Black Pauldron		
2	Darth Vader	12.00	25.00
	Episode VI		
3	Luke Skywalker	25.00	50.00
	Episode VI		
4	Chewbacca	20.00	40.00
5	TIE Pilot	15.00	30.00
6	Yoda	25.00	50.00
7	Clone Trooper Sergeant	12.00	25.00
8	Obi-Wan Kenobi	10.00	20.00
	Reissue		
9	Han Solo Stormtrooper	12.00	25.00
10	Bossk	20.00	40.00
11	Luke Skywalker	12.00	25.00
	Stormtrooper		
12	Emperor Palpatine	15.00	30.00
13	Clone Trooper Captain	12.00	25.00
14	IG-88	20.00	40.00
15	Princess Leia	30.00	60.00
16	Clone Commander Cody	12.00	25.00

2014-15 Star Wars Black Series 6-Inch Blue Deluxe

1	Han Solo (w/Tauntaun)	25.00	50.00
2	Jabba the Hutt	25.00	50.00
3	Luke Skywalker (w/Wampa)	20.00	40.00
4	Scout Trooper (w/Speeder Bike)	20.00	40.00

2013-18 Star Wars Black Series 6-Inch Exclusives

NNO	Admiral Ackbar & First Order Officer 2-Pack	10.00	20.00
	(2017 Toys R Us Exclusive)		
NNO	Admiral Ackbar	15.00	30.00
	(2017 Toys R Us Exclusive)		
NNO	Astromech 3-Pack	50.00	100.00
	(2016 Toys R Us Exclusive)		
NNO	AT-ACT Driver	15.00	30.00
	(2017 Target Exclusive)		
NNO	Boba Fett (Prototype Armor)	25.00	50.00
	(2014 Walgreens Exclusive)		
NNO	Boba Fett and Han Solo in Carbonite	200.00	400.00
	(2013 SDCC Exclusive)		
NNO	C-3PO	25.00	50.00
	(2016 Walgreens Exclusive)		
NNO	Cantina Showdown	50.00	100.00
	(2014 Toys R Us Exclusive)		
NNO	Captain Rex	50.00	100.00
	(2017 Hascon Exclusive)		
NNO	Chewbacca	20.00	40.00
	(2018 Target Exclusive)		
NNO	Commander Gree	30.00	75.00
	(2017 Toys R Us Exclusive)		
NNO	Commander Wolffe	20.00	40.00
	(2017 Disney Store Exclusive)		
NNO	Darth Vader Emperor's Wrath	15.00	30.00
	(2015 Walgreen's Exclusive)		
NNO	Elite Praetorian Guard (w/heavy blade)	20.00	40.00
	(2017 Amazon Exclusive)		
NNO	First Order Officer	10.00	20.00
	(2017 Toys R Us Exclusive)		
NNO	First Order Snowtrooper Officer	15.00	30.00
	(2015 Toys R Us Exclusive)		
NNO	First Order Stormtrooper Officer	30.00	75.00
	(2015 SDCC Exclusive)		
NNO	Gamorrean Guard	30.00	75.00
	(2018 Target Exclusive)		
NNO	Guards 4-Pack	60.00	120.00
	(2017 Barnes & Noble/GameStop Exclusive)		
NNO	Imperial Forces 4-Pack	50.00	100.00
	(2015 Entertainment Earth Exclusive)		
NNO	Imperial Hovertank Pilot	15.00	30.00
	(2016 Toys R Us Exclusive)		
NNO	Imperial Shadow Squadron	60.00	120.00
	(2014 Target Exclusive)		
NNO	Imperial Shock Trooper	25.00	50.00
	(2015 Walmart Exclusive)		
NNO	Inferno Squad Agent	20.00	40.00
	(2017 GameStop Exclusive)		
NNO	Jabba's Throne Room	100.00	200.00
	(2014 SDCC Exclusive)		
NNO	Kylo Ren (unmasked)	30.00	75.00
	(2016 Celebration/SDCC Exclusive)		
NNO	Kylo Ren	15.00	30.00
	(2015 Kmart Exclusive)		
NNO	Kylo Ren	12.50	25.00
	(2017 Walmart Exclusive)		
NNO	Luke Skywalker (w/Ach-to base)	15.00	30.00
	(2017 Target Exclusive)		
NNO	Moloch	30.00	75.00
	(2018 Target Exclusive)		
NNO	Obi-Wan Kenobi	50.00	100.00
	(2016 SDCC Exclusive)		
NNO	Obi-Wan Kenobit (Force ghost)	10.00	20.00
	(2017 Walgreens Exclusive)		
NNO	Phase II Clone Trooper 4-Pack	50.00	100.00
	(2016 Entertainment Earth Exclusive)		
NNO	Poe Dameron and Riot Control Stormtrooper	20.00	40.00
	(2015 Target Exclusive)		
NNO	Red Squadron 3-Pack	60.00	120.00
	(2018 Amazon Exclusive)		
NNO	Resistance Tech Rose	7.50	15.00
	(2017 Walmart Exclusive)		
NNO	Rey (Jedi Training) & Luke Skywalker (Jedi Master) 2-Pack	30.00	60.00
	(2017 SDCC Exclusive)		
NNO	Rey (Starkiller Base)	12.50	25.00
	(2016 Kmart Exclusive)		
NNO	Rey (w/Crait base)	15.00	30.00
	(2017 Toys R Us Exclusive)		
NNO	Rogue One 3-Pack	30.00	75.00
	Imperial Death Trooper/Captain Cassian Andor Sergeant Jyn Erso (Jedha)/(2016 Target Exclusive)		
NNO	Scarif Stormtrooper	15.00	30.00
	(2016 Walmart Exclusive)		
NNO	Sergeant Jyn Erso (Eadu)	10.00	20.00
	(2016 Kmart Exclusive)		
NNO	Sergeant Jyn Erso	60.00	120.00
	(2016 SDCC Exclusive)		
NNO	Stormtrooper (w/blast accessories)	50.00	100.00
	(2018 Toys R Us International Exclusive)		
NNO	Stormtrooper (w/extra gear)	15.00	30.00
	(2017 Amazon Exclusive)		
NNO	Stormtrooper Evolution 4-Pack	50.00	100.00
	(Amazon Exclusive)		
NNO	Stormtrooper Executioner	10.00	20.00
	(2017 Target Exclusive)		
NNO	Supreme Leader Snoke (Throne Room)	15.00	30.00
	(2017 GameStop Exclusive)		

2013-14 Star Wars Black Series 6-Inch Orange

1	Luke Skywalker X-Wing Pilot	50.00	100.00
2	Darth Maul	30.00	60.00
3	Sandtrooper	20.00	40.00
4	R2-D2	40.00	80.00
5	Princess Leia Organa (Slave attire)	40.00	80.00
6	Boba Fett	40.00	80.00
7	Greedo	20.00	40.00
8	Han Solo	20.00	40.00
9	Stormtrooper	12.00	25.00
10	Obi-Wan Kenobi	20.00	40.00
	Episode II		
11	Luke Skywalker Bespin Gear	30.00	60.00
12	Anakin Skywalker	40.00	80.00
	Episode III		
13	Clone Trooper	12.00	25.00
	Episode II		

2015-17 Star Wars Black Series 6-Inch Red

1A Finn Jakku (Glossy Head)	12.00	25.00
1B Finn Jakku (Matte Head)	12.00	25.00
2A Rey and BB-8 (Clean)	12.00	25.00
2B Rey and BB-8 (Dirty)	12.00	25.00
3 Kylo Ren	10.00	20.00
4 First Order Stormtrooper	10.00	20.00
5 Chewbacca	10.00	20.00
6 Captain Phasma	20.00	40.00
7 Poe Dameron	10.00	20.00
8 Guavian Enforcer	12.00	25.00
9A Constable Zuvio (green helmet)	10.00	20.00
9B Constable Zuvio (brown helmet)	10.00	20.00
10A Resistance Soldier (green helmet)	20.00	40.00
10B Resistance Soldier (brown helmet)	10.00	20.00
11 First Order TIE Fighter Pilot	15.00	30.00
12 First Order Snowtrooper	12.00	25.00
13 First Order General Hux	15.00	30.00
14 X-Wing Pilot Asty	15.00	30.00
15 Jango Fett	10.00	20.00
16 First Order Flametrooper	10.00	20.00
17 Finn (FN-2187)	20.00	40.00
18 Han Solo	12.00	25.00
19 Kanan Jarrus	15.00	30.00
20 Ahsoka Tano	20.00	40.00
21 Luke Skywalker	10.00	20.00
22 Sergeant Jyn Erso (Jedha)	15.00	30.00
23 Captain Cassian Andor (Eadu)	10.00	20.00
24 K-2SO	12.50	25.00
25 Imperial Death Trooper	12.50	25.00
26 Kylo Ren (unmasked)	12.50	25.00
27 Director Krennic	10.00	20.00
28 Scarif Stormtrooper Squad Leader	20.00	40.00
29 C-3PO (Resistance Base)	10.00	20.00
30 Princess Leia Organa	12.50	25.00
31 AT-AT Pilot/AT-AT Driver	20.00	40.00
32 Obi-Wan Kenobi	15.00	30.00
33 Sabine Wren	25.00	50.00
34 Darth Revan	20.00	40.00
35 Snowtrooper	10.00	20.00
36 Chirrut Imwe	20.00	40.00
37 Baze Malbus	15.00	30.00
38 Imperial Royal Guard	10.00	20.00
39 Lando Calrissian	12.50	25.00
40 Qui-Gon Jinn	15.00	30.00
41 Tusken Raider	15.00	30.00
42 Hera Syndulla	20.00	40.00
43 Darth Vader	12.50	25.00
44 Rey (Jedi Training)	12.50	25.00
45 Kylo Ren	12.50	25.00
46 Luke Skywalker (Jedi Master)	12.50	25.00
47 Grand Admiral Thrawn	25.00	50.00
48 Stormtrooper	15.00	30.00
49 Maz Kanata	10.00	20.00
50 Elite Praetorian Guard	15.00	30.00
51 Finn (First Order Disguise)	10.00	20.00
52 General Leia Organa	12.50	25.00
53 Poe Dameron	10.00	20.00
54 Supreme Leader Snoke	12.50	25.00
55 Rose Tico	10.00	20.00
56 Jaina Solo	20.00	40.00
57 DJ	10.00	20.00
58 Rey	10.00	20.00
59 Captain Rex	12.50	25.00
60 Death Squad Commander	15.00	30.00
61 Jawa	10.00	20.00
62 Han Solo	12.50	25.00
63 Grand Moff Tark (w/IT-O Droid)	20.00	40.00
64 Range Trooper	10.00	20.00
65 Lando Calrissian	12.50	25.00
66 Qi'Ra	12.50	25.00
67 4-LOM	25.00	50.00
68 Tobias Beckett	20.00	40.00
69 Rebel Fleet Trooper	20.00	40.00

2017-18 Star Wars Black Series Centerpieces

NNO Rey vs. Kylo Ren (2018 SDCC Exclusive)	75.00	150.00
NNO Darth Vader	30.00	60.00
NNO Luke Skywalker	20.00	40.00
NNO Kylo Ren	20.00	40.00
NNO Rey	30.00	60.00

2018 Star Wars Black Series Multi-Pack

NNO Porgs 2-Pack	10.00	20.00

2013-16 Star Wars Black Series Vehicles

1 Millennium Falcon	10.00	20.00
2 Resistance X-Wing	8.00	15.00
3A Kylo Ren's Command Shuttle	6.00	12.00
3B Kylo Ren Command Shuttle (black)	6.00	12.00
4 First Order Special Forces Tie Fighter	6.00	12.00
5 Rey's Speeder (Jakku)	10.00	20.00
6 First Order Star Destroyer	8.00	15.00
7 X-Wing	12.00	25.00
8 Y-Wing	15.00	30.00
9 Luke Skywalker Landspeeder	10.00	20.00
10 Slave I	12.00	25.00
11 First Order Snowspeeder	5.00	10.00
12 Poe's X-Wing Fighter	5.00	10.00
13 First Order Tie Fighter	4.00	8.00
14 First Order Transporter	4.00	8.00
15 Tie Advanced	5.00	10.00
16 B-Wing	12.00	25.00
17 Snowspeeder	8.00	15.00
18 AT-AT	30.00	60.00
19 Jakku Landspeeder	8.00	15.00
20 A-Wing	15.00	30.00
21 Sith Infiltrator	8.00	15.00
22 Anakin Skywalker's Jedi Starfighter	12.00	30.00
23 Republic Gunship	12.00	25.00
24 Star Destroyer	6.00	12.00
25 Imperial Shuttle	30.00	60.00
26 The Ghost	6.00	12.00
27 Jango Fett's Slave I	8.00	15.00
28 Inquisitor's Tie Advanced Prototype	6.00	12.00
29 Rebel U-Wing Fighter	8.00	15.00
30 TIE Striker	8.00	15.00
31 Imperial Cargo Shuttle SW-0608	8.00	15.00

2003-05 Star Wars Clone Wars

NNO Anakin Skywalker	6.00	12.00
NNO ARC Trooper (blue)	5.00	10.00
NNO ARC Trooper (blue w/gray shoulder pad and thick blue chin paint)	5.00	10.00
NNO ARC Trooper (red)	5.00	10.00
NNO Yoda	5.00	10.00
NNO Obi-Wan Kenobi (General of The Republic Army)	4.00	8.00
NNO Durge Commander of the Seperatist Forces	10.00	20.00
NNO Asajj Ventress (Sith Apprentice)	5.00	10.00
NNO Mace Windu (General of the Republic Army)	5.00	10.00
NNO Kit Fisto	8.00	15.00
NNO Clone Trooper (facing left)	8.00	15.00
NNO Clone Trooper (facing right)	30.00	60.00
NNO Saesee Tiin	8.00	15.00

2003-05 Star Wars Clone Wars Deluxe

1 Clone Trooper (w/speeder bike)	8.00	15.00
2 Spider Droid	6.00	12.00
3 Durge (w/swoop bike)	15.00	30.00

2003-05 Star Wars Clone Wars Multipacks

NNO Clone Trooper Army	8.00	15.00
NNO Clone Trooper Army (w/blue lieutenant)	10.00	20.00
NNO Clone Trooper Army (w/green sergeant)	8.00	15.00
NNO Clone Trooper Army (w/red captain)	8.00	15.00
NNO Clone Trooper Army (w/yellow commander)	8.00	15.00
NNO Droid Army	6.00	12.00
NNO Jedi Knight Army	6.00	12.00

2003-05 Star Wars Clone Wars Value Packs

NNO Anakin Skywalker/Clone Trooper (blue)	5.00	10.00
NNO ARC Trooper/Clone Trooper	10.00	20.00
NNO Yoda/Clone Trooper (yellow)	5.00	10.00

2003-05 Star Wars Clone Wars Vehicles

NNO Anakin Skywalker's Jedi Starfighter	25.00	50.00
NNO Armored Assault/ Tank (AAT)	50.00	100.00
NNO Command Gunship	30.00	75.00
NNO Geonosian Starfighter	15.00	30.00
NNO Hailfire Droid	12.00	25.00
NNO Jedi Starfighter	15.00	30.00

2003-05 Star Wars Clone Wars Animated Series

NNO	Anakin Skywalker	12.50	25.00
NNO	Anakin Skywalker (no sleeves torn pants)	5.00	12.00
NNO	ARC Trooper		
NNO	Asajj Ventress	12.50	25.00
NNO	Clone Trooper	5.00	10.00
NNO	Clone Trooper (blue)	12.00	30.00
NNO	Clone Trooper (red)		
NNO	Clone Trooper (yellow)	6.00	12.00
NNO	Count Dooku	5.00	10.00
NNO	Durge	5.00	10.00
NNO	General Grievous		
NNO	Mace Windu	5.00	10.00
NNO	Obi-Wan Kenobi		
NNO	Yoda		

2003-05 Star Wars Clone Wars Animated Series Commemorative DVD Collection

NNO	Volume 1 Jedi Force	15.00	30.00
	(Anakin Skywalker/ARC Trooper/Obi-Wan Kenobi)		
NNO	Volume 1 Sith Attack	12.00	25.00
	(Asojj Ventress/Durge/General Grievous)		
NNO	Volume 2 (Anakin Skywalker tattoo		
	Clone Trooper/Saesee Tiin)		
NNO	Volume 2 (Clone Commander Cody		
	General Grievous/Obi-Wan Kenobi)		

2008-13 Star Wars The Clone Wars Battle Packs

NNO	Ambush at Abregado	30.00	75.00
NNO	Ambush on the Vulture's Claw	30.00	75.00
NNO	Anti-Hailfire Droid Squad	30.00	75.00
NNO	ARC Troopers	120.00	250.00
NNO	Army of the Republic		
NNO	Assault on Ryloth	30.00	60.00
NNO	Assault on Geonosis	15.00	30.00
NNO	AT-TE Assault Squad	20.00	40.00
NNO	Battle of Orto Plutonia	15.00	30.00
NNO	B'omarr Monastery Assault	30.00	60.00
NNO	Cad Bane's Escape	30.00	60.00
NNO	Capture of the Droids	12.50	25.00
NNO	Clone Troopers & Droids	25.00	50.00
NNO	Defend Kamino	75.00	150.00

NNO	Holocron Heist	20.00	40.00
NNO	Hunt for Grievous	25.00	50.00
NNO	Jabba's Palace	15.00	30.00
NNO	Jedi Showdown	20.00	40.00
NNO	Mandalorian Warriors	75.00	150.00
NNO	Republic Troopers	30.00	75.00
NNO	Rishi Moon Outpost Attack	50.00	100.00
NNO	Speeder Bike Recon	15.00	30.00
NNO	Stop the Zillo Beast	20.00	40.00

2008-13 Star Wars The Clone Wars Battle Packs Exclusives

1	Assassin Spider Droid & Clones		
	(Toys R Us Exclusive)		
2	Battle of Christophsis (ultimate)	90.00	175.00
	(2008 Target Exclusive)		
3	Darth Maul Returns	25.00	50.00
	(2012 Target Exclusive)		
4	Hidden Enemy (w/DVD)	30.00	75.00
	(2010 Target Exclusive)		
5	Hostage Crisis (w/DVD)	15.00	30.00
	(Target Exclusive)		
6	Obi-Wan & 212th Attack Battalion	50.00	100.00
	(2008 Target Exclusive)		
7	Rise of Boba Fett (ultimate)	120.00	250.00
	(2010 Toys R Us Exclusive)		
8	Yoda & Coruscant Guard	30.00	60.00
	(2008 Target Exclusive)		

2008-13 Star Wars The Clone Wars Blue and Black

CW1	Captain Rex	12.50	25.00
CW2	Obi-Wan Kenobi	10.00	20.00
CW3	Clone Commander Cody	7.50	15.00
CW4	Destroyer Droid	7.50	15.00
CW5	Yoda	7.50	15.00
CW6	Count Dooku	10.00	20.00
CW7	Anakin Skywalker	10.00	20.00
CW8	Pre Vizsla	15.00	30.00
CW9	Mandalorian Police Officer	6.00	12.00
CW10	General Grievous	15.00	30.00
CW11	Aurra Sing	12.50	25.00
CW12	Captain Rex (cold weather gear)	12.50	25.00
CW13	Cad Bane	10.00	20.00
CW14	Clone Pilot Odd Ball	12.50	25.00
CW15	Asajj Ventress	20.00	40.00
CW16	Super Battle Droid	10.00	20.00
CW17	Ahsoka Tano	20.00	40.00
CW18	ARF Trooper	12.50	25.00
CW19	Battle Droid	10.00	20.00
CW20	Mace Windu	10.00	20.00
CW21	Commander Gree	15.00	30.00
CW22	Battle Droid Commander	15.00	30.00
CW23	Kit Fisto	10.00	20.00
CW24	ARF Trooper (jungle deco)	12.50	25.00
CW25	Ki-Adi-Mundi	12.50	25.00
CW26	Clone Trooper (flamethrower)	15.00	30.00
CW27	R2-D2	8.00	15.00
CW28	Clone Pilot Goji	15.00	30.00
CW29	Mandalorian Warrior	25.00	50.00
CW30	R4-P17	10.00	20.00
CW31	Shaak Ti	20.00	40.00
CW32	Boba Fett	10.00	20.00
CW33	Embo	15.00	30.00
CW34	Undead Geonosian	7.50	15.00
CW35	Clone Trooper Draa	20.00	40.00
CW36	Quinlan Vos	15.00	30.00
CW37	Cato Parasiti	10.00	20.00
CW38	Clone Commander Jet	25.00	50.00
CW39	Hondo Ohnaka	20.00	40.00
CW40	Obi-Wan Kenobi (new outfit)	10.00	20.00
CW41	Clone Trooper Hevy (training armor)	12.50	25.00
CW42	Cad Bane (w/TODO-360)	15.00	30.00

CW43	R7-A7	12.50	25.00
CW44	Ahsoka (new outfit)	60.00	120.00
CW45	Anakin Skywalker (new outfit)	12.50	25.00
CW46	Aqua Battle Droid	7.50	15.00
CW47	El-Les	12.50	25.00
CW48	Clone Commander Wolffe	30.00	75.00
CW49	Riot Control Clone Trooper	25.00	50.00
CW50	Barriss Offee	20.00	40.00
CW51	Eeth Koth	20.00	40.00
CW52	Clone Commander Colt	60.00	120.00
CW53	Plo Koon (cold weather gear)	7.50	15.00
CW54	Saesee Tin	25.00	50.00
CW55	Savage Opress (shirtless)	12.50	25.00
CW56	ARF Trooper (Kamino)	20.00	40.00
CW57	Stealth Ops Clone Trooper	15.00	30.00
CW58	Even Piell	25.00	50.00
CW59	Savage Opress (armored apprentice)	30.00	60.00
CW60	Kit Fisto (cold weather gear)	12.50	25.00
CW61	Seripas	30.00	60.00
CW62	Captain Rex (jet propulsion pack)	30.00	75.00
CW63	Chewbacca	10.00	20.00
CW64	R7-D4 (Plo Koon's astromech droid)	7.50	15.00
CW65	Jar Jar Binks	10.00	20.00

2008-13 Star Wars The Clone Wars Blue and White

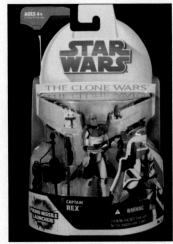

1	Anakin Skywalker		
2	Obi-Wan Kenobi		
3	Yoda		
4	Captain Rex		
5	Clone Trooper		
6	General Grievous		
7	Battle Droid		
8	R2-D2		
9	Ahsoka Tano		
10	Clone Commander Cody		
11	Clone Pilot Odd Ball		
12	Super Battle Droid	15.00	30.00
13	Count Dooku		
14	Plo Koon	10.00	20.00
15	Asajj Ventress		
16	C-3PO	6.00	12.00
17	Destroyer Droid	7.50	15.00
18	IG-86 Assassin Droid		
19	Clone Trooper (212th Attack Battalion)		
20	Padme Amidala (diplomat)		
21	Clone Trooper (space gear)		
22	Magnaguard	10.00	20.00
23	R3-S6 (Goldie)		
24	Jar Jar Binks		
25	Rocket Battle Droid		
26	Clone Trooper (41st Elite Corps)	10.00	20.00
27	Kit Fisto		

2008-13 Star Wars The Clone Wars Darth Maul Pack

CW1 Anakin Skywalker (new sculpt)	7.50	15.00
CW2 Clone Trooper (Phase II armor)	15.00	30.00
CW3 Savage Opress (shirtless)	12.50	25.00
CW4 Cad Bane	12.50	25.00
CW5 Yoda	6.00	12.00
CW6 Plo Koon (cold weather gear)	10.00	20.00
CW7 Clone Commander Cody (jet propulsion pack)	15.00	30.00
CW8 Mace Windu	6.00	12.00
CW9 Chewbacca	7.50	15.00
CW10 Aqua Battle Droid	7.50	15.00
CW11 Republic Commando Boss	12.50	25.00
CW12 Obi-Wan Kenobi	12.50	25.00
CW13 Captain Rex (Phase II)	15.00	30.00
CW14 Aayla Secura	15.00	30.00
CW15 Ahsoka Tano (scuba gear)	30.00	75.00
CW16 Training Super Battle Droid	10.00	20.00
CW17 Clone Commander Wolffe (Phase II)	25.00	50.00
CW18 Clone Commander Fox (Phase II)	20.00	40.00

2008-13 Star Wars The Clone Wars Deluxe Figures and Vehicles

NNO 212th Battalion Clone Troopers & Jet Backpacks	25.00	50.00
NNO Armored Scout Tank (w/Battle Droid)	12.50	25.00
NNO Armored Scout Tank (w/Tactical Droid)	15.00	30.00
NNO AT-RT (w/ARF Trooper Boil)	20.00	40.00
NNO Attack Cycle (w/General Grievous)	15.00	30.00
NNO Attack Recon Fighter (w/Anakin Skywalker)	20.00	40.00
NNO BARC Speeder (w/Commander Cody)	15.00	30.00
NNO BARC Speeder (w/Clone Trooper)	15.00	30.00
NNO BARC Speeder Bike (w/Clone Trooper Jesse)	25.00	50.00
NNO BARC Speeder Bike (w/Obi-Wan Kenobi)	15.00	30.00
NNO Can-Cell (w/Anakin Skywalker)	15.00	30.00
NNO Crab Droid	20.00	40.00
NNO Desert Skiff (w/Anakin Skywalker)	12.50	25.00
NNO Freeco Speeder (w/Clone Trooper)	10.00	20.00
NNO Freeco Speeder (w/Obi-Wan Kenobi)	15.00	30.00
NNO Mandalorian Speeder (w/Mandalorian Warrior)	30.00	60.00
NNO Naboo Star Skiff (w/Anakin Skywalker)	15.00	30.00
NNO Pirate Speeder Bike (w/Cad Bane)	12.50	25.00
NNO Republic Assault Submarine with Scuba Clone Trooper	25.00	50.00
NNO Republic Attack Dropship with Clone Pilot		
NNO Republic Scout Speeder with ARF Trooper	15.00	30.00
NNO Separatist Droid Speeder with Battle Droid	15.00	30.00
NNO Speeder Bike with Castas	10.00	20.00
NNO Speeder Bike with Count Dooku	20.00	40.00
NNO Speeder Bike with Plo Koon		
NNO Turbo Tank Support Squad	25.00	50.00
NNO Y-Wing Scout Bomber with Clone Trooper Pilot	20.00	40.00

2008-13 Star Wars The Clone Wars Deluxe Figures and Vehicles Exclusives

1 AT-RT with ARF Trooper (Walmart Exclusive)	25.00	50.00
2 BARC Speeder with Clone Trooper Buzz (Walmart Exclusive)	30.00	60.00
3 Separatist Speeder with Geonosian Warrior (2011 Toys R Us Exclusive)	15.00	30.00
4 STAP with Battle Droid (2010 Toys R Us Exclusive)		

2008-13 Star Wars The Clone Wars Exclusives

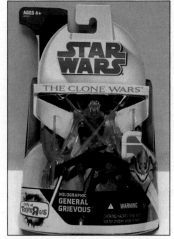

1 Captain Rex (2008 Sneak Preview Mailaway Exclusive)	12.50	25.00
2 Clone Captain Lock (2011 K-Mart Exclusive)	12.50	25.00
3 Clone Trooper: 501st Legion (2008 Wal-Mart Exclusive)	15.00	30.00
4 Clone Trooper: Senate Security (2008 SDCC Exclusive)	15.00	30.00
5 Commander Fox (2008 Target Exclusive)	20.00	40.00
6 Commander Ponds (2009 Toys R Us Exclusive)	25.00	50.00
7 General Grievous: Holographic (2008 Toys R Us Exclusive)	10.00	20.00
8 Kul Teska (2010 Toys R Us Exclusive)	15.00	30.00
9 Nahdar Vebb (2009 Mailaway Exclusive)	15.00	30.00
10 Nikto Skiff Guard Puko Naga (2010 Toys R Us Exclusive)	10.00	20.00
11 Sgt. Bric & Galactic Battle Mat (2010 Mailaway Exclusive)	20.00	40.00
12 Stealth Operation Clone Trooper: Commander Blackout (2011 Toys R Us Exclusive)	15.00	30.00

2008-13 Star Wars The Clone Wars Red and White

CW1 General Grievous	10.00	20.00
CW2 Clone Trooper (space gear)	15.00	30.00
CW3 Rocket Battle Droid	10.00	20.00
CW4 Clone Trooper (41st Elite Corps)	15.00	30.00
CW5 Kit Fisto	10.00	20.00
CW6 Mace Windu	10.00	20.00
CW7 Admiral Yularen	15.00	30.00
CW8 Jawas	10.00	20.00
CW9 Commander Gree	20.00	40.00
CW10 ARF Trooper	12.50	25.00
CW11 Heavy Assault Super Battle Droid	7.50	15.00
CW12 Obi-Wan Kenobi (space suit)	7.50	15.00
CW13 4A-7	10.00	20.00
CW14 Yoda	10.00	20.00

CW15 Whorm Loathsom	10.00	20.00
CW16 Commando Droid	15.00	30.00
CW17 Clone Trooper Echo	20.00	40.00
CW18 Anakin Skywalker	7.50	15.00
CW19 Obi-Wan Kenobi	10.00	20.00
CW20 Clone Trooper Denal	20.00	40.00
CW21 Anakin Skywalker (space suit)	7.50	15.00
CW22 Cad Bane	10.00	20.00
CW23 Ahsoka Tano (space suit)	15.00	30.00
CW24 Captain Rex	12.50	25.00
CW25 R2-D2	7.50	15.00
CW26 Ahsoka Tano	15.00	30.00
CW27 Count Dooku	10.00	20.00
CW28 Commander Cody	12.50	25.00
CW29 Destroyer Droid	7.50	15.00
CW30 Luminara Unduli	12.50	25.00
CW31 Captain Argyus	15.00	30.00
CW32 Clone Commander Thire	20.00	40.00
CW33 Battle Droid (AAT Driver)	15.00	30.00
CW34 Matchstick	15.00	30.00
CW35 Padme Amidala (adventurer suit)	15.00	30.00
CW36 Clone Tank Gunner	20.00	40.00
CW37 Ziro's Assassin Droid	10.00	20.00
CW38 Clone Trooper Jek	30.00	60.00
CW39 Commander Bly	30.00	75.00
CW40 Aayla Secura	10.00	20.00
CW41 Hondo Ohnaka	30.00	75.00
CW42 Anakin Skywalker (cold weather gear)	7.50	15.00
CW43 Thi-Sen	15.00	30.00
CW44 Clone Commander Stone	25.00	50.00
CW45 Darth Sidious	75.00	150.00
CW46 Commander TX-20	20.00	40.00
CW47 Firefighter Droid	25.00	50.00
CW48 Obi-Wan Kenobi (cold weather gear)	10.00	20.00
CW49 Magnaguard (w/cape)	20.00	40.00
CW50 Captain Rex (cold assault gear)	12.50	25.00

2008-13 Star Wars The Clone Wars Vehicles

NNO Ahsoka Tano's Delta Starfighter		
NNO Anakin's Delta Starfighter	8.00	15.00
NNO Anakin's Modified Jedi Starfighter	15.00	40.00
NNO ARC-170 Starfighter (Imperial Shadow Squadron)		
NNO AT-AP Walker		
NNO AT-TE (All Terrain Tactical Enforcer)		
NNO Clone Turbo Tank	150.00	300.00
NNO Corporate Alliance Tank Droid	30.00	60.00
NNO Droid Tri-Fighter		
NNO General Grievous' Starfighter	20.00	40.00
NNO Hailfire Droid (Remote Control)	20.00	40.00
NNO Homing Spider Droid	25.00	50.00
NNO Hyena Bomber	25.00	50.00
NNO Jedi Turbo Speeder	30.00	60.00
NNO MagnaGuard Fighter	12.50	25.00
NNO Mandalorian Assault Gunship	50.00	100.00
NNO Obi-Wan Kenobi's Delta Starfighter		
NNO Obi-Wan's Jedi Starfighter (Utapau)		
NNO Plo Koon's Delta Starfighter	15.00	30.00
NNO Republic Attack Shuttle	75.00	150.00
NNO Republic AV-7 Mobile Cannon	30.00	75.00

NNO	Republic Fighter Tank		
NNO	Republic Fighter Tank (blue deco)		
NNO	Republic Fighter Tank (green deco)		
NNO	Republic Fighter Tank (Remote Control)	25.00	50.00
NNO	Republic Swamp Speeder	30.00	60.00
NNO	Separatist Droid Gunship	30.00	75.00
NNO	Trade Federation Armored Assault Tank (AAT - brown/blue)	20.00	40.00
NNO	Trade Federation Armored Assault Tank (AAT)	30.00	60.00
NNO	V-19 Torrent Starfighter		
NNO	Vulture Droid	20.00	40.00
NNO	V-Wing Starfighter	20.00	40.00
NNO	Xanadu Blood	30.00	75.00
NNO	Y-Wing Bomber	75.00	150.00

2008-13 Star Wars The Clone Wars Vehicles Exclusives

NNO	ARC-170 Starfighter (flaming wampa)		
	(Toys R Us Exclusive)		
NNO	Hailfire Droid & General Grievous		
	(Toys R Us Exclusive)		
NNO	Kit Fisto's Delta Starfighter		
	(Walmart Exclusive)		
NNO	Octuptarra Droid	30.00	75.00
	(Walmart Exclusive)		
NNO	Republic Gunship (crumb bomber)		
	(Toys R Us Exclusive)		
NNO	Republic Gunship (Lucky Lekku)	125.00	250.00
	(Walmart Exclusive)		
NNO	V-Wing Starfighter & V-Wing Pilot		
	(Toys R Us Exclusive)		
NNO	V-Wing Starfighter (Imperial)	30.00	75.00
	(Toys R Us Exclusive)		

2008-13 Star Wars The Clone Wars Yoda Pack

CW1	Obi-Wan Kenobi		
CW2	Savage Opress (armoured apprentice)		
CW3	Anakin Skywalker		
CW4	Captain Rex	15.00	30.00
CW5	R2-D2		
CW6	501st Legion Clone Trooper	60.00	120.00
CW7	Clone Commander Cody (jet propulsion pack)		
CW8	Darth Maul	30.00	60.00
CW9	Battle Droid	15.00	30.00

1996-99 Star Wars Collector Series

1	Admiral Ackbar	20.00	40.00
2	AT-AT Driver	15.00	30.00
3	Boba Fett	25.00	50.00
4	C-3PO	20.00	40.00
5	Cantina Band - Doikk Na'ts (w/Fizzz)	12.00	25.00
	(Walmart Exclusive)		
6	Cantina Band - Figrin D'an (w/Kloo Horn)	10.00	20.00
	(Walmart Exclusive)		
7	Cantina Band - Ickabel (w/fanfar)	12.00	25.00
	(Walmart Exclusive)		
8	Cantina Band - Nalan (w/Bandfill)	10.00	20.00
	(Walmart Exclusive)		
9	Cantina Band - Tech (w/Omni Box)	12.00	25.00
	(Walmart Exclusive)		
10	Cantina Band - Tedn (w/fanfar)	10.00	20.00
	(Walmart Exclusive)		
11	Chewbacca	20.00	40.00
12	Darth Vader	15.00	30.00
13	Greedo	15.00	30.00
	(JC Penney Exclusive)		
14	Han Solo	15.00	30.00
15	Lando Calrissian	12.00	25.00
16	Luke Skywalker	15.00	30.00
17	Luke Skywalker (Bespin)	12.00	25.00
18	Luke Skywalker (X-Wing Pilot)	20.00	40.00
19	Obi-Wan Kenobi	15.00	30.00
20	Princess Leia	15.00	30.00
21	Sandtrooper	15.00	30.00
22	Stormtrooper	15.00	30.00
23	TIE Fighter Pilot	20.00	40.00
24	Tusken Raider (blaster and binoculars)	12.00	25.00
25	Tusken Raider (gaderffi stick)	12.00	25.00

1996-99 Star Wars Collector Series 2-Packs

1	Grand Moff Tarkin and Imperial Gunner	25.00	50.00
	(FAO Schwarz Exclusive)		
2	Han Solo and Luke Skywalker (stormtrooper gear)	30.00	60.00
	(KB Toys Exclusive)		
3	Han Solo and Tauntaun	30.00	60.00
4	Luke Hoth and Wampa	25.00	50.00
5	Luke Jedi and Bib Fortuna	25.00	50.00
	(FAO Schwarz Exclusive)		
6	Obi-Wan Kenobi vs. Darth Vader (electronic)	25.00	50.00
	(JC Penney/KB Toys Exclusive)		
7	Princess Leia and R2-D2 (Jabba's prisoners)		
	(FAO Schwarz/KB Toys Exclusive)		

1996-99 Star Wars Collector Series European Exclusives

1	Han Solo (drawing action)	12.00	25.00
2	Luke Skywalker (drawing action)		

1996-99 Star Wars Collector Series Masterpiece Edition

1	Anakin Skywalker/Story of Darth Vader	10.00	20.00
2	Aurra Sing/Dawn of the Bounty Hunters	12.00	25.00
3	C-3PO/Tales of the Golden Droid	20.00	40.00

2012-13 Star Wars Discover the Force

NNO	Aurra Sing	12.50	25.00
NNO	Darth Maul	8.00	15.00
NNO	Destroyer Droid	6.00	12.00
NNO	G8-R3	12.00	25.00
NNO	Gungan Warrior	8.00	15.00
NNO	Mawhonic	6.00	12.00
NNO	Obi-Wan Kenobi	8.00	15.00
NNO	Qui-Gon Jinn	6.00	12.00
NNO	Ric Olie	6.00	12.00
NNO	Naboo Pilot	5.00	10.00
NNO	Tusken Raider	5.00	10.00
NNO	Yoda	8.00	15.00

2012-13 Star Wars Discover the Force Battle Packs

NNO	Mos Espa Arena	20.00	40.00

	(C-3PO/Anakin/Sebulba/2 Pit Droids)		
NNO	Royal Starship Droids		
	(R2-B1/R2-R9/R2-D2/R2-N3)		

2012-13 Star Wars Discover the Force Vehicles-Creatures

NNO	Dewback	20.00	40.00
NNO	Vulture Droid		

2010-15 Star Wars Disney Characters Exclusives

NNO	Bad Pete as Jango Fett	20.00	40.00
	(2015 Star Wars Weekends Exclusive)/2002		
NNO	Donald Duck as Darth Maul	25.00	50.00
	(2012 Star Wars Weekends Exclusive)		
NNO	Donald Duck as Savage Opress	25.00	50.00
	(2012 Star Wars Weekends Exclusive)/2012		
NNO	Donald Duck as Shadow Trooper	30.00	60.00
	(2010 Star Wars Celebration Exclusive)/5000		
NNO	Mickey Mouse and Donald Duck as X-Wing Luke and Han Solo	15.00	30.00
	(2014 Star Wars Weekends Exclusive)/1980		
NNO	Mickey Mouse/Chip & Dale as Luke Skywalker and Ewoks	20.00	40.00
	(2013 Star Wars Weekends Exclusive)/1983		
NNO	Pluto and Minnie Mouse as R2-D2 and Princess Leia	30.00	60.00
	(2015 Star Wars Weekends Exclusive)/1977		
NNO	Stitch as Emperor Palpatine	15.00	30.00
	(2010 Star Wars Weekends Exclusive)/1980		
NNO	Stitch as Hologram Yoda	15.00	30.00
	(2011 Star Tours Opening Exclusive)/2011		

2007 Star Wars Disney Characters Series 1

NNO	Donald Duck as Han Solo	12.50	25.00
NNO	Goofy as Darth Vader	10.00	20.00
NNO	Mickey Mouse as Luke Skywalker	12.50	25.00
NNO	Minnie Mouse as Princess Leia	7.50	15.00
NNO	Stitch as Emperor Palpatine	12.50	25.00

2009 Star Wars Disney Characters Series 3

NNO	Chip & Dale as Ewoks	20.00	40.00
NNO	Donald Duck as Stormtrooper	12.50	25.00
NNO	Goofy as Chewbacca	15.00	30.00
NNO	Mickey Mouse as Luke Skywalker (X-Wing Pilot)	12.50	25.00
NNO	Minnie Mouse as Slave Leia		

2010 Star Wars Disney Characters Series 4

NNO	Bad Pete as Boba Fett	20.00	40.00
NNO	Donald Duck as Han in Carbonite	10.00	20.00
NNO	Goofy as C-3PO	20.00	40.00
NNO	Mickey Mouse as Jedi Knight Luke Skywalker		
NNO	Minnie Mouse as Princess Leia Boushh	15.00	30.00

2011 Star Wars Disney Characters Series 5

NNO	Daisy Duck as Aurra Sing	15.00	30.00
NNO	Donald Duck as Commander Cody		
NNO	Goofy as Cad Bane		
NNO	Dewey/Huey/Louie as Jawas	20.00	40.00
NNO	Stitch as General Grievous	25.00	50.00

2012 Star Wars Disney Characters Series 6

NNO	Donald Duck as Darth Maul	20.00	40.00
NNO	Goofy as TC-14	12.50	25.00
NNO	Mickey Mouse as Anakin Skywalker	25.00	50.00
NNO	Minnie Mouse as Queen Amidala	12.50	25.00
NNO	Pluto as R2-D2	20.00	40.00
NNO	Stitch as Yoda		

2015-17 Star Wars Disney Parks Droid Factory

NNO	BB-8	7.50	15.00
NNO	C1-10P Chopper	15.00	30.00
NNO	R2-B00	20.00	40.00
(2016 Halloween Exclusive)			
NNO	R2-D60	25.00	50.00
(2015 Disneyland 60th Anniversary Exclusive)			
NNO	R2-H15	30.00	75.00
(2015 Holiday Exclusive)			
NNO	R2-H16	15.00	30.00
(2016 Holiday Exclusive)			
NNO	R3-B0017 (glow-in-the-dark)	60.00	120.00
(2017 Halloween Exclusive)			
NNO	R-3D0	10.00	20.00
NNO	R3-H17	20.00	40.00
(2017 Holiday Exclusive)			
NNO	R5-M4	12.50	25.00
(2016 May 4th Exclusive)			

2015-17 Star Wars Disney Parks Droid Factory Multipacks

NNO	Artoo Detoo (R2-D2)/See-Threepio (C-3PO)	30.00	75.00
(2017 40th Anniversary Exclusive)			
NNO	BB-8/2BB-2/BB-4/BB-9E	25.00	50.00
NNO	C2-B5/R2-BHD/R3-M2/R5-SK1	30.00	75.00
NNO	R4-X2/Y5-X2	20.00	40.00
NNO	R5-013/R2-C2/R5-S9/R5-P8	25.00	50.00

2017-18 Star Wars Disney Store Toybox

1	Kylo Ren	10.00	20.00
2	Rey	10.00	20.00
3	Stormtrooper	7.50	15.00
4	Darth Vader	7.50	15.00
5	Luke Skywalker	12.50	25.00
6	Boba Fett	10.00	20.00
7	Princess Leia Organa	7.50	15.00
8	Han Solo	10.00	20.00
9	Chewbacca		

2015 Star Wars Elite Series

NNO	Anakin Skywalker	25.00	50.00
NNO	Boba Fett (w/cape)	20.00	40.00
NNO	Boba Fett (w/o cape)	30.00	75.00
NNO	Darth Maul	30.00	60.00
NNO	Darth Vader	20.00	40.00
NNO	General Grievous	50.00	100.00
NNO	Prototype Boba Fett	30.00	75.00
NNO	Stormtrooper	15.00	30.00

2016-17 Star Wars Elite Series 11-Inch

NNO	Darth Vader	20.00	40.00
NNO	Death Trooper	15.00	30.00
NNO	Director Orson Krennic	20.00	40.00
NNO	Jyn Erso	20.00	40.00
NNO	Kylo Ren	15.00	30.00
NNO	Princess Leia Organa	25.00	50.00
NNO	Rey	15.00	30.00

2015-17 Star Wars Elite Series Multipacks and Exclusives

NNO	8-Piece Gift Set	500.00	750.00
Darth Maul/Anakin/Grievous/Stormtrooper/Vader/C-3PO/R2-D2/Boba Fett)/(2016 D23 Exclusive)			
NNO	Deluxe Gift Set	60.00	120.00
Stormtrooper/Phasma/Kylo Ren/Finn/Flametrooper			
NNO	Droid Gift Pack	25.00	50.00
BB-8, C-3PO, R2-D2			
NNO	Han Solo & Luke Skywalker	50.00	100.00
w/blond hair (Stormtrooper Disguise)			
NNO	Han Solo & Luke Skywalker	25.00	50.00
w/brown hair (Stormtrooper Disguise)			
NNO	Princess Leia & Darth Vader/1000*	75.00	150.00
(2017 D23 Exclusive)			

1999-00 Star Wars Episode I 2-Packs

1	Darth Maul and Sith Infiltrator	8.00	15.00
2	Final Jedi Duel (Qui-Gon Jinn/Darth Maul break apart)	20.00	50.00

1999-00 Star Wars Episode I Accessory Sets

1	Flash Cannon	8.00	15.00
2	Gungan Catapult	10.00	20.00
3	Hyperdrive Repair Kit	25.00	50.00
4	Naboo Accessory Set	8.00	15.00
5	Pod Race Fuel Station	8.00	15.00
6	Rappel Line Attach	12.00	25.00
7	Sith Accessory Set	8.00	15.00
8	Tatooine Accessory Set	8.00	15.00
9	Tatooine Disguise Set	12.00	25.00
10	Underwater Accessory Set	8.00	15.00

1999-00 Star Wars Episode I Action Collection 12-Inch

1	Anakin Skywalker (fully poseable)	10.00	20.00
2	Anakin Skywalker (w/Theed Hangar Droid)	20.00	40.00
3	Battle Droid (w/blaster rifle)	15.00	30.00
4	Battle Droid Commander(#(w/electrobinoculars)	10.00	20.00
5	Boss Nass	15.00	30.00
6	Chancellor Valorum & Coruscant Guard	20.00	40.00
7	Darth Maul (w/lightsaber)	12.00	25.00
8	Darth Maul & Sith Speeder	20.00	40.00
(Walmart Exclusive)			
9	Jar Jar Binks (fully poseable)	12.00	25.00
10	Mace Windu (w/lightsaber)	15.00	30.00
11	Obi-Wan Kenobi (w/lightsaber)	12.00	25.00
12	Pit Droids (fully poseable)	12.00	20.00
13	Qui-Gon Jinn (w/lightsaber)	15.00	30.00
14	Qui-Gon Jinn (Tatooine)	10.00	20.00
15	R2-A6 (metalized dome)	20.00	40.00
16	Sebulba (w/Chubas)	12.00	25.00
17	Watto (w/data pad)	10.00	20.00

1999-00 Star Wars Episode I Battle Bags

1	Sea Creatures I	6.00	12.00
2	Sea Creatures II	6.00	12.00
3	Swamp Creatures I	6.00	12.00
4	Swamp Creatures II	6.00	12.00

1999-00 Star Wars Episode I Bonus Battle Droid 2-Packs

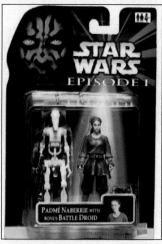

NNO	Anakin Skywalker (Naboo)/Battle Droid (tan clean)		
NNO	Anakin Skywalker (Tatooine)	10.00	20.00
	Battle Droid (tan clean)		
NNO	Battle Droid (tan clean)/Battle Droid (tan clean)		
NNO	Battle Droid (tan clean)/Battle Droid (gold/dirty)		
NNO	Battle Droid (tan clean)/Battle Droid (tan/blast on chest)		
NNO	Battle Droid (tan clean)/Battle Droid		
	(tan/slash on chest/burn marks)		
NNO	C-3PO/Battle Droid (tan clean)	15.00	30.00
NNO	Captain Panaka/Battle Droid (tan clean)		
NNO	Darth Maul (Jedi duel)/Battle Droid (tan clean)	7.50	15.00
NNO	Darth Maul (Tatooine)/Battle Droid (tan clean)	7.50	15.00
NNO	Darth Sidious/Battle Droid (tan clean)		
NNO	Destroyer Droid/Battle Droid (tan clean)	12.50	25.00
NNO	Jar Jar Binks/Battle Droid (tan clean)	12.50	25.00
NNO	Naboo Royal Security/Battle Droid (tan clean)		
NNO	Nute Gunray/Battle Droid (tan clean)	15.00	30.00
NNO	Obi-Wan Kenobi (Jedi duel)	6.00	12.00

Battle Droid (tan clean)		
NNO Obi-Wan Kenobi (Jedi Knight)	6.00	12.00
Battle Droid (tan clean)		
NNO Padme Naberrie/Battle Droid (tan clean)		
NNO Queen Amidala (Naboo)	6.00	12.00
Battle Droid (tan clean)		
NNO Queen Amidala (red senate gown)/Battle Droid (tan clean)		
NNO Qui-Gon Jinn/Battle Droid (tan clean)		
NNO Qui-Gon Jinn (Jedi Master)	12.50	25.00
Battle Droid (tan clean)		
NNO R2-D2/Battle Droid (tan clean)	15.00	30.00
NNO Ric Olie/Battle Droid (tan clean)		
NNO Rune Haako/Battle Droid (tan clean)		
NNO Senator Palpatine/Battle Droid (tan clean)		
NNO Watto/Battle Droid (tan clean)	20.00	40.00
NNO Yoda/Battle Droid (tan clean)	6.00	12.00

1999-00 Star Wars Episode I Bonus Pit Droid 2-Packs

NNO Anakin Skywalker (Tatooine)/Pit Droid (maroon)		
NNO Anakin Skywalker (Tatooine)/Pit Droid (orange)		
NNO Anakin Skywalker (Tatooine)/Pit Droid (white)		
NNO Darth Maul (Jedi duel)/Pit Droid (maroon)	25.00	50.00
NNO Darth Maul (Jedi duel)/Pit Droid (orange)		
NNO Darth Maul (Jedi duel)/Pit Droid (white)		
NNO Darth Sidius (hologram)/Pit Droid (maroon)		
NNO Darth Sidius (hologram)/Pit Droid (orange)		
NNO Darth Sidius (hologram)/Pit Droid (white)		
NNO Naboo Royal Guard/Pit Droid (maroon)	10.00	20.00
NNO Naboo Royal Guard/Pit Droid (orange)	20.00	40.00
NNO Naboo Royal Guard/Pit Droid (white)	15.00	30.00
NNO Obi-Wan Kenobi (Jedi Knight)/Pit Droid (maroon)		
NNO Obi-Wan Kenobi (Jedi Knight)/Pit Droid (orange)		
NNO Obi-Wan Kenobi (Jedi Knight)/Pit Droid (white)		

1999-00 Star Wars Episode I CommTech Cinema Scenes

1 Mos Espa Encounter	12.00	25.00
(Sebulba/Jar Jar Binks/Anakin Skywalker)		
2 Tatooine Showdown (Darth Maul	8.00	20.00
Qui-Gon Jinn Tatooine/Anakin Skywalker Tatooine)		
3 Watto's Box (Watto/Graxol Kelvyyn/Shakka)	25.00	50.00

1999-00 Star Wars Episode I CommTech Collection 1

1a Anakin Skywalker Naboo (new sticker)	6.00	12.00
1b Anakin Skywalker Naboo (no new sticker)	12.00	25.00
2a Anakin Skywalker Naboo pilot (new sticker)	6.00	12.00
2b Anakin Skywalker Naboo pilot (no new sticker)	3.00	6.00
3a Anakin Skywalker Tatooine (.00)	10.00	20.00
3b Anakin Skywalker Tatooine (.0100)	3.00	6.00
3c Anakin Skywalker Tatooine (.01 innovision back)	3.00	6.00
4a Battle Droid (tan clean .00)	5.00	10.00
4b Battle Droid (tan clean .01)	5.00	10.00
4c Battle Droid (tan clean .02 innovision back)	5.00	10.00
5a Battle Droid (tan slash on chest w/burn marks .00)	8.00	15.00
5b Battle Droid (tan slash on chest w/burn marks .01)	4.00	8.00
5c Battle Droid (tan slash on chest w/burn marks .02 innovision back)	3.00	6.00
6a Battle Droid (tan blast on chest .00)	4.00	8.00

6b Battle Droid (tan blast on chest .01)	3.00	6.00
6c Battle Droid (tan blast on chest .02 innovision back)	6.00	12.00
7a Battle Droid (gold/dirty .00)	3.00	6.00
7b Battle Droid (gold/dirty .01)	3.00	6.00
7c Battle Droid (gold/dirty .02 innovision back)	3.00	6.00
8a Darth Maul Jedi duel (.00)	8.00	15.00
8b Darth Maul Jedi duel (.01/ innovision back)	3.00	6.00
8c Darth Maul Jedi duel (.02)	5.00	10.00
8d Darth Maul Jedi duel (.0000 large eyes different face more red paint on)	4.00	8.00
8e Darth Maul Jedi duel (white strip on package card instead of yellow)	3.00	6.00
9a Darth Maul Sith Lord (new sticker)	5.00	10.00
9b Darth Maul Sith Lord (no new sticker)	5.00	10.00
10a Darth Maul Tatooine (new sticker)	4.00	8.00
10b Darth Maul Tatooine (new sticker hologram chip sticker)	3.00	6.00
10c Darth Maul Tatooine (no new sticker)	4.00	6.00
10d Darth Maul Tatooine (no new sticker hologram chip sticker)	3.00	6.00
10e Darth Maul Sith Lord (new sticker white strip on package card)	3.00	6.00
11a Destroyer Droid battle damaged (new sticker)	5.00	10.00
11b Destroyer Droid battle damaged (no new sticker)	3.00	6.00
12a Jar Jar Binks (.00 large package photo)	12.00	25.00
12b Jar Jar Binks (.0100 small package photo)	3.00	6.00
12c Jar Jar Binks (.0200/ innovision back)	3.00	6.00
13 Jar Jar Binks (Naboo swamp)	4.00	8.00
14a Obi-Wan Kenobi Jedi duel (.00)	4.00	8.00
14b Obi-Wan Kenobi Jedi duel (.0100)	3.00	6.00
15a Obi-Wan Kenobi Jedi Knight (new sticker)	4.00	8.00
15b Obi-Wan Kenobi Jedi Knight (no new sticker)	3.00	6.00
16a Obi-Wan Kenobi Naboo (new sticker)	6.00	12.00
16b Obi-Wan Kenobi Naboo (no new sticker)	3.00	6.00
17a Padme Naberrie (.00)	10.00	20.00
17b Padme Naberrie (.0100 innovision back)	3.00	6.00
18a Queen Amidala Coruscant (new sticker)	4.00	8.00
18b Queen Amidala Coruscant (no new sticker)	4.00	8.00
19a Queen Amidala Naboo (.00)	3.00	6.00
19b Queen Amidala Naboo (.0100 innovision back)	6.00	12.00
20a Qui-Gon Jinn (.00)	6.00	12.00
20b Qui-Gon Jinn (.0100 innovision back)	4.00	8.00
21a Qui-Gon Jinn Jedi Master (new sticker)	3.00	6.00
21b Qui-Gon Jinn Jedi Master (no new sticker)	3.00	6.00
22a Qui-Gon Jinn Naboo (new sticker)	5.00	10.00
22b Qui-Gon Jinn Naboo (no new sticker)	3.00	6.00

1999-00 Star Wars Episode I CommTech Collection 2

1a C-3PO (.00)	5.00	10.00
1b C-3PO (.01 innovision back)	20.00	40.00
2a Captain Panaka (wrong chip line on back they need her to sign a treaty)	5.00	10.00

2b Captain Panaka (correct chip line on back this battle I do not think)	5.00	10.00
3a Darth Sidious (.00)	5.00	10.00
3b Darth Sidious (.01/innovision back)	3.00	6.00
4 Darth Sidious (holograph)	15.00	30.00
5a Destroyer Droid (new sticker)	6.00	12.00
5b Destroyer Droid (no new sticker)	4.00	8.00
6a Naboo Royal Guard	8.00	15.00
6b Naboo Royal Security	3.00	6.00
7a Nute Gunray (new sticker)	5.00	10.00
7b Nute Gunray (no new sticker)	8.00	15.00
8a R2-B1 (.0000/Astromech back/no space)	8.00	15.00
8b R2-B1 (.0100/Astromech back/space)	8.00	15.00
9a R2-D2 (large packing bubble/new sticker)	6.00	12.00
9b R2-D2 (small packing bubble)	6.00	12.00
10 Pit Droids	5.00	10.00
11 Queen Amidala (battle)	6.00	12.00
12a Ric Olie (.00)	3.00	6.00
12b Ric Olie (.0100/innovision back)	4.00	8.00
13a Rune Haako (new sticker)	3.00	6.00
13b Rune Haako (no new sticker)	3.00	6.00
14a Senator Palpatine (.00)	3.00	6.00
14b Senator Palpatine (.0100/innovision back)	3.00	6.00
15 Sio Bibble	10.00	20.00
16a Watto (.00)	3.00	6.00
16b Watto (.0100 innovision back)	3.00	6.00
17a Yoda (episode 1 on front)	3.00	6.00
17b Yoda (no episode 1 on front)	5.00	10.00

1999-00 Star Wars Episode I CommTech Collection 3

1 Adi Gallia	4.00	8.00
2a Boss Nass (.00)	3.00	6.00
2b Boss Nass (.01/innovision back)	3.00	6.00
3a Captain Tarpals (.00)	5.00	10.00
3b Captain Tarpals (.01)	3.00	6.00
4a Chancellor Valorum (.00/warning)	3.00	6.00
4b Chancellor Valorum (.00/no warning)	3.00	6.00
4c Chancellor Valorum (.01/no warning)	3.00	6.00
4d Chancellor Valorum (.02/no warning)	3.00	6.00
5a Gasgano with Pit Droid (.0100)	5.00	10.00
5b Gasgano with Pit Droid (.0200)	3.00	6.00
6a Ki-Adi-Mundi (.0000)	3.00	6.00
6b Ki-Adi-Mundi (.0100/innovision back)	3.00	6.00
7a Mace Windu (.0000)	3.00	6.00
7b Mace Windu (.0100/innovision back)	3.00	6.00
8a Ody Mandrell and Otoga (222 Pit Droid)	3.00	6.00
8b Ody Mandrell and Otoga (222 Pit Droid hologram chip sticker)	3.00	6.00
9a OOM-9 (binoculars in package)	3.00	6.00
9b OOM-9 (binoculars in package hologram chip sticker)	3.00	6.00
9c OOM-9 (binoculars in right hand)	3.00	6.00
9d OOM-9 (binoculars in left hand hologram chip sticker)	5.00	10.00
10 TC-14 Protocol Droid	8.00	15.00

1999-00 Star Wars Episode I CommTech Figure Collector 2-Packs

1 Anakin Skywalker naboo/Obi-Wan Kenobi naboo	12.00	25.00
2 Battle Droid (tan blast on chest)/Darth Maul Tatooine		
3 Battle Droid (tan slash on chest w/burn marks)/Darth Maul Tatooine		
4 Darth Maul Jedi duel/Anakin Skywalker Tatooine	10.00	20.00
5 Jar Jar Binks/Qui-Gon Jinn	6.00	12.00
6 Padme Naberrie/Obi-Wan Kenobi Jedi Knight		
7 Queen Amidala Naboo/Qui-Gon Jinn Jedi Knight		

1999-00 Star Wars Episode I Creature 2-Packs

1 Ammo Wagon and Falumpaset	20.00	40.00
2 Eopie (w/Qui-Gon Jinn)		
3 Fambaa (w/Gungan warrior)	50.00	100.00
4 Jabba the Hut (w/two-headed announcer)	10.00	20.00

| 5 Kaadu and Jar Jar Binks | 10.00 | 20.00 |
| 6 Opee and Qui-Gon Jinn | 10.00 | 20.00 |

1999-00 Star Wars Episode I Deluxe

1 Darth Maul	3.00	6.00
2 Obi-Wan Kenobi	3.00	6.00
3 Qui-Gon Jinn	5.00	10.00

1999-00 Star Wars Episode I Electronic Talking 12-Inch

1 C-3PO	15.00	30.00
2 Darth Maul	10.00	20.00
3 Jar Jar Binks	15.00	30.00
4 Qui-Gon Jinn	12.00	25.00
5 TC-14	20.00	40.00

1999-00 Star Wars Episode I Epic Force

1 Darth Maul	8.00	15.00
2 Obi-Wan Kenobi	10.00	20.00
3 Qui-Gon Jinn	8.00	15.00

1999-00 Star Wars Episode I Invasion Force

1 Armored Scout Tank (w/Battle Droid tan clean)	6.00	12.00
2 Gungan Assault Cannon (w/Jar Jar Binks)	6.00	12.00
3 Gungan Scout Sub (w/Obi-Wan Kenobi Naboo water)	8.00	15.00
4 Sith Attack Speeder (w/Darth Maul Tatooine)	10.00	20.00

1999-00 Star Wars Episode I Jabba Glob

| 1 Jabba the Hutt | 10.00 | 20.00 |

1999-00 Star Wars Episode I Light-Up

1 Darth Maul hologram/ Wal-Mart exclusive		
2 Qui-Gon Jinn Hologram	10.00	20.00
(Walmart Exclusive)		

1999-00 Star Wars Episode I Playsets

1 R2-D2 Carryall	12.00	25.00
2 Theed Generator Complex (w/Battle Droid)	12.00	25.00
3 Theed Hangar Power Spin Qui-Gon Jinn/Battle Droid break up	25.00	50.00

1999-00 Star Wars Episode I Portrait Edition 12-Inch

1 Princess Leia (ceremonial dress)	20.00	40.00
2 Queen Amidala (black travel gown)	12.00	25.00
3 Queen Amidala (return to Naboo)	15.00	30.00
4 Queen Amidala (Senate gown)	15.00	30.00
5 Return to Naboo 2-Pack/Padme/Qui Gon Ginn		

1999-00 Star Wars Episode I Vehicles

1 Anakin's Podracer	20.00	40.00
2 Flash Speeder	15.00	30.00
3 Naboo Fighter	15.00	30.00
4 Naboo Royal Starship	100.00	200.00
5 Sith Speeder (w/Darth Maul Jedi duel)	8.00	15.00
6 Stap and Battle Droid (burn marks on arms and legs)	8.00	15.00
7 Sebulba's Podracer (w/Sebulba podrace gear)	15.00	30.00
8 Trade Federation Droid Fighters	15.00	30.00
9 Trade Federation Tank	20.00	40.00

2015-16 Star Wars The Force Awakens 12-Inch

1 BB-8	10.00	20.00
2 Chewbacca	20.00	40.00
3 Darth Vader	12.00	25.00
4 Fifth Brother Inquisitor	7.50	15.00
5 Finn (Jakku)	10.00	20.00
6 First Order Flametrooper	10.00	20.00
7 First Order Stormtrooper	8.00	15.00
8 First Order TIE Fighter Pilot	7.50	15.00
9 Kylo Ren	7.50	15.00
10 R2-D2	10.00	20.00
11 Rey (Jakku)	10.00	20.00

2015-16 Star Wars The Force Awakens 12-Inch Vehicles

| NNO Assault Walker (w/Riot Control Stormtrooper) | 12.00 | 25.00 |
| NNO Speeder Bike (w/Poe Dameron) | 12.00 | 25.00 |

2015-16 Star Wars The Force Awakens Armor Up 1

NNO Boba Fett	7.50	15.00
NNO Captain Phasma (Epic Battles)	10.00	20.00
(Toys R Us Exclusive)		
NNO Chewbacca	7.50	15.00
NNO Finn (Jakku)	7.50	15.00
NNO Finn (Starkiller Base)	6.00	12.00
NNO First Order Flametrooper	6.00	12.00
NNO First Order Stormtrooper	10.00	20.00
NNO First Order TIE Fighter Pilot	10.00	20.00
NNO Kylo Ren	7.50	15.00
NNO Luke Skywalker	7.50	15.00
NNO Poe Dameron	7.50	15.00
NNO Poe Dameron (Epic Battles)	6.00	12.00
(Toys R Us Exclusive)		

2015-16 Star Wars The Force Awakens Build-a-Weapon Collection

NNO Admiral Ackbar	6.00	12.00
NNO Captain Phasma	7.50	15.00
NNO Captain Rex	10.00	20.00
NNO Constable Zuvio	6.00	12.00
NNO Darth Maul		
NNO Darth Vader	6.00	12.00
NNO Ezra Bridger	6.00	12.00
NNO Fifth Brother	7.50	15.00
NNO Finn (FN-2187)	7.50	15.00
NNO Finn (Jakku)	7.50	15.00
NNO First Order Flametrooper	6.00	12.00
NNO First Order Snowtrooper	5.00	10.00
NNO First Order Stormtrooper (running image)	6.00	12.00
NNO First Order Stormtrooper (shooting blaster image)	6.00	12.00
NNO First Order Stormtrooper Squad Leader	10.00	20.00
NNO First Order TIE Fighter Pilot	5.00	10.00
NNO General Hux	5.00	10.00
NNO Goss Toowers	5.00	10.00
NNO Guavian Enforcer	6.00	12.00
NNO Han Solo	7.50	15.00
NNO Hassk Thug	5.00	10.00

NNO Inquisitor	10.00	20.00
NNO Kanan Jarrus	5.00	10.00
NNO Kanan Jarrus (stormtrooper disguise)	6.00	12.00
NNO Kylo Ren (Force grip image)	7.50	15.00
NNO Kylo Ren (lightsaber image)	6.00	12.00
NNO Kylo Ren Unmasked	7.50	15.00
NNO Luke Skywalker (Episode V)	6.00	12.00
NNO Nien Nunb	6.00	12.00
NNO Poe Dameron	6.00	12.00
NNO Princess Leia		
NNO PZ-4CO	5.00	10.00
NNO Resistance Trooper	6.00	12.00
NNO Rey (Resistance fatigues)	7.50	15.00
NNO Rey (Starkiller Base)	7.50	15.00
NNO Sabine Wren	6.00	12.00
NNO Sarco Plank	6.00	12.00
NNO Seventh Sister		
NNO Tasu Leech	6.00	12.00
NNO Unkar Plutt	6.00	12.00
NNO X-Wing Pilot Asty	3.00	6.00

2015-16 Star Wars The Force Awakens Elite Series

NNO C-3PO	20.00	40.00
NNO Captain Phasma	10.00	20.00
NNO Finn	10.00	20.00
NNO Finn (w/lightsaber)	10.00	20.00
NNO Flametrooper	15.00	30.00
NNO FN-2187 (Finn)	12.50	25.00
NNO Han Solo	15.00	30.00
NNO Kylo Ren	10.00	20.00
NNO Kylo Ren (unmasked)	12.00	25.00
NNO Poe Dameron	10.00	20.00
NNO R2-D2	20.00	40.00
NNO Rey and BB-8	12.00	25.00
NNO Rey and BB-8 (w/lightsaber)	15.00	30.00
NNO Stormtrooper	10.00	20.00
NNO Stormtrooper (squad leader)	12.50	25.00
NNO Stormtrooper (w/riot gear)	12.50	25.00
NNO Stormtrooper Officer	15.00	30.00
NNO TIE Fighter Pilot	12.50	25.00

2015-16 Star Wars The Force Awakens Multi-Packs

1 BB-8, Unkar's Thug, Jakku Scavenger 3-Pack	8.00	15.00
2 Forest Mission 5-Pack	20.00	40.00
BB-8, Kylo Ren, Chewbacca, Stormtrooper, Resistance Trooper/(Amazon Exclusive)		
3 Takodana Encounter 4-Pack	12.00	25.00
Maz Kanata, Rey, Finn, BB-8		
4 Troop Builder 7-Pack	30.00	60.00
(Kohl's Exclusive)		

2015-16 Star Wars The Force Awakens 2-Packs

NNO	Anakin Skywalker & Yoda	12.00	25.00
NNO	Clone Commander Cody & Obi-Wan Kenobi	8.00	15.00
NNO	Darth Vader & Ahsoka Tano	12.00	25.00
NNO	First Order Snowtrooper Officer & Snap Wexley	8.00	15.00
NNO	Garazeb Orrelios & C1-10P Chopper	8.00	20.00
NNO	Han Solo & Princess Leia	8.00	15.00
NNO	R2-D2 & C-3PO	10.00	20.00
NNO	Sidon Ithano & First Mate Quiggold	6.00	12.00

2015-16 Star Wars The Force Awakens Vehicles

1	Assault Walker (w/Stormtrooper Sergeant)	12.50	25.00
2	Battle Action Millennium Falcon	60.00	120.00
	(w/Finn, BB-8, Chewbacca)		
3	Desert Assault Walker (w/Stormtrooper Officer)	12.50	25.00
	(2015 Entertainment Earth Exclusive)		
4	Desert Landspeeder (w/Jakku Finn)	15.00	30.00
5	Elite Speeder Bike	10.00	20.00
	(w/Special Edition Stormtrooper)		
6	First Order Snowspeeder (w/Snowspeeder Officer)	15.00	30.00
7	First Order Special Forces TIE Fighter	12.50	25.00
	(w/TIE Fighter Pilot)		
8	Poe Dameron's Black Squadron X-Wing	30.00	75.00
	(w/Poe Dameron)		
9	Rey's Speeder (w/Special Edition Rey)	10.00	20.00
10	Slave I (w/Boba Fett)	25.00	50.00
11	Y-Wing Scout Bomber (w/Kanan Jarrus)	12.50	25.00

2004-10 Star Wars Galactic Heroes

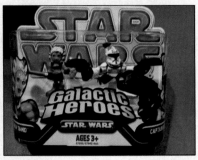

1	4-LOM/Bossk	8.00	15.00
2	Ahsoka Tano/Captain Rex	15.00	30.00
3	Ahsoka Tano/R3-S6 Goldie	8.00	15.00
4	Anakin Skywalker/Clone Trooper (white)	6.00	12.00
5	Anakin Skywalker/Clone Trooper (blue)	6.00	12.00
6	Anakin Skywalker/Count Dooku	6.00	12.00
7	Anakin Skywalker/STAP		
8	Asajj Ventress/Count Dooku	12.00	25.00
9	AT-AT Commander/AT-AT Driver	8.00	15.00
10	Battle Droid/Clone Trooper	6.00	12.00
11	C-3PO/Chewbacca	8.00	15.00
12	Chewbacca/Clone Trooper	6.00	12.00
13	Chewbacca/Death Star Droid/Mouse Droid	8.00	15.00
14	Chewbacca/Disassembled C-3PO	10.00	20.00
15	Clone Trooper/Dwarf Spider Droid	8.00	15.00
16	Clone Trooper/Mace Windu	8.00	15.00
17	Commander Bly/Aayla Secura	12.00	25.00
18	Dark Side Anakin/Clone Trooper	8.00	12.00
19	Darth Maul/Sith Speeder	8.00	15.00
20	Darth Vader/Holographic Emperor Palpatine		
21	Death Star Trooper/Imperial Officer	6.00	12.00
22	Dengar/Boba Fett	12.00	25.00
23	Duros/Garindan		
24	Emperor Palpatine/Shock Trooper		
25	Emperor Palpatine/Yoda	6.00	15.00
26	Figrin D'an/Hammerhead	6.00	12.00
27	Grand Moff Tarkin/Imperial Officer	5.00	10.00

28	Greedo/Han Solo	15.00	30.00
29	Han Solo/Logray	8.00	15.00
30	IG-86/Clone Commander Thire		
31	IG-88/Zuckuss	6.00	12.00
32	Jango Fett/Obi-Wan Kenobi	8.00	15.00
33	Jar Jar Binks/Destroyer Droid		
34	Jawa/Tusken Raider	6.00	12.00
35	Ki-Adi-Mundi/Commander Bacara		
36	Kit Fisto/General Grievous	8.00	15.00
37	Kit Fisto/Mace Windu	10.00	20.00
38	Luke Skywalker (w/Yoda)/Spirit of Obi-Wan	6.00	12.00
39	Luke Skywalker Stormtrooper	10.00	20.00
	Han Solo Stormtrooper		
40	Luke Skywalker/Darth Vader	8.00	15.00
41	Luke Skywalker/Gamorrean Guard	6.00	12.00
42	Luke Skywalker/Han Solo		
43	Luke Skywalker/Lando Calrissian	6.00	12.00
44	Luke Skywalker/R2-D2	6.00	12.00
45	Luke Skywalker/Speeder	15.00	30.00
46	Nien Nunb/Admiral Ackbar	10.00	20.00
47	Obi-Wan Kenobi/Clone Commander Cody		
48	Obi-Wan Kenobi/Clone Trooper (blue Star Wars logo)		
49	Obi-Wan Kenobi/Clone Trooper (red Star Wars logo)		
50	Obi-Wan Kenobi/Darth Maul	8.00	15.00
51	Obi-Wan Kenobi/Darth Vader	6.00	12.00
52	Obi-Wan Kenobi/Durge	6.00	12.00
53	Obi-Wan Kenobi/General Grievous		
54	Padme Amidala/Anakin Skywalker	12.00	25.00
55	Padme Amidala/Clone Trooper		
56	Padme Amidala/Jar Jar Binks		
57	Plo Koon/Captain Jag		
58	Ponda Baba/Snaggletooth		
59	Princess Leia (Endor general)/Rebel Commando (Battle of Endor)		
60	Princess Leia Boushh/Han Solo		
61	Princess Leia/Darth Vader		
62	Princess Leia/Han Solo	12.00	25.00
63	R2-D2 (serving tray)/Princess Leia (slave)		
64	R2-D2/Jawas		
65	Royal Guard/Imperial Gunner		
66	Saesee Tiin/Agen Kolar		
67	Sandtrooper/Obi-Wan Kenobi		
68	Scout Trooper/Speeder Bike	6.00	12.00
69	Shaak Ti/Magna Guard		
70	Skiff Guard/Lando Calrissian	8.00	15.00
71	Snowtrooper/Rebel Trooper		
72	Stormtrooper/Rebel Trooper		
73	Super Battle Droid/Luminara Unduli		
74	Super Battle Droid/R2-D2		
75	Tarfful/Commander Gree		
76	Wedge/TIE Pilot		
77	Weequay/Barada		
78	Yoda/Clone Trooper		
79	Yoda/Kashyyyk Trooper		

2015 Star Wars Hero Mashers

NNO	Boba Fett	5.00	10.00
NNO	Bossk	5.00	10.00
NNO	Darth Vader	6.00	12.00
NNO	General Grievous	7.50	15.00
NNO	Jar Jar Binks	5.00	10.00
NNO	Kanan Jarrus	7.50	15.00
NNO	Zeb Orrelios		

2015 Star Wars Hero Mashers Deluxe

NNO	Anakin Skywalker with Speeder Bike	12.50	25.00
NNO	Darth Maul with Sith Speeder Bike	10.00	20.00
NNO	Han Solo vs. Boba Fett	10.00	20.00
NNO	Luke Skywalker vs. Darth Vader	15.00	30.00
NNO	Yoda vs. Emperor Palpatine	15.00	30.00

2017 Star Wars The Last Jedi Big Figs

NNO	Captain Phasma	15.00	30.00
NNO	Elite Praetorian Guard	12.50	25.00
NNO	First Order Executioner	25.00	50.00
NNO	First Order Stormtrooper	10.00	20.00
NNO	Kylo Ren	12.50	25.00
NNO	Poe Dameron	10.00	20.00
NNO	Rey	12.50	25.00

2017 Star Wars The Last Jedi Elite Series

NNO	Elite Praetorian Guard	15.00	30.00
NNO	First Order Judicial	30.00	60.00
NNO	Kylo Ren	15.00	30.00
NNO	Luke Skywalker	15.00	30.00
NNO	R2-D2	20.00	40.00
NNO	Rey	20.00	40.00

2017 Star Wars The Last Jedi Force Link

1	C-3PO	6.00	12.00
2	C'Ai Threnalli	6.00	12.00
	(Entertainment Earth Exclusive)		
3	Chewbacca (w/porg)	7.50	15.00
4	DJ (Canto Bight)	5.00	10.00
5	Emperor Palpatine		
6	Finn (Resistance Fighter)	6.00	12.00
7	First Order Flametrooper	7.50	15.00
	(Entertainment Earth Exclusive)		
8	First Order Stormtrooper	7.50	15.00
9	General Hux (w/mouse droid)	5.00	10.00
10	General Leia Organa	7.50	15.00
11	Jyn Erso (Jedha)	6.00	12.00

12	Kylo Ren	7.50	15.00
13	Luke Skywalker (Jedi Exile)	7.50	15.00
14	Luke Skywalker (Jedi Master)	7.50	15.00
15	Obi-Wan Kenobi	7.50	15.00
16	Poe Dameron (Resistance Pilot)	5.00	10.00
17	R2-D2	6.00	12.00
18	Resistance Gunner Paige	6.00	12.00
19	Resistance Gunner Rose	6.00	12.00
20	Rey (Island Journey)	6.00	12.00
21	Rey (Jedi Training)	10.00	20.00
22	Yoda	10.00	20.00

2017 Star Wars The Last Jedi Force Link 2-Packs

NNO	Bala-Tik (w/Rathtar)	7.50	15.00
NNO	Chirrut Imwe & Baze Malbus	12.50	25.00
NNO	Darth Vader (w/Imperial probe droid)		
NNO	Finn & Captain Phasma	15.00	30.00
	(Entertainment Earth Exclusive)		
NNO	Han Solo & Boba Fett	10.00	20.00
NNO	Rey (Jedi Training) & Elite Praetorian Guard	7.50	15.00
NNO	Rose Tico (w/BB-8 & BB-9E)	7.50	15.00

2017 Star Wars The Last Jedi Force Link Multipacks

NNO	Battle on Crait 4-Pack	15.00	30.00
	Rey/First Order Walker Driver/First Order Gunner/Rose		
NNO	Emperor Palpatine/Luke Skywalker	10.00	20.00
	Emperor's Royal Guard 3-Pack		
	(Target Exclusive)		
NNO	Era of the Force 8-Pack		
	Yoda/Luke/Kylo Ren/Rey/Darth Maul/Mace Windu/Obi-Wan Kenobi/Darth Vader/(Target Exclusive)		
NNO	Luke Skywalker/Resistance Tech Rose	20.00	40.00
	Rey (Jedi Training)/First Order Stormtrooper 4-Pack		

2017 Star Wars The Last Jedi Force Link Sets

NNO	BB-8 2-in-1 Mega Playset	20.00	40.00
NNO	Starter Set (w/Elite Praetorian Guard)		
	(Toys R Us Exclusive)		
NNO	Starter Set (w/Kylo Ren)	7.50	15.00
NNO	Starter Set (w/Stormtrooper Executioner)	15.00	30.00
	(Toys R Us Exclusive)		

2017 Star Wars The Last Jedi Force Link Vehicles

NNO	Canto Bight Police Speeder (w/Canto Bight Police)	10.00	20.00
NNO	Kylo Ren's TIE Silencer (w/Kylo Ren)	20.00	40.00
NNO	Resistance A-Wing Fighter	12.50	25.00
	(w/Resistance Pilot Tallie)		
NNO	TIE Fighter (w/TIE Fighter Pilot)	15.00	30.00
	(Walmart Exclusive)		
NNO	X-Wing Fighter (w/Poe Dameron)	30.00	75.00
	(Toys R Us Exclusive)		

2017 Star Wars The Last Jedi S.H. Figuarts

NNO	Captain Phasma	30.00	60.00
NNO	Elite Praetorian Guard (w/dual blades)	20.00	40.00
NNO	Elite Praetorian Guard (w/single blade)	20.00	40.00
NNO	Elite Praetorian Guard (w/whip staff)	25.00	50.00
NNO	First Order Executioner	25.00	50.00
NNO	First Order Stormtrooper	30.00	75.00
NNO	Kylo Ren	50.00	100.00
NNO	Rey	50.00	100.00

2008-10 Star Wars The Legacy Collection Battle Packs

NNO	Battle at the Sarlaac Pit (ultimate)	50.00	100.00
	(2008 Target Exclusive)		
NNO	Battle of Endor		
NNO	Birth of Darth Vader	20.00	40.00
NNO	Clone Attack on Coruscant	20.00	40.00
NNO	Disturbance at Lars Homestead	75.00	150.00
	(2008 Toys R Us Exclusive)		
NNO	Duel on Mustafar		
NNO	Gelagrub Patrol	20.00	50.00
NNO	Genosis Assault	50.00	100.00
NNO	Hoth Recon Patrol	30.00	60.00
NNO	Hoth Speeder Bike Patrol	25.00	50.00
NNO	Jedi Training on Dagobah		
NNO	Jedi vs. Darth Sidious	15.00	30.00
NNO	Kamino Conflict		
NNO	Resurgence of the Jedi	20.00	40.00
NNO	Scramble on Yavin	100.00	175.00
NNO	Shield Generator Assault	25.00	50.00
NNO	Tatooine Desert Ambush		
NNO	Training on the Falcon	30.00	75.00

2008-10 Star Wars The Legacy Collection Build-A-Droid Wave 1

BD1a	Han Solo/ with R4-D6 left leg	6.00	12.00
BD1b	Han Solo/ with R4-D6 left leg/ first day of issue sticker		
BD2a	Luke Skywalker/ with R4-D6 right leg		
BD2b	Luke Skywalker/ with R5-A2 head/ and center leg		
BD2c	Luke Skywalker/ with R4-D6 right leg/ first day of issue sticker		
BD3a	Chewbacca/ with R4-D6 head/ and center leg		
BD3b	Chewbacca/ with R4-D6 head/ and center leg/ first day of issue sticker		
BD4a	Leektar/Nippet/ with R4-D6 torso		
BD4b	Leektar/Nippet/ with R4-D6 torso/ first day of issue sticker		

BD5a	Ak-Rev/ with R7-Z0 left leg		
BD5b	Ak-Rev/ with R7-Z0 left leg	6.00	12.00
	first day of issue sticker		
BD6a	Yarna D'Al'Gargan/ with R7-Z0 right leg	8.00	15.00
BD6b	Yarna D'Al'Gargan/ with R7-Z0 right leg	6.00	12.00
	first day of issue sticker		
BD7a	Bane Malar/ with R7-Z0 torso		
BD7b	Bane Malar/ with R7-Z0 torso/ first day of issue sticker		
BD8a	Darth Vader/ multi-piece helmet/ with R7-Z0 head		
BD8b	Darth Vader/ multi-piece helmet/ with R7-Z0 head/ first day of issue sti		
BD8c	Darth Vader/ multi-piece helmet/ with MB-RA-7 head		

2008-10 Star Wars The Legacy Collection Build-A-Droid Wave 2

BD9	Obi-Wan Kenobi general/ with R4-J1 left leg	10.00	20.00
BD10	Clone Scuba Trooper/ with R4-J1 head	6.00	12.00
	and center leg		
BD11	Saesee Tiin general/ with R7-T1 right leg		
BD12	Padme Amidala snow/ with R4-J1 left leg		
BD13	IG Lancer Droid/ with R4-J1 torso		
BD14	Mon Calimari Warrior/ with R7-T1 Torso	8.00	15.00
BD15	Quarren Soldier/ with R7-T1 head/ and center leg		
BD16	Clone Trooper blue/ with cannon/with R4-J1 right leg		

2008-10 Star Wars The Legacy Collection Build-A-Droid Wave 3

BD17a	Clone Trooper coruscant	10.00	20.00
	landing platform/ with RD6-RA7 torso		
BD17b	Clone Trooper coruscant/ landing platform/ with MB-RA-7 right arm		
BD18a	Jodo Kast/ with RD6-RA7 head	10.00	20.00
BD18b	Jodo Kast/ with MB-RA-7 left leg		
BD19	Yaddle/Evan Piell/ with RD6-RA7 right leg	15.00	30.00
BD20a	Saleucami Trooper/ with 5D6-RA7 left leg		
BD20b	Saleucami Trooper/ with MB-RA-7 right leg		
BD21	Count Dooku/ holographic transmission/ with RD6-RA7 right arm		
BD22	Imperial Engineer/ with RD6-RA7 left arm		

2008-10 Star Wars The Legacy Collection Build-A-Droid Wave 4

BD23	Stass Allie/ with MB-RA-7 left arm	12.00	25.00
BD24a	Commander Faie/ with MB-RA-7 torso	10.00	20.00
BD24b	Commander Faie/ with R5-A2 left leg	10.00	20.00
BD25a	General Grievous/ with MB-RA-7 head	12.00	25.00
BD25b	General Grievous/ with R5-A2 right leg		
BD26a	Bail Organa/ light skin/ with MB-RA-7 left arm		
BD26b	Bail Organa/ dark skin/ with MB-RA-7 left arm		
BD27a	Breha Organa/ light skin/ with MB-RA-7 left leg		
BD27b	Breha Organa/ dark skin/ with MB-RA-7 left leg		
BD28	FX-6/ with MB-RA-7 right leg	10.00	20.00
BD29	Clone Trooper 327th Star/ Corps yellow shoulder/ with MB-RA-7 torso		
BD29a	Clone Trooper 327th Star/ Corps yellow shoulder/ with R5-A2 torso		
BD29b	Clone Trooper 327th Star/ Corps yellow shoulder/ with MB-RA-7 torso		
BD29c	Clone Trooper 327th Star/ Corps yellow shoulder/ with R5-A2 torso		

2008-10 Star Wars The Legacy Collection Comic Packs Blue and White Exclusives

NNO	Ibtisam and Nrin Vakil	25.00	50.00
	(2008 Walmart Exclusive)		
NNO	Janek Sunber and Amanin	15.00	30.00
	(2008 Walmart Exclusive)		
NNO	Machook/Keoulkeech/Ketch	30.00	60.00
	(2008 Walmart Exclusive)		

2008-10 Star Wars The Legacy Collection Creatures

1	Dewback (w/Imperial sandtrooper)	25.00	50.00
	(2009 Walmart Exclusive)		
2	Jabba's Rancor (w/Luke Skywalker)	60.00	120.00
	(2008 Target Exclusive)		

2008-10 Star Wars The Legacy Collection Evolutions

1 Clone Commandos	50.00	100.00
(2009 Walmart Exclusive)		
2 Imperial Pilot Legacy I	15.00	30.00
3 Imperial Pilot Legacy II	15.00	30.00
(2009 Walmart Exclusive)		
4 Rebel Pilot Legacy I	15.00	40.00
5 Rebel Pilot Legacy II	25.00	50.00
6 Rebel Pilot Legacy III	30.00	75.00
(2009 Walmart Exclusive)		
7 The Fett Legacy	15.00	40.00
8 The Jedi Legacy		
9 The Padme Amidala Legacy	12.00	25.00
10 The Sith Legacy	60.00	120.00
11 Vader's Secret Apprentice	30.00	60.00

2008-10 Star Wars The Legacy Collection Greatest Hits 2008

GH1 Commander Gree	6.00	12.00
GH2 Kashyyyk Trooper	6.00	12.00
GH3 Darth Vader (Battle Damage)	10.00	20.00
GH4 Imperial EVO Trooper	6.00	12.00

2008-10 Star Wars The Legacy Collection Vehicles

1 AT-ST	30.00	75.00
(2009 Walmart Exclusive)		
2 Dagger Squadron B-Wing Fighter	50.00	100.00
(2008 Toys R Us Exclusive)		
3 Darth Vader's TIE Advanced x1 Starfighter	15.00	30.00
4 Green Leader's A-Wing Fighter	50.00	100.00
(2008 Walmart Exclusive)		
5 Millennium Falcon	300.00	600.00
6 Speeder Bike (w/biker scout)	25.00	50.00
(Toys R Us Exclusive)		
7 TIE Fighter		
8 TIE Fighter Pirate		
(PX Previews Exclusive)		
9 TIE Fighter Shadows of the Empire	150.00	300.00
(2009 Target Exclusive)		
10 TIE Interceptor	30.00	60.00
(2009 Toys R Us Exclusive)		
11 Wedge Antilles' X-Wing Starfighter	120.00	200.00
(2009 Target Exclusive)		

2008-09 Star Wars Mighty Muggs

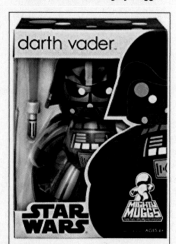

NNO Anakin Skywalker		
NNO Asajj Ventress		
NNO Boba Fett	8.00	15.00

NNO C-3PO	8.00	15.00
NNO Captain Rex	6.00	12.00
NNO Chewbacca	8.00	15.00
NNO Commander Cody	12.00	25.00
NNO Count Dooku	6.00	12.00
NNO Darth Maul	6.00	12.00
NNO Darth Maul (shirtless)	6.00	12.00
NNO Darth Revan	10.00	20.00
NNO Darth Vader	8.00	15.00
NNO Darth Vader (unmasked)		
NNO Emperor	5.00	10.00
NNO Gamorrean Guard	5.00	10.00
NNO General Grievous	12.00	25.00
NNO Grand Moff Tarkin		
NNO Han Solo	8.00	15.00
NNO Han Solo (Hoth)	10.00	20.00
NNO Jango Fett	6.00	12.00
NNO Lando Calrissian	8.00	15.00
NNO Luke (Bespin)	8.00	15.00
NNO Luke Skywalker	8.00	15.00
NNO Luke Skywalker (Hoth)	8.00	15.00
NNO Mace Windu		
NNO Obi-Wan Kenobi (old)	6.00	12.00
NNO Obi-Wan Kenobi (young)		
NNO Plo Koon		
NNO Princess Leia		
NNO Qui-Gon Jinn	8.00	15.00
NNO Royal Guard		
NNO Stormtrooper	6.00	12.00
NNO Wampa	5.00	10.00
NNO Wicket	5.00	10.00
NNO Yoda	8.00	15.00

2008-09 Star Wars Mighty Muggs Exclusives

1 Admiral Ackbar		
(2008 PX Previews Exclusive)		
2 Biggs Darklighter		
(2009 Target Exclusive)		
3 Bossk		
(2009 Target Exclusive)		
4 Commander Gree		
(2008 SDCC Exclusive)		
5 Shadow Trooper		
(2008 PX Previews Exclusive)		
6 Shock Trooper	8.00	15.00
(2009 Target Exclusive)		
7 Snowtrooper	8.00	15.00
(2009 Target Exclusive)		
8 Teebo		
(2009 Target Exclusive)		

2012 Star Wars Movie Heroes

MH1 Shock Trooper	10.00	20.00
MH2 Super Battle Droid	7.50	15.00
MH3 R2-D2	10.00	20.00
MH4 Battle Droid (repaint)	6.00	12.00
MH4 Battle Droid (variant)	6.00	12.00
MH5 Darth Maul (repaint)		
MH6 Darth Vader	7.50	15.00
MH7 General Grievous	15.00	30.00
MH8 Obi-Wan Kenobi	5.00	10.00
MH9 Yoda	6.00	12.00
MH10 Qui-Gon Jinn	5.00	10.00
MH11 Clone Trooper (with Jetpack)	6.00	12.00
MH12 Destroyer Droid	5.00	10.00
MH13 Jar Jar Binks	5.00	10.00
MH14 Anakin Skywalker	5.00	10.00
MH15 Darth Maul (Spinning Action)		
MH16 Obi-Wan Kenobi (Light-Up Lightsaber)		
MH17 Padme Amidala	6.00	12.00
MH18 Qui-Gon Jinn (Light-Up Lightsaber)	5.00	10.00
MH19 Anakin Skywalker (Light-Up Lightsaber)		
MH20 Darth Vader (Light-Up Lightsaber)	12.50	25.00
MH21 Luke Skywalker (zipline backpack)	7.50	15.00
MH22 Battle Droid (The Phantom Menace)(exploding action)		
MH23 Sandtrooper (Light-Up Weapon)		
MH24 Boba Fett (zipline jetpack)		

2012 Star Wars Movie Heroes Battle Packs

NNO Bespin Battle	20.00	40.00
NNO Duel on Naboo	15.00	30.00
NNO Ewok Pack		
NNO Geonosis Arena Battle		
NNO Rebel Heroes		
NNO Rebel Pilots		
NNO Republic Troopers		

2012 Star Wars Movie Heroes Vehicles

NNO Anakin Skywalker's Jedi Starfighter (The Clone Wars)		
NNO Anakin Skywalker's Podracer	20.00	40.00
NNO Attack Recon Fighter with Anakin Skywalker		
NNO BARC Speeder with Clone Trooper		
NNO Naboo Royal Fighter with Obi-Wan Kenobi		
NNO Naboo Starfighter	60.00	120.00
NNO Republic Assault Submarine with Scuba Clone Trooper		
NNO Republic Attack Dropship with Clone Pilot		
NNO Sebulba's Podracer		
NNO Sith Infiltrator		
NNO Sith Speeder with Darth Maul		
NNO Speeder Bike with Scout and Cannon		
(Toys R Us Exclusive)		
NNO STAP with Battle Droid		
NNO Trade Federation AAT (Armored Assault Tank)		

2005 Star Wars M&M's Chocolate Mpire

1 Chewbacca/Mace Windu	6.00	12.00
2 Clone Trooper/Darth Vader	6.00	12.00
3 Count Dooku/Darth Maul	12.00	25.00
4 Emperor Palpatine/Anakin Skywalker	12.00	25.00
5 General Grievous/Obi-Wan Kenobi	8.00	15.00
6 Han Solo/Boba Fett	10.00	20.00
7 Luke Skywalker/Princess Leia	8.00	15.00
8 Queen Amidala/R2-D2/C-3PO	8.00	15.00

2007 Star Wars Order 66 Target Exclusives

1 Emperor Palpatine/Commander Thire	12.00	25.00
2 Mace Windu/Galactic Marine	10.00	20.00
3 Darth Vader/Commander Bow	12.00	25.00
4 Obi-Wan Kenobi/AT-RT Driver	10.00	20.00
5 Anakin Skywalker/Airborne Trooper	12.00	25.00
6 Yoda/Kashyyyk Trooper	10.00	20.00

2008 Star Wars Order 66 Target Exclusives

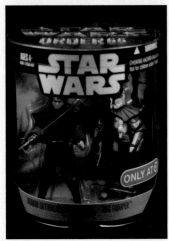

1 Obi-Wan Kenobi/ARC Trooper Commander	12.00	25.00
2 Anakin Skywalker/ARC Trooper	10.00	20.00
3 Tsui Choi/BARC Trooper	15.00	30.00
4 Emperor Palpatine/Commander Vill	12.00	25.00
5 Luminara Unduli/AT-RT Driver	10.00	20.00
6 Master Sev/ARC Trooper	15.00	30.00

2004-05 Star Wars The Original Trilogy Collection

1 Luke Skywalker (Dagobah training)	6.00	12.00
2 Yoda (Dagobah training)	3.00	6.00
3 Spirit Obi-Wan Kenobi	8.00	15.00
4 R2-D2 (Dagobah training)	6.00	12.00
5 Luke Skywalker (X-Wing pilot)	8.00	15.00
6 Luke Skywalker (Jedi Knight)	8.00	15.00
7 Han Solo (Mos Eisley escape)	3.00	6.00
8 Chewbacca (Hoth escape)	6.00	12.00
9 Princess Leia	10.00	20.00
10 Darth Vader (throne room)	8.00	15.00
11 Scout Trooper	6.00	12.00
12 R2-D2	8.00	15.00
13 C-3PO	8.00	15.00
14 Boba Fett	12.00	25.00
15 Obi-Wan Kenobi	12.00	25.00
16 Stormtrooper (Death Star attack)	8.00	15.00
17 Wicket	3.00	6.00
18 Princess Leia (Cloud City)	8.00	15.00
19 Cloud Car Pilot	3.00	6.00
20 Lobot	3.00	6.00
21 TIE Fighter Pilot	8.00	15.00
22 Greedo	6.00	12.00
23 Tusken Raider	10.00	20.00
24 Jawas	3.00	6.00
25 Snowtrooper	6.00	12.00
26 Luke Skywalker (Bespin)	8.00	15.00
27 IG-88	12.00	25.00
28 Bossk	6.00	12.00
29 Darth Vader (Hoth)	10.00	20.00
30 Gamorrean Guard	10.00	20.00
31 Bib Fortuna	3.00	6.00
32 Darth Vader	3.00	6.00
33 Lando Calrissian (skiff guard)	6.00	12.00
34 Princess Leia (sail barge)	15.00	30.00
35 Han Solo (AT-ST driver uniform)	3.00	6.00
36 General Madine	3.00	6.00
37 Lando Calrissian (General)	8.00	15.00
38a Imperial Trooper (white)	3.00	6.00
38b Imperial Trooper (gray)	3.00	6.00

2004-05 Star Wars The Original Trilogy Collection 12-Inch

1 Boba Fett	30.00	60.00
2 Chewbacca	20.00	40.00
3 Luke Skywalker	20.00	40.00
4 Stormtrooper	15.00	30.00

2004-05 Star Wars The Original Trilogy Collection DVD Collection

1 A New Hope	6.00	12.00
2 Empire Strikes Back	10.00	20.00
3 Return of the Jedi	8.00	15.00

2004-05 Star Wars The Original Trilogy Collection Exclusives

1 Darth Vader (silver)	10.00	20.00
(2004 Toys R Us Exclusive)		
2 Emperor Palpatine (executor transmission)		
(2004 StarWarsShop.com Exclusive)		
3 Holiday Darth Vader	30.00	60.00
(2005 StarWarsShop.com Exclusive)		
4 Holographic Princess Leia	12.00	25.00
(2005 SDCC Exclusive)		
5 Holiday Edition Jawas	15.00	30.00
(2004 Entertainment Earth Exclusive)		
6 Luke Skywalker's Encounter with Yoda		
(2004 Encuentros Mexico Exclusive)		
7 Wedge Antilles		
(2005 Internet Exclusive)		

2004-05 Star Wars The Original Trilogy Collection Multipacks

1 Clone Trooper/Troop Builder 4-Pack	25.00	50.00
Clone Trooper/Clone Trooper/Clone Tr		
2 Clone Trooper Builder 4-Pack	30.00	60.00
(white w/battle damage)		
3 Clone Trooper Builder 4-Pack (colored)		
4 Clone Trooper Builder 4-Pack	20.00	40.00
(colored w/battle damage)		
5 Endor Ambush (Han Solo/Logray/Rebel Trooper/Wicket/Speeder)	12.00	25.00
6 Naboo Final Combat (Battle Droid tan	20.00	40.00
Gungan Soldier/Captain Tarpals/Kaad)		

2004-05 Star Wars The Original Trilogy Collection Screen Scenes

1 Mos Eisley Cantina I/Dr. Evanzan	30.00	60.00
Wuher/Kitik Keed'kak		
2 Mos Eisley Cantina II (Obi-Wan Kenobi	30.00	60.00
Ponda Baba/Zutton)		
3 Jedi High Council I (Qui-Gon Jinn/Ki-Adi Mundi/Yoda)		
4 Jedi High Council II (Plo Koon/Obi-Wan Kenobi/Eeth Koth)		
5 Jedi High Council III (Anakin Skywalker/Saesee Tiin/Adi Gallia)		
6 Jedi High Council IV (Shaak Ti/Agen Kolar/Stass Alli)		

2004-05 Star Wars The Original Trilogy Collection Transitional

1 Pablo-Jill (Geonosis Arena)	6.00	12.00
2 Yarua (Wookiee Senator)	10.00	20.00
3 Sly Moore	5.00	10.00
4 Queen Amidala (Naboo Celebration)	5.00	10.00
5 Rabe (Royal Handmaiden)	4.00	10.00
6 Feltipern Trevagg (Cantina)	8.00	15.00
7 Myo (Cantina)	8.00	15.00
8 Dannik Jerriko (Cantina Encounter)	8.00	15.00
9 Luke Skywalker (Dagobah Training)		
10 Darth Vader (Death Star Hangar)	15.00	30.00
11 Stormtrooper (Death Star Attack)		
12 Sandtrooper (Tatooine Search)		
13 Scout Trooper (Endor Raid)		
14 Han Solo (Mos Eisley Escape)		
15 Chewbacca (Hoth Escape)	12.00	25.00
16 Yoda (Dagobah Training)		

2004-05 Star Wars The Original Trilogy Collection Vehicles

1 Darth Vader's TIE Fighter	30.00	75.00
2 Millennium Falcon		
3 Millennium Falcon (w/Chewbacca/Han/Luke/Obi-Wan/C-3PO/R2-D2)		
(2004 Sam's Club Exclusive)		
4 Sandcrawler (w/RA-7 and Jawas)	100.00	200.00
5 Slave I (w/Boba Fett in tan cape)	75.00	150.00
6 TIE Fighter	30.00	75.00
7 TIE Fighter & X-Wing Fighter	30.00	75.00
8 X-Wing Fighter		
9 Y-Wing Fighter (w/pilot)		

2004-05 Star Wars The Original Trilogy Collection Vintage

1 Boba Fett (ROTJ)	15.00	30.00
2 C-3PO (ESB)	6.00	12.00
3 Chewbacca (ROTJ)	12.00	25.00
4 Darth Vader (ESB)	8.00	15.00
5 Han Solo (SW)	6.00	12.00
6 Lando Calrissian (ESB)	12.00	25.00
7 Luke Skywalker (SW)	6.00	12.00
8 Obi-Wan Kenobi (SW)	5.00	10.00
9 Princess Leia Organa (SW)	5.00	10.00
10 R2-D2 (ROTJ)	15.00	30.00
11 Stormtrooper (ROTJ)	8.00	15.00
12 Yoda ESB	6.00	12.00

2000-02 Star Wars Power of the Jedi Action Collection 12-Inch

1 4-LOM	12.00	25.00
2 Bossk	15.00	30.00
3 Captain Tarpals (w/Kaadu)	20.00	40.00
4 Death Star Droid	15.00	30.00
5 Death Star Trooper	20.00	40.00
6 Han Solo Stormtrooper	15.00	30.00
7 IG-88	8.00	15.00
8 Luke Skywalker & Yoda	20.00	40.00
9 Luke Skywalker (100th figure)	30.00	60.00
10 Luke Skywalker (w/speeder bike)	40.00	80.00

2000-02 Star Wars Power of the Jedi Attack of the Clones Sneak Preview

1	Clone Trooper	4.00	8.00
2	Jango Fett	5.00	10.00
3	R3-T7	6.00	12.00
4	Zam Wesell	4.00	8.00

2000-02 Star Wars Power of the Jedi Collection 1

1	Anakin Skywalker (mechanic)	8.00	15.00
2	Aurra Sing (bounty hunter)	6.00	12.00
3	Battle Droid (boomer damage)	4.00	8.00
4	Ben Obi Wan Kenobi (Jedi Knight)	5.00	10.00
5	Chewbacca (Millennium Falcon mechanic)	10.00	20.00
6	Darth Maul (final duel)	6.00	12.00
7	Darth Maul (Sith Apprentice)	5.00	10.00
8	Darth Vader (Dagobah)	8.00	15.00
9	Darth Vader (Emperor's wrath)	5.00	10.00
10	Han Solo (Bespin capture)	4.00	8.00
11	Han Solo (Death Star escape)	6.00	12.00
12	Leia Organa (general)	5.00	10.00
13	Luke Skywalker (X-Wing Pilot)	4.00	8.00
14	Obi-Wan Kenobi (cold weather gear)	4.00	8.00
15	Obi-Wan Kenobi (Jedi)	4.00	8.00
16	Qui-Gon Jinn (Jedi training gear)	8.00	15.00
17	Qui-Gon Jinn (Mos Espa disguise)	4.00	8.00
18	R2-D2 (Naboo escape)	5.00	10.00
19	Sandtrooper (Tatooine patrol)	6.00	12.00

2000-02 Star Wars Power of the Jedi Collection 2

1	Battle Droid (security)	4.00	8.00
2	Bespin Guard (cloud city security)	4.00	8.00
3	BoShek	8.00	15.00
4	Boss Nass (Gungan sacred place)	4.00	8.00
5	Chewbacca (Dejarik Champion)	10.00	20.00
6	Coruscant Guard	5.00	10.00
7	Eeth Koth (Jedi Master)	6.00	12.00
8	Ellorrs Madak (Fan's Choice Figure #1)	5.00	10.00
9	Fode and Beed (pod race announcers)	5.00	10.00
10	FX-7 (medical droid)	10.00	20.00
11	Gungan Warrior	4.00	8.00
12	IG-88 (bounty hunter)	12.00	25.00
13	Imperial Officer	4.00	8.00
14	Jar Jar Binks (Tatooine)	4.00	8.00
15	Jek Porkins (X-Wing pilot)	10.00	20.00
16	K-3PO (Echo Base protocol droid)	6.00	12.00
17	Ketwol	4.00	8.00
18	Lando Calrissian (Bespin escape)	6.00	12.00
19	Leia Organa (Bespin escape)	8.00	15.00
20	Mas Amedda	5.00	10.00
21	Mon Calamari (officer)	8.00	15.00
22	Obi-Wan Kenobi (Jedi training gear)	4.00	8.00
23	Plo Koon (Jedi Master)	4.00	8.00
24	Queen Amidala (royal decoy)	6.00	12.00
25	Queen Amidala (Theed invasion)	6.00	12.00
26	R4-M9	8.00	15.00
27	R2-Q5 (Imperial astromech droid)	8.00	15.00
28	Rebel Trooper (Tantive IV defender)	4.00	8.00
29	Sabe (Queen's decoy)	5.00	10.00
30	Saesee Tiin (Jedi Master)	4.00	8.00
31	Scout Trooper (Imperial patrol)	6.00	12.00
32	Sebulba (Boonta Eve Challenge)	5.00	10.00
33	Shmi Skywalker	5.00	10.00
34	Teebo	6.00	12.00
35	Tessek	5.00	10.00
36	Tusken Raider (desert sniper)	6.00	12.00
37	Zutton (Snaggletooth)	5.00	10.00

2000-02 Star Wars Power of the Jedi Deluxe

1	Amanaman (w/Salacious Crumb)	10.00	20.00
	(Fan's Choice Figure #2)		
2	Darth Maul (w/Sith Attack Droid)	8.00	15.00

3	Luke Skywalker (in Echo Base Bacta Tank)	10.00	20.00
4	Princess Leia (Jabba's prisoner w/sail barge cannon)	8.00	15.00

2000-02 Star Wars Power of the Jedi Masters of the Darkside

1	Darth Vader and Darth Maul	6.00	30.00

2000-02 Star Wars Power of the Jedi Mega Action

1	Darth Maul	12.00	25.00
2	Destroyer Droid	20.00	40.00
3	Obi-Wan Kenobi	12.00	25.00

2000-02 Star Wars Power of the Jedi Playsets

1	Carbon Freezing Chamber (w/Bespin guard)	40.00	80.00

2000-02 Star Wars Power of the Jedi Special Edition

1	Boba Fett (300th figure)	15.00	30.00
2	Rorworr (Wookiee scout)	5.00	10.00

2000-02 Star Wars Power of the Jedi Vehicles

1	B-Wing Fighter (w/Sullustan pilot)	40.00	80.00
2	Imperial AT-ST & Speeder Bike (w/Paploo)	25.00	50.00
3	Luke Skywalker's Snowspeeder (w/Dack Ralter)	40.00	80.00
4	TIE Bomber	25.00	50.00
5	TIE Interceptor (w/Imperial pilot)	30.00	60.00

1995-00 Star Wars Power of the Force 3-Packs

NNO	Lando/Chewbacca/Han Solo	10.00	20.00
NNO	Lando/Luke Dagobah/TIE Fighter Pilot	10.00	20.00
NNO	Luke Jedi/AT-ST Driver/Leia Boushh	20.00	40.00
NNO	Luke Stormtrooper/Tusken Raider/Ben Kenobi	12.50	25.00
NNO	Luke/Ben Kenobi/Darth Vader	10.00	20.00
NNO	Stormtrooper/R2-D2/C-3PO	10.00	20.00

1995-00 Star Wars Power of the Force Accessories

1	Escape the Death Star Action Figure Game	10.00	20.00
2	Millennium Falcon Carrying Case (w/Imperial Scanning Trooper)	20.00	40.00
3	Millennium Falcon Carrying Case (w/Wedge)	15.00	30.00
4	Power of the Force Carrying Case	6.00	12.00
5	Talking C-3PO Carrying Case	25.00	50.00

1995-00 Star Wars Power of the Force Cinema Scenes

1	Cantina Aliens	10.00	20.00
2a	Cantina Showdown (.00)	6.00	12.00
2b	Cantina Showdown (.01)	6.00	12.00
3a	Death Star Escape (.00)	12.00	25.00
3b	Death Star Escape (.01)	12.00	25.00
4a	Final Jedi Duel (.00)	10.00	20.00
4b	Final Jedi Duel (.01)	12.50	25.00
5	Jabba the Hutt's Dancers	10.00	20.00
6	Jabba's Skiff Guards	10.00	20.00
7	Jedi Spirits	10.00	20.00
8	Mynock Hunt	15.00	30.00
9	Purchase of the Droids	8.00	15.00
10	Rebel Pilots	10.00	20.00

1995-00 Star Wars Power of the Force Comm-Tech

1	Admiral Motti	20.00	40.00
2a	Darth Vader (holographic chip)	8.00	15.00
2b	Darth Vader (white chip)	8.00	15.00
3	Greedo	6.00	12.00
4	Han Solo	6.00	12.00
5a	Jawa (w/Gonk Droid holographic chip)	8.00	15.00
5b	Jawa (w/Gonk Droid white chip)	8.00	15.00
6	Luke Skywalker (w/T16 Skyhopper)	6.00	12.00
7	Princess Leia	8.00	15.00
8	R2-D2 (w/Princess Leia)	12.00	25.00
9	Stormtrooper	8.00	15.00
10a	Wuher (no sticker)	8.00	15.00
	(2000 Fan Club Exclusive)		
10b	Wuher (sticker)	6.00	12.00
	(2000 Fan Club Exclusive)		

1995-00 Star Wars Power of the Force Complete Galaxy

1	Dagobah (w/Yoda)	8.00	15.00
2	Death Star (w/Darth Vader)	12.00	25.00
3a	Endor (w/Ewok) (.00)	15.00	30.00
3b	Endor (w/Ewok) (.01)	15.00	30.00
4	Tatooine (w/Luke)	10.00	20.00

1995-00 Star Wars Power of the Force Creatures

1	Bantha & Tusken Raider	30.00	60.00
2	Dewback & Sandtrooper	20.00	40.00
3a	Jabba the Hutt & Han Solo (Han on left)		
3b	Jabba the Hutt & Han Solo (Han on right)	15.00	30.00
4	Rancor & Luke Skywalker	30.00	60.00
5	Ronto & Jawa	12.00	25.00
6	Tauntaun & Han Solo	25.00	50.00
7	Tauntaun & Luke Skywalker	12.00	25.00
8	Wampa & Luke Skywalker	25.00	50.00

1995-00 Star Wars Power of the Force Deluxe

NNO	Boba Fett (photon torpedo)	8.00	15.00
NNO	Boba Fett (proton torpedo)	10.00	20.00
NNO	Han Solo (Smuggler's Flight)	6.00	12.00
NNO	Hoth Rebel Soldier	8.00	15.00
NNO	Luke Skywalker (Desert Sport Skiff)	25.00	50.00
NNO	Probe Droid (printed warning/green cardback)	6.00	12.00
NNO	Probe Droid (printed warning/red cardback)	6.00	12.00
NNO	Probe Droid (warning sticker/red cardback)	6.00	12.00
NNO	Snowtrooper (Tripod Cannon)	6.00	12.00
NNO	Stormtrooper (Crowd Control)(no sticker)	5.00	10.00
NNO	Stormtrooper (Crowd Control)(warning sticker)	5.00	10.00

1995-00 Star Wars Power of the Force Epic Force

1	Bespin Luke Skywalker	5.00	12.00
2	Boba Fett	5.00	12.00
3	C-3PO	8.00	15.00
4	Chewbacca	5.00	12.00
5	Darth Vader	5.00	12.00
6	Han Solo	5.00	12.00

7 Obi-Wan Kenobi	5.00	12.00
8 Princess Leia	4.00	8.00
9 Stormtrooper	4.00	8.00

1995-00 Star Wars Power of the Force Exclusives

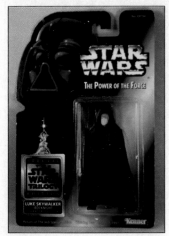

1a B-Omarr Monk (.00)	12.50	25.00
(1997 Online Exclusive)		
1b B-Omarr Monk (.01)	12.50	25.00
(1997 Online Exclusive)		
2 C-3PO (greenish tint)	15.00	30.00
(Japanese Exclusive)		
3 Cantina Band Member	6.00	15.00
(1997 Fan Club Exclusive)		
4 Han Solo (w/Tauntaun)	15.00	30.00
(1997 Toys R Us Exclusive)		
5 Han Solo Stormtrooper	8.00	15.00
(Kellogg's Mail Order Exclusive)		
6 Kabe and Muftak	10.00	20.00
(1998 Online Exclusive)		
7 Luke Skywalker Jedi Knight	10.00	20.00
(Theater Edition Exclusive)		
8 Oola & Salacious Crumb	12.00	25.00
(1998 Fan Club Exclusive)		
9 Spirit of Obi-Wan Kenobi	8.00	15.00
(Frito-Lay Mail Order Exclusive)		
10 Spirit of Obi-Wan Kenobi		
(UK Special Edition Exclusive)		

1995-00 Star Wars Power of the Force Expanded Universe Vehicles

1 Airspeeder (w/pilot)	20.00	40.00
2 Cloud Car (w/pilot)	10.00	20.00
3 Rebel Speeder Bike (w/pilot)	12.00	25.00

1995-00 Star Wars Power of the Force Flashback

1 Anakin Skywalker	6.00	12.00
2 Aunt Beru	5.00	10.00
3 C-3PO (removable arm)	5.00	10.00
4 Darth Vader	8.00	15.00
5 Emperor Palpatine	8.00	15.00
6 Hoth Chewbacca	8.00	15.00
7 Luke Skywalker	6.00	12.00
8 Obi-Wan Kenobi	5.00	10.00
9 Princess Leia (ceremonial dress)	6.00	12.00
10a R2-D2 (pop-up lightsaber)(forward position)	6.00	12.00
10b R2-D2 (pop-up lightsaber)(slanted)	4.00	8.00
11 Yoda	10.00	20.00

1995-00 Star Wars Power of the Force Freeze Frame Collection 1

1 C-3PO (removable limbs)	7.50	15.00
2a Endor Rebel Commando (.00)	5.00	10.00
2b Endor Rebel Commando (.01)	5.00	10.00

3 Garindan (long snoot)	10.00	20.00
4 Han Solo	6.00	12.00
5 Han Solo (Bespin)	6.00	12.00
6a Han Solo (carbonite)(.04)	7.50	15.00
6b Han Solo (carbonite)(.05)	7.50	15.00
7a Han Solo (Endor)(.01)	5.00	10.00
7b Han Solo (Endor)(.02)	5.00	10.00
8a Hoth Rebel Soldier (.02)	5.00	10.00
8b Hoth Rebel Soldier (.03)	5.00	10.00
9a Lando Calrissian (General)(.00)	5.00	10.00
9b Lando Calrissian (General)(.01)	5.00	10.00
10a Lando Calrissian (Skiff guard)(.01)	5.00	10.00
10b Lando Calrissian (Skiff guard)(.02)	5.00	10.00
11 Lobot	3.00	6.00
12a Luke Skywalker (Bespin)(w/gold buckle)(.00)	6.00	12.00
12b Luke Skywalker (Bespin)(w/gold buckle)(.01)	6.00	12.00
12c Luke Skywalker (Bespin)(w/silver buckle)(.00)	6.00	12.00
12d Luke Skywalker (Bespin)(w/silver buckle)(.01)	6.00	12.00
13 Luke Skywalker (blast shield helmet)	7.50	15.00
14 Luke Skywalker (ceremonial)	5.00	10.00
15a Luke Skywalker (stormtrooper disguise)(.03)	5.00	10.00
15b Luke Skywalker (stormtrooper disguise)(.04)	5.00	10.00
16 Mon Mothma	6.00	12.00
17a Obi-Wan Kenobi (.03)	7.50	15.00
17b Obi-Wan Kenobi (.04)	7.50	15.00
18 Orrimaarko (Prune Face)	4.00	8.00
19 Princess Leia Organa (Ewok celebration)	5.00	10.00
20a Princess Leia Organa (Jabba's prisoner)(.01)	7.50	15.00
20b Princess Leia Organa (Jabba's prisoner)(.02)	7.50	15.00
21 Princess Leia Organa (new likeness)	5.00	10.00
22a R2-D2 (Death Star slide)	6.00	12.00
22b R2-D2 (Imperial slide)	6.00	12.00
23a Rebel Fleet Trooper (.01)	5.00	10.00
23b Rebel Fleet Trooper (.02)	5.00	10.00
23c Rebel Fleet Trooper (w/sticker)(.01)	5.00	10.00

1995-00 Star Wars Power of the Force Freeze Frame Collection 2

1 8D8	6.00	12.00
2a Admiral Ackbar (comlink wrist blaster)	6.00	12.00
2b Admiral Ackbar (wrist blaster)	6.00	12.00
3 Biggs Darklighter	4.00	8.00
4 EV-9D9	5.00	10.00
5 Ewoks Wicket & Logray	10.00	20.00
6 Gamorrean Guard	6.00	12.00
7a Han Solo (Bespin)(.02)	6.00	12.00
7b Han Solo (Bespin)(.03)	6.00	12.00
8 Lak Sivrak	6.00	12.00
9 Malakili (Rancor Keeper)	5.00	10.00
10 Nien Nunb	5.00	10.00
11 Saelt-Marae (Yak Face)	5.00	10.00
12 Ugnaughts	6.00	12.00

1995-00 Star Wars Power of the Force Freeze Frame Collection 3

1 AT-AT Driver	10.00	20.00
(1998 Fan Club Exclusive)		
2 Boba Fett	6.00	15.00
3a Captain Piett (baton sticker)	5.00	10.00
3b Captain Piett (pistol sticker)	5.00	10.00
4 Darth Vader	6.00	12.00
5 Darth Vader (removable helmet)	8.00	15.00
6 Death Star Droid (w/mouse droid)	8.00	15.00
7 Death Star Trooper	12.00	25.00
8 Emperor Palpatine	8.00	15.00
9 Emperor's Royal Guard	8.00	15.00
10 Grand Moff Tarkin	6.00	12.00
11a Ishi Tib (brown pouch)	5.00	10.00
11b Ishi Tib (gray pouch)	5.00	10.00
12 Pote Snitkin	12.00	25.00
(1999 Internet Exclusive)		
13 Princess Leia Organa (Hoth)	8.00	15.00
(1999 Fan Club Exclusive)		
14 Ree-Yees	6.00	12.00
15 Sandtrooper	25.00	50.00
16 Snowtrooper	5.00	10.00
17 Stormtrooper	5.00	10.00
18 TIE Fighter Pilot	5.00	10.00
19 Weequay	90.00	175.00
20 Zuckuss	4.00	8.00

1995-00 Star Wars Power of the Force Green Collection 1

1a Bib Fortuna (hologram)	6.00	12.00
1b Bib Fortuna (photo)	6.00	12.00
2 Boba Fett (hologram)	15.00	30.00
3 C-3PO (hologram)	8.00	15.00
4a Chewbacca	10.00	20.00
4b Chewbacca (hologram)	4.00	8.00
5a Darth Vader	6.00	12.00
5b Darth Vader (hologram)	8.00	15.00
6a Death Star Gunner	6.00	12.00
6b Death Star Gunner (hologram)	6.00	12.00
7a Emperor Palpatine	6.00	12.00
7b Emperor Palpatine (hologram)	6.00	12.00
8 Garindan (long snoot)	4.00	8.00
9a Greedo	6.00	12.00
9b Greedo (hologram)	6.00	12.00
10a Han Solo	5.00	10.00
10b Han Solo (hologram)	6.00	12.00
11a Han Solo (Bespin)	6.00	12.00
11b Han Solo (Bespin)(hologram)	6.00	12.00
12a Han Solo (carbonite stand-up bubble)	8.00	15.00

12b Han Solo (carbonite stand-up bubble) (hologram)	8.00	15.00
13a Han Solo (Endor blue pants)	8.00	15.00
13b Han Solo (Endor blue pants)(hologram)	8.00	15.00
13c Han Solo (Endor brown pants)	10.00	20.00
14 Hoth Rebel Soldier (hologram)	5.00	10.00
15 Lando Calrissian	20.00	40.00
16 Lando Calrissian (Skiff guard)(hologram)	6.00	12.00
17a Luke Skywalker (ceremonial)	5.00	10.00
17b Luke Skywalker (ceremonial)(hologram)	5.00	10.00
18 Luke Skywalker (Hoth)(hologram)	5.00	10.00
19a Luke Skywalker (Jedi Knight)	6.00	12.00
19b Luke Skywalker (Jedi Knight)(hologram)	6.00	12.00
20 Luke Skywalker (stormtrooper disguise) (hologram)	6.00	12.00
21 Luke Skywalker (X-Wing pilot)(hologram)	8.00	15.00
22a Obi-Wan Kenobi (hologram)	5.00	10.00
22b Obi-Wan Kenobi (photo)	5.00	10.00
23a Princess Leia Organa (Jabba's prisoner)	5.00	10.00
23b Princess Leia Organa (Jabba's prisoner) (hologram)	5.00	10.00
24a Princess Leia Organa (photo)		
24b Princess Leia Organa (three-ring belt)	10.00	20.00
24c Princess Leia Organa (two-ring belt)(hologram)	8.00	15.00
25 R2-D2	10.00	20.00
26 Rebel Fleet Trooper (hologram)	5.00	10.00
27a Sandtrooper	8.00	15.00
27b Sandtrooper (hologram)	8.00	15.00
28a Yoda	6.00	12.00
28b Yoda (hologram)	6.00	12.00

1995-00 Star Wars Power of the Force Green Collection 2

1a 2-1B (.00)	5.00	10.00
1b 2-1B (.00)(hologram)	6.00	12.00
1c 2-1B (.01)	4.00	8.00
1d 2-1B (.01)(hologram)	6.00	12.00
2a 4-LOM	6.00	12.00
2b 4-LOM (hologram)	6.00	12.00
3 Admiral Ackbar	4.00	8.00
4a ASP-7 (hologram)	5.00	10.00
4b ASP-7 (photo)	5.00	10.00
5a AT-ST Driver	7.50	15.00
5b AT-ST Driver (hologram)	5.00	10.00
6a Bib Fortuna (hologram/stand-up bubble)	4.00	8.00
6b Bib Fortuna (hologram/straight bubble)	5.00	10.00
7a Bossk (.00)(hologram)	4.00	8.00
7b Bossk (.00)(photo)	4.00	8.00
7c Bossk (.01)(photo)	6.00	12.00
8 Clone Emperor Palpatine (Expanded Universe)	8.00	15.00
9 Darktrooper (Expanded Universe)	10.00	20.00
10a Dengar (hologram)	7.50	15.00
10b Dengar (photo)	6.00	12.00
11a EV-9D9 (hologram)	6.00	12.00
11b EV-9D9 (photo)	6.00	12.00
12 Gamorrean Guard (hologram)	5.00	10.00
13 Grand Admiral Thrawn (Expanded Universe)	20.00	40.00
14a Grand Moff Tarkin	5.00	10.00
14b Grand Moff Tarkin (hologram)	5.00	10.00
15a Han Solo (carbonite)	6.00	12.00
15b Han Solo (carbonite)(hologram)	7.50	15.00
16a Hoth Rebel Soldier	5.00	10.00
16b Hoth Rebel Soldier (hologram)	5.00	10.00
17 Imperial Sentinel (Expanded Universe)	10.00	20.00
18a Jawas	5.00	10.00
18b Jawas (hologram)	5.00	10.00
18c Jawas (new bubble)	6.00	12.00
18d Jawas (new bubble)(hologram)	6.00	12.00
19 Kyle Katarn (Expanded Universe)	10.00	20.00

20a Luke Skywalker (ceremonial)(hologram)	5.00	10.00
20b Luke Skywalker (ceremonial/different head)		
21 Luke Skywalker (Expanded Universe)	10.00	20.00
22a Luke Skywalker (Hoth)	5.00	10.00
22b Luke Skywalker (Hoth)(hologram)	5.00	10.00
23a Luke Skywalker (Jedi Knight)	6.00	12.00
23b Luke Skywalker (Jedi Knight)(hologram)	7.50	15.00
24a Luke Skywalker (stormtrooper disguise)	7.50	15.00
24b Luke Skywalker (stormtrooper disguise) (hologram)	6.00	12.00
25 Malakili (Rancor Keeper)(hologram)	4.00	8.00
26 Mara Jade (Expanded Universe)	15.00	30.00
27a Momaw Nadon (Hammerhead)	3.00	8.00
27b Momaw Nadon (Hammerhead)(hologram)	4.00	8.00
28 Nien Nunb (hologram)	4.00	8.00
29a Ponda Baba (black beard) (hologram)	5.00	10.00
29b Ponda Baba (gray beard) (hologram)	5.00	10.00
30 Princess Leia (Expanded Universe)	8.00	15.00
31a R5-D4 (no warning sticker/L-latch)	5.00	10.00
31b R5-D4 (no warning sticker/L-latch)(hologram)	5.00	10.00
31c R5-D4 (no warning sticker/straight latch)	5.00	10.00
31d R5-D4 (no warning sticker/straight latch) (hologram)	5.00	10.00
31e R5-D4 (warning sticker/L-latch)	5.00	10.00
31f R5-D4 (warning sticker/L-latch)(hologram)	5.00	10.00
31g R5-D4 (warning sticker/straight latch)	5.00	10.00
31h R5-D4 (warning sticker/straight latch) (hologram)	5.00	10.00
32a Rebel Fleet Trooper		
32b Rebel Fleet Trooper (hologram)		
33 Saelt-Marae (Yak Face)(hologram)		
34 Spacetrooper (Expanded Universe)	8.00	15.00
35 TIE Fighter Pilot (hologram)		
36 Tusken Raider (hologram)	4.00	8.00
37 Weequay		
38a Yoda		
38b Yoda (hologram)		

1995-00 Star Wars Power of the Force Green Collection 3

1 AT-ST Driver	5.00	10.00
2 AT-ST Driver (hologram)	5.00	10.00
3 Boba Fett (hologram)	12.00	25.00
4 Darth Vader (hologram)	4.00	8.00
5a Death Star Gunner	5.00	10.00
5b Death Star Gunner (hologram)	5.00	10.00
6 Emperor Palpatine (hologram)	4.00	8.00
7a Emperor's Royal Guard	6.00	12.00
7b Emperor's Royal Guard (hologram)	6.00	12.00
8a Garindan (long snoot)(hologram)	4.00	8.00
8b Garindan (long snoot)(photo)	4.00	8.00
9 Grand Moff Tarkin	4.00	8.00
10a Ponda Baba (black beard)	5.00	10.00
10b Ponda Baba (gray beard)	50.00	100.00
11a Sandtrooper	5.00	10.00
11b Sandtrooper (hologram)	5.00	10.00
12a Snowtrooper		
12b Snowtrooper (hologram)		
13a Stormtrooper	5.00	10.00
13b Stormtrooper (holosticker)	5.00	10.00
14 TIE Fighter Pilot (hologram)	6.00	12.00
15 Weequay (hologram)	4.00	8.00

1995-00 Star Wars Power of the Force Gunner Stations

1a Gunner Station (Millennium Falcon w/Han Solo)(.00)	6.00	12.00
1b Gunner Station (Millennium Falcon w/Han Solo)(.01)	6.00	12.00
2a Gunner Station (Millennium Falcon w/Luke Skywalker)(.00)	6.00	12.00
2b Gunner Station (Millennium Falcon w/Luke Skywalker)(.01)	6.00	12.00
3 Gunner Station (TIE Fighter w/Darth Vader)	8.00	15.00

1995-00 Star Wars Power of the Force Max Rebo Band Pairs

1a Droopy McCool & Barquin D'an (CGI Sy Snootles on back) (1998 Walmart Exclusive)	12.00	25.00
1b Droopy McCool & Barquin D'an (puppet Sy Snootles on back) (1998 Walmart Exclusive)	8.00	15.00
2 Max Rebo & Doda Bodonawieedo	15.00	30.00
3a Sy Snootles & Joh Yowza (CGI Sy Snootles on back) (1998 Walmart Exclusive)	12.00	25.00
3b Sy Snootles & Joh Yowza (puppet Sy Snootles on back) (1998 Walmart Exclusive)	8.00	15.00

1995-00 Star Wars Power of the Force Millennium Mint

1 C-3PO	5.00	12.00
2a Chewbacca (.00) (1998 Toys R Us Exclusive)	6.00	12.00
2b Chewbacca (.01/new insert) (1998 Toys R Us Exclusive)	6.00	12.00
3 Emperor Palpatine (1998 Toys R Us Exclusive)	5.00	12.00
4a Han Solo (Bespin)(.00) (1998 Toys R Us Exclusive)	6.00	12.00
4b Han Solo (Bespin)(.01/new insert) (1998 Toys R Us Exclusive)	12.00	25.00
5a Luke Skywalker (Endor gear)(.00) (1998 Toys R Us Exclusive)	10.00	20.00
5b Luke Skywalker (Endor gear)(.01) (1998 Toys R Us Exclusive)	8.00	15.00
6a Princess Leia (Endor gear)(.00) (1998 Toys R Us Exclusive)	12.00	25.00
6b Princess Leia (Endor gear)(.01) (1998 Toys R Us Exclusive)	10.00	20.00
7a Snowtrooper (.00) (1998 Toys R Us Exclusive)	6.00	12.00
7b Snowtrooper (.01) (1998 Toys R Us Exclusive)	8.00	15.00

1995-00 Star Wars Power of the Force Orange

1	Chewbacca	6.00	12.00
2a	Darth Vader (long saber)	8.00	15.00
2b	Darth Vader (short saber/long tray)	10.00	20.00
2c	Darth Vader (short saber/short tray)	6.00	12.00
3	Han Solo	6.00	12.00
4a	Stormtrooper	6.00	12.00
4b	Stormtrooper (holosticker)	6.00	12.00

1995-00 Star Wars Power of the Force Playsets

1a	Cantina Pop-Up Diorama (w/sandtrooper)	12.00	25.00
	(Retail Store Version - 25" sticker correction)		
1b	Cantina Pop-Up Diorama (w/sandtrooper)	15.00	30.00
	(Retail Store Version - 25" wide description)		
1c	Cantina Pop-Up Diorama (w/sandtrooper)		
	(Retail Store Version - 26" wide description)		
2	Cantina Pop-Up Diorama		
	(1997 Mail Order Exclusive)		
3	Death Star Escape	12.50	25.00
4	Detention Block Rescue	15.00	30.00
5a	Endor Attack (no warning sticker)		
5b	Endor Attack (warning sticker)	30.00	60.00
6a	Hoth Battle (no warning sticker)	25.00	50.00
6b	Hoth Battle (warning sticker)	20.00	40.00
7a	Jabba's Palace (w/Han Solo)(podrace arena bio card)		
7b	Jabba's Palace (w/Han Solo)(podracer bio card)	15.00	30.00
8	Millennium Falcon Cockpit	20.00	40.00
	(PC Explorer Game)		

1995-00 Star Wars Power of the Force Power F/X

1	Ben (Obi-Wan) Kenobi	5.00	10.00
2	Darth Vader	5.00	10.00
3a	Emperor Palpatine (.00)	6.00	12.00
3b	Emperor Palpatine (.01)	4.00	8.00
4	Luke Skywalker	6.00	12.00
5a	R2-D2 (.00)	4.00	8.00
5b	R2-D2 (.01)	4.00	8.00
5c	R2-D2 (.02)	4.00	8.00
5d	R2-D2 (.103)	4.00	8.00

1995-00 Star Wars Power of the Force Princess Leia Collection

1a	Princess Leia & Han Solo (gold border)	4.00	8.00
1b	Princess Leia & Han Solo (gray border)	10.00	20.00
2a	Princess Leia & Luke Skywalker (gold border)	8.00	15.00
2b	Princess Leia & Luke Skywalker (gray border)	10.00	20.00
3a	Princess Leia & R2-D2 (gold border)	25.00	50.00
3b	Princess Leia & R2-D2 (gray border)	10.00	20.00
4a	Princess Leia & Wicket (gold border)	4.00	8.00
4b	Princess Leia & Wicket (gray border)	10.00	20.00

1995-00 Star Wars Power of the Force Red

1995-00 Star Wars Power of the Force Vehicles

1a	Boba Fett (full circle)	7.50	15.00
1b	Boba Fett (half circle)	20.00	40.00
1c	Boba Fett (no circle)	12.00	25.00
2	C-3PO (.00)	6.00	12.00
3	Death Star Gunner	7.50	15.00
4	Greedo	5.00	10.00
5a	Han Solo (carbonite block)	7.50	15.00
5b	Han Solo (carbonite freezing chamber)	6.00	12.00
6a	Han Solo (Hoth - closed hand)	6.00	12.00
6b	Han Solo (Hoth - open hand)	6.00	12.00
7	Jawas	6.00	12.00
8	Lando Calrissian	3.00	6.00
9a	Luke Skywalker (Dagobah - long saber)	6.00	12.00
9b	Luke Skywalker (Dagobah - short saber/long tray)	10.00	20.00
9c	Luke Skywalker (Dagobah - short saber/short tray)		
10a	Luke Skywalker (Jedi Knight - black vest)	6.00	12.00
10b	Luke Skywalker (Jedi Knight - brown vest)	10.00	20.00
11a	Luke Skywalker (long saber)	8.00	15.00
11b	Luke Skywalker (short saber/long tray)	6.00	12.00
11c	Luke Skywalker (short saber/short tray)	6.00	12.00
12a	Luke Skywalker (stormtrooper disguise)	8.00	15.00
12b	Luke Skywalker (stormtrooper disguise)	7.50	15.00
	(hologram)		
13a	Luke Skywalker (X-Wing pilot - long saber)	10.00	20.00
13b	Luke Skywalker (X-Wing pilot - short saber/long tray)	5.00	10.00
13c	Luke Skywalker (X-Wing pilot - short saber/short tray)		
14	Momaw Nadon (Hammerhead) (warning sticker)	4.00	8.00
15a	Obi-Wan Kenobi (hologram)	5.00	10.00
15b	Obi-Wan Kenobi (short saber/long tray)	5.00	10.00
15c	Obi-Wan Kenobi (short saber/short tray)	5.00	10.00
15d	Obi-Wan Kenobi (long saber)	15.00	30.00
15e	Obi-Wan Kenobi (photo)		
16a	Princess Leia Organa (2-band belt)	6.00	12.00
16b	Princess Leia Organa (3-band belt)	6.00	12.00
16c	Princess Leia Organa (hologram)		
17a	R2-D2	12.50	25.00
17b	R2-D2 (hologram)		
18a	R5-D4 (no warning sticker/straight latch)	6.00	12.00
18b	R5-D4 (warning sticker/straight latch)		
19	Sandtrooper		
20a	TIE Fighter Pilot (printed warning)	4.00	8.00
20b	TIE Fighter Pilot (SOTE)		
20c	TIE Fighter Pilot (warning sticker)		
21a	Tusken Raider (closed left hand)	6.00	12.00
21b	Tusken Raider (open left hand)		
22a	Yoda (.00)	6.00	12.00
22b	Yoda (.00)(hologram)		
22c	Yoda (.01)		

1995-00 Star Wars Power of the Force Vehicles

NNO	AT-AT Walker (electronic)(no sticker)	60.00	120.00
NNO	AT-AT Walker (electronic)(sticker of figure's legs)		
NNO	AT-ST Scout Walker	30.00	60.00
NNO	A-Wing Fighter	25.00	50.00
NNO	Cruisemissile Trooper (.00)		
NNO	Cruisemissile Trooper (.01)		
NNO	Darth Vader's TIE Fighter	25.00	50.00
NNO	Landspeeder	12.00	25.00
NNO	Luke Skywalker's Red Five X-Wing Fighter	50.00	100.00
NNO	Millennium Falcon (electronic)	60.00	120.00
NNO	Power Racing Speeder Bike (w/scout)		
NNO	Rebel Snowspeeder (electronic)	30.00	75.00
NNO	Speeder Bike (w/Leia in Endor fatigues)(grassy background)		
NNO	Speeder Bike (w/Leia in Endor fatigues)	15.00	30.00
	(rocky background)		
NNO	Speeder Bike (w/Luke in Endor fatigues glove)	30.00	60.00
NNO	Speeder Bike (w/Luke in Endor fatigues no glove)	12.50	25.00
NNO	Speeder Bike (w/scout)(aggressiveness removed)		
NNO	Speeder Bike (w/scout)(aggressiveness)		
NNO	Speeder Bike (w/scout)(Canadian windowless package)		
NNO	Speeder Bike (w/scout)(Topps Widevision card)	10.00	20.00

NNO	STAP and Battle Droid	10.00	20.00
	Sneak Preview (beige rod)		
NNO	STAP and Battle Droid	12.00	25.00
	Sneak Preview (brown rod)		
NNO	T-16 Skyhopper		
NNO	Tatooine Skiff	60.00	120.00
NNO	TIE Fighter	25.00	50.00
NNO	X-Wing Fighter (electronic green box)	15.00	30.00
NNO	X-Wing Fighter (electronic red box)	30.00	60.00
NNO	Y-Wing Fighter	40.00	80.00

2014-15 Star Wars Rebels Hero Series

1	Agent Kallus	12.00	25.00
2	Clone Trooper	6.00	12.00
3	Darth Vader	7.50	15.00
4	Ezra Bridger	10.00	20.00
5	Garazeb Orrelios	15.00	30.00
6	Heroes and Villains	20.00	50.00
	(2014 Target Exclusive)		
7	Kanan Jarrus	12.00	25.00
8	Luke Skywalker	12.00	25.00
9	Stormtrooper	10.00	20.00
10	The Inquisitor	8.00	15.00

2014-15 Star Wars Rebels Mission Series

MS1	Garazeb Orrelios/Stormtrooper	8.00	15.00
MS2	R2-D2/C-3PO	15.00	30.00
MS3	Luke Skywalker/Darth Vader	10.00	20.00
MS4	Darth Sidious/Yoda	12.00	25.00
MS5	Boba Fett/Stormtrooper	12.00	25.00
MS7	Wullffwarro/Wookiee Warrior	8.00	15.00
MS8	Sabine Wren/Stormtrooper	20.00	40.00
MS9	Cikatro Vizago/IG-RM	10.00	20.00
MS10	Wicket/Biker Scout	8.00	15.00
MS11	Bossk/IG-88	10.00	20.00
MS15	Luke Skywalker/Han Solo	12.00	25.00
MS16	R2-D2/Yoda	15.00	30.00
MS17	TIE Pilot/Stormtrooper	8.00	15.00
MS18	Ezra Bridger/Kanan Jarrus	8.00	15.00
MS19	Stormtrooper Commander/Hera Syndulla	12.00	25.00
MS20	Princess Leia/Luke Skywalker Stormtrooper	10.00	20.00

2014-15 Star Wars Rebels Saga Legends

SL1	Stormtrooper	6.00	12.00
SL2	Ezra Bridger	8.00	15.00
SL3	The Inquisitor	7.50	15.00
SL4	Kanan Jarrus	6.00	12.00
SL5	Agent Kallus	12.00	30.00
SL6	C1-10P (Chopper)	12.00	30.00
SL7	Jango Fett	6.00	12.00
SL8	Clone Trooper	6.00	12.00
SL9	Darth Vader	10.00	20.00
SL10	Luke Skywalker (Jedi Knight)	7.50	15.00

SL11 Obi-Wan Kenobi	7.50	15.00
SL12 Snowtrooper	10.00	20.00
SL13 TIE Pilot	5.00	10.00
SL14 AT-DP Driver	20.00	40.00
SL15 Clone Commander Gree	6.00	12.00
SL16 Plo Koon	5.00	10.00
SL17 Jedi Temple Guard	30.00	75.00
SL18 AT-AT Driver	6.00	12.00
SL22 Luke Skywalker (X-Wing Pilot)	7.50	15.00
SL23 Lando Calrissian	7.50	15.00
SL24 Han Solo	8.00	15.00
SL25 Luke Skywalker (Endor)	7.50	15.00
SL26 Commander Bly	6.00	12.00
SL27 Han Solo (Endor)	8.00	15.00
SL28 Princess Leia (Endor)	6.00	12.00

2005 Star Wars Revenge of the Sith

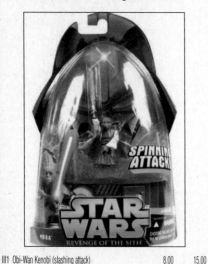

III1 Obi-Wan Kenobi (slashing attack)	8.00	15.00
III2 Anakin Skywalker (slashing attack straight saber red)	6.00	12.00
III2a Anakin Skywalker (slashing attack bent saber red)	4.00	8.00
III2b Anakin Skywalker (slashing attack bent saber pink)	4.00	8.00
III3 Yoda (firing cannon)	4.00	8.00
III4 Super Battle Droid (firing arm blaster)	10.00	20.00
III5 Chewbacca (Wookiee rage)	8.00	15.00
III6a Clone Trooper (white - quick draw attack)	6.00	12.00
III6b Clone Trooper (red - quick draw attack)	6.00	12.00
III7 R2-D2 (droid attack)	5.00	10.00
III8 Grievous's Bodyguard (battle attack)	4.00	8.00
III9 General Grievous (four lightsaber attack)	4.00	8.00
III10 Mace Windu (Force combat)	6.00	12.00
III11 Darth Vader (lightsaber attack)	4.00	8.00
III12 Emperor Palpatine (firing Force lightning)	5.00	10.00
III13 Count Dooku (Sith Lord)	5.00	10.00
III14 Chancellor Palpatine (supreme chancellor)	4.00	8.00
III15 Bail Organa (Republic Senator)	5.00	10.00
III16 Plo Koon (Jedi Master)	4.00	8.00
III17 Battle Droid (separatist army)	5.00	10.00
III18 C-3PO (protocal droid)	4.00	8.00
III19 Padme republic senator	10.00	20.00
III20 Agen Kolar (Jedi Master)	6.00	12.00
III21 Shaak Ti (Jedi Master)	10.00	20.00
III22 Kit Fisto (Jedi Master)	6.00	12.00
III23a Royal Guard (blue - senate security)	6.00	12.00
III23b Royal Guard (red - senate security)	8.00	15.00
III24 Mon Mothma (Republic Senator)	6.00	12.00
III25 Tarfful (firing bowcaster)	4.00	8.00
III26 Yoda (spinning attack)	6.00	12.00

III27 Obi-Wan Kenobi (Jedi kick)	4.00	8.00
III28 Anakin Skywalker (slashing attack)	8.00	15.00
III29 Ki-Adi-Mundi (Jedi Master)	5.00	10.00
III30 Saesee Tiin (Jedi Master)	5.00	10.00
III31 Luminara Unduli (Jedi Master)	6.00	12.00
III32 Aayla Secura (Jedi Knight)	8.00	15.00
III33a Clone Commander (red - battle gear)	8.00	15.00
III33b Clone Commander (green - battle gear)	8.00	15.00
III34a Clone Pilot (firing cannon)	5.00	10.00
III34b Clone Pilot (black - firing cannon)	5.00	10.00
III35a Palpatine (red lightsaber - lightsaber attack)	6.00	12.00
III35b Palpatine (blue lightsaber - lightsaber attack)	6.00	12.00
III36 General Grievous (exploding body)	10.00	20.00
III37 Vader's Medical Droid (chopper droid)	4.00	8.00
III38 AT-TE Tank Gunner (clone army)	6.00	12.00
III39 Polis Massan (medic droid)	4.00	8.00
III40 Mas Amedda (Republic Senator)	5.00	10.00
III41 Clone Trooper (white - super articulation)	5.00	10.00
III42 Neimoidian Warrior (Neimoidian weapon attack)	4.00	8.00
III43a Warrior Wookiee (dark - wookiee battle bash)	4.00	8.00
III43b Warrior Wookiee (light - wookiee battle bash)	12.00	25.00
III44 Destroyer Droid (firing arm blaster)	8.00	15.00
III45 Tarkin (Governor)	4.00	8.00
III46 Ask Aak (Senator)	6.00	12.00
III47 Meena Tills (Senator)	4.00	8.00
III48 R2-D2 (try me electronic)	6.00	12.00
III49 Commander Bacara (quick-draw attack)	5.00	10.00
III50 Anakin Skywalker (battle damaged)	8.00	15.00
III51 Captain Antilles (Senate security)	4.00	8.00
III52 Jett Jukassa (Jedi Padawan)	4.00	8.00
III53 Utapaun Warrior (Utapaun security)	5.00	10.00
III54 AT-RT Driver (missile-firing blaster)	12.00	25.00
III55 Obi-Wan Kenobi (w/pilot gear)	8.00	15.00
III56 Mustafar Sentury (spinning energy bolt)	5.00	10.00
III57 Commander Bly (battle gear)	8.00	15.00
III58 Wookie Commando (Kashyyyk battle gear)	6.00	12.00
III59 Commander Gree (battle gear)	10.00	20.00
III60 Grievous's Bodyguard (battle attack)	6.00	12.00
III61 Passel Argente (separatist leader)	6.00	12.00
III62 Cat Miin (separatist)	4.00	8.00
III63 Neimoidian Commander (separatist bodyguard)	4.00	8.00
III64 R4-P17 (rolling action)	8.00	15.00
III65 Tactical Ops Trooper (Vader's legion)	6.00	12.00
III66 Plo Koon (Jedi hologram transmission)	8.00	15.00
III67 Aayla Secura (Jedi hologram transmission)	5.00	10.00
III68 Wookiee Heavy Gunner (blast attack)	5.00	10.00

2005 Star Wars Revenge of the Sith 12-Inch

1 Anakin Skywalker/Darth Vader (ultimate villain)	30.00	60.00
2 Barriss Offee	15.00	30.00
3 Chewbacca	20.00	40.00
(2005 KB Toys Exclusive)		
4 Clone Trooper	12.00	25.00
5 Darth Sidious		
6 General Grievous	30.00	60.00
7 Shaak Ti	15.00	30.00

2005 Star Wars Revenge of the Sith Accessories

10 Darth Vader Carrying Case (w/Clone Trooper & Anakin Skywalker)		
20 Darth Vader Carrying Case (w/Darth Vader & Obi-Wan Kenobi)		

2005 Star Wars Revenge of the Sith Battle Arena

1 Bodyguard vs. Obi-Wan (Utapau landing platform)	8.00	15.00
2 Dooku vs Anakin (Trade Federation cruiser)	8.00	15.00
3 Sidius vs. Mace (Chancellor's office)	8.00	15.00

2005 Star Wars Revenge of the Sith Battle Packs

NNO Assault on Hoth (General Veers/Probot/3 Snowtroopers)		
NNO Attack on Coruscant (5 Clone Troopers)	30.00	60.00
NNO Imperial Throne Room (Emperor Palpatine Imperial Dignitary/2 Royal Guards/Stormtrooper)		
NNO Jedi Temple Assault (Anakin/Clone Pilot/3 Special Ops Troopers)		
NNO Jedi vs. Sith (Anakin/Asajj Ventress General Grievous/Obi-Wan/Yoda)	20.00	40.00
NNO Jedi vs. Separatists (Anakin/Darth Maul Jango Fett/Obi-Wan/Mace Windu)	15.00	30.00
NNO Rebel vs. Empire (Chewbacca/Vader Han/Luke/Stormtrooper)	20.00	40.00

2005 Star Wars Revenge of the Sith Collectible Cup Figures

1 Boba Fett	12.00	25.00
2 Clone Trooper		
3 Darth Vader	10.00	20.00
4 General Grievous		
5 Han Solo	10.00	20.00
6 Obi-Wan Kenobi	10.00	20.00
7 Princess Leia		
8 Stormtrooper	8.00	15.00
9 Yoda	8.00	15.00

2005 Star Wars Revenge of the Sith Commemorative Episode III DVD Collection

1 Jedi Knights (Anakin Skywalker Mace Windu/Obi-Wan Kenobi)	10.00	20.00
2 Sith Lords (Emperor Palpatine Darth Vader/Count Dooku)	10.00	20.00
3 Clone Troopers (3 Clone Troopers)	12.00	25.00

2005 Star Wars Revenge of the Sith Creatures

10 Boga (w/Obi-Wan Kenobi)	20.00	40.00

2005 Star Wars Revenge of the Sith Deluxe

1 Anakin Skywalker (changes to Darth Vader)	15.00	30.00
2 Clone Trooper (firing jet pack)	5.00	10.00
3 Clone Troopers (Build Your Army - 3 white)	8.00	15.00
4 Clone Troopers (Build Your Army - 2 white and 1 red)	10.00	20.00
5 Clone Troopers (Build Your Army - 2 white and 1 green)	8.00	15.00
6 Clone Troopers (Build Your Army - 2 white and 1 blue)	12.00	25.00
7 Crab Droid (moving legs/missile launcher)	12.00	25.00
8 Darth Vader (rebuild Darth Vader)	10.00	20.00
9 Emperor Palpatine (changes to Darth Sidious)	8.00	15.00
10 General Grievous (secret lightsaber attack)	15.00	30.00
11 Obi-Wan Kenobi (Force jump attack - w/super battle droid)	5.00	10.00
12 Spider Droid (firing laser action)	5.00	10.00
13 Stass Allie (exploding action - w/BARC speeder)	5.00	10.00
14 Vulture Droid (blue - firing missile launcher)	6.00	12.00
15 Vulture Droid (brown - firing missile launcher)	10.00	20.00
16 Yoda (fly into battle - w/can-cell)	8.00	15.00

2005 Star Wars Revenge of the Sith Evolutions

1 Anakin Skywalker to Darth Vader	12.00	25.00
2 Clone Trooper (Attack of the Clones Revenge of the Sith/A New Hope)	15.00	30.00
3 Clone Trooper (Attack of the Clones Revenge of the Sith - gray/A New Hope - gray)	15.00	30.00
4 Sith Lords (Darth Maul Darth Tyranus/Darth Sidious)	15.00	30.00

2005 Star Wars Revenge of the Sith Exclusives

1 Anakin Skywalker Paris-Mai		
(2005 Star Wars Reunion Convention Exclusive)		
2 Clone Trooper (Neyo logo)		
(2005 Target Exclusive)		
3 Clone Trooper (Sith logo)	12.00	25.00
(2005 Target Exclusive)		
4 Covert Ops Clone Trooper		
(2005 StarWarsShop.com Exclusive)		
5 Darth Vader (Duel at Mustafar)	8.00	15.00
(2005 Target Exclusive)		
6 Darth Vader (lava reflection)	8.00	15.00
(2005 Target Exclusive)		
7 Darth Vader	12.00	25.00
(2005 Celebration III Exclusive)		
8 Holographic Emperor	6.00	12.00
(2005 Toys R Us Exclusive)		
9 Holographic Yoda (Kashyyyk transmission)	6.00	12.00
(2005 Toys R Us Exclusive)		
10 Obi-Wan Kenobi (Duel at Mustafar)	12.00	25.00
(2005 Target Exclusive)		
11 R2-D2 (remote control)		
(2005 Japanese Exclusive)		
12 Utapau Shadow Trooper (super articulation)	10.00	20.00
(2005 Target Exclusive)		

2005 Star Wars Revenge of the Sith Kay Bee Toys Collector Packs

1 Luminara Unduli/Count Dooku	20.00	40.00
Royal Guard/Kit Fisto		
Darth Vader/Bail Organa/C-3PO/Ki-Adi-Mundi/Chancellor Palpatine		

2005 Star Wars Revenge of the Sith Playsets

1 Mustafar Final Duel/Anakin		
Skywalker/Obi-Wan Kenobi		
2 Mustafar Final Duel (w/Obi-Wan	40.00	80.00
Darth Vader/4 Clone Troopers)		

2005 Star Wars Revenge of the Sith Sneak Preview

1 General Grievous	8.00	15.00
2 Tion Medon	4.00	8.00
3 Wookie Warrior	4.00	8.00
4 R4-G9	4.00	8.00
NNO Anakin's Jedi Starfighter (vehicle)	15.00	30.00

2005 Star Wars Revenge of the Sith Super Deformed

1 Boba Fett	6.00	12.00
2 C-3PO	6.00	12.00
3 Chewbacca	6.00	12.00

4 Darth Maul	6.00	12.00
5 Darth Vader	6.00	12.00
6 R2-D2	6.00	12.00
7 Stormtrooper	6.00	12.00
8 Yoda	6.00	12.00

2005 Star Wars Revenge of the Sith Vehicles

1 Anakin's Jedi Starfighter (w/Anakin)	20.00	40.00
(2005 Toys R Us Exclusive)		
2 ARC-170 Fighter	50.00	100.00
3 ARC-170 Fighter (w/4 Troopers)	75.00	150.00
4 AR-RT/AR-RT Driver		
5 AR-RT/AR-RT Driver (w/Clone Trooper white)		
6 Barc Speeder (w/Barc Trooper & Wookiee warrior)		
7 Barc Speeder (w/Barc Trooper)		
8 Droid Tri-Fighter		
9 Grievous's Wheel Bike (w/General Grievous)	25.00	50.00
10 Millennium Falcon		
11 Obi-Wan's Jedi Starfighter	20.00	40.00
12 Obi-Wan's Jedi Starfighter (w/Obi-Wan)	12.00	25.00
(2005 Toys R Us Exclusive)		
13 Plo Koon's Jedi Starfighter	15.00	30.00
(2005 Target Exclusive)		
14 Republic Gunship	100.00	200.00
15 Wookiee Flyer (w/Wookiee warrior)		

2016 Star Wars Rogue One 2-Packs

NNO Baze Malbus vs. Imperial Stormtrooper	7.50	15.00
NNO Captain Cassian Andor vs.	12.50	25.00
Imperial Stormtrooper		
NNO First Order Snowtrooper Officer vs.	8.00	15.00
Poe Dameron		
NNO Moroff vs. Scariff Stormtrooper Squad Leader	7.50	15.00
NNO Rebel Commander Pao vs.	10.00	20.00
Imperial Death Trooper		
NNO Seventh Sister Inquisitor vs. Darth Maul	15.00	30.00
NNO Captain Phasma vs. Finn	10.00	20.00

2016 Star Wars Rogue One Big Figs

NNO Imperial Death Trooper	15.00	30.00
NNO Imperial Stormtrooper	15.00	30.00
NNO K-2SO	15.00	30.00
NNO Sergeant Jyn Erso	12.00	25.00

2016 Star Wars Rogue One Build-A-Weapon

1 Admiral Raddus	10.00	20.00
2 Bodhi Rook	12.00	25.00
3 Captain Cassian Andor (Eadu)	8.00	15.00
4 Chirrut Imwe	8.00	15.00
5 Darth Vader	8.00	15.00
6 Director Krennic	6.00	12.00
7 Fenn Rau	60.00	120.00
8 Galen Erso	12.00	25.00
9 Grand Admiral Thrawn (admiral rank)	15.00	30.00
10 Grand Admiral Thrawn (director rank)	30.00	60.00
11 Imperial Death Trooper (Specialist Gear)	10.00	20.00
12 Imperial Ground Crew	6.00	12.00
13 Imperial Stormtrooper	6.00	12.00
14 K-2SO	6.00	12.00
15 Kanan Jarrus (stormtrooper disguise)	10.00	20.00
(Star Wars Rebels)		
16 Kylo Ren (The Force Awakens)	8.00	15.00
17 Lieutenant Sefla	6.00	12.00
18 Princess Leia Organa (Star Wars Rebels)	6.00	12.00
19 Rey (Jakku)(The Force Awakens)	6.00	12.00
20 Sabine Wren (Star Wars Rebels)	6.00	12.00
21 Sergeant Jyn Erso (Eadu)	6.00	12.00
22 Sergeant Jyn Erso	8.00	15.00
(Imperial Ground Crew Disguise)		
23 Sergeant Jyn Erso (Jedha)	6.00	12.00
24 Shoretrooper	8.00	15.00

2016 Star Wars Rogue One Elite Series

NNO Baze Malbus	10.00	20.00
NNO Bodhi Rook	10.00	20.00
NNO C2-B5	12.00	25.00
NNO Captain Cassian Andor	8.00	15.00
NNO Chirrut Imwe	10.00	20.00
NNO Imperial Death Trooper	15.00	30.00
NNO K-2SO	10.00	20.00
NNO Sergeant Jyn Erso	10.00	20.00
NNO Stormtrooper	10.00	20.00

2016 Star Wars Rogue One Hero Series

NNO Captain Cassian Andor	8.00	15.00
NNO First Order Stormtrooper		
NNO Imperial Death Trooper	8.00	15.00
NNO Sergeant Jyn Erso	8.00	15.00
NNO Shoretrooper		

2016 Star Wars Rogue One Multipacks

NNO Eadu 3-Pack	12.00	25.00
Sergeant Jyn Erso/Captain Cassian Andor/K-2SO/(Walmart Exclusive)		
NNO Jedha Revolt 4-Pack	15.00	30.00
Edrio Two Tubes/Saw Gerrera/Sergeant Jyn Erso/Imperial Hovertank Pilot		
NNO Rey vs. Kylo Ren		
Poe Dameron vs. First Order TIE Fighter Pilot/Finn vs. FN-2199		
NNO Scarif 4-Pack	12.00	25.00
Rebel Commando Pao/Moroff/Imperial Death Trooper/Imperial Stormtrooper/(Kohl's Exclusive)		
NNO Star Wars 8-Pack	15.00	30.00
Darth Maul/Jango Fett/Obi-Wan/Chewbacca/Darth Vader/Luke/Rey/BB-8		
(Target Exclusive)		

2016 Star Wars Rogue One Vehicles

NNO Assault Walker (w/stormtrooper sergeant)	20.00	40.00
(The Force Awakens)		
NNO A-Wing (w/Hera Syndulla)(Star Wars Rebels)	20.00	40.00
NNO Ezra Bridger's Speeder (w/Ezra Bridger)	12.00	25.00
(Star Wars Rebels)		
NNO First Order Snowspeeder (w/stormtrooper)	15.00	30.00
(The Force Awakens)		
NNO Imperial AT-ACT Playset	75.00	150.00
(w/Jyn Erso/astromech droid/driver)		
NNO Imperial Speeder (w/AT-DP pilot)	12.00	25.00
(Star Wars Rebels)		
NNO Imperial TIE Striker (w/pilot)	20.00	40.00
NNO Imperial TIE Striker (w/pilot)	10.00	20.00
(Toys R Us Exclusive)		
NNO Rebel U-Wing Fighter (w/Cassian Andor)	20.00	40.00
NNO Y-Wing Scout Bomber (w/Kanan Jarrus)	20.00	40.00

2015-16 Star Wars S.H. Figuarts

NNO Battle Droid	30.00	60.00
NNO Captain Phasma	30.00	60.00
NNO Clone Trooper (Phase 1)	25.00	50.00
NNO Darth Maul	50.00	100.00
NNO Darth Vader (w/display stand)	80.00	150.00
NNO First Order Riot Control Stormtrooper	30.00	60.00
NNO First Order Stormtrooper	30.00	60.00
NNO First Order Stormtrooper Heavy Gunner	40.00	80.00
NNO Jango Fett	40.00	80.00
NNO Kylo Ren		
NNO Luke Skywalker (Episode IV)	40.00	80.00
NNO Luke Skywalker (Episode VI)	60.00	120.00
NNO Mace Windu	40.00	80.00
NNO Obi-Wan Kenobi (Episode I)	30.00	60.00
NNO Scout Trooper and Speeder Bike	120.00	200.00
NNO Shadow Trooper	40.00	80.00
NNO Stormtrooper	50.00	100.00

2002-04 Star Wars Saga 12-Inch

NNO Anakin Skywalker	12.50	25.00
NNO Anakin Skywalker (w/slashing lightsaber)	15.00	30.00
NNO AT-ST Driver	15.00	30.00
NNO Biker Scout	30.00	75.00
NNO Clone Commander	8.00	15.00
NNO Clone Trooper (black-and-white)	12.50	25.00
NNO Clone Trooper (red-and-white)	12.50	25.00
NNO Count Dooku	25.00	50.00
NNO Dengar	12.50	25.00
NNO Ewok 2-Pack (Logray & Keoulkeech)	20.00	40.00
NNO Gamorrean Guard	25.00	50.00
NNO Garindan	20.00	40.00
NNO Geonosian Warrior	12.50	25.00
NNO Han Solo		
NNO Imperial Officer	10.00	20.00
NNO Jango Fett	30.00	75.00
NNO Jango Fett (electronic battling)	20.00	40.00
NNO Jawas	25.00	50.00
NNO Ki-Adi-Mundi	20.00	40.00
NNO Lando Calrissian (Skiff disguise)	12.00	25.00
NNO Luke Skywalker & Tauntaun	50.00	100.00
NNO Luke Skywalker (w/slashing lightsaber)	25.00	50.00
NNO Mace Windu	15.00	30.00
NNO Obi-Wan Kenobi	12.00	25.00
NNO Obi-Wan Kenobi (electronic battling)	10.00	20.00
NNO Obi-Wan Kenobi (Tatooine encounter)	20.00	40.00
NNO Padme Amidala	15.00	30.00
NNO Plo Koon		
NNO Princess Leia (Boushh) & Han Solo (carbonite)	30.00	60.00

NNO Princess Leia (w/speeder bike)	30.00	75.00
NNO Super Battle Droid	12.00	25.00
NNO Yoda (w/hoverchair)	20.00	40.00
NNO Zam Wesell	12.00	25.00
NNO Zuckuss	20.00	40.00

2002-04 Star Wars Saga 12-Inch Character Collectibles

NNO Anakin Skywalker		
NNO Darth Vader		
NNO Jango Fett	30.00	60.00
NNO Mace Windu	10.00	20.00

2002-04 Star Wars Saga Accessory Sets

NNO Arena Conflict with/Battle Droid brown	12.00	25.00
NNO Death Star (w/Death Star trooper and droids)	10.00	20.00
NNO Endor Victory (w/scout trooper)	10.00	20.00
NNO Hoth Survival (w/Hoth Rebel soldier)	7.50	15.00

2002-04 Star Wars Saga Arena Battle Beasts

NNO Acklay	25.00	50.00
NNO Reek	15.00	30.00

2002-04 Star Wars Saga Cinema Scenes

NNO Death Star Trash Compactor (Chewbacca & Princess Leia)	20.00	40.00
NNO Death Star Trash Compactor (Luke Skywalker & Han Solo)	25.00	50.00
NNO Geonosian War Chamber (Nute Gunray/Passel Argente/Shu Mai)	12.00	25.00
NNO Geonosian War Chamber (Poggle the Lesser/Count Dooku/San Hill)	12.00	25.00
NNO Jedi High Council (Mace Windu Oppo Rancisis/Even Piell)	20.00	40.00
NNO Jedi High Council (Yarael Poof Depa Billaba/Yaddle)	10.00	20.00

2002-04 Star Wars Saga Collectible Cup Figures

NNO Episode I/Darth Maul	10.00	20.00
NNO Episode II	10.00	20.00
Anakin Skywalker		
NNO Episode IV	10.00	20.00
Obi-Wan Kenobi		
NNO Episode V	10.00	20.00
Luke Skywalker		
NNO Episode VI	12.00	25.00
Princess Leia Organa		

2002-04 Star Wars Saga Collection 1 (2002)

1 Anakin Skywalker (outland peasant disguise)	6.00	12.00
2 Padme Amidala (arena escape)	6.00	12.00
3 Obi-Wan Kenobi (Coruscant chase)	6.00	12.00
4 C-3PO (protocol droid)	5.00	10.00
5 Kit Fisto (Jedi Master)	5.00	10.00

6 Super Battle Droid	5.00	10.00
17 Clone Trooper	6.00	12.00
18 Zam Wesell (bounty hunter)	6.00	12.00
22 Anakin Skywalker (hangar duel)	12.00	25.00
23 Yoda (Jedi Master)		
27 Count Dooku (Dark Lord)	6.00	12.00
28 Mace Windu (Geonosian rescue)	8.00	15.00
29 Luke Skywalker (Bespin duel)	8.00	15.00
30 Darth Vader (Bespin duel)	6.00	12.00
31 Jango Fett (final battle)	5.00	10.00
36 Obi-Wan Kenobi (Jedi starfighter)	12.00	25.00
37 Han Solo (Endor bunker)		
38 Chewbacca (Cloud City capture w/C-3PO)	6.00	12.00
40 Djas Puhr (bounty hunter)	6.00	12.00
41 Padme Amidala (Coruscant attack)	6.00	12.00
43 Anakin Skywalker (Tatooine attack)	6.00	12.00
47 Jango Fett (Slave-1 pilot)	5.00	10.00
48 Destroyer Droid (Geonosis battle)		
49 Clone Trooper (Republic gunship pilot)	8.00	15.00
53 Yoda (Jedi High Council)		

2002-04 Star Wars Saga Collection 1 (2003)

1 Obi-Wan Kenobi (acklay battle)	5.00	10.00
2 Mace Windu (arena confrontation)	5.00	10.00
3 Darth Tyranus (Geonosian escape)	8.00	15.00
7 Anakin Skywalker (secret ceremony)	8.00	15.00
8 Boba Fett (The Pit of Carkoon)	8.00	15.00
9 R2-D2 (droid factory)	6.00	12.00
13 Han Solo (Hoth rescue)		
14 Chewbacca (mynock hunt)	5.00	10.00
17 Luke Skywalker (throne room duel)	5.00	10.00
18 Darth Vader (throne room duel)	6.00	12.00
19 Snowtrooper (The Battle of Hoth)	8.00	15.00
20 Jango Fett (Kamino duel)		
21 C-3PO (Tatooine attack)		

2002-04 Star Wars Saga Collection 2 (2002)

7 Boba Fett (Kamino escape)	8.00	15.00
8 Tusken Raider Female (w/Tusken child)	6.00	12.00
9 Captain Typho (Padme's head of security)	5.00	10.00
10 Shaak Ti (Jedi Master)	5.00	10.00
11a Battle Droid (arena battle tan)	5.00	10.00
11b Battle Droid (arena battle brown)	12.00	25.00
12 Plo Koon (arena battle)		
13 Jango Fett (Kamino escape)	8.00	15.00
14 R2-D2 (Coruscant sentry)	8.00	15.00
15 Geonosian Warrior	5.00	10.00
16 Dexter Jettster (Coruscant informant)	5.00	10.00
19 Royal Guard (Coruscant security)	6.00	12.00
20 Saesee Tin (Jedi Master)	5.00	10.00

21 Nikto (Jedi Knight)	6.00	12.00
24 Jar Jar Binks (Gungan Senator)	5.00	10.00
25 Taun We (Kamino cloner)	6.00	12.00
26 Luminara Unduli	5.00	10.00
32 Qui-Gon Jinn (Jedi Master)	6.00	12.00
33a Endor Rebel Soldier (facial hair)		
33a Endor Rebel Soldier (no facial hair)		
34 Massiff (w/Geonosian handler)	8.00	15.00
35 Orn Free Taa (senator)		
39 Supreme Chancellor Palpatine		
42 Darth Maul (Sith training)	5.00	10.00
44 Ki-Adi-Mundi (Jedi Master)	5.00	10.00
45 Ephant Man (Jabba's head of security)		
46 Teemto Pagalies (pod racer)		
50 Watto (Mos Espa junk dealer)	5.00	10.00
51 Lott Dod (Neimoidian Senator)		
52 Tusken Raider (w/massiff)	6.00	12.00
54 Rebel Trooper (Tantive IV defender)		
55 Imperial Officer		
56 Eeth Koth (Jedi Master)		
57 Teebo		

2002-04 Star Wars Saga Collection 2 (2003)

4 Padme Amidala (droid factory chase)		
5 SP-4 & JN-66 (research droids)	6.00	12.00
6 Tusken Raider (Tatooine camp ambush)	5.00	10.00
10 Lama Su (w/clone child)	10.00	20.00
11 Aayla Secura (Battle of Geonosis)	8.00	15.00
12 Barriss Offee (Luminara Unduli's Padawan)	6.00	12.00
15 Yoda and Chian (Padawan lightsaber training)		
16 Ashla & Jempa (Jedi Padawans)	8.00	15.00
22 Padme Amidala (secret ceremony)	10.00	20.00
23 Wat Tambor (Geonosis war room)	10.00	20.00
24 Coleman Trebor (Battle of Geonosis)		
25 Darth Maul (Theed hangar duel)	8.00	15.00
26 Princess Leia Organa (Imperial captive)	5.00	10.00
27 Han Solo (fight to Alderaan)		
28 WA-7 (Dexter's diner)	8.00	15.00
29 Lt. Dannl Faytonni (Coruscant Outlander club)		
30 The Emperor (throne room)		
31 Luke Skywalker (Tatooine encounter)	5.00	10.00
32 Darth Vader (Death Star clash)	8.00	15.00
33 Bail Organa (Alderaan Senator)	6.00	12.00
34 Stormtrooper (McQuarrie concept)	8.00	15.00
35 Imperial Dignitary Janus Greejatus		
(Death Star procession)		
36 Padme Amidala (Lars' homestead)	15.00	30.00
37 Achk Med-Beq (Coruscant Outlander club)	6.00	12.00
38 Ayy Vida (Outlander nightclub patron)	10.00	20.00
39 Obi-Wan Kenobi (Outlander nightclub patron)	6.00	12.00
40 Elan Sleazebaggano	8.00	15.00
(Outlander nightclub encounter)		
41 Imperial Dignitary Kren Blista-Vanee		
(Death Star procession)		

2002-04 Star Wars Saga Deluxe

NNO Anakin Skywalker (w/Force flipping attack)	4.00	8.00
NNO Anakin Skywalker	6.00	12.00
(w/lightsaber slashing action)		
NNO C-3PO (w/droid factory assembly line)	4.00	8.00
NNO Clone Trooper (w/speeder bike)	6.00	12.00
NNO Darth Tyranus (w/Force flipping attack)	4.00	8.00
NNO Flying Geonosian	4.00	8.00
(w/sonic blaster and attack pod)		
NNO Jango Fett (Kamino showdown)	4.00	8.00
NNO Jango Fett	4.00	8.00
(w/electronic backpack and snap-on armor)		
NNO Mace Windu (w/blast apart droid tan)	4.00	8.00
NNO Mace Windu (w/blast apart droid brown)	4.00	8.00
NNO Nexu (w/snapping jaw and attack roar)	12.00	25.00
NNO Obi-Wan Kenobi (Kamino showdown)	4.00	8.00
NNO Obi-Wan Kenobi (w/Force flipping attack)	4.00	8.00

NNO Spider Droid	4.00	8.00
(w/rotating turret and firing cannon)		
NNO Super Battle Droid Builder	4.00	8.00
(w/droid factory assembly mold)		
NNO Yoda (w/Force powers)	10.00	20.00

2002-04 Star Wars Saga Exclusives

NNO Boba Fett (silver)	15.00	30.00
(2003 Convention Exclusive)		
NNO C-3PO (Santa) & R2-D2 (reindeer)	12.00	25.00
(2002 Holiday Edition Exclusive)		
NNO Clone Trooper (silver)	6.00	12.00
(2003 Toys R Us Exclusive)		
NNO Clone Trooper/Super Battle Droid	12.00	25.00
(2004 Jedi Con Exclusive)		
NNO Commander Jorg Sacul	20.00	40.00
(2002 Celebration 2 Exclusive)		
NNO Darth Vader (silver)	30.00	60.00
(2002 New York Toy Fair Exclusive)		
NNO R2-D2 (silver)	15.00	30.00
(2002 Toys R Us Silver Anniversary Exclusive)		
NNO Sandtrooper (silver)		
(2004 SDCC Exclusive)		
NNO Yoda (Santa)		
(2003 Holiday Edition Exclusive)		

2002-04 Star Wars Saga Mos Eisley Cantina Bar

NNO Dr. Evezan		
NNO Greedo	8.00	15.00
NNO Kitik Keed'kak		
NNO Momaw Nadon		
NNO Ponda Baba		
NNO Wuher		

2002-04 Star Wars Saga Multipacks

NNO Endor Soldiers (w/four soldiers paint may vary slightly)		
NNO Imperial Forces (Darth Vader	15.00	30.00
Stormtrooper/AT-ST Driver/R4-I9)		
NNO Jedi Warriors (Obi-Wan Kenobi	10.00	20.00
Saesee Tiin/Plo Koon/Fi-Ek Sirch)		
NNO Light Saber Action Pack		
(Anakin Skywalker/Count Dooku/Yoda)		
NNO Rebel Troopers Builder Set		
NNO Sandtroopers Builder Set		
(orange, black, gray, & white shoulder pad)		
NNO Skirmish at Karkoon	10.00	20.00
(Han Solo/Klaatu/Nikto/Barada)		
NNO Stormtroopers Builder Set		
NNO The Battle of Hoth (Luke	20.00	40.00
Leia/Chewbacca/R3-A2/Tauntaun)		
NNO Ultimate Bounty (Boba Fett	12.00	25.00
Bossk/IG-88/Aurra Sing w/swoop vehicle)		
NNO Value 4-Pack (Zam Wesell		
Battle Droid/Kit Fisto/Super Battle Droid)		

2002-04 Star Wars Saga Playsets

NNO Geonosian Battle Arena	60.00	120.00

2002-04 Star Wars Saga Playskool

NNO Arena Adventure	12.00	25.00
NNO Duel with Darth Maul	25.00	50.00
NNO Fast through the Forest	8.00	15.00
NNO Millennium Falcon Adventure	20.00	40.00
NNO The Stompin' Wampa		
NNO X-Wing Adventure	25.00	50.00

2002-04 Star Wars Saga Ultra With Accessories

NNO C-3PO with Escape Pod	12.00	25.00
NNO Ewok (w/attack glider)		
NNO General Rieekan (w/Hoth tactical screen)	20.00	40.00
NNO Jabba's Palace Court Denizens		
NNO Jabba the Hutt (w/pipe stand)		
NNO Jango Fett (Kamino confrontation)		
NNO Obi-Wan Kenobi (Kamino confrontation)	15.00	30.00
NNO Wampa (w/Hoth cave)		

2002-04 Star Wars Saga Vehicles

NNO Anakin Skywalker's Speeder	10.00	20.00
NNO Anakin Skywalker's Swoop Bike (w/Anakin)	20.00	40.00
NNO A-Wing Fighter	20.00	40.00
NNO Darth Tyranus's Speeder Bike	15.00	30.00
(w/Darth Tyranus)		
NNO Imperial Dogfight TIE Fighter	20.00	40.00
NNO Imperial Shuttle	120.00	200.00
NNO Jango Fett's Slave 1	25.00	50.00
NNO Jedi Starfighter	15.00	30.00
NNO Jedi Starfighter (w/Obi-Wan Kenobi)	20.00	40.00
NNO Landspeeder (w/Luke Skywalker)	20.00	40.00
NNO Luke Skywalker's X-Wing Fighter (w/R2-D2)	60.00	120.00
NNO Red Leader's X-Wing Fighter (w/Red Leader)	30.00	60.00
NNO Republic Gunship	75.00	150.00
NNO TIE Bomber	30.00	75.00
NNO Zam Wesell's Speeder	10.00	20.00

2002-04 Star Wars Saga Wave 1 Hoth

1 Hoth Trooper (Hoth evacuation)	8.00	15.00
2 R-3PM (Hoth evacuation)		
3 Luke Skywalker (Hoth attack)		

2002-04 Star Wars Saga Wave 2 Tatooine

4 Luke Skywalker (Jabba's Palace)	6.00	12.00
5 R2-D2 (Jabba's sail barge)	8.00	15.00
6 R1-G4 (Tatooine transaction)		

2002-04 Star Wars Saga Wave 3 Jabba's Palace

7 Lando Calrissian (Jabba's sail barge)	5.00	10.00
8 Rappertunie (Jabba's Palace)		
9 J'Quille (Jabba's sail barge)	12.00	25.00
10 Tanus Spojek		
11 TIE Fighter Pildof		

2002-04 Star Wars Saga Wave 4 Battle of Yavin

12 General Jan Dodonna (Battle of Yavin)		
13 Dutch Vander Gold Leader (Battle of Yavin)		
14 TIE Fighter Pilot (Battle of Yavin)	6.00	12.00
15 Captain Antilles		

2002-04 Star Wars Saga Wave 6 Battle of Endor

19 Han Solo (Endor strike)		
20 General Madine (Imperial shuttle capture)		
21 Lando Calrissian (Death Star attack)	6.00	12.00

2006-07 Star Wars The Saga Collection

SAGA1 Princess Leia boushh	7.50	15.00
SAGA2 Han Solo carbonite	7.50	15.00
SAGA3 Bib Fortuna	12.50	25.00
SAGA4 Barada skiff	4.00	8.00
SAGA5 Chewbacca/ boushh prisoner	6.00	12.00
SAGA6 Boba Fett	7.50	15.00
SAGA7 General Veers	12.50	25.00
SAGA8 Major Bren Derlin	6.00	12.00
SAGA9 AT-AT Driver	4.00	8.00
SAGA10 R2-D2	6.00	12.00
SAGA11 Snowtrooper	5.00	10.00
SAGA12 General Rieeken	4.00	8.00
SAGA13 Darth Vader	7.50	15.00
SAGA14 Power Droid	10.00	20.00
SAGA15 Sora Bulq	6.00	12.00
SAGA16 Sun Fac	10.00	20.00
SAGA17 C-3PO w/ battle droid head droid head on	4.00	8.00
SAGA18 Poggle the Lesser	4.00	8.00
SAGA19 Yoda	7.50	15.00
SAGA20 Jango Fett	5.00	10.00
SAGA21 Scorch	15.00	30.00
SAGA22 Firespeeder Pilot	4.00	8.00
SAGA23 Lushros Dofine	6.00	12.00
SAGA24 Clone Commander Cody/ orange highlights	7.50	15.00
SAGA25 Anakin Skywalker	5.00	10.00
SAGA26 Utapau Clone Trooper	7.50	15.00
SAGA27 Holographic Ki-Adi-Mundi	5.00	10.00
SAGA28 Obi-Wan Kenobi beard	4.00	8.00
SAGA29 Faul Maudama	6.00	12.00
SAGA30 General Grievous	7.50	15.00
SAGA31 Momaw Nadon/ clear cup	5.00	10.00
SAGA32 R5-D4	4.00	8.00
SAGA33 Hem Dazon blue cup	4.00	8.00
SAGA34 Garindan	10.00	20.00
SAGA35 Han Solo	6.00	12.00
SAGA36 Luke Skywalker	4.00	8.00
SAGA37 Sandtrooper	6.00	12.00
SAGA38 Darth Vader bespin/ saber fight	7.50	15.00
SAGA39 Chief Chirpa	10.00	20.00
SAGA40 Moff Jerjerrod	6.00	12.00
SAGA41 Death Star Gunner	7.50	15.00
SAGA42 C-3PO (with/ ewok throne unpainted knees)	10.00	20.00
SAGA43 Emperor Palpatine	6.00	12.00
SAGA44 Luke Skywalker	4.00	8.00
SAGA45 Darth Vader/ shocked by emperor	6.00	12.00
SAGA46 Rebel Trooper/ endor black	4.00	8.00
SAGA47 Obi-Wan Kenobi/ no beard	5.00	10.00
SAGA48 Holographic Darth Maul	4.00	8.00
SAGA49 Rep Been	5.00	10.00
SAGA50 Naboo Soldier yellow	6.00	12.00
SAGA51 Dud Bolt & Mars Guo	5.00	10.00
SAGA52 Gragra	7.50	15.00
SAGA53 Sith Training Darth Maul	7.50	15.00
SAGA54 Chewbacca with/ electronic C-3PO	10.00	20.00
SAGA55 Kit Fisto	4.00	8.00
SAGA56 Holographic Clone Commander Cody	5.00	10.00
SAGA57 Clone Trooper 442nd Siege Batallion (green highlights)	15.00	30.00
SAGA58 R5-J2	12.50	25.00
SAGA59 Clone Trooper Fifth Fleet Security/ (blue stripes on head/shoulder)	10.00	20.00
SAGA60 Clone Trooper Sergeant	7.50	15.00
SAGA61 Super Battle Droid	6.00	12.00
SAGA62 Battle Droids (green and yellow)	4.00	8.00
SAGA63 Holographic Obi-Wan Kenobi	7.50	15.00
SAGA64 Commander Oppo (blue highlights blue shoulder)	5.00	10.00
SAGA65 Elite Corps Clone Commander	4.00	8.00
SAGA66 R4-K5 Darth Vader's Astromech Droid	4.00	8.00
SAGA67 Padme Amidala	4.00	8.00
SAGA68 Combat Engineer Clone Trooper (brown highlights)	4.00	8.00
SAGA69 Yareal Poof	4.00	8.00
SAGA70 Aurra Sing	4.00	8.00
SAGA71 Kitik Keed'Kak	4.00	8.00
SAGA72 Nabrun Leids & Kabe	4.00	8.00
SAGA73 Labria	4.00	8.00
SAGA74 R4-M6 Mace Windu's Astromech Droid	4.00	8.00
SAGA17a C-3PO with/ battle droid head C-3PO head on	4.00	8.00
SAGA31a Momaw Nadon/ blue cup	5.00	10.00
SAGA33a Hem Dazon white cup	4.00	8.00
SAGA42a C-3PO (with/ ewok throne/ painted knees)	10.00	20.00
SAGA46a Rebel Trooper/ endor white	4.00	8.00

2006-07 Star Wars The Saga Collection Battle Packs

1 Battle Above the Sarlacc (Boba Fett Lando Calrissian skiff/Han Solo carbonite)	25.00	50.00
2 Jedi vs. Darth Sidious (Darth Sidious Kit Fisto/Mace Windu/Saesee Tiin)	25.00	50.00
3 Sith Lord Attack (Obi-Wan Kenobi Qui-Gon Jinn/Darth Maul/Battle Droid tan)	20.00	40.00

2006-07 Star Wars The Saga Collection Battle Packs Exclusives

1 Mace Windu's Attack Batallion (Mace Windu Clone Trooper purple/ with sk)	50.00	100.00
2 Skirmish in the Senate (Emperor Palpatine Yoda/Clone Trooper red/Clone)	20.00	40.00
3 The Hunt for Grievous (Clone Trooper red Clone Trooper blue/Clone Trooper	30.00	75.00

2006-07 Star Wars The Saga Collection Commemorative DVD Collection

1 Luke Skywalker/Darth Vader/Obi-Wan Kenobi	10.00	20.00
2 Han Solo/Chewbacca/Stormtrooper	10.00	20.00
3 Luke Skywalker/Emperor Palpatine/R2-D2/C-3PO	15.00	30.00

2006-07 Star Wars The Saga Collection Episode III Greatest Battles Collection

1 501st Legion Trooper (blue with orange feet)	6.00	12.00
2 AT-TE Tank Gunner (gold helmet highlights)	6.00	12.00
3 C-3PO	4.00	8.00
4 Count Dooku	10.00	20.00
5 Royal Guard Blue	5.00	10.00
6 Padme	5.00	10.00
7 R4-G9	4.00	8.00
8 Kit Fisto	6.00	12.00
9 Wookiee Warrior	4.00	8.00
10 R2-D2	6.00	12.00
11 Shock Trooper	4.00	8.00
12 Obi-Wan Kenobi (flight helmet)	4.00	8.00
13 Emperor Palpatine	4.00	8.00
14a Clone Commander (green with skirt sash)	7.50	15.00
14b Clone Commander (red with skirt sash)	10.00	20.00

2006-07 Star Wars The Saga Collection Episode III Heroes & Villains Collection

1 Darth Vader	4.00	8.00
2 Anakin Skywalker	4.00	8.00
3 Yoda	4.00	8.00
4 Commander Bacara	4.00	8.00
5 Clone Trooper	4.00	8.00
6 Clone Pilot black	4.00	8.00
7 Chewbacca	4.00	8.00
8 Obi-Wan Kenobi	4.00	8.00
9 General Grievous cape	4.00	8.00
10 Mace Windu	4.00	8.00
11 R2-D2	4.00	8.00
12 Destroyer Droid	4.00	8.00
9a General Grievous/ no cape	4.00	8.00

2006-07 Star Wars The Saga Collection Exclusives

1 501st Stormtrooper (2006 SDCC Exclusive)	15.00	30.00
2 Clone Trooper (Saleucami) (2006 Toys R Us French Exclusive)		
3 Darth Vader (2006 UK Woolworth's Exclusive)	30.00	75.00
4 Demise of General Grievous (2006 Target Exclusive)	6.00	12.00
5 Early Bird Certificate Package (2005 Walmart Exclusive)		
6 Early Bird Kit (Luke Skywalker Princess Leia, Chewbacca, and R2-D2) (2005 Mailaway Exclusive)	30.00	75.00
7 George Lucas Stormtrooper (2006 Mailaway Exclusive)	30.00	75.00
8 Separation of the Twins Leia Organa (w/Bail Organa) (2005 Walmart Exclusive)	15.00	30.00
9 Separation of the Twins Luke Skywalker (w/Obi-Wan Kenobi) (2005 Walmart Exclusive)	12.00	25.00
10 Shadow Stormtrooper (2006 Starwarsshop.com Exclusive)	12.00	25.00

2006-07 Star Wars The Saga Collection Multipacks

NNO Droid Pack I/R4-A22/R2-C4/R3-T2	30.00	60.00

R2-Q2/R3-T6

(2006 Entertainment Earth Exclusive)

NNO Droid Pack II/R4-E1/R2-X2	30.00	60.00

R2-M5/R2-A6/R3-Y2

(2006 Entertainment Earth Exclusive)

NNO Episode III Gift Pack/Darth Vader	20.00	40.00

General Grievous/Obi-Wan Kenobi/R2-D2/(2006 UK Woolworth's Exclusive)

NNO Jedi Knights/Anakin Skywalker

Mace Windu/Obi-Wan Kenobi/(2005 UK Argos Exclusive)

NNO Lucas Collector's Set/Zett Jukassa	12.50	25.00

Baron Papanoida/Terr Taneel/Chi Eekway/(2006 Starwarsshop.com Exclusive)

NNO Revenge of the Sith Collector's Set

(UK Exclusive)

2006-07 Star Wars The Saga Collection Previews Exclusives

NNO Death Star Briefing (Darth Vader	60.00	120.00
Grand Moff Tarkin/Admiral Motti/General)		
NNO The Hunt For the Millenium Falcon	30.00	60.00
(Darth Vader/Dengar/IG-88/Boba Fett)		
NNO Republic Commando Delta Squad		
(Delta Three-Eight orange/Scoarch blue)		

2006-07 Star Wars The Saga Collection Ultimate Galactic Hunt

NNO AT-AT Driver (ESB Stand)	6.00	12.00
NNO Anakin Skywalker (ROTS Stand)	4.00	8.00
NNO Boba Fett (ROTJ Stand)	30.00	60.00
NNO Commander Cody (ROTS Stand)	4.00	8.00
NNO Darth Vader (ESB Stand)	4.00	8.00
NNO General Grievous (ROTS Stand)	6.00	12.00
NNO Han Solo Carbonite (ROTJ Stand)	6.00	12.00
NNO Obi-Wan Kenobi (ROTS Stand)	4.00	8.00
NNO Scorch Republic Commando (SW Stand)	8.00	15.00
NNO Snowtrooper (ESB Stand)	8.00	15.00

2006-07 Star Wars The Saga Collection Ultimate Galactic Hunt Vehicles

NNO Republic Gunship	150.00	300.00
(Toys R Us Exclusive)		

2006-07 Star Wars The Saga Collection Ultimate Galactic Hunt Vintage

NNO Bossk	10.00	20.00
NNO IG-88	12.50	25.00
NNO Han Solo Hoth	15.00	30.00
NNO Luke Skywalker Bespin	15.00	30.00
NNO Princess Leia Organa (Endor combat poncho)	10.00	20.00
NNO Imperial Stormtrooper Hoth	12.50	25.00

2006-07 Star Wars The Saga Collection Vehicles

NNO Anakin's Jedi Starfighter	20.00	40.00
NNO Darth Vader's TIE Advanced X1 Starfighter		
NNO Droid Tri-Fighter		
NNO General Grievous's Wheel Bike		
NNO Obi-Wan's Jedi Starfighter		
NNO Mace Windu's Jedi Starfighter		

2006-07 Star Wars The Saga Collection Vehicles Exclusives

NNO Luke Skywalker's X-Wing	75.00	150.00
(w/Luke Skywalker Dagobah)		
(Toys R Us Exclusive)		
NNO TIE Fighter (w/Tie Fighter Pilot)		
(Toys R Us Exclusive)		
NNO Imperial Shuttle (Royal Guard red/Darth Vader)	250.00	400.00
(Target Exclusive)		
NNO Kit Fisto's Jedi Starfighter	20.00	40.00
(Target Exclusive		
NNO Rogue Two Snowspeeder (w/Zev Senesca)	50.00	100.00

2006-07 Star Wars The Saga Collection Vintage

NNO Biker Scout	8.00	15.00
NNO Greedo	6.00	12.00
NNO Han Solo (w/cape)	6.00	12.00
NNO Luke Skywalker X-Wing Pilot	10.00	20.00
NNO Sand People	6.00	12.00

2010 Star Wars Saga Legends

SL1 Bossk	12.00	25.00
SL2 IG-88	10.00	20.00
SL3 Zuckuss	8.00	15.00
SL4 Greedo	8.00	15.00
SL5 Jango Fett	6.00	12.00
SL6a Darth Vader	6.00	12.00
SL6b Darth Vader (unmasked)	8.00	15.00
SL7 Princess Leia Boushh	10.00	20.00
SL8 Darth Maul	6.00	12.00
SL9 General Grievous	10.00	20.00
SL10 Clone Trooper	8.00	15.00
SL11 Darth Vader (Anakin Skywalker)	8.00	15.00
SL12 Obi-Wan Kenobi	6.00	12.00
SL13 Yoda	8.00	15.00
SL14 R2-D2	8.00	15.00
SL15 Shocktrooper	15.00	30.00
SL16 Clone Trooper (Revenge of the Sith)	8.00	15.00
SL17 C-3PO	8.00	15.00
SL18 Chewbacca	8.00	15.00
SL19 501st Legion Trooper	12.00	25.00
SL20 Battle Droid 2-Pack	6.00	12.00
SL21 Luke Skywalker	8.00	15.00
SL22 Han Solo (Hoth)	8.00	15.00
SL23 Snowtrooper	10.00	20.00

2013 Star Wars Saga Legends

SL1 Mace Windu	6.00	12.00
SL2 Clone Trooper		
SL3 Anakin Skywalker	6.00	12.00
SL4 Obi-Wan Kenobi (ROTS)	8.00	15.00
SL5 Super Battle Droid	8.00	15.00
SL6 R4-P17		
SL7 Yoda		
SL8 Shock Trooper		
SL9 Boba Fett		
SL10 Captain Rex		
SL11 Stormtrooper		
SL12 Clone Commander Cody		
SL13 Obi-Wan Kenobi (Clone Wars)		
SL14 Luke Skywalker		
SL15 Darth Maul		
SL16 Snowtrooper		

2013 Star Wars Saga Legends Mission Series

MS1 Darth Vader/Seeker Droid (Star Destroyer)	7.50	15.00
MS2 Anakin/501st Legion Trooper (Coruscant)	6.00	12.00
MS3 Battle Droid/Jango Fett (Geonosis)	10.00	20.00
MS4 Battle Droid/212th Battalion	15.00	30.00
Clone Trooper (Utapau)		
MS5 R2-D2/C-3PO (Tantive IV)	12.50	25.00
MS6 Obi-Wan Kenobi/Darth Maul (Mandalore)	15.00	30.00
MS7 Han Solo/Chewbacca (Death Star)	10.00	20.00
MS8 Obi-Wan Kenobi/General Grievous (Utapau)	7.50	15.00
MS9 Luke Skywalker/Darth Vader (Bespin)	15.00	30.00
MS10 Darth Sidious/Yoda (Senate Duel)	12.50	25.00

1996 Star Wars Shadows of the Empire

1 Boba Fett vs IG-88/ with comic book	12.00	25.00
2 Chewbacca/ bounty hunter disguise	8.00	15.00
3 Darth Vader vs Prince Xizor	12.00	25.00
with comic book		
4 Dash Rendar	10.00	20.00
5 Luke Skywalker/ imperial guard	10.00	20.00
6 Prince Xizor	6.00	12.00
7 Princess Leia/ boushh disguise	10.00	20.00

1996 Star Wars Shadows of the Empire European

1 Chewbacca bounty/ hunter disguise	12.50	25.00
2 Dash Rendar	10.00	20.00
3 Luke Skywalker/ imperial guard	15.00	30.00
4 Princess Leia/ boushh disguise	10.00	20.00
5 Prince Xizor	15.00	30.00

ACTION FIGURES AND FIGURINES

1996 Star Wars Shadows of the Empire Vehicles

1	Boba Fett's Slave I	40.00	80.00
2	Dash Rendar's Outrider	25.00	50.00
3	Swoop with Swoop Trooper	12.00	25.00
4	Speeder Bike/ with Endor Trooper	12.00	25.00

2013 Star Wars Titan Heroes 12-Inch

NNO	Anakin Skywalker	12.50	25.00
NNO	Clone Trooper		
NNO	Darth Vader	12.50	25.00
NNO	Luke Skywalker	7.50	15.00
NNO	Obi-Wan Kenobi		

2002-07 Star Wars Unleashed

NNO	Aayla Secura	15.00	30.00
NNO	Anakin Skywalker (2005)	15.00	30.00
NNO	Anakin Skywalker (rage)	12.00	25.00
NNO	Asajj Ventress	15.00	30.00
NNO	Aurra Sing	15.00	30.00
NNO	Boba Fett	25.00	50.00
NNO	Bossk	15.00	30.00
NNO	Chewbacca (2004)	10.00	20.00
NNO	Chewbacca (2006)	15.00	30.00
NNO	Clone Trooper (red)	15.00	30.00
NNO	Clone Trooper (white)	12.00	25.00
NNO	Count Dooku	15.00	30.00
NNO	Darth Maul (fury)	15.00	30.00
NNO	Darth Sidious	25.00	50.00
NNO	Darth Tyranus (dissension)	6.00	12.00
NNO	Darth Vader (2005)	15.00	30.00
NNO	Darth Vader (power)	12.00	25.00
NNO	Darth Vader (redemption)	30.00	75.00
NNO	General Grievous	15.00	30.00
NNO	General Grievous	20.00	40.00
	(2006 Target Exclusive)		
NNO	Han Solo	20.00	40.00
NNO	Han Solo Stormtrooper	15.00	30.00
NNO	IG-88	15.00	30.00
NNO	Jango and Boba Fett (intensity)	15.00	30.00
NNO	Luke Skywalker	20.00	40.00
NNO	Luke Skywalker (snowspeeder pilot)	15.00	30.00
NNO	Mace Windu (honor)	12.00	25.00
NNO	Obi-Wan Kenobi (2003)	15.00	30.00
NNO	Obi-Wan Kenobi (2005)	15.00	30.00
NNO	Padme Amidala (courage)	30.00	60.00
NNO	Palpatine vs. Yoda	20.00	40.00
NNO	Princess Leia	30.00	75.00
NNO	Shock Trooper	15.00	30.00
NNO	Stormtrooper	20.00	40.00
NNO	Tusken Raider	10.00	20.00
NNO	Yoda	15.00	30.00

2005-07 Star Wars Unleashed Tubed Packs

NNO	Anakin Skywalker	25.00	50.00
NNO	ARC Heavy Gunner		
NNO	Boba Fett	25.00	50.00
	(2006 Target Exclusive)		
NNO	Darth Vader	12.00	25.00
	(2005 Best Buy Exclusive)		
NNO	Darth Vader		
	(2006 KB Toys Exclusive)		
NNO	Darth Vader	10.00	20.00
	(2006 Walmart Exclusive)		
NNO	Luke Skywalker		
	(2006 Walmart Exclusive)		
NNO	Obi-Wan Kenobi	15.00	30.00
NNO	Shadow Stormtrooper	8.00	15.00

2010-18 Star Wars The Vintage Collection

VC1a	Dengar (age warning on left back)	20.00	40.00
VC1b	Dengar (age warning on bottom back)	30.00	60.00
VC2a	Leia (Hoth)(age warning on left back)	25.00	50.00
VC2b	Leia (Hoth)(age warning on bottom back)	20.00	40.00
VC3a	Han Solo (Echo Base)	15.00	30.00
	(age warning on left back)		
VC3b	Han Solo (Echo Base)	12.50	25.00
	(age warning on bottom back)		
VC3c	Han Solo (Echo Base)(FOIL card)	15.00	30.00
VC4a	Luke Skywalker (Bespin)	25.00	50.00
	(age warning on left back)		
VC4b	Luke Skywalker (Bespin)	50.00	100.00
	(age warning on bottom back)		
VC4c	Luke Skywalker (Bespin)(FOIL card)	30.00	60.00
VC5	AT-AT Commander (age warning on left back)	20.00	40.00
VC5	AT-AT Commander	20.00	40.00
	(age warning on bottom back)		
VC6	See-Threepio (C-3PO)	15.00	30.00
	(age warning on left back)		
VC6	See-Threepio (C-3PO)	20.00	40.00
	(age warning on bottom back)		
VC7	Dack Ralter	15.00	30.00
VC8a	Darth Vader (age warning on left back)	15.00	30.00
VC8b	Darth Vader (age warning on bottom back)	12.50	25.00
VC8c	Darth Vader (Boba Fett sticker	20.00	40.00
	plus shipping and handling)		
VC8d	Darth Vader (barcode #54674 sticker)	20.00	40.00
VC8e	Darth Vader (barcode #54674 printed)	20.00	40.00
VC8f	Darth Vader (Revenge of the Jedi)		
VC8g	Darth Vader (Return of the Jedi)	25.00	50.00
VC8h	Darth Vader (Wave 1 ESB figure back)	15.00	30.00
VC8i	Darth Vader (FOIL card)	25.00	50.00
VC9aa	Boba Fett (age warning on left back)	30.00	60.00
VC9ab	Boba Fett (age warning on bottom back)	20.00	40.00
VC9ac	Boba Fett (black gun barrel)	25.00	50.00
VC9ad	Boba Fett (no warning on card back)	60.00	120.00
VC9ae	Boba Fett (FOIL card)	30.00	75.00
VC9ba	Boba Fett (Revenge of the Jedi)	30.00	75.00
VC9bb	Boba Fett (Return of the Jedi)	25.00	50.00
VC10a	4-LOM (age warning on left back)	12.50	25.00
VC10b	4-LOM (age warning on bottom back)	17.50	35.00
VC11a	(Twin-Pod) Cloud Car Pilot	15.00	30.00
	(age warning on left back)		
VC11b	(Twin-Pod) Cloud Car Pilot	12.50	25.00
	(age warning on bottom back		
VC12	Darth Sidious	25.00	50.00
VC12	Darth Sidious (FOIL card)	30.00	75.00
VC13a	Anakin Skywalker (Darth Vader)	30.00	60.00
	(Boba Fett mailway sticker front)		
VC13b	Anakin Skywalker (Darth Vader)	20.00	40.00
	(Darth Vader title on front and back)		
VC13c	Anakin Skywalker (Darth Vader)		
	(Boba Fett sticker/shipping and handling)		
VC13d	Anakin Skywalker (Darth Vader)(barcode #54885)		
VC13e	Anakin Skywalker (Darth Vader)(FOIL card)	30.00	60.00
VC14a	Sandtrooper (dim photo front)	10.00	20.00
VC14b	Sandtrooper (bright photo front)	10.00	20.00
VC14c	Sandtrooper (Boba Fett sticker	17.50	35.00
	shipping and handling)		
VC14d	Sandtrooper (barcode #54573 sticker)	12.50	25.00
VC14e	Sandtrooper (barcode #54573 printed)	25.00	50.00
VC14e	Sandtrooper (FOIL card)	15.00	30.00
VC15a	Clone Trooper (dim photo front)	15.00	30.00
VC15b	Clone Trooper (bright photo front)		
VC15c	Clone Trooper (Boba Fett sticker	12.50	25.00
	shipping and handling)		
VC15d	Clone Trooper (barcode #54888 sticker)	15.00	30.00
VC15e	Clone Trooper (barcode #54888 printed)	12.50	25.00
VC15f	Clone Trooper (FOIL card)	20.00	40.00
VC16a	Obi-Wan Kenobi	20.00	40.00
VC16b	Obi-Wan Kenobi (FOIL card)	30.00	60.00
VC17a	General Grievous (Boba Fett sticker on front)	30.00	75.00
VC17b	General Grievous (barcode #54572 sticker)	30.00	60.00
VC17c	General Grievous (barcode #54572 printed)	30.00	60.00
VC17d	General Grievous (FOIL card)	25.00	50.00
VC18a	MagnaGuard	25.00	50.00
VC18b	MagnaGuard (FOIL card)	30.00	75.00
VC19a	Clone Commander Cody (dim photo front)	30.00	75.00
VC19b	Clone Commander Cody (bright photo front)	75.00	150.00
VC19c	Clone Commander Cody (FOIL card)	30.00	60.00
VC20a	Yoda	25.00	50.00
VC20b	Yoda (Boba Fett sticker front)	25.00	50.00
VC21a	Gamorrean Guard	25.00	50.00
	(1st Boba Fett rocket sticker)		
VC21b	Gamorrean Guard (2nd Boba Fett rocket sticker)		
VC21c	Gamorrean Guard (barcode #54898 sticker)	30.00	60.00
VC21d	Gamorrean Guard (barcode #54898 printed)	20.00	40.00
VC21e	Gamorrean Guard (Darth Maul sticker front)	30.00	60.00
VC22a	Admiral Ackbar (1st Boba Fett rocket sticker)	12.50	25.00
VC22b	Admiral Ackbar (2nd Boba Fett rocket sticker)	15.00	30.00
VC22c	Admiral Ackbar (barcode #54900)	15.00	30.00
VC22d	Admiral Ackbar (barcode #52864)	15.00	30.00
VC23a	Luke Skywalker	25.00	50.00
	(Jedi Knight Outfit / Endor Captive)		
	(1st Boba Fett rocket sticker)		
VC23b	Luke Skywalker	15.00	30.00
	(Jedi Knight Outfit / Endor Captive)		
	(2nd Boba Fett rocket sticker)		
VC23c	Luke Skywalker (Jedi Knight Outfit / Endor Captive)		
VC23d	Luke Skywalker	20.00	40.00
	(Jedi Knight Outfit / Endor Captive)		
	(barcode #54902)		
VC23e	Luke Skywalker (Jedi Knight Outfit / Endor Captive)		
	(portrait back)		
VC23f	Luke Skywalker (Jedi Knight Outfit / Endor Captive)		
	(no warning on back)		
VC23g	Luke Skywalker (Jedi Knight Outfit / Endor Captive)		
	(Revenge of the Jedi)		
VC23h	Luke Skywalker	20.00	40.00
	(Jedi Knight Outfit / Endor Captive)		
	(barcode #52867)		
VC24a	Wooof (Klaatu)(1st Boba Fett rocket sticker)	30.00	75.00
VC24b	Wooof (Klaatu)(2nd Boba Fett rocket sticker)	25.00	50.00
VC24c	Wooof (Klaatu)(barcode #54905)	20.00	40.00
VC24d	Wooof (Klaatu)(figures left off backs)		
VC25a	R2-D2 (w/Pop-Up Lightsaber)	20.00	40.00
	(1st Boba Fett rocket sticker)		
VC25b	R2-D2 (w/Pop-Up Lightsaber)	17.50	35.00
	(2nd Boba Fett rocket sticker)		
VC25c	R2-D2 (w/Pop-Up Lightsaber)	20.00	40.00
	(R2-D2 back)		
VC25d	R2-D2 (w/Pop-Up Lightsaber)	17.50	35.00
	(Revenge of the Jedi)		
VC25e	R2-D2 (w/Pop-Up Lightsaber)		
	(no warning on back)		
VC26aa	Rebel Commando	15.00	30.00
	(1st Boba Fett rocket sticker)		
VC26ab	Rebel Commando	20.00	40.00
	(2nd Boba Fett rocket sticker)		
VC26ac	Rebel Commando (barcode #54907)	15.00	30.00

VC26ba Rebel Commando	15.00	30.00
(Version II)(Return of the Jedi logo)		
VC26bb Rebel Commando	30.00	75.00
(Version II)(Revenge of the Jedi logo)		
VC27a Wicket (1st Boba Fett rocket sticker)	25.00	50.00
VC27b Wicket (2nd Boba Fett rocket sticker)	25.00	50.00
VC27c Wicket (barcode #54908)	25.00	50.00
VC27d Wicket (barcode #52900)	25.00	50.00
VC27e Wicket (no warning on back)		
VC28a Wedge Antilles (card image on back)	12.50	25.00
VC28b Wedge Antilles (film image on back)		
VC28ca Wedge Antilles (light violet background)	25.00	50.00
VC28cb Wedge Antilles (dark blue to violet background)		
VC29 Kit Fisto	20.00	40.00
VC30 Zam Wesell	15.00	30.00
VC31a Obi-Wan Kenobi (figures left of cardbacks)	20.00	40.00
VC31b Obi-Wan Kenobi	30.00	60.00
(Prototype Boba Fett sticker)		
VC32a Anakin Skywalker (Peasant Disguise)	12.50	25.00
VC32b Anakin Skywalker	12.50	25.00
(Peasant Disguise)(Boba Fett sticker front)		
VC33 Padme Amidala (Peasant Disguise)	17.50	35.00
VC34a Jango Fett (figures left of cardbacks)	25.00	50.00
VC34b Jango Fett (no warning on back)	20.00	40.00
VC34c Jango Fett (Prototype Boba Fett sticker)	25.00	50.00
VC35 Mace Windu	30.00	60.00
VC36a Senate Guard (close-up photo front)	12.50	25.00
VC36b Senate Guard (wide photo front)	10.00	20.00
VC37 Super Battle Droid	15.00	30.00
VC38 Clone Trooper (212th Battalion)	15.00	30.00
VC39 Luke Skywalker (Death Star Escape)	15.00	30.00
VC40 R5-D4	20.00	40.00
VC41a Stormtrooper (barcode #62162 sticker)	15.00	30.00
VC41b Stormtrooper (barcode #62162 printed)	15.00	30.00
VC41c Stormtrooper (warning sticker on front)		
VC41d Stormtrooper (Revenge of the Jedi)	20.00	40.00
VC41e Stormtrooper (Return of the Jedi)	12.50	25.00
VC42 Han Solo (Yavin Ceremony)	25.00	50.00
VC43 Commander Gree (Greatest Hits)	17.50	35.00
VC44 Luke Skywalker (Dagobah Landing)	50.00	100.00
VC45 Clone Trooper (Phase I)	12.50	25.00
VC46 AT-RT Driver	20.00	40.00
VC47 General Lando Calrissian	15.00	30.00
VC48 Weequay (Skiff Master)	20.00	40.00
VC49 Fi-Ek Sirch (Jedi Knight)	20.00	40.00
VC50 Han Solo (Bespin Outfit)	25.00	50.00
VC51 Barriss Offee (Jedi Padawan)	30.00	60.00
VC52 Rebel Fleet Trooper	30.00	60.00
VC53 Bom Vimdin (Cantina Patron)	12.50	25.00
VC54 ARC Trooper Commander (Captain Fordo)	25.00	50.00
VC55 Logray (Ewok Medicine Man)	12.50	25.00
VC56a Kithaba (Skiff Guard)(black headband)	15.00	30.00
VC56b Kithaba (Skiff Guard)(red headband)	20.00	40.00
VC57a Dr. Cornelius Evazan (pink scar)	20.00	40.00
VC57b Dr. Cornelius Evazan (no pink scar)	12.50	25.00
VC58 Aayla Secura	20.00	40.00
VC59 Nom Anor	12.50	25.00
VC60 Clone Trooper (501st Legion)	25.00	50.00
VC61 Prototype Armour Boba Fett	17.50	35.00
(2011 Mailaway Exclusive)		
VC62 Han Solo (In Trench Coat)	15.00	30.00
VC63 B-Wing Pilot (Keyan Farlander)	12.50	25.00
VC64 Princess Leia (Slave Outfit)	50.00	100.00
VC65 TIE Fighter Pilot	20.00	40.00
VC66 Salacious Crumb	12.50	25.00
(2011 SDCC Exclusive)		
VC67 Mouse Droid		
(2011 SDCC Exclusive)		
VC68 Rebel Soldier (Echo Base Battle Gear)	50.00	100.00
VC69 Bastila Shan	45.00	90.00
VC70 Ponda Baba (Walrus Man)	30.00	60.00
VC71 Mawhonic	12.50	25.00
VC72 Naboo Pilot	12.50	25.00
VC73 Aurra Sing	25.00	50.00

VC74 Gungan Warrior	12.50	25.00
VC75 Qui-Gon Jinn	12.50	25.00
VC76 Obi-Wan Kenobi (Jedi Padawan)	12.50	25.00
VC77 Ratts Tyerell & Pit Droid	12.50	25.00
VC78 Battle Droid	12.50	25.00
VC79 Darth Sidious	15.00	30.00
VC80 Anakin Skywalker (Jedi Padawan)	12.50	25.00
VC81 Ben Quadinaros & Pit Droid	10.00	20.00
VC82 Daultay Dofine	10.00	20.00
VC83 Naboo Royal Guard	10.00	20.00
VC84 Queen Amidala (Post-Senate)	12.50	25.00
VC85 Quinlan Vos (Mos Espa)	10.00	20.00
VC86 Darth Maul	20.00	40.00
VC87 Luke Skywalker (Lightsaber Construction)	20.00	40.00
VC88 Princess Leia (Sandstorm Outfit)	25.00	50.00
VC89 Lando Calrissian (Sandstorm Outfit)	25.00	50.00
VC90 Colonel Cracken (Millennium Falcon Crew)	15.00	30.00
VC91 Rebel Pilot (Mon Calamari)	15.00	30.00
VC92 Anakin Skywalker (The Clone Wars)	20.00	40.00
VC93 Darth Vader (A New Hope)	15.00	30.00
VC94 Imperial Navy Commander	12.50	25.00
VC95 Luke Skywalker (Hoth Outfit)	15.00	30.00
VC96 Darth Malgus (The Old Republic)	20.00	40.00
VC97 Clone Pilot Davijaan (Oddball)	15.00	30.00
VC98 Grand Moff Tarkin	75.00	150.00
VC99 Nikto (Vintage)	25.00	50.00
VC100 Galen Marek (The Force Unleashed II)		
VC101 Shae Vizsla	100.00	200.00
VC102 Ahsoka Tano (The Clone Wars)	125.00	250.00
VC103 Obi-Wan Kenobi (The Clone Wars)	50.00	100.00
VC104 Lumat	30.00	60.00
VC105 Emperor's Royal Guard	30.00	75.00
VC106 Nien Nunb	30.00	75.00
VC107 Weequay (Hunter)	25.00	50.00
VC108a Jar Jar Binks	30.00	60.00
VC108b Jar Jar Binks (lost line)		
VC109a Clone Trooper Lieutenant	20.00	40.00
VC109b Clone Trooper Lieutenant (lost line)		
VC110a Shock Trooper	25.00	50.00
VC110b Shock Trooper (lost line)		
VC111a Leia Organa (Bespin)	25.00	50.00
VC111b Leia Organa (Bespin) (lost line)		
VC112a Sandtrooper (with Patrol Droid)	20.00	40.00
VC112b Sandtrooper (with Patrol Droid) (lost line)		
VC113 Republic Trooper	90.00	175.00
VC114 Orrimarko	20.00	40.00
VC115a Darth Vader (Emperor's Wrath)	30.00	75.00
VC115b Darth Vader (Emperor's Wrath) (lost line)		
VC116 Rey (Jakku)	10.00	20.00
VC117 Kylo Ren	12.50	25.00
VC118 First Order Stormtrooper	10.00	20.00
VC119 Jyn Erso	7.50	15.00
VC120 Rebel Soldier (Hoth)	7.50	15.00
VC121 Supreme Leader Snoke	6.00	12.00
VC122 Rey (Island Journey)	25.00	50.00
VC123 Stormtrooper (Mimban)	17.50	35.00
VC124 Han Solo	15.00	30.00
VC125 Enfys Nest	15.00	30.00
VC126 Imperial Assault Tank Driver	15.00	30.00
VC127 Imperial Death Trooper	12.50	25.00
VC128 Range Trooper	20.00	40.00
VC129 Doctor Aphra	20.00	40.00
VC130 Captain Cassian Andor	15.00	30.00
VC131 Luke Skywalker	20.00	40.00

2010-13 Star Wars The Vintage Collection Creatures

NNO Luke Skywalker's Tauntaun	30.00	60.00
(Target Exclusive)		

2010-13 Star Wars The Vintage Collection Exclusives

NNO Jocasta Nu	60.00	120.00
(Brian's Toys Exclusive)		

VCP3 Boba Fett (rocket-firing)	30.00	75.00
(Mailaway Exclusive)		
VCP12 4-LOM/Zuckuss 2-Pack	30.00	60.00
(TVC Convention Exclusive)		

2010-13 Star Wars The Vintage Collection Multipacks

NNO Android 3-Pack	30.00	75.00
C-3PO, R2-D2, Chewbacca/(Target Exclusive)		
NNO Death Star Scanning Crew	20.00	40.00
(K-Mart Exclusive)		
NNO Droid 3-Pack	12.00	25.00
R5-D4, Death Star Droid, Power Droid/(Target Exclusive)		
NNO Endor AT-ST Crew 2-Pack	20.00	40.00
(K-Mart Exclusive)		
NNO Ewok Assault Catapult	25.00	50.00
(K-Mart Exclusive)		
NNO Ewok Scouts 2-Pack	15.00	30.00
(K-Mart Exclusive)		
NNO Hero 3-Pack	15.00	30.00
Luke Skywalker, Ben Kenobi, Han Solo/(Target Exclusive)		
NNO Imperial 3-Pack	20.00	40.00
Imperial Commander, Dengar, AT-AT Driver/(Target Exclusive)		
NNO Imperial Forces 3-Pack	20.00	40.00
Bossk, IG-88, Snowtrooper/(Target Exclusive)		
NNO Imperial Scanning Crew	20.00	40.00
(K-Mart Exclusive)		
NNO Lost Line Carbon Freeze Chamber 7-Figure Set	120.00	200.00
(2012 SDCC Exclusive)		
NNO Rebel 3-Pack	20.00	40.00
2-1B, Leia (Hoth), Rebel Commander/(Target Exclusive)		
NNO Revenge of the Jedi 14-Figure Death Star Set	750.00	1500.00
(2011 SDCC Exclusive)		
NNO Special Action Figure Set	15.00	30.00
Han Solo (Hoth), Hoth Rebel Trooper, FX-7/(Target Exclusive)		
NNO Villain 3-Pack 2012	15.00	30.00
Sand People, Boba Fett, Snaggletooth/(Target Exclusive)		
NNO Villain 3-Pack	20.00	40.00
Stormtrooper, Darth Vader, Death Star Trooper/(Target Exclusive)		

2010-13 Star Wars The Vintage Collection Vehicles

NNO AT-AP	30.00	75.00
NNO B-Wing Starfighter	75.00	150.00
(K-Mart Exclusive)		
NNO Biggs' Red 3 X-Wing Fighter	100.00	175.00
(Toys R Us Exclusive)		
NNO Imperial AT-AT (ESB)	250.00	400.00
(Toys R Us Exclusive)		
NNO Imperial AT-AT (ROTJ)	200.00	350.00
(Toys R Us Exclusive)		
NNO Imperial TIE Fighter	50.00	100.00
(Target Exclusive)		
NNO Landspeeder	60.00	120.00
(Target Exclusive)		
NNO Millennium Falcon	300.00	500.00
(Toys R Us Exclusive)		
NNO Obi-Wan Kenobi's Jedi Starfighter	50.00	100.00
NNO Rebel Armored Snowspeeder	50.00	100.00
(Target Exclusive)		
NNO Republic Gunship	175.00	300.00
(Toys R Us Exclusive)		
NNO Scout Walker AT-ST	60.00	120.00
(K-Mart Exclusive)		
NNO Slave I	120.00	200.00
(Amazon Exclusive)		
NNO TIE Interceptor	50.00	100.00
(Amazon Exclusive)		
NNO V-19 Torrent Starfighter	30.00	75.00
NNO Y-Wing Starfighter	60.00	120.00
(Toys R Us Exclusive)		

ACTION FIGURES AND FIGURINES

2011-12 Funko Blox

23	Darth Vader	10.00	20.00
24	Boba Fett	8.00	15.00
25	Stormtrooper	8.00	12.00

2017-18 Funko Dorbz Star Wars

1	Luke Skywalker	7.50	15.00
2	Princess Leia	7.50	15.00
3A	Darth Vader	10.00	20.00
(2017)			
3B	Darth Vader HOLO CH	10.00	20.00
4	Han Solo	6.00	12.00
5A	Chewbacca	10.00	20.00
5B	Chewbacca FLK CH	15.00	30.00
6	C-3PO	7.50	15.00
7	Stormtrooper	10.00	20.00
8	Jawa	7.50	15.00
9	Luke Skywalker w/Speeder	20.00	40.00
10	Tusken Raider w/Bantha	20.00	40.00
11	Han Solo	10.00	20.00
(2018)			
12A	Chewbacca	7.50	15.00
(2018)			
12B	Chewbacca FLK CH	15.00	30.00
13	Qi'Ra	6.00	12.00
(2018)			
14A	Lando Calrissian		
(2018)			
14B	Lando Calrissian White Cape CH	20.00	40.00

2017-18 Funko Dorbz Star Wars Multi-Pack

NNO	Greedo/Walrus Man/Snaggletooth D23	20.00	40.00

2014-16 Funko Fabrikations

2	Yoda	8.00	15.00
3	Boba Fett	6.00	12.00
4	Greedo	6.00	12.00
12	Darth Vader	6.00	12.00
13	Chewbacca	6.00	12.00
26	Wicket Warrick	10.00	20.00
27	Princess Leia	12.00	25.00
29	Stormtrooper	6.00	12.00

2009 Funko Force Star Wars

NNO	501st Clone Trooper/1008* SDCC	30.00	60.00
NNO	Boba Fett	7.50	15.00
NNO	Chewbacca	6.00	12.00
NNO	Darth Maul	15.00	30.00
NNO	Darth Vader	7.50	15.00
NNO	Emperor Palpatine	12.50	25.00

NNO	Shadow Trooper	12.50	25.00
NNO	Shocktrooper	20.00	40.00
NNO	Stormtrooper	12.50	25.00
NNO	Yoda	7.50	15.00

2017-18 Funko Galactic Plushies Star Wars

NNO	Ahsoka ECCC	15.00	30.00
NNO	Ahsoka SCE	10.00	20.00
NNO	BB-8	6.00	12.00
NNO	BB-9E	7.50	15.00
NNO	Boba Fett	5.00	10.00
NNO	C-3PO	5.00	10.00
NNO	Chewbacca 12" WG	7.50	15.00
NNO	Chewbacca	7.50	15.00
NNO	Darth Vader	6.00	12.00
NNO	Finn	6.00	12.00
NNO	First Order Executioner	6.00	12.00
NNO	First Order Stormtrooper	7.50	15.00
NNO	Han Solo	6.00	12.00
NNO	Jabba the Hutt & Salacious B. Crumb 2-Pack		
(2017 Galactic Convention Exclusive)			
NNO	Jabba the Hutt/Salacious Crumb 2Pk SWC		
NNO	Kylo Ren	5.00	10.00
NNO	Luke Skywalker/Wampa 2Pk GS	7.50	15.00
NNO	Luke Skywalker	6.00	12.00
NNO	Maz Kanata	6.00	12.00
NNO	Porg Brown	12.50	25.00
NNO	Porg Gray	10.00	20.00
NNO	Porg (gray/yellow eyes)	10.00	20.00
(2017)			
NNO	Porg (talking)	25.00	50.00
(2018)			
NNO	Praetorian Guard WG	6.00	12.00
NNO	Princess Leia	6.00	12.00
NNO	R2-D2	7.50	15.00
NNO	Resistance BB Unit	6.00	12.00
NNO	Rey	6.00	12.00
NNO	Rey TLJ	6.00	12.00
NNO	Stormtrooper	7.50	15.00
NNO	Supreme Leader Snoke WG	6.00	12.00
NNO	Tusken Raider/Bantha 2Pk TAR	6.00	12.00
NNO	Wampa SB	5.00	10.00
NNO	Wicket	6.00	12.00
NNO	Yoda SB	5.00	10.00
NNO	Yoda	7.50	15.00

2015-18 Funko Hikari Star Wars

NNO	Boba Fett Clear Glitter/750* NYCC	25.00	50.00
NNO	Boba Fett Glitter/1200*	20.00	40.00
NNO	Boba Fett Infrared/1000* SDCC	25.00	50.00
NNO	Boba Fett Infrared/1000* SCE	25.00	50.00
NNO	Boba Fett Midnight/1000* SWC	60.00	120.00
NNO	Boba Fett Prism/750*	30.00	60.00
NNO	Boba Fett Proto/250* FS	30.00	75.00
NNO	Boba Fett/1500*	20.00	40.00
NNO	Bossk MET/1000*	25.00	50.00
NNO	Bossk Planet X/600*	20.00	40.00
NNO	Bossk Prism/500* EE	25.00	50.00
NNO	Bossk Rainbow/550* SLCC	30.00	75.00
NNO	Bossk Starfield/500* NYCC	30.00	75.00
NNO	Bossk/1000*	25.00	50.00
NNO	C-3PO Clear Glitter/750* SLCC	30.00	60.00

NNO	C-3PO Dirty Penny/500* TT	30.00	75.00
NNO	C-3PO Red/750* SLCC	25.00	50.00
NNO	C-3PO Rusty/500* Gemini	25.00	50.00
NNO	C-3PO/1500*	20.00	40.00
NNO	Captain Phasma Alloy/250*	30.00	60.00
NNO	Captain Phasma Blue Steel/400*	30.00	75.00
NNO	Captain Phasma Classic/500*	25.00	50.00
NNO	Captain Phasma Cold Steel/250*	30.00	60.00
NNO	Captain Phasma Meltdown/100* HT	100.00	175.00
NNO	Clone Trooper Dirty Penny/250* EE	25.00	50.00
NNO	Clone Trooper Rusty White/250* GS	20.00	40.00
NNO	Clone Trooper 442 Siege Glitter/100*	60.00	120.00
NNO	Clone Trooper 442 Siege/900*	20.00	40.00
NNO	Clone Trooper 501st Glitter/250*	30.00	75.00
NNO	Clone Trooper 501st/1500* SDCC	20.00	40.00
NNO	Clone Trooper Starfield/1000* SWC	25.00	50.00
NNO	Clone Trooper Utapau Glitter/100* EE	50.00	100.00
NNO	Clone Trooper Utapau/600* EE	25.00	50.00
NNO	Clone Trooper/1500*	15.00	30.00
NNO	Darth Vader Holographic GITD/300* Gemini	30.00	75.00
NNO	Darth Vader Holographic/750*	25.00	50.00
NNO	Darth Vader Infrared/500* EE	30.00	60.00
NNO	Darth Vader Lightning/1500*	20.00	40.00
NNO	Darth Vader Matte Back/1200* SDCC	25.00	50.00
NNO	Darth Vader Starfield/750*Gemini	30.00	75.00
NNO	Darth Vader/1500*	20.00	40.00
NNO	E-3PO/500*	20.00	40.00
NNO	FO Snowtrooper Ice Storm/500*	20.00	40.00
NNO	FO Snowtrooper Iron Age/250*	25.00	50.00
NNO	Stormtrooper Inferno/250*	30.00	75.00
NNO	FO Stormtrooper Kiln/400*	30.00	75.00
NNO	FO Stormtrooper Nocturne/400*	30.00	60.00
NNO	FO Stormtrooper Phantasm/250*	30.00	60.00
NNO	FO Stormtrooper/500*	15.00	30.00
NNO	Greedo Mystic Powers/750*	30.00	75.00
NNO	Greedo Platinum/600* NYCC	25.00	50.00
NNO	Greedo Sublime/750*	15.00	30.00
NNO	Greedo Verdigris/500* SWC	30.00	60.00
NNO	Greedo Original/2000*	20.00	40.00
NNO	K-3PO/750*	20.00	40.00
NNO	Kylo Ren Alchemy/300*	25.00	50.00
NNO	Kylo Ren Dark Side/500*	20.00	40.00
NNO	Kylo Ren Live Wire/250*	60.00	120.00
NNO	Kylo Ren Onyx/150* HT	75.00	150.00
NNO	Kylo Ren Rage/250* HT	60.00	120.00
NNO	Shadow Trooper/1000*	20.00	40.00
NNO	Snowtrooper Celsius/400*	30.00	60.00
NNO	Snowtrooper Galaxy/250*	20.00	40.00
NNO	Stormtrooper Blue MET/1000*	20.00	40.00
NNO	Stormtrooper Cosmic/2000* SDCC LC	15.00	30.00
NNO	Stormtrooper Green/100* ECCC	75.00	150.00
NNO	Stormtrooper Ice/750* SWC	60.00	120.00
NNO	Stormtrooper Prism/750* TT	30.00	75.00
NNO	Stormtrooper Relic/500*	20.00	40.00
NNO	Stormtrooper Rusty Silver/750*	25.00	50.00
NNO	Stormtrooper Starfield/750*	20.00	40.00
NNO	Stormtrooper/1500*	30.00	60.00
NNO	Wampa Bloody/750*	20.00	40.00
NNO	Wampa Glitter/750*	20.00	40.00
NNO	Wampa Grey Skull/250* EE	20.00	40.00
NNO	Wampa Ice/500* Gemini	30.00	60.00

2017-18 Funko Hikari XS Star Wars

NNO Chopper (black)	7.50	15.00
(2017 Smuggler's Bounty Exclusive)		
NNO Chopper (clear)	4.00	8.00
(2017 Smuggler's Bounty Exclusive)		
NNO Chopper (gold)	5.00	10.00
(2017 Smuggler's Bounty Exclusive)		
NNO Chopper (orange)	4.00	8.00
(2017 Smuggler's Bounty Exclusive)		
NNO Chopper (red)	4.00	8.00
(2017 Smuggler's Bounty Exclusive)		
NNO Darth Vader (black)	6.00	12.00
(2017 Smuggler's Bounty Exclusive)		
NNO Darth Vader (blue)	4.00	8.00
(2017 Smuggler's Bounty Exclusive)		
NNO Darth Vader (gold)	15.00	30.00
(2017 Smuggler's Bounty Exclusive)		
NNO Darth Vader (red)	5.00	10.00
(2017 Smuggler's Bounty Exclusive)		
NNO Darth Vader (silver)	4.00	8.00
(2017 Smuggler's Bounty Exclusive)		
NNO Greedo 2-Pack (blue & clear)	10.00	20.00
(2017 Galactic Convention Exclusive)		
NNO Greedo 2-Pack (blue & clear)	10.00	20.00
(2017 Star Wars Celebration Exclusive)		
NNO Greedo 2-Pack (green & gold)	6.00	12.00
(2017 Galactic Convention Exclusive)		
NNO Greedo 2-Pack (green & gold)	12.50	25.00
(2017 Star Wars Celebration Exclusive)		

2005-18 Funko Mini Wacky Wobblers Star Wars

NNO C-3PO	12.50	25.00
NNO C-3PO/R2-D2 Ulta Mini	7.50	15.00
NNO Chewbacca	20.00	40.00
NNO Darth Vader	10.00	20.00
NNO Darth Vader/Stormtrooper	7.50	15.00
NNO Darth Vader Holiday	7.50	15.00
NNO Jawa Holiday	12.50	25.00
NNO R2-D2	7.50	15.00
NNO R2-D2 Holiday	7.50	15.00
NNO Star Wars 5Pk	15.00	30.00
NNO Stormtrooper	7.50	15.00
NNO Yoda	5.00	10.00
NNO Yoda & Chewbacca (ultra mini)	7.50	15.00
NNO Yoda (holiday)	6.00	12.00

2012 Funko Mini Wacky Wobblers Star Wars Monster Mash-Ups

NNO Chewbacca	7.50	15.00
NNO Darth Vader	7.50	15.00
NNO Jawa	12.50	25.00
NNO Stormtrooper	10.00	20.00
NNO Tusken Raider	7.50	15.00
NNO Yoda	7.50	15.00

2017 Funko MyMoji Star Wars

NNO Chewbacca (laughing)	4.00	8.00
NNO Chewbacca (smiling)	4.00	8.00
NNO Chewbacca (surprised)	2.50	5.00
NNO Darth Vader (angry)	4.00	8.00
NNO Darth Vader (sad)	2.50	5.00
NNO Darth Vader (staring)	2.50	5.00
NNO Jabba (bored)	2.50	5.00
NNO Jabba (closed eyes)	4.00	8.00
NNO Jabba (sad)	4.00	8.00
NNO Luke Skywalker (big smile)	2.50	5.00
NNO Luke Skywalker (closed eyes)	2.50	5.00
NNO Luke Skywalker (sad)	2.50	5.00
NNO Princess Leia (big smile)	3.00	6.00
NNO Princess Leia (closed eyes)	2.50	5.00
NNO Princess Leia (sad)	2.50	5.00
NNO Wampa (angry)	2.50	5.00
NNO Wampa (bored)	2.50	5.00
NNO Wampa (sad)	2.50	5.00
NNO Wicket (laughing)	2.50	5.00
NNO Wicket (sad)	2.50	5.00
NNO Wicket (smiling)	2.50	5.00
NNO Yoda (closed eyes)	2.50	5.00
NNO Yoda (curious)	2.50	5.00
NNO Yoda (smiling)	4.00	8.00

2018 Funko Mystery Mini Plushies Solo A Star Wars Story Keychains

NNO Chewbacca	4.00	8.00
NNO Han Solo	4.00	8.00
NNO Han Solo (goggles)	5.00	10.00
NNO L3-37	7.50	15.00
NNO Lando Calrissian	4.00	8.00
NNO Qi'Ra	5.00	10.00
NNO Range Trooper	4.00	8.00
NNO Tobias Beckett	4.00	8.00

2018 Funko Mystery Mini Plushies Star Wars Classic Keychains

NNO Boba Fett	6.00	12.00
NNO C-3PO	6.00	12.00
NNO Darth Vader	6.00	12.00
NNO Ewok	7.50	15.00
NNO Greedo	12.50	25.00
NNO Jawa	12.50	25.00
NNO Princess Leia	6.00	12.00
NNO Yoda	7.50	15.00

2018 Funko Mystery Mini Plushies Star Wars The Last Jedi Keychains

NNO BB-8		
NNO BB-9E		
NNO Chewbacca	6.00	12.00
NNO Finn		
NNO Kylo Ren		
NNO Porg		
NNO Rey		
NNO Stormtrooper		

2018 Funko Mystery Minis Solo A Star Wars Story

NNO Chewbacca	4.00	8.00
NNO Chewbacca (prisoner)	4.00	8.00
(Target Exclusive)		
NNO Dryden Voss	7.50	15.00
NNO Enfys Nest	3.00	6.00
NNO Han Solo	4.00	8.00
NNO Han Solo (pilot)	125.00	250.00
(Target Exclusive)		
NNO Han Solo (prisoner)	7.50	15.00
(Target Exclusive)		
NNO L3-37	15.00	30.00
NNO Lando Calrissian	4.00	8.00
NNO Patrol Trooper	6.00	12.00
NNO Qi'Ra	3.00	6.00
NNO Qi'Ra (dress)	7.50	15.00
(Target Exclusive)		
NNO Range Trooper	10.00	20.00
(Target Exclusive)		
NNO Rio Durant	5.00	10.00
NNO Tobias Beckett	4.00	8.00
NNO Tobias Beckett (w/rifle)	15.00	30.00
(Target Exclusive)		
NNO Val	15.00	30.00
NNO Weazel	5.00	10.00

2017 Funko Mystery Minis Star Wars

NNO C-3PO	3.00	6.00
NNO Chewbacca	4.00	8.00
NNO Chewbacca (w/bowcaster)	10.00	20.00
NNO Darth Vader (Force Choke)	75.00	150.00
NNO Darth Vader (Force Lift)	15.00	30.00
NNO Darth Vader (lightsaber)	25.00	50.00
(GameStop Exclusive)		
NNO Grand Moff Tarkin	4.00	8.00
NNO Greedo	4.00	8.00
NNO Greedo (pistol up)	20.00	40.00
NNO Hammerhead	4.00	8.00
NNO Han Solo	6.00	12.00
NNO Han Solo (stormtrooper)	12.00	25.00
(GameStop Exclusive)		
NNO Jawa	6.00	12.00
NNO Luke Skywalker	10.00	20.00
NNO Luke Skywalker (stormtrooper)	15.00	30.00
NNO Obi Wan Kenobi	4.00	8.00
NNO Obi Wan Kenobi (Force Ghost)	30.00	75.00
NNO Ponda Baba	3.00	6.00
NNO Princess Leia	2.50	5.00
NNO Shadow Trooper	5.00	10.00
NNO Snaggletooth	2.50	5.00
NNO Stormtrooper	4.00	8.00
NNO TIE Pilot	30.00	75.00
NNO Tusken Raider	20.00	40.00

2018 Funko Mystery Minis Star Wars Empire Strikes Back

NNO 4-LOM	25.00	50.00
(GameStop Exclusive)		
NNO Boba Fett	30.00	60.00
NNO Bossk	75.00	150.00
(Hot Topic Exclusive)		
NNO Chewbacca	3.00	6.00
NNO Darth Vader	3.00	6.00
NNO Dengar	30.00	75.00
NNO Han Solo (Bespin)	3.00	6.00
NNO Han Solo (Hoth)	12.50	25.00
(Hot Topic Exclusive)		
NNO IG-88	12.50	25.00
NNO Imperial AT-AT Driver	15.00	30.00
(GameStop Exclusive)		
NNO Lando Calrissian	6.00	12.00
NNO Lobot	25.00	50.00
(Target Exclusive)		
NNO Luke Skywalker (Bespin)	12.50	25.00
(Target Exclusive)		
NNO Luke Skywalker (Hoth)	15.00	30.00
NNO Princess Leia (Bespin)	7.50	15.00
(GameStop Exclusive)		
NNO Princess Leia (Hoth)	7.50	15.00
NNO R2-D2	3.00	6.00
NNO Snowtrooper	20.00	40.00
(Hot Topic Exclusive)		
NNO Wampa	7.50	15.00
NNO Yoda	4.00	8.00

NNO	Zuckuss	60.00	120.00
	(Target Exclusive)		

2017 Funko Mystery Minis Star Wars The Last Jedi

NNO	BB-8	2.50	5.00
NNO	BB-9E	6.00	12.00
NNO	C'ai Threnalli	50.00	100.00
	(Walgreens Exclusive)		
NNO	Captain Phasma	4.00	8.00
NNO	Chewbacca (w/porg)	4.00	8.00
NNO	DJ	4.00	8.00
NNO	Finn	7.50	15.00
NNO	Finn (First Order uniform)	3.00	6.00
NNO	First Order Executioner	7.50	15.00
NNO	Kylo Ren	25.00	50.00
NNO	Kylo Ren (unmasked)	60.00	120.00
NNO	Poe Dameron	3.00	6.00
NNO	Porg	12.00	25.00
NNO	Porg (wings open)	15.00	30.00
NNO	Praetorian Guard	5.00	10.00
NNO	Praetorian Guard (w/staff)	6.00	12.00
NNO	Praetorian Guard (w/whip)	12.50	25.00
NNO	Princess Leia	6.00	12.00
NNO	Resistance BB Unit	6.00	12.00
NNO	Rey	4.00	8.00
NNO	Rey (cloaked)	8.00	15.00
	(GameStop Exclusive)		
NNO	Rose	3.00	6.00
NNO	Supreme Leader Snoke	3.00	6.00
NNO	Supreme Leader Snoke (holographic)	10.00	20.00

2015-18 Funko Pop Vinyl Conan O'Brien

6	Stormtrooper Conan COCO SDCC	60.00	120.00
10	Jedi Conan COCO SDCC	60.00	120.00
14	Rebel Pilot Conan COCO SDCC	50.00	100.00

2011-18 Funko Pop Vinyl Freddy Funko

A9A	Clone Trooper/48* SDCC	250.00	500.00
A9B	Cl.Trooper Blue Hair/12* SDCC	1600.00	2100.00
28A	Boba Fett/196* SDCC	500.00	650.00
28B	B.Fett Red Hair/24* SDCC	2500.00	3200.00
46	Kylo Ren/400* FD	250.00	400.00
SE	Poe Dameron/200* FD	550.00	800.00
SE	Yoda/450* FD		

2011-18 Funko Pop Vinyl Star Wars

1A	Darth Vader	7.50	15.00
1B	Darth Vader MET HT	15.00	30.00
2A	Yoda	6.00	12.00
2B	Yoda Spirit WG ERR	6.00	12.00
2C	Yoda Spirit WG COR	6.00	12.00
2C	Yoda Spirit WG COR Sticker	6.00	12.00
3A	Han Solo V	100.00	200.00
3B	Han Solo VAULT	12.50	25.00
4	Princess Leia	5.00	10.00
5A	Stormtrooper	5.00	10.00
5B	Stormtrooper Red TAR	7.50	15.00
6A	Chewbacca	6.00	12.00
6B	Chewbacca FLK/480* SDCC	800.00	1200.00
6C	Chewbacca Hoth GS	12.50	25.00
7A	Greedo V	120.00	250.00
7B	Greedo VAULT	5.00	10.00
8A	Boba Fett	5.00	10.00
8B	Boba Fett Prototype WG ERR	6.00	12.00
8D	Boba Fett Prototype WG COR Sticker	6.00	12.00
8C	Boba Fett Prototype WG COR	6.00	12.00
9	Darth Maul	7.50	15.00
10A	Obi-Wan Kenobi V	90.00	175.00
10B	Obi-Wan VAULT	15.00	30.00
11A	Luke Skywalker Jedi Knight V	30.00	60.00
11B	Jedi Luke Skywalker VAULT	20.00	40.00
12A	Gamorrean Guard V	50.00	100.00
12B	Gamorrean Guard VAULT	5.00	10.00
13A	C-3PO	7.50	15.00
13B	C-3PO Gold Chrome SDCC	15.00	30.00
13C	C-3PO Gold Chrome SCE	15.00	30.00
14	Shadow Trooper/480* SDCC	900.0	1500.00
15	H.Solo Stormtrooper/1000* ECCC	300.00	550.00
16	L.Skywalker Stormtrooper/1000* ECCC	400.00	700.00
17	Luke Skywalker X-Wing	12.50	25.00
18A	Slave Leia V	30.00	60.00
18B	Slave Leia VAULT	20.00	40.00
19A	Tusken Raider V	30.00	60.00
19B	Tusken Raider VAULT	10.00	20.00
20A	Jawa V	50.00	100.00
20B	Jawa VAULT	10.00	20.00
21A	Clone Trooper V	50.00	100.00
21B	Clone Trooper VAULT	7.50	15.00
22	Jabba the Hutt	5.00	10.00
23	Darth Maul HOLO/480* SDCC	1500.00	2000.00
24	Biggs Darklighter/480* SDCC	800.00	1200.00
25	501st Clone Trooper/480* SDCC	400.00	600.00
26A	Wicket the Ewok	6.00	12.00
26B	Wicket the Ewok FLK FT	75.00	150.00
27	Jar Jar Binks V	30.00	75.00
28	Admiral Ackbar V	30.00	60.00
29	Queen Amidala V	75.00	150.00
30	Lando Calrissian V	30.00	75.00
31	R2-D2	7.50	15.00
32	Boba Fett Droids/480* SDCC	450.00	600.00
33A	Darth Vader HOLO GITD DCC	350.00	500.00
33B	Darth Vader HOLO GITD PE	350.00	500.00
34	Luke Skywalker Hoth V	10.00	20.00
35	Bossk V	25.00	50.00
36	The Emperor V	30.00	60.00
37	Hammerhead V	12.50	25.00
38	Biker Scout V	15.00	30.00
39A	6" Wampa V	12.50	25.00
39B	Wampa 6" FLK HT	15.00	30.00
40	Emperor HOLO TW	30.00	60.00
41A	R2-Q5 GCE	15.00	30.00
41B	R2-Q5 SWC	60.00	120.00
42A	Shock Trooper GCE	30.00	75.00
42B	Shock Trooper SWC	75.00	150.00
43A	Unmasked Vader GCE	5.00	10.00
43B	Unmasked Vader SWC	75.00	150.00
44A	R2-R9 GCE	20.00	40.00
44B	R2-R9 SWC	30.00	60.00
45	R2-B1 GS	6.00	12.00
46A	E-3PO GCE	12.50	25.00
46B	E-3PO SWC	12.50	25.00
47	Han Solo Hoth GS	5.00	10.00
48	Figrin D'an GS	6.00	12.00
49	Luke Skywalker Tatooine	10.00	20.00
50	Princess Leia Boussh	6.00	12.00
51A	TIE Fighter Pilot	5.00	10.00
51B	TIE Pilot MET	12.50	25.00
52	Nalan Cheel	5.00	10.00
53	Bib Fortuna	5.00	10.00
54A	Leia Boussh Unmasked SDCC	450.00	600.00
54B	Leia Boussh Unmasked SCE	450.00	600.00
55	K-3PO B&N	7.50	15.00
56A	Snowtrooper WG ERR	5.00	10.00
56B	Snowtrooper WG COR	5.00	10.00
56C	Snowtrooper WG COR Sticker	5.00	10.00
57A	Imperial Guard WG ERR	6.00	12.00
57B	Imperial Guard WG COR	6.00	12.00
57C	Imperial Guard WG COR Sticker	6.00	12.00
58A	Rey	5.00	10.00
59	Finn	5.00	10.00
60	Kylo Ren	5.00	10.00
61	BB-8	5.00	10.00
62	Poe Dameron V	5.00	10.00
63A	Chewbacca	5.00	10.00
63B	Chewbacca FLK SB	7.50	15.00
64A	C-3PO	6.00	12.00
64B	C-3PO MET B&N	10.00	20.00
65A	Captain Phasma	5.00	10.00
65B	Captain Phasma Last Jedi Box	6.00	12.00
66	First Order Stormtrooper	5.00	10.00
67A	First Order Snowtrooper	5.00	10.00
67B	First Order Snowtrooper Last Jedi Box	5.00	10.00
68A	First Order Flametrooper	5.00	10.00
68B	First Order Flametrooper Last Jedi Box	6.00	12.00
69	Blue Snaggletooth CH SB	25.00	50.00
70	Red Snaggletooth SB	5.00	10.00
71	Shadow Guard WG	10.00	20.00
72	Poe Dameron No Helmet WM	5.00	10.00
73	Rey w/Goggles HT	5.00	10.00
74	FO Stormtrooper w/Rifle AMZ	7.50	15.00
75	FO Stormtrooper w/Shield WG	6.00	12.00
76	Finn Stormtrooper GS	7.50	15.00
77	Kylo Ren Unhooded TAR	6.00	12.00
78	R2-L3 Dorkside Toys	15.00	30.00
79	Han Solo	5.00	10.00
80	Princess Leia	5.00	10.00
81	Admiral Ackbar	5.00	10.00
82	Nien Nunb	5.00	10.00
83	Sidon Ithano	5.00	10.00
84	Varmik	5.00	10.00
85	Finn w/Lightsaber B&N	5.00	10.00
86	Han Solo Snow Gear LC	5.00	10.00
87	Kylo Ren Unmasked WM	5.00	10.00
88	Nien Nunb w/Helmet GS	5.00	10.00
89	TIE Fighter Pilot SB	5.00	10.00
A90	TIE Fighter Pilot Red Stripe SB CH	25.00	50.00
B90	Luke Ceremony SWC	10.00	20.00
A91	Captain Phasma MET SB	10.00	20.00
B91A	Han Ceremony SWC	7.50	15.00
B91B	Han Ceremony GCE	7.50	15.00
92	AT-AT Driver WG	6.00	12.00
93	Luke Skywalker Bespin V	6.00	12.00
94A	Luke Skywalker Bespin SWC	7.50	15.00
94B	Luke Skywalker Bespin GCE	7.50	15.00
95	Ree Yees WG	5.00	10.00
96	Kit Fisto WG	7.50	15.00
97	Plo Koon WG	6.00	12.00
98	Blue Senate Guard SWC	15.00	30.00
99	Old Ben Kenobi SB	12.50	25.00
100	FN-2187 TAR	20.00	40.00
101A	4-LOM SWC	15.00	30.00
101B	4-LOM GCE	20.00	40.00
102	Bobe Fett Action SB	15.00	30.00
103	IG-88 SB	7.50	15.00
104	Rey w/Lightsaber	6.00	12.00

#	Item	Low	High
105	Kylo Ren Unmasked Action	6.00	12.00
106	Luke Skywalker Force Awakens	6.00	12.00
107	General Leia	6.00	12.00
108	Maz Kanata	6.00	12.00
109	General Hux	6.00	12.00
110	Snap Wexley	6.00	12.00
111	FN-2199 V	6.00	12.00
112	Guavian	6.00	12.00
113	ME-8D9	6.00	12.00
114	Rey Jedi Temple WG	10.00	20.00
115A	Han Solo w/Bowcaster SDCC	7.50	15.00
115B	Han Solo w/Bowcaster SCE	7.50	15.00
116A	BB-8 w/Lighter SDCC	10.00	20.00
116B	BB-8 w/Lighter SCE	10.00	20.00
117	Poe Dameron Jacket/Blaster HT	6.00	12.00
118	Maz Kanata Goggles Up TAR	6.00	12.00
119	Rey X-Wing Helmet GS	7.50	15.00
120	Poe Dameron X-Wing Jumpsuit FYE	6.00	12.00
121	R2-D2 Jabba's Sail Barge SB	6.00	12.00
122	Zuckuss TW	10.00	20.00
123	Luke Skywalker (Endor)	6.00	12.00
124	Dagobah Yoda	6.00	12.00
A125	Hoth Han Solo w/Tauntaun SB	30.00	60.00
B125A	Princess Leia Hoth SWC	15.00	30.00
B125B	Princess Leia Hoth GCE	15.00	30.00
126A	Luke Skywalker Hood SWC	30.00	75.00
126B	Luke Skywalker Hood GCE	25.00	50.00
127A	Garindan SWC	12.50	25.00
127B	Garindan GCE	12.50	25.00
128A	Qui Gon Jinn NYCC	250.00	400.00
128B	Qui Gon Jinn HOLO SWC	25.00	50.00
128C	Qui Gon Jinn HOLO GCE	25.00	50.00
129	General Grievous WG	25.00	50.00
130A	Ahsoka HT	10.00	20.00
130B	Ahsoka GITD Comikaze	10.00	20.00
131	Sabine Masked WG	7.50	15.00
132	Kanan	6.00	12.00
133A	Chopper	6.00	12.00
133B	Chopper Imperial SWC	6.00	12.00
133C	Chopper Imperial GCE	6.00	12.00
134	Ezra	6.00	12.00
135	Sabine	6.00	12.00
136	Hera	6.00	12.00
137	Zeb	6.00	12.00
138	Jyn Erso	6.00	12.00
139	Captain Cassian Andor	6.00	12.00
140	Chirrut Imwe	6.00	12.00
141	Baze Malbus	6.00	12.00
142	Director Orson Krennic	6.00	12.00
143	Darth Vader	6.00	12.00
144	Imperial Death Trooper	6.00	12.00
145	Scarif Stormtrooper	6.00	12.00
146	K-2SO	6.00	12.00
147	C2-B5	6.00	12.00
148	Jyn Erso Mountain Gear SB	6.00	12.00
149	Death Trooper Sniper SB	6.00	12.00
150	Jyn Erso Hooded HT	6.00	12.00
151	Capt. C.Andor Brown Jacket TAR	6.00	12.00
152	Jyn Erso Imperial Disguise TAR	6.00	12.00
153	Saw Gerrera WM	6.00	12.00
154	Imp. Death Trooper Black MET WM	7.50	15.00
155	Bistan NYCC	12.50	25.00
156	Scarif Stormtrooper Striped WG	6.00	12.00
157	Vader Force Choke GS	7.50	15.00
158	Darth Vader Bespin SB	15.00	30.00
159	Grand Moff Tarkin SB	12.50	25.00
160	Max Rebo SS	6.00	12.00
161	Rey w/Jacket TAR	8.00	12.00
162	Young Anakin	7.50	15.00
164	Captain Rex SB	6.00	12.00
165	Darth Maul Rebels SB	15.00	30.00
166	The Inquisitor	7.50	15.00

#	Item	Low	High
167	Seventh Sister	6.00	12.00
168	Fifth Brother	6.00	12.00
169A	Han Solo SWC	7.50	15.00
169B	Han Solo GCE	7.50	15.00
170A	Grand Admiral Thrawn SWC	20.00	40.00
170B	Grand Admiral Thrawn GCE	20.00	40.00
171A	442nd Clone Trooper SWC	12.50	25.00
171B	442nd Clone Trooper GCW	12.50	25.00
172	Mace Windu WG	7.50	15.00
173A	Muftak ECCC	12.50	25.00
173B	Muftak SPCE	12.50	25.00
174A	Rey w/Speeder SWC	30.00	60.00
174B	Rey w/Speeder GCE	30.00	60.00
175	Luke w/Speeder SB	20.00	40.00
A176	Darth Vader w/TIE Fighter TAR	20.00	40.00
B176	Commander Cody WG	12.50	25.00
177A	Saw Gerrera w/Hair NYCC	12.50	25.00
177B	Saw Gerrera w/Hair FCE	12.50	25.00
178A	Jyn Erso w/Helmet NYCC	12.50	25.00
178B	Jyn Erso w/Helmet FCE	12.50	25.00
179A	K-2SO Action Pose NYCC	10.00	20.00
179B	K-2SO Action Pose FCE	10.00	20.00
180	R5-D4 SB	7.50	15.00
181	C-3PO Unfinished SB	10.00	20.00
182A	Snoke GITD SDCC	12.50	25.00
182B	Supreme Leader Snoke GITD SCE	12.50	25.00
183A	Bodhi Rook SDCC	7.50	15.00
183B	Bodhi Rook SCE	7.50	15.00
184B	Tank Trooper SDCC	6.00	12.00
184C	Combat Assault Tank Trooper SCE	6.00	12.00
185	Young Jyn Erso	6.00	12.00
186	Galen Erso	6.00	12.00
187	Weeteef Cyubee	6.00	12.00
188A	Death Star Droid Rogue One NYCC	7.50	15.00
188B	Death Star Droid Rogue One FCE	7.50	15.00
189	Death Star Droid Black	6.00	12.00
190A	Rey	6.00	12.00
190B	Rey GITD COST	20.00	40.00
191	Finn	6.00	12.00
192	Poe Dameron	6.00	12.00
193	Luke Skywalker	6.00	12.00
194A	Kylo Ren	6.00	12.00
194B	Kylo Ren GITD COST	20.00	40.00
194C	Kylo Ren HOLO TAR OL	20.00	40.00
195A	Chewbacca w/Porg	6.00	12.00
195B	Chewbacca w/Porg FLK FYE	12.50	25.00
196	BB-8	6.00	12.00
197	Rose	6.00	12.00
198A	Porg	6.00	12.00
198B	Porg Open Mouth CH	15.00	30.00
198C	Porg FLK HT	10.00	20.00
198D	Porg Open Mouth FLK HT	30.00	60.00
198E	Porg Wings Open TAR	12.50	25.00
198F	Porg 10" TAR	25.00	50.00
199	Supreme Leader Snoke	6.00	12.00
200	Praetorian Guard	6.00	12.00
201	First Order Executioner	6.00	12.00
202A	BB-9E	6.00	12.00
202B	BB-9E Chrome BL	10.00	20.00
203	Kylo Ren w/Helmet TRU	10.00	20.00
205	Rose SS	10.00	20.00
207	DJ GS	6.00	12.00
208	Praetorian Guard w/Swords WG	10.00	20.00
209	Praetorian Guard w/Whip WG	7.50	15.00
210	Resistance BB Unit Orange NBC	7.50	15.00
211	Resistance BB Unit WM	6.00	12.00
212	Medical Droid WG	10.00	20.00
213A	Boba Fett w/Slave I NYCC	30.00	60.00
213B	Boba Fett w/Slave I FCE	30.00	60.00
214	Obi-Wan Kenobi ROTS SB	20.00	40.00
215	Kylo Ren w/TIE Fighter	15.00	30.00
217	Aayla Secura SB	6.00	12.00

#	Item	Low	High
218	Princess Leia WM	7.50	15.00
219	Wedge Antilles w/Snow Speeder WG	15.00	30.00
220	BB-8 Baseball and Bat Giants	30.00	60.00
221	Tie Fighter w/Tie Pilot	7.50	15.00
222	Escape Pod Landing WM	20.00	40.00
223	Cantina Faceoff WM	25.00	50.00
224	Trash Compactor Escape WM	20.00	40.00
225	Death Star Duel WM	20.00	40.00
226	Cloud City Duel WG	20.00	40.00
227	Poe Dameron w/X-Wing SB	15.00	30.00
228	Princess Leia w/Speeder Bike	15.00	30.00
229	Luke Skywalker w/Speeder Bike CH	25.00	50.00
230A	Dengar NYCC	12.50	25.00
230B	Dengar FCE	12.50	25.00
231	Young Anakin Podracing WG	7.50	15.00
232	Luke Skywalker w/X-Wing 40th Anniv.	20.00	40.00
234	Scout Trooper w/Speeder SB	20.00	40.00
235	Vice Admiral Holdo	6.00	12.00
236	Chewbacca w/AT-ST	15.00	30.00
237A	Padme Amidala ECCC	12.50	25.00
237B	Padme Amidala SCE	10.00	20.00
238	Han Solo	6.00	12.00
239A	Chewbacca	6.00	12.00
239B	Chewbacca FLK BL	6.00	12.00
239C	Chewbacca FLK MCM	25.00	50.00
240	Lando Calrissian	6.00	12.00
241	Qi'Ra	6.00	12.00
242	Tobias Beckett	6.00	12.00
243	Val	6.00	12.00
244	Rio Durant	6.00	12.00
245	L3-37	6.00	12.00
246	Range Trooper	6.00	12.00
247	Enfys Nest	6.00	12.00
248A	Han Solo Goggles TAR	10.00	20.00
248B	Mudtrooper FS	20.00	40.00
250	Tobias Beckett WM	7.50	15.00
251	Lando Calrissian White Cape HT	7.50	15.00
252A	Stormtrooper SDCC	25.00	50.00
252B	Stormtrooper SCE	15.00	30.00
253	Dryden Voss FYE	12.50	25.00
254	Dryden Gangster TAR	12.50	25.00
255	Han Solo Vest WG	12.50	25.00
257	Rematch on the Supremacy	15.00	30.00
262A	Cad Bane SDCC	30.00	60.00
262B	Cad Bane SCE	12.50	25.00
268	Ahsoka	10.00	20.00
269	Yoda		
270	Obi-Wan Kenobi	6.00	12.00
271	Anakin Skywalker	6.00	12.00
272	Ahsoka Force Push HT	10.00	20.00
273	Obi-Wan Kenobi Hooded WG	25.00	50.00
274A	Captain Rex NYCC	25.00	50.00
274B	Captain Rex FCE	20.00	40.00
275	R2-D2 w/Antlers		
276	C-3PO w/Santa Hat		
277	Yoda Santa Outfit		
278	Chewbacca Christmas Lights		
279A	Darth Vader Candy Cane Lightsaber		
279B	Darth Vader GITD Candy Cane Lightsaber CH		

2011-18 Funko Pop Vinyl Star Wars Multi-Packs

#	Item	Low	High
NNO	BB-8/BB-9E BB	10.00	20.00
NNO	BB-8 Gold Dome HT BF	10.00	20.00
NNO	Biggs/Wedge/Porkins WM	10.00	20.00
NNO	Fighting Droids GS	10.00	20.00
NNO	First Order Kylo Ren/Snoke/BB-9E COSTCO	30.00	60.00
NNO	First Order Kylo Ren/Snoke	20.00	40.00
	Executioner/BB-9E COSTCO		
NNO	Greedo/Hammerhead/Walrus Man WM	10.00	20.00
NNO	Gunner/Officer/Trooper WM	10.00	20.00
NNO	Han Solo/Chewbacca SB	20.00	40.00
NNO	Jabba/Slave Leia/Salacious Crumb WM	30.00	60.00

NNO Jango Fett GITD/LEGO Star Wars III Bundle	25.00	50.00
NNO Lobot/Ugnaught/Bespin Guard WM	7.50	15.00
NNO Luke Skywalker & Wampa SDCC	90.00	175.00
NNO Praetorian Guards POPCULTCHA	30.00	60.00
NNO Princess Leia/R2-D2 SDCC	10.00	20.00
NNO Princess Leia/R2-D2 SCE	10.00	20.00
NNO R2-D2 Gold Dome HT BF	10.00	20.00
NNO Rancor/Luke/Slave Oola PX	20.00	40.00
NNO Rebel Rey/Chewbacca/BB-8 COSTCO	20.00	40.00
NNO Rebel Rey/Luke/Chewbacca/BB-8 COSTCO	20.00	40.00
NNO Rogue One Jyn/Cassian/K-2SO/C2-B5/Krennic Vader/Scarif/Death Trooper	90.00	175.00
NNO Sandtrooper/Dewback WM	15.00	30.00
NNO Tarfful/Unhooded Emperor/Clone Trooper WM	7.50	15.00
NNO Teebo/Chirpa/Logray WM	7.50	15.00

2015-16 Funko Super Shogun

2 Shadowtrooper SWC	120.00	200.00
3 Boba Fett ROTJ SWC	120.00	200.00
4 Boba Fett ESB	60.00	120.00
5 Boba Fett Proto/400* FS	150.00	250.00

2017-18 Funko Vynl Star Wars

NNO Darth Vader + Stormtrooper	15.00	30.00
NNO Han Solo + Greedo		
NNO Han Solo + Lando Calrissian	12.50	25.00
NNO Luke Skywalker + Princess Leia		

2007-16 Funko Wacky Wobblers Star Wars

NNO 4-LOM	6.00	12.00
NNO 501st Clone Trooper	15.00	30.00
NNO Admiral Ackbar	25.00	50.00
NNO Ahsoka Tano	25.00	50.00
NNO Anakin Skywalker Clone Wars	7.50	15.00
NNO Battle Droid	10.00	20.00
NNO Boba Fett	7.50	15.00
NNO Boba Fett Chrome Base	15.00	30.00
NNO Bossk	7.50	15.00
NNO C-3PO	7.50	15.00
NNO C-3PO TFA	7.50	15.00
NNO Cantina Band	10.00	20.00
NNO Captain Phasma	6.00	12.00
NNO Captain Rex	10.00	20.00
NNO Captain Red Chrome Base	12.50	25.00
NNO Chewbacca	7.50	15.00
NNO Chewbacca Chrome Base	25.00	50.00
NNO Chewbacca TFA	5.00	10.00
NNO Clone Trooper	25.00	50.00
NNO Clone Trooper Utapau AFE	10.00	20.00
NNO Clone Trooper (yellow)	15.00	30.00
(2008)		
NNO Clone Trooper Denal Chrome Base WM	12.50	25.00
NNO Clone Trooper Sinker	75.00	150.00
NNO Clone Troooper Denal WM	7.50	15.00
NNO Commander Gree/1500* DIAMOND	7.50	15.00

NNO Darth Maul	15.00	30.00
NNO Darth Maul HOLO Chrome Base/12* SDCC	90.00	175.00
NNO Darth Maul HOLO/480* SDCC	60.00	120.00
NNO Darth Vader	7.50	15.00
NNO Darth Vader (chrome base)	25.00	50.00
NNO Darth Vader Holiday EE	7.50	15.00
NNO Darth Vader HOLO SDCC/WWC	20.00	40.00
NNO Darth Vader HOLO Chrome Base SDCC/WWC	25.00	50.00
NNO Emperor Palpatine	25.00	50.00
NNO Emperor Palpatine (chrome base)	25.00	50.00
NNO Finn	6.00	12.00
NNO Finn/Kylo Ren HMV	15.00	30.00
NNO Finn Stormtrooper	5.00	10.00
NNO First Order Flametrooper	6.00	12.00
NNO First Order Snowtrooper	5.00	10.00
NNO First Order Stormtrooper	6.00	12.00
NNO Gamorrean Guard	12.50	25.00
NNO General Grievous	10.00	20.00
NNO Greedo	7.50	15.00
NNO Greedo Chrome Base	25.00	50.00
NNO Han Solo	12.50	25.00
NNO Han Solo Stormtrooper/1008* SDCC	20.00	40.00
NNO Holiday C-3PO	7.50	15.00
NNO Holiday Special Boba Fett	10.00	20.00
NNO Holiday Yoda	7.50	15.00
NNO Jango Fett	7.50	15.00
NNO Jawa	10.00	20.00
NNO K-3PO/1500*	6.00	12.00
NNO Kylo Ren	5.00	10.00
NNO Kylor Ren No Hood	6.00	12.00
NNO Luke Skywalker	20.00	40.00
NNO Luke Skywalker (stormtrooper)	25.00	50.00
(2008 Entertainment Earth Exclusive)		
NNO Luke Skywalker X-Wing Pilot	20.00	40.00
NNO Obi-Wan Kenobi	25.00	50.00
NNO Obi-Wan Kenobi (Clone Wars)	12.50	25.00
NNO Obi-Wan Kenobi Force Ghost NYCC	15.00	30.00
NNO Obi-Wan Kenobi Force Ghost Chrome Base	25.00	50.00
NNO Princess Leia	7.50	15.00
NNO R2-D2	7.50	15.00
NNO R2-Q2/756* EE		
NNO R2-R9/756* EE	7.50	15.00
NNO R2-X2/756* EE	20.00	40.00
NNO Rey	6.00	12.00
NNO Shadow Stormtrooper SDCC	12.50	25.00
NNO Shock Trooper/1008* SDCC	30.00	75.00
NNO Slave Leia	10.00	20.00
NNO Stormtrooper	7.50	15.00
NNO TC-14/480* SDCC	25.00	50.00
NNO TIE Fighter Pilot	12.50	25.00
NNO Tusken Raider	7.50	15.00
NNO Wicket	7.50	15.00
NNO Wicket Chrome Base	30.00	60.00
NNO Yoda	6.00	12.00
NNO Yoda Chrome Base	15.00	30.00
NNO Yoda Force Ghost	6.00	12.00
NNO Yoda Force Ghost/1500* DIAMOND SDCC	25.00	50.00
NNO Yoda (holiday)	6.00	12.00

2010 Funko Wacky Wobblers Star Wars Monster Mash-Ups

NNO Chewbacca	6.00	12.00
NNO Darth Vader	6.00	12.00
NNO Stormtrooper	7.50	15.00
NNO Yoda	5.00	10.00

2016-18 Funko Wobblers Star Wars

COMMON FIGURINE

NNO Boba Fett (prototype)	15.00	30.00
(2017 Galactic Convention Exclusive)		
NNO Boba Fett Proto SWC	15.00	30.00
NNO Boba Fett	6.00	12.00

NNO Captain Cassian Andor	4.00	8.00
NNO Chewbacca	6.00	12.00
NNO Darth Vader	7.50	15.00
NNO First Order Executioner	6.00	12.00
NNO Han Solo (Solo film)	7.50	15.00
(2018)		
NNO Imperial Death Trooper	6.00	12.00
NNO Jyn Erso	5.00	10.00
NNO Lando Calrissian	6.00	12.00
(2018)		
NNO Princess Leia	7.50	15.00
NNO Rey	7.50	15.00
NNO Scarif Stormtrooper	6.00	12.00

2017 Vinylmation Eachez Star Wars The Last Jedi

NNO Praetorian Guard Single Blade	30.00	75.00
NNO Praetorian Guard Double Blade (chaser)	50.00	100.00
NNO Praetorian Guard Whip	12.00	25.00

2012-13 Vinylmation Star Wars Disney Characters

NNO Boba Fett Pete	6.00	12.00
NNO Chewbacca Goofy	20.00	40.00
(LE 1500)		
NNO Darth Vader Goofy	8.00	15.00
NNO Emperor Stitch	25.00	50.00
(LE 2000)		
NNO Ewok Chip	20.00	40.00
(LE 1500)		
NNO Ewok Dale	20.00	40.00
(LE 1500)		
NNO Han Solo Donald	30.00	60.00
(LE 1500)		
NNO Jedi Mickey	20.00	40.00
(LE 2000)		
NNO Princess Leia Minnie	10.00	20.00
NNO Stormtrooper Donald	6.00	12.00
NNO X-Wing Pilot Luke Mickey	12.00	25.00
NNO Yoda Stitch	20.00	40.00

2016 Vinylmation Star Wars The Force Awakens Series 2

NNO Admiral Ackbar	5.00	10.00
NNO Captain Phasma		
NNO Ello Asty (w/ helmet)	6.00	12.00
NNO Ello Asty (helmetless)		
NNO First Mate Guiggold	4.00	8.00
NNO First Order Snowtrooper	6.00	12.00
NNO First Order TIE Fighter Pilot	8.00	15.00
NNO First Order TIE Fighter Pilot (red mark)		
NNO Princess Leia	12.00	25.00
NNO Sidon Ithano	5.00	10.00

2015 Vinylmation Star Wars The Force Awakens Series 1

NNO	BB-8	10.00	20.00
NNO	C-3PO	4.00	8.00
NNO	Finn (leather jacket)	5.00	10.00
NNO	Finn (stormtrooper)		
NNO	First Order Stormtrooper	12.00	25.00
NNO	Han Solo (chaser)	15.00	30.00
NNO	Kylo Ren	10.00	20.00
NNO	Poe Dameron	4.00	8.00
NNO	Rey		
NNO	Rey (desert wear)	30.00	75.00

2016 Vinylmation Star Wars Rogue One

NNO	Admiral Raddus	8.00	15.00
NNO	Baze Malbus	6.00	12.00
NNO	Bistan	4.00	8.00
NNO	C2-B5	6.00	12.00
NNO	Cassian Andor	8.00	15.00
NNO	Chirrut Imwe	8.00	15.00
NNO	Director Orson Krennic	6.00	12.00
NNO	Imperial Death Trooper (w/o shoulder pad)	8.00	15.00
NNO	Imperial Death Trooper (w/ shoulder pad)	30.00	75.00
NNO	Jyn Erso (w/o helm)	8.00	15.00
NNO	Jyn Erso (w/ helm)	60.00	120.00
NNO	K-2SO	10.00	20.00
NNO	Rebel Commando Pao	8.00	15.00
NNO	Saw Gererra	12.00	25.00

2011 Vinylmation Star Wars Series 1

NNO	Boba Fett	12.00	25.00
NNO	C-3PO	8.00	15.00
NNO	Chewbacca	6.00	12.00
NNO	Darth Vader	10.00	20.00
NNO	Han Solo	12.00	25.00
NNO	Lando	10.00	20.00
NNO	Leia	6.00	12.00
NNO	Luke	6.00	12.00
NNO	Obi-Wan Kenobi Ghost	30.00	60.00
(super chaser)			
NNO	Obi-Wan Kenobi	8.00	15.00
(chaser)			
NNO	R2-D2	6.00	12.00
NNO	Stormtrooper	8.00	15.00
NNO	Yoda	8.00	15.00

2012 Vinylmation Star Wars Series 2

NNO	Darth Vader	20.00	40.00
NNO	Garindan	25.00	50.00
(chaser)			
NNO	Grand Moff Tarkin	6.00	12.00
NNO	Greedo	6.00	12.00

NNO	Han Solo	6.00	12.00
NNO	Hologram Princess Leia	30.00	60.00
(LE 2500) Celebration VI Exclusive			
NNO	Jawa	15.00	30.00
(LE 2000)			
NNO	Luke Skywalker	8.00	15.00
NNO	Muftak	6.00	12.00
NNO	Obi-Wan Kenobi	8.00	15.00
NNO	Ponda Baba	6.00	12.00
NNO	Princess Leia	8.00	15.00
NNO	R5-D4		
(LE 2000)			
NNO	Tusken Raider	8.00	15.00
NNO	Wedge Antilles	6.00	12.00

2013 Vinylmation Star Wars Series 3

NNO	Admiral Ackbar	10.00	20.00
NNO	Bib Fortuna	6.00	12.00
NNO	Biker Scout	8.00	15.00
NNO	Emperor Palpatine	30.00	60.00
(chaser)			
NNO	Emperor's Royal Guard	10.00	20.00
NNO	Gamorrean Guard	6.00	12.00
NNO	Helmetless Princess Leia in Boushh Disguise		
(variant)			
NNO	Lando Calrissian Skiff Guard Disguise	8.00	15.00
NNO	Logray	10.00	20.00
NNO	Luke Skywalker Jedi	8.00	15.00
NNO	Nien Nunb	6.00	12.00
NNO	Princess Leia in Boushh Disguise	15.00	30.00
NNO	Wicket	10.00	20.00

2014 Vinylmation Star Wars Series 4

NNO	4-LOM	6.00	12.00
NNO	Bespin Princess Leia	6.00	12.00
NNO	Boba Fett Concept	20.00	40.00
(combo topper)			
NNO	Boba Fett Holiday Special		
(LE 1500)			
NNO	Boba Fett	15.00	30.00
(combo topper)			
NNO	Bossk	6.00	12.00
NNO	Dagobah Luke Skywalker 9-Inch	30.00	60.00
(LE 2000)			
NNO	Dengar	6.00	12.00
NNO	Han Solo Carbonite	50.00	100.00
(LE 2000)			
NNO	Han Solo Hoth	6.00	12.00
NNO	Holographic Emperor	12.00	25.00
(LE 2000)			
NNO	Jabba the Hutt and Salacious Crumb 9-Inch	30.00	60.00
(LE 2000)			
NNO	Luke Skywalker Hoth	6.00	12.00

NNO	R2-D2 Dagobah	12.00	25.00
NNO	R2-D2	15.00	30.00
(variant)			
NNO	R2-MK	8.00	15.00
NNO	Rancor and Malakili 9-and-3-Inch Combo	40.00	80.00
NNO	Snowtrooper	10.00	20.00
NNO	Tauntaun	6.00	12.00
NNO	Ugnaught	6.00	12.00
NNO	Wampa Attacked Luke		
(variant)			
NNO	Wampa	15.00	30.00
(chaser)			
NNO	Yoda 9-Inch		
(LE 2000)			
NNO	Zuckuss	6.00	12.00

2015 Vinylmation Star Wars Series 5

NNO	Death Star and Trooper 9-and-3-Inch Combo	40.00	80.00
(LE 1000)			
NNO	Death Star Droid	8.00	15.00
NNO	Dr. Evazan	6.00	12.00
NNO	Duros		
NNO	Figrin D'an	15.00	30.00
(instrument 1)			
NNO	Figrin D'an	20.00	40.00
(instrument 2)			
NNO	Figrin D'an	20.00	40.00
(instrument 3)			
NNO	Figrin D'an	15.00	30.00
(instrument 4)			
NNO	Figrin D'an	20.00	40.00
(instrument 5)			
NNO	Han Solo Stormtrooper	12.00	25.00
NNO	Heroes of Yavin Han		
(LE 2500)			
NNO	Heroes of Yavin Luke	12.00	25.00
(LE 2500)			
NNO	Jabba the Hutt	6.00	12.00
NNO	Jawa	20.00	40.00
(LE 2500)			
NNO	Labria	6.00	12.00
NNO	Luke Skywalker Stormtrooper	50.00	100.00
(variant)			
NNO	Luke Skywalker X-Wing Pilot	10.00	20.00
(combo topper)			
NNO	Momaw Nadon	6.00	12.00
NNO	Power Droid	10.00	25.00
(LE 2500)			
NNO	Princess Leia	6.00	12.00
NNO	Sandtrooper	8.00	15.00
NNO	Snaggletooth	10.00	20.00
(chaser)			
NNO	Tie Fighter Pilot	10.00	20.00

2016 Vinylmation Star Wars Series 6

NNO	Anakin/Yoda/Obi-Wan Spirits		
(LE 2500)			
NNO	Han Solo		
NNO	Klaatu		
NNO	Luke Skywalker		
NNO	Luke Skywalker (w/o helmet)		
NNO	Max Rebo		
NNO	Oola		
NNO	Princess Leia		
NNO	Princess Leia (chaser)		
NNO	Stormtrooper		
NNO	Stormtrooper Battle Damaged (variant)		
NNO	Teebo		
NNO	Wicket 9"		
(LE 1000)			

Trading Cards

PRICE GUIDE

FILMS

1977 Star Wars

COMPLETE SET W/STICKERS (330)	125.00	250.00
COMP.SER.1 SET W/STICKERS (66)	30.00	80.00
COMP.SER.2 SET W/STICKERS (66)	20.00	50.00
COMP.SER.3 SET W/STICKERS (66)	20.00	50.00
COMP.SER.4 SET W/STICKERS (66)	20.00	50.00
COMP.SER.5 SET W/STICKERS (66)	25.00	60.00
UNOPENED SER.1 BOX (36 PACKS)	1600.00	2000.00
UNOPENED SER.1 PACK (7 CARDS+1 STICKER)		
UNOPENED SER.2 BOX (36 PACKS)	500.00	600.00
UNOPENED SER.2 PACK (7 CARDS+1 STICKER)		
UNOPENED SER.3 BOX (36 PACKS)	400.00	500.00
UNOPENED SER.3 PACK (7 CARDS+1 STICKER)		
UNOPENED SER.4 BOX (36 PACKS)	450.00	600.00
UNOPENED SER.4 PACK (7 CARDS+1 STICKER)		
UNOPENED SER.5 BOX (36 PACKS)	350.00	500.00
UNOPENED SER.5 PACK (7 CARDS+1 STICKER)		
COMMON BLUE (1-66)	.30	.75
COMMON RED (67-132)	.25	.60
COMMON YELLOW (133-198)	.25	.60
COMMON GREEN (199-264)	.25	.60
COMMON ORANGE (265-330)	.25	.60
207A C-3PO Anthony Daniels ERR Obscene	30.00	80.00
207B C-3PO Anthony Daniels COR Airbrushed	.25	.60

1977 Star Wars Stickers

COMPLETE SET (55)	40.00	80.00
COMPLETE SERIES 1 (11)	6.00	15.00
COMPLETE SERIES 2 (11)	6.00	15.00
COMPLETE SERIES 3 (11)	6.00	15.00
COMPLETE SERIES 4 (11)	6.00	15.00
COMPLETE SERIES 5 (11)	6.00	15.00
COMMON STICKER (1-11)	.75	2.00
COMMON STICKER (12-22)	.60	1.50
COMMON STICKER (23-33)	.60	1.50
COMMON STICKER (34-44)	.60	1.50
COMMON STICKER (45-55)	.60	1.50
1 Luke Skywalker	1.25	3.00
7 Lord Darth Vader	1.25	3.00
36 Star Pilot Luke Skywalker	1.25	3.00
43 Stormtrooper Tool of the Empire	1.25	3.00

1977 Star Wars Mexican

COMPLETE SET (66)	250.00	400.00
UNOPENED PACK (2 CARDS)	35.00	40.00
COMMON CARD (1-66)	3.00	8.00

1977 Star Wars OPC

COMPLETE SET (264)	200.00	400.00
COMPLETE SERIES 1 SET (66)	100.00	200.00
COMPLETE SERIES 2 SET (66)	60.00	120.00
COMPLETE SERIES 3 SET (132)	50.00	100.00
UNOPENED SERIES 1 BOX (36 PACKS)		
UNOPENED SERIES 1 PACK (7 CARDS+1 STICKER)		
UNOPENED SERIES 2 BOX (36 PACKS)		
UNOPENED SERIES 2 PACK (7 CARDS+1 STICKER)		

UNOPENED SERIES 3 BOX (36 PACKS)		
UNOPENED SERIES 3 PACK (7 CARDS+1 STICKER)		
COMMON BLUE (1-66)	2.50	5.00
COMMON RED (67-132)	1.25	3.00
COMMON ORANGE (133-264)	.50	1.25

1978 Star Wars General Mills

COMPLETE SET (18)	12.00	30.00
COMMON CARD (1-18)	1.00	2.50

1977 Star Wars Tip Top Ice Cream

COMPLETE SET (15)	80.00	150.00
COMMON CARD	5.00	12.00
UNNUMBERED SET LISTED ALPHABETICALLY		
ALSO KNOWN AS R2-D2 SPACE ICE		

1977 Star Wars Wonder Bread

COMPLETE SET (16)	8.00	20.00
COMMON CARD (1-16)	.75	2.00

1995 Star Wars Widevision

COMPLETE SET (120)	15.00	40.00
UNOPENED BOX (36 PACKS)	80.00	100.00
UNOPENED PACK (10 CARDS)	2.50	3.00
COMMON CARD (1-120)	.20	.50

1995 Star Wars Widevision Finest

COMPLETE SET (10)	40.00	100.00
COMMON CARD (1-10)	5.00	12.00
STATED ODDS 1:11		

2007 Star Wars 30th Anniversary

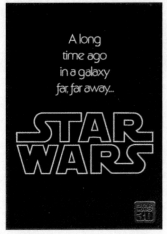

COMPLETE SET (120)	5.00	12.00
UNOPENED HOBBY BOX (24 PACKS)	200.00	225.00
UNOPENED HOBBY PACK (7 CARDS)	10.00	12.00
UNOPENED RETAIL BOX (24 PACKS)		
UNOPENED RETAIL PACK (7 CARDS)		
COMMON CARD (1-120)	.15	.40
*BLUE: 4X TO 10X BASIC CARDS		
*RED: 8X TO 20X BASIC CARDS		
*GOLD/30: 80X TO 150X BASIC CARDS		

2007 Star Wars 30th Anniversary Animation Cels

COMPLETE SET (9)	6.00	15.00
COMMON CARD (1-9)	1.50	4.00
STATED ODDS 1:6 RETAIL		

2007 Star Wars 30th Anniversary Autographs

COMMON AUTO (UNNUMBERED)	10.00	20.00
STATED ODDS 1:43 HOBBY		
NNO Anthony Daniels	700.00	1200.00
NNO Carrie Fisher	600.00	1000.00
NNO Christine Hewett	12.00	30.00
NNO Colin Higgins	15.00	40.00
NNO David Prowse	300.00	600.00
NNO Gary Kurtz	30.00	75.00
NNO George Roubichek	12.00	30.00
NNO Harrison Ford		
NNO Joe Viskocil	15.00	40.00
NNO John Dykstra	20.00	50.00
NNO John Williams	750.00	1200.00
NNO Jon Berg	12.00	30.00
NNO Ken Ralston	15.00	40.00
NNO Kenny Baker	120.00	250.00
NNO Lorne Peterson	12.00	30.00
NNO Maria De Aragon	15.00	40.00
NNO Norman Reynolds	25.00	60.00
NNO Peter Mayhew	150.00	300.00
NNO Phil Tippet	30.00	75.00
NNO Richard Edlund	15.00	40.00
NNO Richard LeParmentier	8.00	20.00
NNO Rusty Goffe	20.00	50.00

2007 Star Wars 30th Anniversary Blister Bonus

COMPLETE SET (3)	3.00	8.00
COMMON CARD (1-3)	1.25	3.00
STATED ODDS 1:BLISTER PACK		

2007 Star Wars 30th Anniversary Magnets

The Tusken Raider

COMPLETE SET (9)	12.00	30.00
COMMON CARD (UNNUMBERED)	1.50	4.00
STATED ODDS 1:8 RETAIL		

2007 Star Wars 30th Anniversary Original Series Box-Toppers

SERIES 1 (1-66) BLUE	12.00	30.00
SERIES 2 (67-132) RED	12.00	30.00
SERIES 3 (133-198) YELLOW	12.00	30.00
SERIES 4 (199-264) GREEN	12.00	30.00
SERIES 5 (265-330) ORANGE SP	30.00	80.00
STATED ODDS 1:BOX		

2007 Star Wars 30th Anniversary Triptych Puzzle

COMPLETE SET (27)	12.00	25.00
COMMON CARD (1-27)	.75	2.00
STATED ODDS 1:3		

2017 Star Wars 40th Anniversary

COMPLETE SET (200)	10.00	25.00
UNOPENED BOX (24 PACKS)	120.00	150.00
UNOPENED PACK (8 CARDS)	5.00	6.50
COMMON CARD (1-200)	.20	.50
*GREEN: .5X TO 1.2X BASIC CARDS	.40	1.00
*BLUE: .6X TO 1.5X BASIC CARDS	.50	1.25
*PURPLE/100: 3X TO 8X BASIC CARDS	2.50	6.00
*GOLD/40: 6X TO 15X BASIC CARDS	5.00	12.00
*RED/1: UNPRICED DUE TO SCARCITY		
*P.P.BLACK/1: UNPRICED DUE TO SCARCITY		
*P.P.CYAN/1: UNPRICED DUE TO SCARCITY		
*P.P.MAGENTA/1: UNPRICED DUE TO SCARCITY		
*P.P.YELLOW/1: UNPRICED DUE TO SCARCITY		

2017 Star Wars 40th Anniversary Autographs

COMMON AUTO	6.00	15.00

*PURPLE/40: .6X TO 1.5X BASIC AUTOS
*GOLD/10: 1X TO 2.5X BASIC AUTOS
*RED/1: UNPRICED DUE TO SCARCITY
*P.P.BLACK/1: UNPRICED DUE TO SCARCITY
*P.P.CYAN/1: UNPRICED DUE TO SCARCITY
*P.P.MAGENTA/1: UNPRICED DUE TO SCARCITY
*P.P.YELLOW/1: UNPRICED DUE TO SCARCITY
RANDOMLY INSERTED INTO PACKS

AAAH	Alan Harris	6.00	15.00
AAAL	Al Lampert	10.00	20.00
AABF	Barbara Frankland	10.00	25.00
AABL	Bai Ling	8.00	20.00
AACR	Clive Revill	10.00	25.00
AADL	Denis Lawson	10.00	25.00
AADR	Deep Roy	10.00	25.00
AAFF	Femi Taylor	8.00	20.00
AAGB	Glyn Baker	8.00	20.00
AAGH	Garrick Hagon	8.00	20.00
AAGR	George Roubicek	10.00	25.00
AAHQ	Hugh Quarshie	10.00	25.00
AAIL	Ian Liston	10.00	25.00
AAJB	Jeremy Bulloch	15.00	40.00
AAJK	Jack Klaff	10.00	25.00
AAKC	Kenneth Colley	8.00	20.00
AAKR	Kipsang Rotich	10.00	25.00
AAMC	Michael Carter	12.00	30.00
AAMW	Matthew Wood	10.00	25.00
AAPS	Paul Springer	8.00	20.00
AARO	Richard Oldfield	10.00	25.00
AASC	Stephen Costantino	8.00	20.00
AATR	Tim Rose	8.00	20.00
AACDW	Corey Dee Williams	8.00	20.00
AAPBL	Paul Blake	10.00	25.00
AAPBR	Paul Brooke	8.00	20.00

2017 Star Wars 40th Anniversary Celebration Orlando Promos

Luke Skywalker

COMPLETE SET (4)	225.00	450.00
COMMON CARD (C1-C4)	50.00	100.00
C1 Luke Skywalker	80.00	150.00
C2 Princess Leia	80.00	150.00
C3 Han Solo	60.00	120.00

2017 Star Wars 40th Anniversary Classic Stickers

COMMON CARD	12.00	30.00

STATED PRINT RUN 100 SER.#'d SETS

2017 Star Wars 40th Anniversary Medallions

COMMON MEDALLION	6.00	15.00
MILLENNIUM FALCON (1-12)		
DEATH STAR (13-23)		
*BLUE/40: .5X TO 1.2X BASIC MEDALLIONS	8.00	20.00
*PURPLE/25: .6X TO 1.5X BASIC MEDALLIONS	10.00	25.00
*GOLD/10: 1.2X TO 3X BASIC MEDALLIONS	20.00	50.00
*RED/1: UNPRICED DUE TO SCARCITY		

2017 Star Wars 40th Anniversary Patches

COMMON CARD (1-20)	5.00	12.00
*BLUE/40: 6X TO 1.5X BASIC CARDS	8.00	20.00
*PURPLE/25: 1X TO 2.5X BASIC CARDS	12.00	30.00
*GOLD/10: 1.5X TO 4X BASIC CARDS	20.00	50.00
RANDOMLY INSERTED INTO PACKS		
TARGET EXCLUSIVE		

2017 Star Wars 1978 Sugar Free Wrappers Set

COMPLETE SET (49)	10.00	25.00
COMPLETE FACTORY SET (51)		
COMMON CARD (1-49)	.30	.75
*BLUE/75: 2X TO 5X BASIC CARDS	1.50	4.00
*GREEN/40: 4X TO 10X BASIC CARDS	3.00	8.00
*GOLD/10: 6X TO 15X BASIC CARDS	5.00	12.00
*RED/1: UNPRICED DUE TO SCARCITY		

2013 Star Wars Illustrated A New Hope

COMPLETE SET (100)	8.00	20.00
COMMON CARD (1-100)	.20	.50
*PURPLE: 2.5X TO 6X BASIC CARDS		
*BRONZE: 5X TO 12X BASIC CARDS		
*GOLD/10: 50X TO 120X BASIC CARDS		
*P.P.BLACK/1: UNPRICED DUE TO SCARCITY		
*P.P.CYAN/1: UNPRICED DUE TO SCARCITY		
*P.P.MAGENTA/1: UNPRICED DUE TO SCARCITY		
*P.P.YELLOW/1: UNPRICED DUE TO SCARCITY		

2013 Star Wars Illustrated A New Hope Film Cels

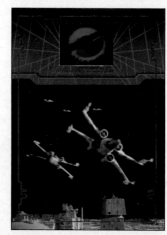

COMPLETE SET (20)	250.00	500.00
COMMON CARD (FR1-FR20)	12.00	30.00
FR8 Greedo's Bounty	15.00	40.00
FR14 The Final Encounter	60.00	120.00

2013 Star Wars Illustrated A New Hope Movie Poster Reinterpretations

COMPLETE SET (9)	5.00	12.00
COMMON CARD (MP1-MP9)	1.25	3.00

*P.P.BLACK/1: UNPRICED DUE TO SCARCITY
*P.P.CYAN/1: UNPRICED DUE TO SCARCITY
*P.P.MAGENTA/1: UNPRICED DUE TO SCARCITY
*P.P.YELLOW/1: UNPRICED DUE TO SCARCITY
STATED ODDS 1:3

2013 Star Wars Illustrated A New Hope One Year Earlier

COMPLETE SET (18)	5.00	12.00
COMMON CARD (OY1-OY18)	.60	1.50

*P.P.BLACK/1: UNPRICED DUE TO SCARCITY
*P.P.CYAN/1: UNPRICED DUE TO SCARCITY
*P.P.MAGENTA/1: UNPRICED DUE TO SCARCITY
*P.P.YELLOW/1: UNPRICED DUE TO SCARCITY
STATED ODDS 1:2

2013 Star Wars Illustrated A New Hope Radio Drama Puzzle

COMPLETE SET (6)	5.00	12.00
COMMON CARD (1-6)	1.50	4.00

*P.P.BLACK/1: UNPRICED DUE TO SCARCITY
*P.P.CYAN/1: UNPRICED DUE TO SCARCITY
*P.P.MAGENTA/1: UNPRICED DUE TO SCARCITY
*P.P.YELLOW/1: UNPRICED DUE TO SCARCITY
STATED ODDS 1:8

2013 Star Wars Illustrated A New Hope The Mission Destroy the Death Star

COMPLETE SET (12)	30.00	60.00
COMMON CARD (1-12)	3.00	8.00

*P.P.BLACK/1: UNPRICED DUE TO SCARCITY
*P.P.CYAN/1: UNPRICED DUE TO SCARCITY
*P.P.MAGENTA/1: UNPRICED DUE TO SCARCITY
*P.P.YELLOW/1: UNPRICED DUE TO SCARCITY
STATED ODDS 1:12

2013 Star Wars Illustrated A New Hope Promos

COMPLETE SET (4)	5.00	12.00

2018 Star Wars A New Hope Black and White

COMPLETE SET (140)	15.00	40.00
UNOPENED BOX (7 PACKS)		
UNOPENED PACK (8 CARDS)		
COMMON CARD (1-140)	.25	.60
*SEPIA: .75X TO 2X BASIC CARDS	.50	1.25
*BLUE: 1X TO 2.5X BASIC CARDS	.60	1.50
*GREEN/99: 3X TO 8X BASIC CARDS	2.00	5.00
*PURPLE/25: 8X TO 20X BASIC CARDS	5.00	12.00
*RED/10: UNPRICED DUE TO SCARCITY		
*METAL/1: UNPRICED DUE TO SCARCITY		

$2018 Star Wars A New Hope Black and White Autographs

COMMON AUTO	6.00	15.00

*BLUE/99: .5X TO 1.2X BASIC AUTOS
*GREEN/25: .6X TO 1.5X BASIC AUTOS
*PURPLE/10: UNPRICED DUE TO SCARCITY
*RED/1: UNPRICED DUE TO SCARCITY
STATED ODDS 1:18

NNO	Al Lampert	8.00	20.00
NNO	Annette Jones	8.00	20.00
NNO	Anthony Daniels		
NNO	Barbara Frankland	8.00	20.00
NNO	Carrie Fisher		
NNO	Denis Lawson	12.00	30.00
NNO	Garrick Hagon	8.00	20.00
NNO	Harrison Ford		
NNO	Kenny Baker		
NNO	Mark Hamill		
NNO	Paul Blake	10.00	25.00
NNO	Peter Mayhew		

2018 Star Wars A New Hope Black and White Autographs Blue

*BLUE: .5X TO 1.2X BASIC AUTOS
STATED ODDS 1:62
STATED PRINT RUN 99 SER.#'d SETS

NNO	Peter Mayhew	30.00	75.00

2018 Star Wars A New Hope Black and White Autographs Green

*GREEN: .6X TO 1.5X BASIC AUTOS
STATED ODDS 1:202
STATED PRINT RUN 25 SER.#'d SETS

NNO	Anthony Daniels	75.00	150.00
NNO	Kenny Baker	60.00	120.00

2018 Star Wars A New Hope Black and White Behind-the-Scenes

COMPLETE SET (41)	20.00	50.00
COMMON CARD (BTS1-BTS41)	2.00	5.00
STATED ODDS 1:2		

2018 Star Wars A New Hope Black and White

Concept Art

COMPLETE SET (12)	10.00	25.00
COMMON CARD (CA1-CA12)	1.50	4.00
STATED ODDS 1:4		

2018 Star Wars A New Hope Black and White

Iconic Characters

COMPLETE SET (12)	15.00	40.00
COMMON CARD (IC1-IC12)	2.00	5.00
STATED ODDS 1:12		
IC1 Luke Skywalker	4.00	10.00
IC2 Han Solo	5.00	12.00
IC3 Princess Leia Organa	4.00	10.00
IC4 Chewbacca	2.50	6.00
IC5 Ben (Obi-Wan) Kenobi	4.00	10.00
IC7 R2-D2	2.50	6.00
IC8 Darth Vader	5.00	12.00

2018 Star Wars A New Hope Black and White

Posters

COMPLETE SET (12)	12.00	30.00
COMMON CARD (PO1-PO12)	1.50	4.00
STATED ODDS 1:6		

1980 Star Wars Empire Strikes Back

"WELCOME, YOUNG LUKE!"

COMPLETE SET (352)	60.00	120.00
COMPLETE SET W/STICKERS (440)	75.00	150.00
COMPLETE SERIES 1 SET (132)	20.00	50.00
COMPLETE SERIES 1 SET W/STICKERS (165)	25.00	60.00
COMPLETE SERIES 2 SET (132)	15.00	40.00
COMPLETE SERIES 2 SET W/STICKERS (165)	20.00	50.00
COMPLETE SERIES 3 SET (88)	12.00	30.00
COMPLETE SERIES 3 SET W/STICKERS (110)	15.00	40.00
UNOPENED SERIES 1 BOX (36 PACKS)	150.00	200.00
UNOPENED SERIES 1 PACK (12 CARDS+1 STICKER)	5.00	6.00
UNOPENED SERIES 2 BOX (36 PACKS)	65.00	80.00
UNOPENED SERIES 2 PACK (12 CARDS+1 STICKER)	2.50	3.00

UNOPENED SERIES 3 BOX (36 PACKS)	65.00	80.00
UNOPENED SERIES 3 PACK (12 CARDS+1 STICKER)	2.50	3.00
COMMON SERIES 1 CARD (1-132)	.10	.25
COMMON SERIES 2 CARD (133-264)	.06	.15
COMMON SERIES 3 CARD (265-352)	.06	.15

1980 Star Wars Empire Strikes Back Stickers

COMPLETE SET (88)	15.00	40.00
COMPLETE SERIES 1 SET (33)	8.00	20.00
COMPLETE SERIES 2 SET (33)	6.00	15.00
COMPLETE SERIES 3 SET (22)	3.00	8.00
COMMON CARD (1-33)	.60	1.50
COMMON CARD (34-66)	.40	1.00
COMMON CARD (67-88)	.20	.50

1980 Star Wars Empire Strikes Back 5X7 Photos

COMPLETE SET (30)	12.00	30.00
COMMON CARD (1-30)	1.00	2.50

1980 Star Wars Empire Strikes Back 5X7 Photos

Test Issue

COMPLETE SET (30)	100.00	200.00
COMMON CARD (1-30)	3.00	8.00

1980 Star Wars Empire Strikes Back Twinkies

New Zealand

COMPLETE SET (6)	15.00	40.00
COMMON CARD (UNNUMBERED)	4.00	10.00

1980 Star Wars Empire Strikes Back York Peanut Butter Discs

COMPLETE SET (6)	12.00	30.00
COMMON CARD (1-6)	3.00	8.00

1995 Star Wars Empire Strikes Back Widevision

COMPLETE SET (144)	12.00	30.00
UNOPENED BOX (36 PACKS)	30.00	40.00
UNOPENED PACK (9 CARDS)	1.00	1.25
COMMON CARD (1-144)	.25	.60

1995 Star Wars Empire Strikes Back Widevision Finest

COMPLETE SET (10)	40.00	100.00
COMMON CARD (C1-C10)	4.00	10.00
STATED ODDS 1:12		

1995 Star Wars Empire Strikes Back Widevision Mini Posters

COMPLETE SET (6)	40.00	80.00
COMMON CARD (1-6)	6.00	15.00
STATED ODDS 1:BOX		

1995 Star Wars Empire Strikes Back Widevision Promos

COMMON CARD	2.00	5.00
NNO 3-Card Sheet	5.00	12.00
P1-P3		

2010 Star Wars Empire Strikes Back 3-D Widevision

COMPLETE SET (48)	10.00	25.00
COMMON CARD (1-48)	.40	1.00
P1 Luke Skywalker PROMO	8.00	20.00

2010 Star Wars Empire Strikes Back 3-D Widevision Autographs

COMMON CARD	150.00	300.00
STATED ODDS 1:1,055		
1 Irvin Kershner	250.00	400.00
2 Ralph McQuarrie	500.00	800.00
4 David Prowse	500.00	800.00
6 Carrie Fisher	500.00	800.00
8 Mark Hamill	400.00	600.00

1996 Star Wars Empire Strikes Back 3-Di

P1 AT-ATs	2.00	5.00

2015 Star Wars Illustrated Empire Strikes Back

COMPLETE SET (100)	10.00	25.00
COMMON CARD (1-100)	.20	.50
*PURPLE: 5X TO 12X BASIC CARDS	2.50	6.00
*BRONZE: 8X TO 20X BASIC CARDS	4.00	10.00
*GOLD/10: 20X TO 50X BASIC CARDS	10.00	25.00

*P.P.BLACK/1: UNPRICED DUE TO SCARCITY	
*P.P.CYAN/1: UNPRICED DUE TO SCARCITY	
*P.P.MAGENTA/1: UNPRICED DUE TO SCARCITY	
*P.P.YELLOW/1: UNPRICED DUE TO SCARCITY	

2015 Star Wars Illustrated Empire Strikes Back Celebration VII Promos

COMPLETE SET (10)	10.00	25.00
COMMON CARD (1-10)	1.50	4.00

2015 Star Wars Illustrated Empire Strikes Back Artist Autographs

COMMON BUSCH	5.00	12.00
COMMON MARTINEZ	6.00	15.00

2015 Star Wars Illustrated Empire Strikes Back Film Cel Relics

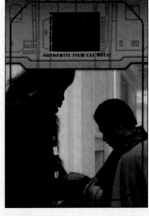

COMPLETE SET (25)	100.00	200.00
COMMON CARD (SKIP #'d)	6.00	15.00
FR2 Back at Echo Base	8.00	20.00
FR3 Monster in the Snow	8.00	20.00
FR6 The Imperial Walkers	10.00	25.00
FR7 Luke Vs. the AT-AT	8.00	20.00
FR8 Imperial Pursuit	10.00	25.00
FR9 Asteroid Field	8.00	20.00
FR10 Dagobah Landing	8.00	20.00
FR13 Message From the Emperor	12.00	30.00
FR15 Bounty Hunters Assemble	8.00	20.00
FR16 Failure at the Cave	10.00	25.00
FR20 A Most Gracious Host	10.00	25.00
FR25 You are not a Jedi Yet	10.00	25.00
FR26 Lando's Redemption	8.00	20.00
FR27 Battle in the Gantry	10.00	25.00
FR28 The Truth Revealed	8.00	20.00
FR29 Rescuing Luke	15.00	40.00
FR30 Saying Farewell	8.00	20.00

2015 Star Wars Illustrated Empire Strikes Back
Movie Poster Reinterpretations

COMPLETE SET (10)	8.00	20.00
COMMON CARD (MP1-MP10)	1.50	4.00
*P.P.BLACK/1: UNPRICED DUE TO SCARCITY		
*P.P.CYAN/1: UNPRICED DUE TO SCARCITY		
*P.P.MAGENTA/1: UNPRICED DUE TO SCARCITY		
*P.P.YELLOW/1: UNPRICED DUE TO SCARCITY		
STATED ODDS 1:3		

2015 Star Wars Illustrated Empire Strikes Back
One Year Earlier

COMPLETE SET (18)	15.00	40.00
COMMON CARD (OY1-OY18)	1.50	4.00
*P.P.BLACK/1: UNPRICED DUE TO SCARCITY		
*P.P.CYAN/1: UNPRICED DUE TO SCARCITY		
*P.P.MAGENTA/1: UNPRICED DUE TO SCARCITY		
*P.P.YELLOW/1: UNPRICED DUE TO SCARCITY		
STATED ODDS 1:2		

2015 Star Wars Illustrated Empire Strikes Back
The Force Awakens Inserts

COMPLETE SET (4)	20.00	50.00
COMMON CARD (SKIP #'d)	8.00	20.00

2015 Star Wars Illustrated Empire Strikes Back
The Mission Capture Skywalker

COMPLETE SET (10)	12.00	30.00
COMMON CARD (1-10)	2.50	6.00
*P.P.BLACK/1: UNPRICED DUE TO SCARCITY		
*P.P.CYAN/1: UNPRICED DUE TO SCARCITY		
*P.P.MAGENTA/1: UNPRICED DUE TO SCARCITY		
*P.P.YELLOW/1: UNPRICED DUE TO SCARCITY		
STATED ODDS 1:8		
3 Han Solo	3.00	8.00
9 Boba Fett	4.00	10.00

1983 Star Wars Return of the Jedi

COMPLETE SET (220)	15.00	40.00
COMMON CARD (1-220)	.15	.40

1983 Star Wars Return of the Jedi Stickers

COMPLETE SET W/O VARIANTS (55)	6.00	15.00
COMMON CARD (1-55)	.20	.50
STATED ODDS 1:1		

2014 Star Wars Return of the Jedi 3-D Widevision

COMPLETE SET (44)	12.00	30.00
COMMON CARD (1-44)	.50	1.25
TOPPS WEBSITE EXCLUSIVE SET		

2014 Star Wars Return of the Jedi 3-D Widevision
Autographs

COMMON CARD (UNNUMBERED)	12.00	30.00
STATED ODDS 1:SET		
NNO Alan Harris	30.00	60.00
NNO Barrie Holland	12.00	30.00
NNO Carrie Fisher		
NNO Femi Taylor	12.00	30.00
NNO Jeremy Bulloch	25.00	60.00
NNO Kenneth Colley	15.00	40.00
NNO Mark Hamill		
NNO Mike Quinn	25.00	50.00
NNO Peter Mayhew	50.00	100.00
NNO Tim Rose	25.00	60.00

2014 Star Wars Return of the Jedi 3-D Widevision
Manufactured Patches

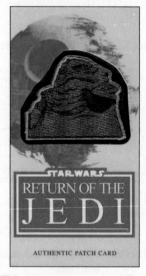

COMPLETE SET (4)	50.00	100.00
COMMON CARD	10.00	25.00
STATED ODDS ONE PATCH/SKETCH PER SET		

1983 Star Wars Return of the Jedi Kellogg's
Stick'R Series

COMPLETE SET (10)	12.00	30.00
COMMON CARD (1-10)	2.00	5.00

1983 Star Wars Return of the Jedi OPC

COMPLETE SET (132)	25.00	60.00
UNOPENED BOX (36 PACKS)	125.00	150.00
UNOPENED PACK	4.00	5.00
COMMON CARD (1-132)	.30	.75

1997 Star Wars Return of the Jedi Special Edition

NNO Crescent City Con XII

1996 Star Wars Return of the Jedi Widevision

COMPLETE SET (144)	10.00	25.00
UNOPENED BOX (24 PACKS)	50.00	60.00
UNOPENED PACK (9 CARDS)	1.50	2.00
COMMON CARD (1-144)	.20	.50

DIII Admiral Akbar

1996 Star Wars Return of the Jedi Widevision Finest

COMPLETE SET (10)	40.00	80.00
COMMON CARD (C1-C10)	4.00	10.00
STATED ODDS 1:12		

1996 Star Wars Return of the Jedi Widevision Mini Posters

COMPLETE SET (6)	40.00	80.00
COMMON CARD (1-6)	6.00	15.00
STATED ODDS 1:BOX		

1996 Star Wars Return of the Jedi Widevision Promos

COMMON CARD	2.00	5.00
P6 Luke, Han, & Chewbacca in Jabba's Palace	25.00	60.00

NNO 1-Card Sheet
Complete the Trilogy

1999 Star Wars Episode One Widevision Series One

COMPLETE SET (80)	8.00	20.00
UNOPENED HOBBY BOX (36 PACKS)	45.00	60.00
UNOPENED HOBBY PACK (8 CARDS)	1.50	2.00
UNOPENED RETAIL BOX (11 PACKS)	30.00	45.00
UNOPENED RETAIL PACK (8 CARDS)	2.75	4.00
COMMON CARD (1-80)	.25	.60

1999 Star Wars Episode One Widevision Series One Chrome

COMPLETE SET (8)	30.00	60.00
COMMON CARD (C1-C8)	4.00	10.00
STATED ODDS 1:12		

1999 Star Wars Episode One Widevision Series One Expansion

COMPLETE SET (40)	30.00	60.00
COMMON CARD (X1-X40)	1.00	2.50
STATED ODDS 1:2		

1999 Star Wars Episode One Widevision Series One Foil

COMPLETE SET (10)	30.00	60.00
COMMON CARD (F1-F10)	3.00	8.00

1999 Star Wars Episode One Widevision Series One Stickers

COMPLETE SET (16)	8.00	20.00
COMMON CARD (S1-S16)	.60	1.50

1999 Star Wars Episode One Widevision Series One Tin Inserts

COMPLETE SET (5)	12.00	30.00
COMMON CARD (1-5)	4.00	10.00
STATED ODDS ONE PER RETAIL TIN		
2 Darth Maul	5.00	12.00

1999 Star Wars Episode One Widevision Series Two

COMPLETE SET (80)	8.00	20.00
UNOPENED HOBBY BOX (36 PACKS)	40.00	50.00
UNOPENED HOBBY PACK (8 CARDS)	1.25	1.50
UNOPENED RETAIL BOX (24 PACKS)	35.00	45.00
UNOPENED RETAIL PACK (8 CARDS)	1.50	1.75
COMMON CARD (1-80)	.25	.60

1999 Star Wars Episode One Widevision Series Two Box-Toppers

COMPLETE SET (3)	10.00	20.00
COMMON CARD (1-3)	4.00	10.00
STATED ODDS 1:HOBBY BOX		

1999 Star Wars Episode One Widevision Series Two Chrome Hobby

COMPLETE SET (4)	12.00	25.00
COMMON CARD (HC1-HC4)	4.00	10.00
STATED ODDS 1:18 HOBBY		

1999 Star Wars Episode One Widevision Series Two Chrome Retail

COMPLETE SET (4)	20.00	40.00
COMMON CARD (C1-C4)	6.00	15.00
STATED ODDS 1:18 RETAIL		

1999 Star Wars Episode One Widevision Series Two Embossed Hobby

COMPLETE SET (6)	8.00	20.00
COMMON CARD (HE1-HE6)	2.50	6.00
STATED ODDS 1:12 HOBBY		

1999 Star Wars Episode One Widevision Series Two Embossed Retail

COMPLETE SET (6)	20.00	40.00
COMMON CARD (E1-E6)	4.00	10.00
STATED ODDS 1:12 RETAIL		

1999 Star Wars Episode One Widevision Series Two Promos

COMPLETE SET (2)	3.00	8.00
COMMON CARD (P1-P2)	2.00	5.00

2000 Star Wars Episode One 3-D

TRADING CARDS

COMPLETE SET (46)	20.00	40.00
UNOPENED BOX (36 PACKS)	45.00	60.00
UNOPENED PACK (2 CARDS)	1.50	2.00
COMMON CARD (1-46)	.50	1.25

2000 Star Wars Episode One 3-D Multi-Motion

COMPLETE SET (2)	10.00	25.00
COMMON CARD (1-2)	6.00	15.00

1999 Star Wars Episode I Bluebird Potato Chips New Zealand

COMPLETE SET (30)	10.00	25.00
COMMON CARD (1-30)	.60	1.50

1999 Star Wars Episode I Family Toy

COMPLETE SET (3)	8.00	20.00
COMMON CARD	4.00	10.00

1999 Star Wars Episode I Flip Images

COMPLETE SET (6)	5.00	12.00
COMMON CARD	1.25	3.00
UNNUMBERED SET		

1999 Star Wars Episode I Hallmark

H1 Anakin Skywalker and Obi-Wan Kenobi	2.00	5.00
H2 Obi-Wan Kenobi and Yoda	2.00	5.00
H3 Qui-Gon Jinn and Obi-Wan Kenobi	2.00	5.00

1999 Star Wars Episode I iKon

COMPLETE SET (60)	6.00	15.00
UNOPENED BOX (36 PACKS)		
UNOPENED PACK (6 CARDS)		
COMMON CARD (1-60)	.20	.50
*SILVER: 1.5X TO 4X BASIC CARDS		
*GOLD: 2.5X TO 6X BASIC CARDS		

1999 Star Wars Episode I KFC Australia

COMPLETE SET (10)	3.00	8.00
COMMON CARD (1-10)	.50	1.25

1999 Star Wars Episode I KFC UK

COMPLETE SET (20)	8.00	20.00
COMMON CARD (1-20)	.60	1.50
STATED ODDS 1:		

1999 Star Wars Episode I Lay's Minis

COMPLETE SET (12)	6.00	15.00
COMMON CARD (1-12)	.75	2.00

1999 Star Wars Episode I The Phantom Menace Harmony Foods

COMPLETE SET (24)	50.00	100.00
COMMON CARD (1-24)	2.00	5.00

1999 Star Wars Episode I The Phantom Menace Kentucky Fried Chicken Employee Stickers

COMPLETE SET (5)	6.00	15.00
COMMON CARD (UNNUMBERED)	2.00	5.00

1999 Star Wars Episode I The Phantom Menace Show Promo

NNO DLP Exclusive Presentation	5.00	12.00

2001 Star Wars Episode I The Phantom Menace Walmart DVD Promos

COMPLETE SET (4)	3.00	8.00
COMMON CARD	1.25	3.00

1999 Star Wars Episode I Star Mart

NNO Anakin Skywalker	2.00	5.00
NNO C-3PO	2.00	5.00
NNO Darth Maul	2.00	5.00
NNO R2-D2	2.00	5.00

2002 Star Wars Attack of the Clones

COMPLETE SET (100)	5.00	12.00
UNOPENED BOX (36 PACKS)	45.00	60.00
UNOPENED PACK (7 CARDS)	1.50	2.00
COMMON CARD (1-100)	.15	.40

2002 Star Wars Attack of the Clones Foil

COMPLETE SET (10)	6.00	15.00
COMMON CARD (1-10)	.75	2.00

2002 Star Wars Attack of the Clones Panoramic Fold-Outs

COMPLETE SET (5)	12.00	30.00
COMMON CARD (1-5)	3.00	8.00
STATED ODDS 1:12		

2002 Star Wars Attack of the Clones Prisms

COMPLETE SET (8)	8.00	20.00
COMMON CARD (1-8)	1.25	3.00

2002 Star Wars Attack of the Clones Promos

COMMON CARD	1.25	3.00
B1 UK Distribution	2.50	6.00
(Album Exclusive)		
P4 Star Wars Insider/Star Wars Gamer Exclusive	3.00	8.00
P6 Star Wars Celebration II Exclusive	3.00	8.00
NNO Best Buy Soundtrack Exclusive	3.00	8.00

2002 Star Wars Attack of the Clones Widevision

COMPLETE SET (80)	5.00	12.00
COMMON CARD (1-80)	.15	.40

2002 Star Wars Attack of the Clones Widevision Autographs

COMPLETE SET (24)	600.00	1200.00
COMMON AUTO (UNNUMBERED)	10.00	25.00
STATED ODDS 1:24		
NNO Ahmed Best	30.00	75.00
NNO Alethea McGrath	25.00	60.00
NNO Amy Allen	30.00	60.00
NNO Andrew Secombe	15.00	40.00
NNO Ayesha Dharker	15.00	40.00
NNO Bodie Taylor	15.00	40.00
NNO Bonnie Piesse	40.00	80.00
NNO Daniel Logan	25.00	60.00
NNO David Bowers	15.00	40.00
NNO Frank Oz	250.00	400.00
NNO Jay Laga'aia	15.00	40.00
NNO Joel Edgerton	20.00	50.00
NNO Kenny Baker	100.00	200.00
NNO Leeanna Walsman	15.00	40.00
NNO Mary Oyaya	15.00	40.00

NNO Rena Owen	15.00	40.00
NNO Ronald Falk	15.00	40.00
NNO Silas Carson/Ki-Adi-Mundi	25.00	50.00
NNO Silas Carson/Nute Gunray	25.00	50.00
NNO Zachariah Jensen	12.00	30.00

2002 Star Wars Attack of the Clones Widevision Promos

P1 Spider Droid	.60	1.50
(Non-Sport Update Exclusive)		
S1 Spider Droid		
(UK Exclusive)		

2002 Star Wars Attack of the Clones Widevision DVD Promos

COMPLETE SET (5)	3.00	8.00
COMMON CARD (W1-W5)	1.00	2.50

2016 Star Wars Attack of the Clones 3-D Widevision

MEETING WITH THE CHANCELLOR

COMPLETE SET (44)	12.00	30.00
COMMON CARD (1-44)	.50	1.25

2016 Star Wars Attack of the Clones 3-D Widevision Autographs

IAN McDIARMID A6
DARTH SIDIOUS

COMMON AUTO	12.00	30.00
*BRONZE/50: X TO X BASIC CARDS		
*SILVER/25: UNPRICED DUE TO SCARCITY		
*GOLD/10: UNPRICED DUE TO SCARCITY		
*RED/1: UNPRICED DUE TO SCARCITY		
STATED ODDS 1:SET		
NNO Alan Ruscoe	15.00	40.00
NNO Amy Allen	12.00	30.00
NNO Daniel Logan	15.00	40.00
NNO Jesse Jensen	15.00	40.00
NNO Jett Lucas	15.00	40.00
NNO Kenny Baker	80.00	150.00
NNO Matthew Wood Magaloof	25.00	60.00
NNO Oliver Ford	15.00	40.00

2016 Star Wars Attack of the Clones 3-D Widevision Medallions

COMPLETE SET (10)	175.00	350.00
COMMON CARD (MC1-MC10)	15.00	40.00
*SILVER/25: X TO X BASIC CARDS		
*GOLD/10: X TO X BASIC CARDS		
*RED/1: UNPRICED DUE TO SCARCITY		
STATED ODDS PATCH OR MEDALLION 1:1		

2016 Star Wars Attack of the Clones 3-D Widevision Patches

COMPLETE SET (12)	200.00	350.00
COMMON CARD (MP1-MP12)	15.00	40.00
*SILVER/25: X TO X BASIC CARDS		
*GOLD/10: X TO X BASIC CARDS		
*RED/1: UNPRICED DUE TO SCARCITY		
STATED ODDS PATCH OR MEDALLION 1:1		

2002 Star Wars Episode II Instant Win

COMPLETE SET (5)	5.00	12.00
COMMON CARD (UNNUMBERED)	1.50	4.00

2002 Star Wars Episode II Jedi Fruit Rolls

COMPLETE SET (6)	5.00	12.00
UNNUMBERED SET		
1 Luke vs. Darth Vader	3.00	8.00
2 Luke vs. Darth Vader	3.00	8.00
3 Obi-Wan vs. Count Dooku	.75	2.00
4 Obi-Wan vs. Darth Vader	2.00	5.00
5 Obi-Wan vs. Jango Fett	.75	2.00
6 Qui-Gon Jinn vs. Darth Maul	1.25	3.00

2005 Star Wars Revenge of the Sith

MACE VS. PALPATINE

COMPLETE SET (90)	5.00	12.00
UNOPENED HOBBY BOX (36 PACKS)	65.00	80.00
UNOPENED HOBBY PACK (7 CARDS)	2.00	2.50
UNOPENED RETAIL BOX (24 PACKS)	30.00	40.00
UNOPENED RETAIL PACK (7 CARDS)	1.50	1.75
COMMON CARD (1-90)	.15	.40

2005 Star Wars Revenge of the Sith Blister Bonus

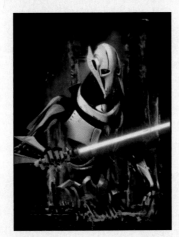

COMPLETE SET (3)	6.00	15.00
COMMON CARD (B1-B3)	2.50	6.00
STATED ODDS ONE PER BLISTER PACK		

2005 Star Wars Revenge of the Sith Embossed Foil

COMPLETE SET (10)	20.00	50.00
COMMON CARD (1-10)	2.50	6.00
STATED ODDS 1:6 RETAIL		

2005 Star Wars Revenge of the Sith Etched Foil Puzzle

COMPLETE SET (6)	12.00	30.00
COMMON CARD (1-6)	2.50	6.00
STATED ODDS 1:6		

2005 Star Wars Revenge of the Sith Flix-Pix

COMPLETE SET (68)	50.00	100.00
UNOPENED BOX (36 PACKS)	100.00	150.00
UNOPENED PACK	3.00	5.00
COMMON CARD (1-68)	1.00	2.50
CL (TRI-FOLD INSERT)	.40	1.00

2005 Star Wars Revenge of the Sith Holograms

CLONE TROOPER

COMPLETE SET (3)	5.00	12.00
COMMON CARD (1-3)	2.00	5.00
STATED ODDS 1:14 RETAIL		

TRADING CARDS

2005 Star Wars Revenge of the Sith Lenticular Morph Hobby

COMPLETE SET (2)	5.00	12.00
COMMON CARD (1-2)	3.00	8.00
STATED ODDS 1:24 HOBBY		

2005 Star Wars Revenge of the Sith Lenticular Morph Retail

COMPLETE SET (2)	5.00	12.00
COMMON CARD (1-2)	3.00	8.00
STATED ODDS 1:24 RETAIL		

2005 Star Wars Revenge of the Sith Stickers

COMPLETE SET (10)	2.50	6.00
COMMON CARD (1-10)	.40	1.00
STATED ODDS 1:3 RETAIL		

2005 Star Wars Revenge of the Sith Tattoos

COMPLETE SET (10)	4.00	10.00
COMMON CARD (1-10)	1.00	2.50
STATED ODDS 1:3 RETAIL		

2005 Star Wars Revenge of the Sith Tin Gold

COMPLETE SET (6)	5.00	12.00
COMMON CARD (A-F)	1.00	2.50
STATED ODDS ONE PER TIN		

2005 Star Wars Revenge of the Sith Tin Story

COMPLETE SET (6)	5.00	12.00
COMMON CARD (1-6)	1.00	2.50
STATED ODDS ONE PER TIN		

2005 Star Wars Revenge of the Sith Promos

COMMON CARD (P1-P5)	1.00	2.50
P3 The Circle is Complete	15.00	40.00
(Star Wars Shop)		

2005 Star Wars Revenge of the Sith Medalionz

COMPLETE SET (24)	15.00	40.00
COMMON CARD (1-24)	1.00	2.50
*GOLD: .8X TO 2X BASIC MED.		
CL Checklist	.20	.50

2005 Star Wars Revenge of the Sith Widevision

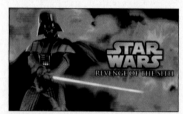

COMPLETE SET (80)	5.00	12.00
UNOPENED HOBBY BOX (24 PACKS)	25.00	40.00
UNOPENED HOBBY PACK (6 CARDS)	1.50	2.00
UNOPENED RETAIL BOX (24 PACKS)	25.00	40.00
UNOPENED RETAIL PACK (6 CARDS)	1.50	2.00
COMMON CARD (1-80)	.15	.40

2005 Star Wars Revenge of the Sith Widevision Autographs

COMMON CARD (UNNUMBERED)	25.00	50.00
STATED ODDS 1:48 HOBBY		
NNO Matthew Wood	50.00	100.00
NNO Peter Mayhew	50.00	100.00
NNO Samuel L. Jackson	600.00	1000.00

2005 Star Wars Revenge of the Sith Widevision Chrome Hobby

COMPLETE SET (10)	12.50	30.00
COMMON CARD (H1-H10)	1.50	4.00
STATED ODDS 1:6 HOBBY		

2005 Star Wars Revenge of the Sith Widevision Chrome Retail

COMPLETE SET (10)	15.00	40.00
COMMON CARD (R1-R10)	2.00	5.00
STATED ODDS 1:60 RETAIL		

2005 Star Wars Revenge of the Sith Widevision Flix-Pix

COMPLETE SET (10)	15.00	40.00
COMMON CARD (1-10)	2.00	5.00
STATED ODDS 1:6		

2015 Star Wars Revenge of the Sith 3-D Widevision

COMPLETE SET (44)	10.00	25.00
COMPLETE FACTORY SET (46)	60.00	120.00
COMMON CARD (1-44)	.40	1.00

2015 Star Wars Revenge of the Sith 3-D Widevision Autographs

COMMON CARD	15.00	40.00
*SILVER/15: UNPRICED DUE TO SCARCITY		
*GOLD/1: UNPRICED DUE TO SCARCITY		
4 Peter Mayhew	60.00	120.00
5 Jeremy Bulloch	25.00	60.00
6 Bai Ling	30.00	80.00

2015 Star Wars Revenge of the Sith 3-D Widevision Medallions

COMPLETE SET (8)	100.00	200.00
COMMON CARD (1-8)	15.00	40.00

*SILVER/30: .6X TO 1.5X BASIC MEDALLIONS

*GOLD/1: UNPRICED DUE TO SCARCITY

2015 Star Wars Revenge of the Sith 3-D Widevision Patches

COMPLETE SET (4)	50.00	100.00
COMMON CARD	15.00	40.00

*SILVER/30: .6X TO 1.5X BASIC PATCHES

*GOLD/1: UNPRICED DUE TO SCARCITY

2017 Star Wars The Force Awakens 3-D Widevision

COMPLETE SET (44)	12.00	30.00
COMPLETE BOXED SET (46)		
COMMON CARD (1-44)	.40	1.00

2016 Star Wars The Force Awakens Chrome

COMPLETE SET (100)	8.00	20.00
UNOPENED BOX (24 PACKS)	50.00	70.00
UNOPENED PACK (6 CARDS)	3.00	3.50
COMMON CARD (1-100)	.25	.60
*REFRACTOR: 1.2X TO 3X BASIC CARDS	.60	1.50
*PRISM REF./99: 5X TO 12X BASIC CARDS	3.00	8.00
*SHIMMER REF./50: 10X TO 25X BASIC CARDS	6.00	15.00
*PULSAR REF./10: 15X TO 40X BASIC CARDS	10.00	25.00

*SUPERFRACTOR/1: UNPRICED DUE TO SCARCITY

*P.P.BLACK/1: UNPRICED DUE TO SCARCITY

*P.P.CYAN/1: UNPRICED DUE TO SCARCITY

*P.P.MAGENTA/1: UNPRICED DUE TO SCARCITY

*P.P.YELLOW/1: UNPRICED DUE TO SCARCITY

2016 Star Wars The Force Awakens Chrome Autographs

COMMON CARD	5.00	12.00

*ATOMIC/99: .5X TO 1.2X BASIC CARDS

*PRISM/50: .6X TO 1.5X BASIC CARDS

*X-FRACTOR/25: .75X TO 2X BASIC CARDS

*SHIMMER/10: UNPRICED DUE TO SCARCITY

*PULSAR/5: UNPRICED DUE TO SCARCITY

*SUPERFRACTOR/1: UNPRICED DUE TO SCARCITY

*P.P.BLACK/1: UNPRICED DUE TO SCARCITY

*P.P.CYAN/1: UNPRICED DUE TO SCARCITY

*P.P.MAGENTA/1: UNPRICED DUE TO SCARCITY

*P.P.YELLOW/1: UNPRICED DUE TO SCARCITY

OVERALL AUTO ODDS 1:24

CAAB Anna Brewster	8.00	20.00
CABV Brian Vernel	10.00	25.00
CAGG Greg Grunberg	10.00	25.00
CAJS Joonas Suotamo	10.00	25.00
CAKS Kipsang Rotich	8.00	20.00
CAMD Mark Dodson	10.00	25.00
CAMQ Mike Quinn	8.00	20.00
CAPM Peter Mayhew	20.00	50.00
CASA Sebastian Armesto	8.00	20.00
CAYR Yayan Ruhian	10.00	25.00
CAMWG Matthew Wood	8.00	20.00

2016 Star Wars The Force Awakens Chrome Autographs Atomic Refractors

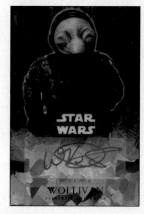

*ATOMIC/99: .5X TO 1.2X BASIC CARDS

CAJB John Boyega	120.00	200.00
CAWD Warwick Davis	12.00	30.00

2016 Star Wars The Force Awakens Chrome Autographs Prism Refractors

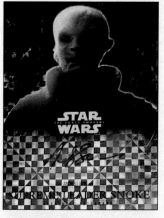

*PRISM/50: .6X TO 1.5X BASIC CARDS

CAAD Anthony Daniels		
CAAS Andy Serkis	120.00	200.00

2016 Star Wars The Force Awakens Chrome Autographs X-fractors

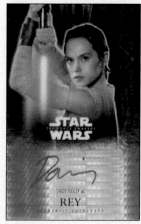

*X-FRACTORS: .75X TO 2X BASIC CARDS

CACF Carrie Fisher	120.00	250.00
CADR Daisy Ridley	1800.00	2200.00
CAEB Erik Bauersfeld		
CAKB Kenny Baker	150.00	300.00
CAMWU Matthew Wood		

2016 Star Wars The Force Awakens Chrome Behind-the-Scenes

COMPLETE SET (12)	10.00	25.00
COMMON CARD (1-12)	1.25	3.00
*SHIMMER REF./50: 1X TO 2.5X BASIC CARDS	3.00	8.00
*PULSAR REF./10: UNPRICED DUE TO SCARCITY		
*SUPERFRACTOR/1: UNPRICED DUE TO SCARCITY		
*P.P.BLACK/1: UNPRICED DUE TO SCARCITY		
*P.P.CYAN/1: UNPRICED DUE TO SCARCITY		
*P.P.MAGENTA/1: UNPRICED DUE TO SCARCITY		
*P.P.YELLOW/1: UNPRICED DUE TO SCARCITY		
STATED ODDS 1:4		

2016 Star Wars The Force Awakens Chrome Heroes of the Resistance

COMPLETE SET (18)	10.00	25.00
COMMON CARD (1-18)	.75	2.00
*SHIMMER REF./50:1 X TO 2.5X BASIC CARDS	2.00	5.00
*PULSAR REF./10: UNPRICED DUE TO SCARCITY		
*SUPERFRACTOR/1: UNPRICED DUE TO SCARCITY		
*P.P.BLACK/1: UNPRICED DUE TO SCARCITY		
*P.P.CYAN/1: UNPRICED DUE TO SCARCITY		
*P.P.MAGENTA/1: UNPRICED DUE TO SCARCITY		
*P.P.YELLOW/1: UNPRICED DUE TO SCARCITY		
STATED ODDS 1:2		
1 Finn	1.25	3.00
2 Rey	1.25	3.00
3 Poe Dameron	1.00	2.50
9 BB-8	1.50	4.00
10 C-3PO	1.00	2.50
11 R2-D2	1.00	2.50
13 Han Solo	1.50	4.00
14 Chewbacca	1.00	2.50
18 General Leia Organa	1.00	2.50

2016 Star Wars The Force Awakens Chrome Medallions

COMPLETE SET (25)	200.00	400.00
COMMON CARD	3.00	8.00
*SILVER/25: .5X TO 1.2X BASIC CARDS		
*GOLD/10: UNPRICED DUE TO SCARCITY		
*PLATINUM/1: UNPRICED DUE TO SCARCITY		
M1 Han Solo	12.00	30.00
M2 General Leia Organa	12.00	30.00
M3 Admiral Ackbar	5.00	12.00
M4 Chewbacca	6.00	15.00
M5 Admiral Statura	5.00	12.00
M6 Snap Wexley	8.00	20.00
M7 Jess Testor Pava	8.00	20.00
M10 Poe Dameron	8.00	20.00
M11 Rey	20.00	50.00
M12 Finn	10.00	25.00
M13 BB-8	10.00	25.00
M14 Riot Control Stormtrooper	8.00	20.00
M16 Colonel Datoo	6.00	15.00
M17 Supreme Leader Snoke	6.00	15.00
M18 Flametrooper	5.00	12.00
M19 Kylo Ren	8.00	20.00
M20 Kylo Ren	8.00	20.00
M21 General Hux	5.00	12.00
M22 Captain Phasma	8.00	20.00
M23 FN-2187	10.00	25.00

2016 Star Wars The Force Awakens Chrome Patches

COMPLETE SET (27)	175.00	350.00
COMMON CARD (P1-P27)	5.00	12.00
*SHIMMER/199: .5X TO 1.2X BASIC CARDS		
*PULSAR/99: .6X TO 1.5X BASIC CARDS		
*SUPERFRACTOR/5: UNPRICED DUE TO SCARCITY		
P1 Rey/686	15.00	40.00
P2 Han Solo/299	8.00	20.00
P4 Finn/686	8.00	20.00
P7 Kylo Ren/401	6.00	15.00
P11 General Leia Organa/755	8.00	20.00
P15 BB-8/686	6.00	15.00
P16 Poe Dameron & BB-8/686	6.00	15.00
P17 Rey & BB-8/686	12.00	30.00
P18 R2-D2/686	6.00	15.00
P19 Rey/299	10.00	25.00
P20 Rey/686	10.00	25.00
P23 Han Solo & Chewbacca/737	10.00	25.00

2016 Star Wars The Force Awakens Chrome Power of the First Order

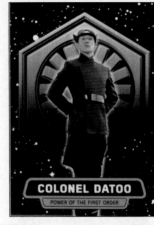

COMPLETE SET (9)	6.00	15.00
COMMON CARD (1-9)	.75	2.00
*SHIMMER REF./50: 1X TO 2.5X BASIC CARDS		
*PULSAR REF./10: UNPRICED DUE TO SCARCITY		
*SUPERFRACTOR/1: UNPRICED DUE TO SCARCITY		
*P.P.BLACK/1: UNPRICED DUE TO SCARCITY		
*P.P.CYAN/1: UNPRICED DUE TO SCARCITY		
*P.P.MAGENTA/1: UNPRICED DUE TO SCARCITY		
*P.P.YELLOW/1: UNPRICED DUE TO SCARCITY		
STATED ODDS 1:12		
1 Supreme Leader Snoke	1.50	4.00
2 Kylo Ren	1.50	4.00
3 General Hux	1.25	3.00
4 Captain Phasma	1.25	3.00

2016 Star Wars The Force Awakens Chrome Ships and Vehicles

COMPLETE SET (11)	6.00	15.00
COMMON CARD (1-11)	1.00	2.50
*SHIMMER REF./50: 1X TO 2.5X BASIC CARDS	2.50	6.00
*PULSAR REF./10: UNPRICED DUE TO SCARCITY		
*SUPERFRACTOR/1: UNPRICED DUE TO SCARCITY		
*P.P.BLACK/1: UNPRICED DUE TO SCARCITY		
*P.P.CYAN/1: UNPRICED DUE TO SCARCITY		
*P.P.MAGENTA/1: UNPRICED DUE TO SCARCITY		
*P.P.YELLOW/1: UNPRICED DUE TO SCARCITY		
STATED ODDS 1:8		

2015 Star Wars The Force Awakens Dog Tags

COMPLETE SET (16)	15.00	40.00
COMMON CARD (1-16)	1.25	3.00
*GOLD: 1X TO 2.5X BASIC TAGS		
1 Kylo Ren	2.00	5.00
2 Rey	2.00	5.00
3 Finn	1.50	4.00
5 Captain Phasma	1.50	4.00
10 BB-8	2.50	6.00
11 Rey	2.00	5.00
12 Finn	1.50	4.00
13 Kylo Ren	2.00	5.00

2015 Star Wars The Force Awakens Dog Tags
Target Exclusives

COMPLETE SET (2)	10.00	25.00
COMMON CARD (T1-T2)	5.00	12.00
*GOLD: .75X TO 2X BASIC TAGS		
EXCLUSIVE TO TARGET		
T2 BB-8	8.00	20.00

2015 Star Wars The Force Awakens Dog Tags Toys 'R' Us Exclusives

COMPLETE SET (2)	10.00	25.00
COMMON CARD (TR1-TR2)	6.00	15.00
*GOLD: 1X TO 2.5X BASIC TAGS		
EXCLUSIVE TO TOYS 'R' US		

2015 Star Wars The Force Awakens Dog Tags Walmart Exclusives

COMPLETE SET (2)	6.00	15.00
COMMON CARD (W1-W2)	4.00	10.00
*GOLD: 1X TO 2.5X BASIC TAGS		
EXCLUSIVE TO WALMART		

2016 Star Wars The Force Awakens Factory Set

COMPLETE FACTORY SET (310)	40.00	80.00
COMMON CARD	.15	.40
JOURNEY TO TFA (1-110)		
TFA SERIES ONE (1-100)		
TFA SERIES TWO (1-100)		
*LIM.ED./100: 6X TO 15X BASIC CARDS	2.50	6.00

2015 Star Wars The Force Awakens Glow-in-the-Dark Decals

COMPLETE SET (7)	10.00	25.00
COMMON CARD	1.25	3.00
STATED ODDS 1:CEREAL BOX		
INSERTED IN BOXES OF GENERAL MILLS CEREAL		
MILLENNIUM FALCON IS KROGER EXCLUSIVE		
1 BB-8	2.50	6.00
2 C-3PO and R2-D2	1.50	4.00
3 Captain Phasma	2.00	5.00
5 Kylo Ren	2.00	5.00
6 Millennium Falcon SP	5.00	12.00
Kroger Exclusive		

2015 Star Wars The Force Awakens Series One

COMPLETE SET w/o SP (100)	10.00	25.00
COMMON CARD (1-100)	.20	.50
*LTSBR GREEN: .5X TO 1.2X BASIC CARDS		
*LTSBR BLUE: .6X TO 1.5X BASIC CARDS		
*LTSBR PURPLE: .75X TO 2X BASIC CARDS		
*FOIL/250: 4X TO 10X BASIC CARDS		
*GOLD/100: 6X TO 15X BASIC CARDS		
*PLATINUM/1: UNPRICED DUE TO SCARCITY		
*P.P.BLACK/1: UNPRICED DUE TO SCARCITY		

*P.P.CYAN/1: UNPRICED DUE TO SCARCITY		
*P.P.MAGENTA/1: UNPRICED DUE TO SCARCITY		
*P.P.YELLOW/1: UNPRICED DUE TO SCARCITY		
TARGET EXCLUSIVES SP 101-103		
100 Han Solo & Chewbacca return home	.75	2.00
101 Maz Kanata SP	3.00	8.00
102 Wollivan SP	3.00	8.00
103 Grummgar SP	3.00	8.00

2015 Star Wars The Force Awakens Series One Autographs

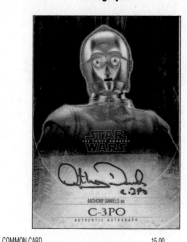

COMMON CARD	15.00	40.00
*LTSBR PURPLE/25: UNPRICED DUE TO SCARCITY		
*GOLD/10: UNPRICED DUE TO SCARCITY		
*IMP. RED/1: UNPRICED DUE TO SCARCITY		
*P.P.BLACK/1: UNPRICED DUE TO SCARCITY		
*P.P.CYAN/1: UNPRICED DUE TO SCARCITY		
*P.P.MAGENTA/1: UNPRICED DUE TO SCARCITY		
*P.P.YELLOW/1: UNPRICED DUE TO SCARCITY		
STATED ODDS 1:106 H; 1:12,334 R		
1 Anthony Daniels	120.00	250.00
2 Carrie Fisher	120.00	250.00
3 Daisy Ridley	800.00	1100.00
Mystery Redemption		
5 John Boyega		
8 Peter Mayhew	30.00	80.00
9 Tim Rose	20.00	50.00

2015 Star Wars The Force Awakens Series One Behind-the-Scenes

COMPLETE SET (7)	5.00	12.00
COMMON CARD (1-7)	1.00	2.50
*LTSBR GREEN: .5X TO 1.2X BASIC CARDS		
*LTSBR BLUE: .6X TO 1.5X BASIC CARDS		
*LTSBR PURPLE: .75X TO 2X BASIC CARDS		
*FOIL/250: 4X TO 10X BASIC CARDS		
*GOLD/100: 6X TO 15X BASIC CARDS		
*PLATINUM/1: UNPRICED DUE TO SCARCITY		
*P.P.BLACK/1: UNPRICED DUE TO SCARCITY		
*P.P.CYAN/1: UNPRICED DUE TO SCARCITY		
*P.P.MAGENTA/1: UNPRICED DUE TO SCARCITY		
*P.P.YELLOW/1: UNPRICED DUE TO SCARCITY		
STATED ODDS 1:8 H; 1:5 R		

2015 Star Wars The Force Awakens Series One Character Montages

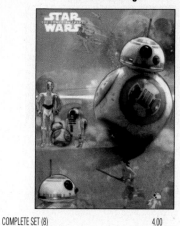

COMPLETE SET (8)	4.00	10.00
COMMON CARD (1-8)	.75	2.00
*LTSBR GREEN: .5X TO 1.2X BASIC CARDS		
*LTSBR BLUE: .6X TO 1.5X BASIC CARDS		
*LTSBR PURPLE: .75X TO 2X BASIC CARDS		
*FOIL/250: 4X TO 10X BASIC CARDS		
*GOLD/100: 6X TO 15X BASIC CARDS		
*PLATINUM/1: UNPRICED DUE TO SCARCITY		
*P.P.BLACK/1: UNPRICED DUE TO SCARCITY		
*P.P.CYAN/1: UNPRICED DUE TO SCARCITY		
*P.P.MAGENTA/1: UNPRICED DUE TO SCARCITY		
*P.P.YELLOW/1: UNPRICED DUE TO SCARCITY		
STATED ODDS 1:7 H; 1:4 R		
1 Rey	1.50	4.00
5 Captain Phasma	1.25	3.00
7 BB-8	1.50	4.00

2015 Star Wars The Force Awakens Series One Character Stickers

COMPLETE SET (18)	6.00	15.00
COMMON CARD (1-18)	.60	1.50
*LTSBR GREEN: .5X TO 1.2X BASIC CARDS		
*LTSBR BLUE: .6X TO 1.5X BASIC CARDS		
*LTSBR PURPLE: .75X TO 2X BASIC CARDS		
*FOIL/250: 4X TO 10X BASIC CARDS		
*GOLD/100: 6X TO 15X BASIC CARDS		
*PLATINUM/1: UNPRICED DUE TO SCARCITY		
*P.P.BLACK/1: UNPRICED DUE TO SCARCITY		
*P.P.CYAN/1: UNPRICED DUE TO SCARCITY		
*P.P.MAGENTA/1: UNPRICED DUE TO SCARCITY		
*P.P.YELLOW/1: UNPRICED DUE TO SCARCITY		
STATED ODDS 1:3 H; 1:2 R		
1 Rey	1.25	3.00
5 Captain Phasma	1.00	2.50
8 BB-8	1.25	3.00
12 Rey	1.25	3.00

2015 Star Wars The Force Awakens Series One
Concept Art

COMPLETE SET (20)	8.00	20.00
COMMON CARD (1-20)	.75	2.00

*LTSBR GREEN: .5X TO 1.2X BASIC CARDS
*LTSBR BLUE: .6X TO 1.5X BASIC CARDS
*LTSBR PURPLE: .75X TO 2X BASIC CARDS
*FOIL/250: 4X TO 10X BASIC CARDS
*GOLD/100: 6X TO 15X BASIC CARDS
*PLATINUM/1: UNPRICED DUE TO SCARCITY
*P.P.BLACK/1: UNPRICED DUE TO SCARCITY
*P.P.CYAN/1: UNPRICED DUE TO SCARCITY
*P.P.MAGENTA/1: UNPRICED DUE TO SCARCITY
*P.P.YELLOW/1: UNPRICED DUE TO SCARCITY
STATED ODDS 1:3 H; 1:2 R

2015 Star Wars The Force Awakens Series One
First Order Rises

COMPLETE SET (9)	6.00	15.00
COMMON CARD (1-9)	1.25	3.00

*LTSBR GREEN: .5X TO 1.2X BASIC CARDS
*LTSBR BLUE: .6X TO 1.5X BASIC CARDS
*LTSBR PURPLE: .75X TO 2X BASIC CARDS
*FOIL/250: 4X TO 10X BASIC CARDS
*GOLD/100: 6X TO 15X BASIC CARDS
*PLATINUM/1: UNPRICED DUE TO SCARCITY
*P.P.BLACK/1: UNPRICED DUE TO SCARCITY
*P.P.CYAN/1: UNPRICED DUE TO SCARCITY
*P.P.MAGENTA/1: UNPRICED DUE TO SCARCITY
*P.P.YELLOW/1: UNPRICED DUE TO SCARCITY
STATED ODDS 1:6 H; 1:4 R

2 Captain Phasma	1.50	4.00

2015 Star Wars The Force Awakens Series One
First Order Stormtrooper Costume Relics

COMMON CARD	12.00	30.00

*BRONZE/99: .75X TO 2X BASIC CARDS
*SILVER/50: 1.2X TO 3X BASIC CARDS
*GOLD/10: 2X TO 5X BASIC CARDS
*PLATINUM/1: UNPRICED DUE TO SCARCITY

2015 Star Wars The Force Awakens Series One
Locations

COMPLETE SET (9)	3.00	8.00
COMMON CARD (1-9)	.60	1.50

*LTSBR GREEN: .5X TO 1.2X BASIC CARDS
*LTSBR BLUE: .6X TO 1.5X BASIC CARDS
*LTSBR PURPLE: .75X TO 2X BASIC CARDS
*FOIL/250: 4X TO 10X BASIC CARDS
*GOLD/100: 6X TO 15X BASIC CARDS
*PLATINUM/1: UNPRICED DUE TO SCARCITY
*P.P.BLACK/1: UNPRICED DUE TO SCARCITY
*P.P.CYAN/1: UNPRICED DUE TO SCARCITY
*P.P.MAGENTA/1: UNPRICED DUE TO SCARCITY
*P.P.YELLOW/1: UNPRICED DUE TO SCARCITY
STATED ODDS 1:6 H; 1:4 R

2015 Star Wars The Force Awakens Series One
Medallions

COMMON CARD (M1-M66)	8.00	20.00
STATED ODDS 1:BOX		

2015 Star Wars The Force Awakens Series One
Movie Scenes

COMPLETE SET (20)	5.00	12.00
COMMON CARD (1-20)	.50	1.25

*LTSBR GREEN: .5X TO 1.2X BASIC CARDS
*LTSBR BLUE: .60X TO 1.5X BASIC CARDS
*LTSBR PURPLE: .75X TO 2X BASIC CARDS
*FOIL/250: 4X TO 10X BASIC CARDS
*GOLD/100: 6X TO 15X BASIC CARDS
*PLATINUM/1: UNPRICED DUE TO SCARCITY
*P.P.BLACK/1: UNPRICED DUE TO SCARCITY
*P.P.CYAN/1: UNPRICED DUE TO SCARCITY
*P.P.MAGENTA/1: UNPRICED DUE TO SCARCITY
*P.P.YELLOW/1: UNPRICED DUE TO SCARCITY
STATED ODDS 1:3 H; 1:2 R

2015 Star Wars The Force Awakens Series One
Weapons

COMPLETE SET (10)	4.00	10.00
COMMON CARD (1-10)	.60	1.50

*LTSBR GREEN: .5X TO 1.2X BASIC CARDS
*LTSBR BLUE: .6X TO 1.5X BASIC CARDS
*LTSBR PURPLE: .75X TO 2X BASIC CARDS
*FOIL/250: 4X TO 10X BASIC CARDS
*GOLD/100: 6X TO 15X BASIC CARDS
*PLATINUM/1: UNPRICED DUE TO SCARCITY
*P.P.BLACK/1: UNPRICED DUE TO SCARCITY
*P.P.CYAN/1: UNPRICED DUE TO SCARCITY
*P.P.MAGENTA/1: UNPRICED DUE TO SCARCITY
*P.P.YELLOW/1: UNPRICED DUE TO SCARCITY
STATED ODDS 1:6 H; 1:3 R

1 Kylo Ren's lightsaber	1.25	3.00
9 Han Solo's Blaster	.75	2.00

2016 Star Wars The Force Awakens Series Two

COMPLETE SET W/O SP (100)	10.00	25.00
COMPLETE SET W/SP (102)	20.00	50.00
UNOPENED HOBBY BOX (24 PACKS)	60.00	100.00
UNOPENED HOBBY PACK (8 CARDS)	2.50	4.00
COMMON CARD (1-100)	.20	.50

*LTSBR GREEN: .5X TO 1.2X BASIC CARDS
*LTSBR BLUE: .6X TO 1.5X BASIC CARDS
*LTSBR PURPLE: .75X TO 2X BASIC CARDS
*FOIL: 4X TO 10X BASIC CARDS
*GOLD/100: 6X TO 15X BASIC CARDS
*PLATINUM/1: UNPRICED DUE TO SCARCITY
*P.P.BLACK/1: UNPRICED DUE TO SCARCITY
*P.P.CYAN/1: UNPRICED DUE TO SCARCITY
*P.P.MAGENTA/1: UNPRICED DUE TO SCARCITY
*P.P.YELLOW/1: UNPRICED DUE TO SCARCITY

101 Finding Luke Skywalker SP	6.00	15.00
102 The Lightsaber Returned SP	10.00	25.00

2016 Star Wars The Force Awakens Series Two
Autographs

COMMON CARD	8.00	20.00

*LTSBR PURPLE/50: .5X TO 1.2X BASIC AUTOS
*FOIL/25: .75X TO 2X BASIC AUTOS
*GOLD/10: UNPRICED DUE TO SCARCITY
*IMP. RED/1: UNPRICED DUE TO SCARCITY
*P.P.BLACK/1: UNPRICED DUE TO SCARCITY
*P.P.CYAN/1: UNPRICED DUE TO SCARCITY
*P.P.MAGENTA/1: UNPRICED DUE TO SCARCITY
*P.P.YELLOW/1: UNPRICED DUE TO SCARCITY

1 David Acord		20.00	50.00
FN-2199			
2 David Acord		15.00	40.00
Teedo			
4 Kenny Baker		50.00	100.00
6 John Boyega		150.00	300.00
7 Anna Brewster		12.00	30.00
8 Dante Briggins		12.00	30.00
9 Thomas Brodie-Sangster		10.00	25.00
10 Aidan Cook		12.00	30.00
11 Anthony Daniels		50.00	100.00
12 Warrick Davis		10.00	25.00
13 Harrison Ford			
14 Greg Grunberg		15.00	40.00
17 Jessica Henwick		15.00	40.00
18 Brian Herring		60.00	120.00
19 Andrew Jack		10.00	25.00
20 Billie Lourd		15.00	40.00
21 Rocky Marshall		10.00	25.00
22 Peter Mayhew		25.00	60.00
25 Arti Shah		12.00	30.00
26 Kiran Shah		10.00	25.00
27 Joonas Suotamo		15.00	40.00
28 Brian Vernel		10.00	25.00
29 Dame Harriet Walter		12.00	30.00
30 Paul Warren		10.00	25.00

2016 Star Wars The Force Awakens Series Two
Card Trader Characters

COMMON CARD (1-9)		50.00	100.00
STATED PRINT RUN 100 SER.#'d SETS			
1 BB-8		60.00	120.00
3 Finn		60.00	120.00
5 Kylo Ren		80.00	150.00
6 Captain Phasma		80.00	150.00
7 Poe Dameron		60.00	120.00
8 Rey		120.00	200.00

2016 Star Wars The Force Awakens Series Two
Character Poster Inserts

COMPLETE SET (5)		5.00	12.00
COMMON CARD (1-5)		1.50	4.00
*P.P.BLACK/1: UNPRICED DUE TO SCARCITY			
*P.P.CYAN/1: UNPRICED DUE TO SCARCITY			
*P.P.MAGENTA/1: UNPRICED DUE TO SCARCITY			
*P.P.YELLOW/1: UNPRICED DUE TO SCARCITY			
STATED ODDS 1:24			
1 Rey		2.50	6.00
2 Finn		2.50	6.00
5 Han Solo		2.00	5.00

2016 Star Wars The Force Awakens Series Two
Character Stickers

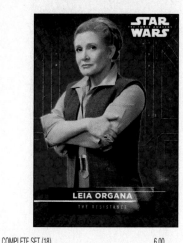

LEIA ORGANA

THE RESISTANCE

COMPLETE SET (18)		6.00	15.00
COMMON CARD (1-18)		.50	1.25
*P.P.BLACK/1: UNPRICED DUE TO SCARCITY			
*P.P.CYAN/1: UNPRICED DUE TO SCARCITY			
*P.P.MAGENTA/1: UNPRICED DUE TO SCARCITY			
*P.P.YELLOW/1: UNPRICED DUE TO SCARCITY			
1 Finn		.75	2.00
2 Rey		1.00	2.50
5 Han Solo		1.00	2.50
6 Leia Organa		.75	2.00
8 Poe Dameron		1.25	3.00
11 BB-8		1.25	3.00
12 Unkar Plutt		.60	1.50
13 General Hux		.75	2.00
15 Admiral Ackbar		.60	1.50
16 Stormtrooper		.75	2.00
18 Maz Kanata		.60	1.50

2016 Star Wars The Force Awakens Series Two
Concept Art

COMPLETE SET (9)		5.00	12.00
COMMON CARD (1-9)		1.00	2.50
*P.P.BLACK/1: UNPRICED DUE TO SCARCITY			
*P.P.CYAN/1: UNPRICED DUE TO SCARCITY			
*P.P.MAGENTA/1: UNPRICED DUE TO SCARCITY			
*P.P.YELLOW/1: UNPRICED DUE TO SCARCITY			

2016 Star Wars The Force Awakens Series Two
Galactic Connexions

COMPLETE SET (5)		120.00	250.00
COMMON CARD (1-5)		30.00	80.00
STATED PRINT RUN 100 ANNCD SETS			
WAL-MART EXCLUSIVE			
3 BB-8		50.00	100.00

2016 Star Wars The Force Awakens Series Two
Heroes of the Resistance

HEROES OF THE RESISTANCE

COMPLETE SET (16)		8.00	20.00
COMMON CARD (1-16)		.75	2.00
*P.P.BLACK/1: UNPRICED DUE TO SCARCITY			
*P.P.CYAN/1: UNPRICED DUE TO SCARCITY			
*P.P.MAGENTA/1: UNPRICED DUE TO SCARCITY			
*P.P.YELLOW/1: UNPRICED DUE TO SCARCITY			
2 Poe Dameron		1.00	2.50
3 Finn		1.00	2.50
4 Rey		1.25	3.00
5 Han Solo		1.50	4.00
16 BB-8		1.50	4.00

2016 Star Wars The Force Awakens Series Two
Maz's Castle

COMPLETE SET (9)		5.00	12.00
COMMON CARD (1-9)		.75	2.00
*P.P.BLACK/1: UNPRICED DUE TO SCARCITY			
*P.P.CYAN/1: UNPRICED DUE TO SCARCITY			
*P.P.MAGENTA/1: UNPRICED DUE TO SCARCITY			
*P.P.YELLOW/1: UNPRICED DUE TO SCARCITY			

2016 Star Wars The Force Awakens Series Two
Medallions

POE DAMERON

COMMON CARD	4.00	10.00
*SILVER p/r 244-399: .5X TO 1.2X BASIC CARDS		
*SILVER p/r 120-199: .6X TO 1.5X BASIC CARDS		
*SILVER p/r 50-99: 1X TO 2.5X BASIC CARDS		
*GOLD p/r 120-199: .6X TO 1.5X BASIC CARDS		
*GOLD p/r 74-100: .75X TO 2X BASIC CARDS		
*GOLD p/r 25-50: 1.2X TO 3X BASIC CARDS		
*PLATINUM p/r 16-25: X TO X BASIC CARDS		
*PLATINUM p/r 5-15: UNPRICED DUE TO SCARCITY		
*PLATINUM/1: UNPRICED DUE TO SCARCITY		
1 Kylo Ren	6.00	15.00
2 General Hux	5.00	12.00
3 Captain Phasma	5.00	12.00
4 FN-2187	5.00	12.00
6 Kylo Ren	6.00	15.00
12 Kylo Ren	6.00	15.00
13 Maz Kanata	5.00	12.00
14 Rey	6.00	15.00
15 BB-8	5.00	12.00
16 Han Solo	8.00	20.00
17 Chewbacca	5.00	12.00
18 Finn	6.00	15.00
19 Rey	6.00	15.00
22 Colonel Datoo	6.00	15.00
23 Captain Phasma	5.00	12.00
24 Finn	5.00	12.00
27 BB-8	5.00	12.00
28 Resistance X-Wing Fighter	5.00	12.00
29 Nien Nunb	6.00	15.00
30 C-3PO	6.00	15.00
31 R2-D2	8.00	20.00
32 Jess Testor Pava	10.00	25.00
33 Snap Wexley	6.00	15.00
34 Admiral Statura	6.00	15.00
35 Admiral Ackbar	6.00	15.00
36 Major Brance	5.00	12.00

2016 Star Wars The Force Awakens Series Two Power of the First Order

COMPLETE SET (11)	5.00	12.00
COMMON CARD (1-11)	.40	1.00
*P.P.BLACK/1: UNPRICED DUE TO SCARCITY		
*P.P.CYAN/1: UNPRICED DUE TO SCARCITY		
*P.P.MAGENTA/1: UNPRICED DUE TO SCARCITY		
*P.P.YELLOW/1: UNPRICED DUE TO SCARCITY		
1 Kylo Ren	1.25	3.00
2 General Hux	1.00	2.50
3 Captain Phasma	1.25	3.00
11 Supreme Leader Snoke	1.00	2.50

2016 Star Wars Rogue One Series One

COMPLETE SET (90)	8.00	20.00
UNOPENED BOX (24 PACKS)	80.00	100.00
UNOPENED PACK (8 CARDS)	3.00	4.00
COMMON CARD (1-90)	.25	.60
*DEATH STAR BL.: .6X TO 1.5X BASIC CARDS		
*GREEN SQ.: .75X TO 2X BASIC CARDS		
*BLUE SQ.: 1X TO 2.5X BASIC CARDS		
*GRAY SQ./100: 4X TO 10X BASIC CARDS		
*GOLD SQ./50: 6X TO 15X BASIC CARDS		
*ORANGE SQ./1: UNPRICED DUE TO SCARCITY		
*P.P.BLACK/1: UNPRICED DUE TO SCARCITY		
*P.P.CYAN/1: UNPRICED DUE TO SCARCITY		
*P.P.MAGENTA/1: UNPRICED DUE TO SCARCITY		
*P.P.YELLOW/1: UNPRICED DUE TO SCARCITY		

2016 Star Wars Rogue One Series One Autographs

COMMON CARD	10.00	25.00
*BLACK/50: .6X TO 1.5X BASIC CARDS		
*GOLD/10: UNPRICED DUE TO SCARCITY		
*P.P.BLACK/1: UNPRICED DUE TO SCARCITY		
*P.P.CYAN/1: UNPRICED DUE TO SCARCITY		
*P.P.MAGENTA/1: UNPRICED DUE TO SCARCITY		
*P.P.YELLOW/1: UNPRICED DUE TO SCARCITY		
RANDOMLY INSERTED INTO PACKS		
1 Donnie Yen as Chirrut Imwe	100.00	200.00
2 Felicity Jones as Jyn Erso	300.00	600.00
3 Forest Whitaker as Saw Gerrera	100.00	200.00
4 Genevieve O'Reilly as Mon Mothma	15.00	40.00

2016 Star Wars Rogue One Series One Blueprints of Ships and Vehicles

COMPLETE SET (8)	5.00	12.00
COMMON CARD (BP1-BP8)	1.00	2.50
*P.P.BLACK/1: UNPRICED DUE TO SCARCITY		
*P.P.CYAN/1: UNPRICED DUE TO SCARCITY		
*P.P.MAGENTA/1: UNPRICED DUE TO SCARCITY		
*P.P.YELLOW/1: UNPRICED DUE TO SCARCITY		
RANDOMLY INSERTED INTO PACKS		

2016 Star Wars Rogue One Series One Character Icons

COMPLETE SET (11)	8.00	20.00
COMMON CARD (CI1-CI11)	1.25	3.00
*P.P.BLACK/1: UNPRICED DUE TO SCARCITY		
*P.P.CYAN/1: UNPRICED DUE TO SCARCITY		
*P.P.MAGENTA/1: UNPRICED DUE TO SCARCITY		
*P.P.YELLOW/1: UNPRICED DUE TO SCARCITY		
RANDOMLY INSERTED INTO PACKS		

2016 Star Wars Rogue One Series One Character Stickers

COMPLETE SET (18)	10.00	25.00
COMMON CARD (CS1-CS18)	.75	2.00
*P.P.BLACK/1: UNPRICED DUE TO SCARCITY		
*P.P.CYAN/1: UNPRICED DUE TO SCARCITY		
*P.P.MAGENTA/1: UNPRICED DUE TO SCARCITY		
*P.P.YELLOW/1: UNPRICED DUE TO SCARCITY		
RANDOMLY INSERTED INTO PACKS		

2016 Star Wars Rogue One Series One Gallery

COMPLETE SET (10)	4.00	10.00
COMMON CARD (G1-G10)	.50	1.25
*P.P.BLACK/1: UNPRICED DUE TO SCARCITY		
*P.P.CYAN/1: UNPRICED DUE TO SCARCITY		
*P.P.MAGENTA/1: UNPRICED DUE TO SCARCITY		
*P.P.YELLOW/1: UNPRICED DUE TO SCARCITY		
RANDOMLY INSERTED INTO PACKS		
G1 Jyn Erso	.75	2.00
G2 Jyn Erso	.75	2.00
G3 Jyn Erso	.75	2.00
G4 Jyn Erso	.75	2.00
G5 Jyn Erso	.75	2.00
G6 Jyn Erso	.75	2.00
G7 Jyn Erso	.75	2.00

2016 Star Wars Rogue One Series One Heroes of the Rebel Alliance

K-2SO
HEROES OF THE REBEL ALLIANCE

COMPLETE SET (14)	8.00	20.00
COMMON CARD (HR1-HR14)	1.00	2.50

*P.P.BLACK/1: UNPRICED DUE TO SCARCITY
*P.P.CYAN/1: UNPRICED DUE TO SCARCITY
*P.P.MAGENTA/1: UNPRICED DUE TO SCARCITY
*P.P.YELLOW/1: UNPRICED DUE TO SCARCITY
RANDOMLY INSERTED INTO PACKS

HR1 Jyn Erso	1.50	4.00
HR4 Chirrut IMWE	1.25	3.00

2016 Star Wars Rogue One Series One Medallions

U-WING

EDRIO TWO TUBES

COMMON CARD	4.00	10.00

*BRONZE: SAME VALUE AS BASIC
*SILVER/99: .5X TO 1.2X BASIC CARDS
*GOLD/50: .6X TO 1.5X BASIC CARDS
*PLATINUM/1: UNPRICED DUE TO SCARCITY
RANDOMLY INSERTED INTO PACKS

5 Captain Cassian Andor with X-Wing	6.00	15.00
6 Captain Cassian Andor with U-Wing	6.00	15.00
7 Chirrut Imwe with Y-Wing	6.00	15.00
8 Darth Vader with Death Star	6.00	15.00
9 Darth Vader with Imperial Star Destroyer	6.00	15.00
10 Death Trooper with Imperial Star Destroyer	6.00	15.00
14 Edrio Two Tubes with U-Wing	6.00	15.00
15 Jyn Erso with X-Wing	8.00	20.00
16 Jyn Erso with U-Wing	8.00	20.00
17 Jyn Erso with Death Star	8.00	20.00
18 K-2SO with X-Wing	5.00	12.00
20 Moroff with U-Wing	5.00	12.00
24 Shoretrooper with AT-ACT	5.00	12.00
25 Stormtrooper with AT-ST	5.00	12.00
27 TIE Fighter Pilot with TIE Striker	5.00	12.00

2016 Star Wars Rogue One Series One Montages

COMPLETE SET (9)	5.00	12.00
COMMON CARD (M1-M9)	1.00	2.50

*P.P.BLACK/1: UNPRICED DUE TO SCARCITY
*P.P.CYAN/1: UNPRICED DUE TO SCARCITY
*P.P.MAGENTA/1: UNPRICED DUE TO SCARCITY
*P.P.YELLOW/1: UNPRICED DUE TO SCARCITY
STATED ODDS 1:

2016 Star Wars Rogue One Series One Villains of the Galactic Empire

DEATH TROOPER
VILLAINS OF THE GALACTIC EMPIRE

COMPLETE SET (8)	6.00	15.00
COMMON CARD (VE1-VE8)	1.00	2.50

*P.P.BLACK/1: UNPRICED DUE TO SCARCITY
*P.P.CYAN/1: UNPRICED DUE TO SCARCITY
*P.P.MAGENTA/1: UNPRICED DUE TO SCARCITY
*P.P.YELLOW/1: UNPRICED DUE TO SCARCITY

2017 Star Wars Rogue One Series Two

KRENNIC AND TARKIN CONFER

COMPLETE SET (100)	6.00	15.00
UNOPENED BOX (24 PACKS)	110.00	120.00
UNOPENED PACK (8 CARDS)	5.00	6.00
COMMON CARD (1-100)	.20	.50

*DTHSTR BLACK: .6X TO 1.5X BASIC CARDS
*GREEN SQ: .75X TO 2X BASIC CARDS
*BLUE SQ: 1X TO 2.5X BASIC CARDS
*GRAY SQ/100: 5X TO 12X BASIC CARDS
*GOLD SQ/50: 10X TO 25X BASIC CARDS
*ORANGE/1: UNPRICED DUE TO SCARCITY

*RED/1: UNPRICED DUE TO SCARCITY
*P.P.BLACK/1: UNPRICED DUE TO SCARCITY
*P.P.CYAN/1: UNPRICED DUE TO SCARCITY
*P.P.MAGENTA/1: UNPRICED DUE TO SCARCITY
*P.P.YELLOW/1: UNPRICED DUE TO SCARCITY

2017 Star Wars Rogue One Series Two Autographs

FELICITY JONES AS
JYN ERSO

COMMON AUTO	10.00	25.00

*BLACK/50: .6X TO 1.5X BASIC AUTOS
*GOLD/10: 1.2X TO 3X BASIC AUTOS
*ORANGE/1: UNPRICED DUE TO SCARCITY
*P.P.BLACK/1: UNPRICED DUE TO SCARCITY
*P.P.CYAN/1: UNPRICED DUE TO SCARCITY
*P.P.MAGENTA/1: UNPRICED DUE TO SCARCITY
*P.P.YELLOW/1: UNPRICED DUE TO SCARCITY
STATED ODDS 1:36
JONES, WHITAKER, AND KELLINGTON
DO NOT HAVE BASE AUTOGRAPHS

DA Derek Arnold	12.00	30.00
DY Donnie Yen	80.00	150.00
GO Genevieve O'Reilly	8.00	20.00
RA Riz Ahmed	120.00	200.00
WD Warwick Davis	12.00	30.00
AC1 Aidan Cook	10.00	25.00
Benthic Two Tubes		
AC2 Aidan Cook	10.00	25.00
Caitken		

2017 Star Wars Rogue One Series Two Autographs Black

*BLACK/50: .6X TO 1.5X BASIC AUTOS
STATED ODDS 1:163
STATED PRINT RUN 50 SER.#'d SETS

FJ Felicity Jones	300.00	600.00
FW Forest Whitaker	100.00	200.00
NK Nick Kellington	20.00	50.00

2017 Star Wars Rogue One Series Two Character Stickers

BISTAN

COMPLETE SET (18)	30.00	80.00
COMMON CARD (CS1-CS18)	2.50	6.00
STATED ODDS 1:12		
CS1 Jyn Erso	5.00	12.00
CS8 Director Krennic	3.00	8.00
CS9 Darth Vader	4.00	10.00
CS10 K-2SO	3.00	8.00
CS14 Chirrut Imwe	4.00	10.00
CS18 Admiral Raddus	3.00	8.00

2017 Star Wars Rogue One Series Two Heroes of the Rebel Alliance

COMPLETE SET (10)	6.00	15.00
COMMON CARD (HR1-HR10)	1.00	2.50
*P.P.BLACK/1: UNPRICED DUE TO SCARCITY		
*P.P.CYAN/1: UNPRICED DUE TO SCARCITY		
*P.P.MAGENTA/1: UNPRICED DUE TO SCARCITY		
*P.P.YELLOW/1: UNPRICED DUE TO SCARCITY		
STATED ODDS 1:7		

2017 Star Wars Rogue One Series Two Movie Posters

COMPLETE SET (10)	30.00	80.00
COMMON CARD (1-10)	3.00	8.00
*P.P.BLACK/1: UNPRICED DUE TO SCARCITY		
*P.P.CYAN/1: UNPRICED DUE TO SCARCITY		
*P.P.MAGENTA/1: UNPRICED DUE TO SCARCITY		
*P.P.YELLOW/1: UNPRICED DUE TO SCARCITY		
STATED ODDS 1:24		
1 United States Theatrical Poster	6.00	15.00
5 Cassian Andor Character Poster	4.00	10.00
6 Bodhi Rook Character Poster	5.00	12.00
7 Chirrut Imwe Character Poster	6.00	15.00
9 K-2SO Character Poster	6.00	15.00

2017 Star Wars Rogue One Series Two Patches

COMMON CARD	5.00	12.00
*SILVER/100: .5X TO 1.2X BASIC CARDS		
*GOLD/50: .6X TO 1.5X BASIC CARDS		
*RED/10: 1.2X TO 3X BASIC CARDS		
*ORANGE/1: UNPRICED DUE TO SCARCITY		

2017 Star Wars Rogue One Series Two Prime Forces

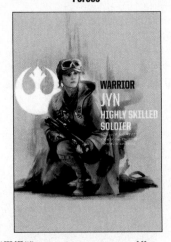

COMPLETE SET (10)	8.00	20.00
COMMON CARD (PF1-PF10)	1.50	4.00
*P.P.BLACK/1: UNPRICED DUE TO SCARCITY		
*P.P.CYAN/1: UNPRICED DUE TO SCARCITY		
*P.P.MAGENTA/1: UNPRICED DUE TO SCARCITY		
*P.P.YELLOW/1: UNPRICED DUE TO SCARCITY		
STATED ODDS 1:2		

2017 Star Wars Rogue One Series Two Troopers

COMPLETE SET (10)	8.00	20.00
COMMON CARD (TR1-TR10)	1.50	4.00
*P.P.BLACK/1: UNPRICED DUE TO SCARCITY		
*P.P.CYAN/1: UNPRICED DUE TO SCARCITY		
*P.P.MAGENTA/1: UNPRICED DUE TO SCARCITY		
*P.P.YELLOW/1: UNPRICED DUE TO SCARCITY		
STATED ODDS 1:2		

2017 Star Wars Rogue One Series Two Villains of the Galactic Empire

COMPLETE SET (10)	12.00	30.00
COMMON CARD (VG1-VG10)	2.50	6.00
*P.P.BLACK/1: UNPRICED DUE TO SCARCITY		
*P.P.CYAN/1: UNPRICED DUE TO SCARCITY		
*P.P.MAGENTA/1: UNPRICED DUE TO SCARCITY		
*P.P.YELLOW/1: UNPRICED DUE TO SCARCITY		
STATED ODDS 1:7		

2017 Star Wars Countdown to The Last Jedi

COMPLETE SET (20)	75.00	150.00
COMMON CARD (1-20)	5.00	12.00
1 Rey Encounters Luke Skywalker/775*	8.00	20.00

2017 Star Wars The Last Jedi Disney Movie Reward Oversized Theater Promos

COMPLETE SET (9)	15.00	40.00
COMMON CARD (UNNUMBERED)	2.00	5.00
THEATER PROMOTION EXCLUSIVE		

2017 Star Wars The Last Jedi Series One

FINN

COMPLETE SET (100)	6.00	15.00
UNOPENED BOX (24 PACKS)	75.00	100.00
UNOPENED PACK (8 CARDS)	4.00	5.00
COMMON CARD (1-100)	.12	.30
*BLUE: 2X TO 5X BASIC CARDS	.60	1.50
*GREEN: 2.5X TO 6X BASIC CARDS	.75	2.00
*PURPLE: 3X TO 8X BASIC CARDS	1.00	2.50
*RED: 4X TO 10X BASIC CARDS	1.25	3.00
*SILVER/99: 10X TO 25X BASIC CARDS	3.00	8.00
*GOLD/25: 20X TO 50X BASIC CARDS	6.00	15.00
*BLACK/1: UNPRICED DUE TO SCARCITY		
*P.P.BLACK/1: UNPRICED DUE TO SCARCITY		
*P.P.CYAN/1: UNPRICED DUE TO SCARCITY		
*P.P.MAGENTA/1: UNPRICED DUE TO SCARCITY		
*P.P.YELLOW/1: UNPRICED DUE TO SCARCITY		

2017 Star Wars The Last Jedi Series One
Autographs

Billie Lourd

BILLIE LOURD

COMMON AUTO	6.00	15.00
*RED/99: .5X TO 1.2X BASIC AUTOS		
*SILVER/25: .6X TO 1.5X BASIC AUTOS		
*GOLD/10: UNPRICED DUE TO SCARCITY		
*BLACK/1: UNPRICED DUE TO SCARCITY		
*P.P.BLACK/1: UNPRICED DUE TO SCARCITY		
*P.P.CYAN/1: UNPRICED DUE TO SCARCITY		
*P.P.MAGENTA/1: UNPRICED DUE TO SCARCITY		
*P.P.YELLOW/1: UNPRICED DUE TO SCARCITY		
STATED ODDS 1:		
NNO Aidan Cook	8.00	20.00
NNO Andy Serkis TFA AU	60.00	120.00
NNO Billie Lourd	60.00	120.00

NNO Brian Herring	12.00	30.00
NNO Crystal Clarke	10.00	25.00
NNO Dave Chapman	12.00	30.00
NNO Ian Whyte	8.00	20.00
NNO Jimmy Vee	15.00	40.00
NNO Mike Quinn	8.00	20.00
NNO Paul Kasey	10.00	25.00
NNO Tom Kane	8.00	20.00
NNO Veronica Ngo	15.00	40.00

2017 Star Wars The Last Jedi Series One
Autographs Red

*RED: .5X TO 1.2X BASIC AUTOS
STATED PRINT RUN 99 SER.#'d SETS

NNO John Boyega		120.00
NNO Joonas Suotamo		75.00

2017 Star Wars The Last Jedi Series One
Autographs Silver

STATED PRINT RUN 25 SER.#'d SETS

NNO Gwendoline Christie	100.00	200.00

2017 Star Wars The Last Jedi Series One
Blueprints and Schematics

COMPLETE SET (8)	6.00	15.00
COMMON CARD (BP1-BP8)	1.25	3.00
*PURPLE/250: .6X TO 1.5X BASIC CARDS	2.00	5.00
*RED/199: .75X TO 2X BASIC CARDS	2.50	6.00
*SILVER/99: 1X TO 2.5X BASIC CARDS	3.00	8.00
*GOLD/25: UNPRICED DUE TO SCARCITY		
*BLACK/1: UNPRICED DUE TO SCARCITY		
*P.P.BLACK/1: UNPRICED DUE TO SCARCITY		
*P.P.CYAN/1: UNPRICED DUE TO SCARCITY		
*P.P.MAGENTA/1: UNPRICED DUE TO SCARCITY		
*P.P.YELLOW/1: UNPRICED DUE TO SCARCITY		
STATED ODDS 1:		

2017 Star Wars The Last Jedi Series One
Character Portraits

COMPLETE SET (16)	12.00	30.00
COMMON CARD (CP1-CP16)	1.50	4.00
*PURPLE/250: .6X TO 1.5X BASIC CARDS	2.50	6.00
*RED/199: .75X TO 2X BASIC CARDS	3.00	8.00
*SILVER/99: 1X TO 2.5X BASIC CARDS	4.00	10.00
*GOLD/25: UNPRICED DUE TO SCARCITY		
*BLACK/1: UNPRICED DUE TO SCARCITY		
*P.P.BLACK/1: UNPRICED DUE TO SCARCITY		
*P.P.CYAN/1: UNPRICED DUE TO SCARCITY		
*P.P.MAGENTA/1: UNPRICED DUE TO SCARCITY		
*P.P.YELLOW/1: UNPRICED DUE TO SCARCITY		
RANDOMLY INSERTED INTO PACKS		

2017 Star Wars The Last Jedi Series One
Character Stickers

COMPLETE SET (6)	8.00	20.00
COMMON CARD (DS1-DS6)	1.25	3.00
RANDOMLY INSERTED INTO PACKS		
DS1 Kylo Ren	1.50	4.00
DS4 Rey	3.00	8.00
DS5 Finn	2.50	6.00
DS6 Poe Dameron	2.00	5.00

2017 Star Wars The Last Jedi Series One
Illustrated

COMPLETE SET (11)	8.00	20.00
COMMON CARD (SWI1-SWI11)	1.25	3.00
*PURPLE/250: .6X TO 1.5X BASIC CARDS	2.00	5.00
*RED/199: .75X TO 2X BASIC CARDS	2.50	6.00
*SILVER/99: 1X TO 2.5X BASIC CARDS	3.00	8.00
*GOLD/25: UNPRICED DUE TO SCARCITY		
*BLACK/1: UNPRICED DUE TO SCARCITY		
*P.P.BLACK/1: UNPRICED DUE TO SCARCITY		
*P.P.CYAN/1: UNPRICED DUE TO SCARCITY		

2017 Star Wars The Last Jedi Series One Medallions

COMMON MEDALLION	4.00	10.00
*PURPLE/99: .5X TO 1.2X BASIC MEDALLIONS	5.00	12.00
*RED/25: 1.2X TO 3X BASIC MEDALLIONS	12.00	30.00
*ORANGE/1: UNPRICED DUE TO SCARCITY		
RANDOMLY INSERTED INTO PACKS		
NNO BB-8 / BB-8	5.00	12.00
NNO BB-8 / Resistance	6.00	15.00
NNO C-3PO / R2-D2	5.00	12.00
NNO Chewbacca / R2-D2	8.00	20.00
NNO Executioner Stormtrooper / First Order	5.00	12.00
NNO Finn / BB-8	5.00	12.00
NNO Finn / Resistance	6.00	15.00
NNO General Hux / First Order	5.00	12.00
NNO General Leia Organa / Resistance	6.00	15.00
NNO Kylo Ren / First Order	6.00	15.00
NNO Luke Skywalker / Millennium Falcon	10.00	25.00
NNO Poe Dameron / BB-8	5.00	12.00
NNO Poe Dameron / Resistance	6.00	15.00
NNO Porg / Millennium Falcon	6.00	15.00
NNO Porg / R2-D2	6.00	15.00
NNO Praetorian Guard / First Order	5.00	12.00
NNO R2-D2 / Resistance	5.00	12.00
NNO Rey / BB-8	8.00	20.00
NNO Rey / Millennium Falcon	8.00	20.00
NNO Rey / Resistance	8.00	20.00
NNO Rose / Resistance	5.00	12.00

2017 Star Wars The Last Jedi Series One Red Character Illustrations

COMPLETE SET (8)	8.00	20.00
COMMON CARD (RL1-RL8)	1.50	4.00
*PURPLE/250: .6X TO 1.5X BASIC CARDS	2.50	6.00
*RED/199: .75X TO 2X BASIC CARDS	3.00	8.00
*SILVER/99: 1X TO 2.5X BASIC CARDS	4.00	10.00
*GOLD/25: UNPRICED DUE TO SCARCITY		
*BLACK/1: UNPRICED DUE TO SCARCITY		
*P.P.BLACK/1: UNPRICED DUE TO SCARCITY		
*P.P.CYAN/1: UNPRICED DUE TO SCARCITY		
*P.P.MAGENTA/1: UNPRICED DUE TO SCARCITY		
*P.P.YELLOW/1: UNPRICED DUE TO SCARCITY		
RANDOMLY INSERTED INTO PACKS		

2017 Star Wars The Last Jedi Series One Resist!

COMPLETE SET (8)	5.00	12.00
COMMON CARD (R1-R8)	1.00	2.50
*PURPLE/250: .6X TO 1.5X BASIC CARDS	1.50	4.00
*RED/199: .75X TO 2X BASIC CARDS	2.00	5.00
*SILVER/99: 1X TO 2.5X BASIC CARDS	2.50	6.00
*GOLD/25: UNPRICED DUE TO SCARCITY		
*BLACK/1: UNPRICED DUE TO SCARCITY		
*P.P.BLACK/1: UNPRICED DUE TO SCARCITY		
*P.P.CYAN/1: UNPRICED DUE TO SCARCITY		
*P.P.MAGENTA/1: UNPRICED DUE TO SCARCITY		
*P.P.YELLOW/1: UNPRICED DUE TO SCARCITY		
RANDOMLY INSERTED INTO PACKS		

2017 Star Wars The Last Jedi Series One Source Material Fabric Relics

COMMON RELIC	12.00	30.00
*SILVER/99: .5X TO 1.2X BASIC RELICS	15.00	40.00
*GOLD/25: UNPRICED DUE TO SCARCITY		
*BLACK/1: UNPRICED DUE TO SCARCITY		
RANDOMLY INSERTED INTO PACKS		

2018 Star Wars The Last Jedi Series Two

COMPLETE SET (100)	6.00	15.00
UNOPENED BOX (24 PACKS)		
UNOPENED PACK (8 CARDS)		
COMMON CARD (1-100)	.12	.30
*BLUE: 2X TO 5X BASIC CARDS	.60	1.50
*PURPLE: 3X TO 8X BASIC CARDS	1.00	2.50
*RED/199: 4X TO 10X BASIC CARDS	1.25	3.00
*BRONZE/99: 10X TO 25X BASIC CARDS	3.00	8.00
*SILVER/25: 20X TO 50X BASIC CARDS	6.00	15.00
*GOLD/10: UNPRICED DUE TO SCARCITY		

2018 Star Wars The Last Jedi Series Two Autographs

COMMON AUTO	6.00	15.00
*RED/99: .5X TO 1.2X BASIC AUTOS		
*SILVER/25: .6X TO 1.5X BASIC AUTOS		
*GOLD/10: UNPRICED DUE TO SCARCITY		
*BLACK/1: UNPRICED DUE TO SCARCITY		
*P.P.BLACK/1: UNPRICED DUE TO SCARCITY		
*P.P.CYAN/1: UNPRICED DUE TO SCARCITY		
*P.P.MAGENTA/1: UNPRICED DUE TO SCARCITY		
*P.P.YELLOW/1: UNPRICED DUE TO SCARCITY		
RANDOMLY INSERTED INTO PACKS		
NNO Adam Driver		
NNO Adrian Edmondson	10.00	25.00
NNO Amanda Lawrence	12.00	30.00
NNO Andy Serkis		
NNO Anthony Daniels		
NNO Billie Lourd		
NNO Brian Herring	8.00	20.00
NNO Crystal Clarke	8.00	20.00
NNO Daisy Ridley		
NNO Gwendoline Christie		
NNO Hermione Corfield	20.00	50.00
NNO Jimmy Vee	10.00	25.00
NNO John Boyega	50.00	100.00
NNO Joonas Suotamo		
NNO Kiran Shah	8.00	20.00
NNO Laura Dern		
NNO Mike Quinn		
NNO Tom Kane		
NNO Veronica Ngo	15.00	40.00

2018 Star Wars The Last Jedi Series Two Autographs Red

*RED: .5X TO 1.2X BASIC AUTOS		
STATED PRINT RUN 99 SER.#'d SETS		
NNO Laura Dern	75.00	150.00

2018 Star Wars The Last Jedi Series Two Autographs Silver

STATED PRINT RUN 25 SER.#'d SETS		
NNO Adam Driver	300.00	500.00
NNO Andy Serkis	60.00	120.00
NNO Anthony Daniels	100.00	200.00
NNO Joonas Suotamo	50.00	100.00

2018 Star Wars The Last Jedi Series Two Character Stickers

POE DAMERON

COMPLETE SET (10)	15.00	40.00
COMMON STICKER (CS1-CS10)	1.25	3.00
CS1 Rey	3.00	8.00
CS2 Kylo Ren	1.50	4.00
CS3 Finn	2.00	5.00
CS4 Poe Dameron	5.00	12.00
CS5 Supreme Leader Snoke	1.50	4.00
CS6 Captain Phasma	2.00	5.00
CS8 General Leia Organa	2.00	5.00
CS10 Luke Skywalker	2.50	6.00

2018 Star Wars The Last Jedi Series Two Commemorative Patches

C'AI THRENALLI — COMMEMORATIVE PATCH

COMMON PATCH	3.00	8.00
*GOLD/25: UNPRICED DUE TO SCARCITY		
NNO BB-8 - BB-8	5.00	12.00
NNO BB-8 - Resist	5.00	12.00
NNO BB-8 - Resistance	5.00	12.00
NNO C-3PO - BB-8	4.00	10.00
NNO C-3PO - Resist	4.00	10.00
NNO C'ai Threnalli - Resistance Pilots	5.00	12.00
NNO Captain Phasma - BB-9E	6.00	15.00
NNO Captain Phasma - First Order	6.00	15.00
NNO Chewbacca - BB-8	4.00	10.00
NNO Chewbacca - Resistance	4.00	10.00
NNO Ensign Pamich Nerro Goode - A-Wing	5.00	12.00
NNO Ensign Pamich Nerro Goode - Resistance	5.00	12.00
NNO Finn - A-Wing	6.00	15.00
NNO Finn - BB-8	6.00	15.00
NNO Finn - Resist	6.00	15.00
NNO General Ematt - A-Wing	5.00	12.00
NNO General Ematt - Resistance	5.00	12.00
NNO General Leia Organa - Resist	8.00	20.00
NNO General Leia Organa - Resistance	8.00	20.00
NNO Kaydel Ko Connix - A-Wing	6.00	15.00
NNO Kaydel Ko Connix - Resistance	6.00	15.00
NNO Kylo Ren - BB-9E	6.00	15.00
NNO Kylo Ren - First Order	6.00	15.00
NNO Luke Skywalker - BB-8	8.00	20.00
NNO Luke Skywalker - Resist	8.00	20.00
NNO Poe Dameron - A-Wing	5.00	12.00
NNO Poe Dameron - BB-8	5.00	12.00

NNO Poe Dameron - Resistance	5.00	12.00
NNO Poe Dameron - Resistance Pilots	5.00	12.00
NNO Praetorian Guard - BB-9E	6.00	15.00
NNO Praetorian Guard - First Order	6.00	15.00
NNO R2-D2 - BB-8	5.00	12.00
NNO R2-D2 - Resist	5.00	12.00
NNO R2-D2 - Resistance	5.00	12.00
NNO Resistance Gunner Paige Tico - Resistance Pilots	5.00	12.00
NNO Rey - A-Wing	6.00	15.00
NNO Rey - BB-8	6.00	15.00
NNO Rey - Resist	6.00	15.00
NNO Rose Tico - Resistance	5.00	12.00
NNO Stormtrooper Executioner - First Order	4.00	10.00
NNO Supreme Leader Snoke - BB-9E	5.00	12.00
NNO Supreme Leader Snoke - First Order	5.00	12.00
NNO Vice Admiral Holdo - Resist	5.00	12.00

2018 Star Wars The Last Jedi Series Two Items and Artifacts

COMPLETE SET (20)	10.00	25.00
COMMON CARD (IA1-IA20)	.75	2.00
*RED/99: .5X TO 1.2X BASIC CARDS		
*BRONZE/50: .75X TO 2X BASIC CARDS		
*SILVER/25: UNPRICED DUE TO SCARCITY		
*GOLD/10: UNPRICED DUE TO SCARCITY		
*BLACK/1: UNPRICED DUE TO SCARCITY		
*P.P.BLACK/1: UNPRICED DUE TO SCARCITY		
*P.P.CYAN/1: UNPRICED DUE TO SCARCITY		
*P.P.MAGENTA/1: UNPRICED DUE TO SCARCITY		
*P.P.YELLOW/1: UNPRICED DUE TO SCARCITY		
STATED ODDS 1:1		
IA1 Skywalker's Lightsaber	2.00	5.00
IA2 Luke Skywalker's Compass	2.00	5.00
IA4 Proton Bomb	1.25	3.00
IA14 Kylo Ren's Lightsaber	3.00	8.00

2018 Star Wars The Last Jedi Series Two Leaders of the Resistance

NIEN NUNB — THE RESISTANCE

COMPLETE SET (10)	5.00	12.00
COMMON CARD (RS1-RS10)	.75	2.00
*RED/99: .5X TO 1.2X BASIC CARDS		
*BRONZE/50: .75X TO 2X BASIC CARDS		
*SILVER/25: UNPRICED DUE TO SCARCITY		
*GOLD/10: UNPRICED DUE TO SCARCITY		
*BLACK/1: UNPRICED DUE TO SCARCITY		
*P.P.BLACK/1: UNPRICED DUE TO SCARCITY		
*P.P.CYAN/1: UNPRICED DUE TO SCARCITY		
*P.P.MAGENTA/1: UNPRICED DUE TO SCARCITY		
*P.P.YELLOW/1: UNPRICED DUE TO SCARCITY		
STATED ODDS 1:2		

2018 Star Wars The Last Jedi Series Two Patrons of Canto Bight

SNOOK UCCORFAY — PATRON OF CANTO BIGHT

COMPLETE SET (10)	6.00	15.00
COMMON CARD (CB1-CB10)	1.25	3.00
*RED/99: .5X TO 1.2X BASIC CARDS	1.50	4.00
*BRONZE/50: .75X TO 2X BASIC CARDS	2.50	6.00
*SILVER/25: UNPRICED DUE TO SCARCITY		
*GOLD/10: UNPRICED DUE TO SCARCITY		
*BLACK/1: UNPRICED DUE TO SCARCITY		
*P.P.BLACK/1: UNPRICED DUE TO SCARCITY		
*P.P.CYAN/1: UNPRICED DUE TO SCARCITY		
*P.P.MAGENTA/1: UNPRICED DUE TO SCARCITY		
*P.P.YELLOW/1: UNPRICED DUE TO SCARCITY		
STATED ODDS 1:6		

2018 Star Wars The Last Jedi Series Two Ships and Vehicles

MILLENNIUM FALCON

COMPLETE SET (10)	8.00	20.00
COMMON CARD (SV1-SV10)	1.50	4.00
*RED/99: .5X TO 1.2X BASIC CARDS	2.00	5.00
*BRONZE/50: .75X TO 2X BASIC CARDS	3.00	8.00
*SILVER/25: UNPRICED DUE TO SCARCITY		
*GOLD/10: UNPRICED DUE TO SCARCITY		
*BLACK/1: UNPRICED DUE TO SCARCITY		
*P.P.BLACK/1: UNPRICED DUE TO SCARCITY		

*P.P.CYAN/1: UNPRICED DUE TO SCARCITY

*P.P.MAGENTA/1: UNPRICED DUE TO SCARCITY

*P.P.YELLOW/1: UNPRICED DUE TO SCARCITY

STATED ODDS 1:8

2018 Star Wars The Last Jedi Series Two Soldiers of the First Order

COMPLETE SET (10)	6.00	15.00
COMMON CARD (FO1-FO10)	1.25	3.00
*RED/99: .5X TO 1.2X BASIC CARDS	1.50	4.00
*BRONZE/50: .75X TO 2X BASIC CARDS	2.50	6.00
*SILVER/25: UNPRICED DUE TO SCARCITY		
*GOLD/10: UNPRICED DUE TO SCARCITY		
*BLACK/1: UNPRICED DUE TO SCARCITY		
*P.P.BLACK/1: UNPRICED DUE TO SCARCITY		
*P.P.CYAN/1: UNPRICED DUE TO SCARCITY		
*P.P.MAGENTA/1: UNPRICED DUE TO SCARCITY		
*P.P.YELLOW/1: UNPRICED DUE TO SCARCITY		
STATED ODDS 1:4		

2018 Star Wars The Last Jedi Series Two Source Material Fabric Swatches

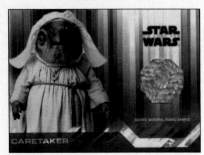

COMMON MEM	20.00	50.00
*GOLD/10: UNPRICED DUE TO SCARCITY		
STATED PRINT RUN 99 SER.#'d SETS		
NNO Captain Peavy's First Order Uniform	25.00	60.00
NNO Caretaker's Smock	60.00	120.00
NNO Praetorian Guard's Ceremonial Battle Skirt	50.00	100.00

2018 Star Wars The Last Jedi Series Two Teaser Posters

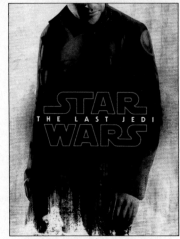

COMPLETE SET (6)	8.00	20.00
COMMON CARD (TP1-TP6)	2.00	5.00
STATED ODDS 1:24		
TP1 Rey	2.50	6.00
TP5 General Leia Organa	2.50	6.00

2018 Countdown to Solo A Star Wars Story

BECKETT & CHEWBACCA ON THE FALCON

COMPLETE SET (25)	75.00	150.00
COMMON CARD (1-25)	5.00	12.00
17 In the Den of the White Worms/241*	6.00	15.00

2018 Solo A Star Wars Story

COMPLETE SET (100)	8.00	20.00
UNOPENED BOX (24 PACKS)	50.00	60.00
UNOPENED PACK (8 CARDS)	2.50	3.00
COMMON CARD (1-100)	.15	.40
*YELLOW: .6X TO 1.5X BASIC CARDS	.25	.60
*BLACK: .75X TO 2X BASIC CARDS	.30	.75
*SILVER: 1.5X TO 4X BASIC CARDS	.60	1.50

*PINK/99: 6X TO 15X BASIC CARDS	2.50	6.00
*ORANGE/25: 15X TO 40X BASIC CARDS	6.00	15.00
*GOLD/10: UNPRICED DUE TO SCARCITY		
*IMPERIAL RED/1: UNPRICED DUE TO SCARCITY		
*P.P.BLACK/1: UNPRICED DUE TO SCARCITY		
*P.P.CYAN/1: UNPRICED DUE TO SCARCITY		
*P.P.MAGENTA/1: UNPRICED DUE TO SCARCITY		
*P.P.YELLOW/1: UNPRICED DUE TO SCARCITY		

2018 Solo A Star Wars Story Autographs

DEE TAILS AS OUAY TOLSITE

COMMON AUTO	8.00	20.00
*PINK/99: .5X TO 1.2X BASIC AUTOS		
*ORANGE/25: .6X TO 1.5X BASIC AUTOS		
*GOLD/10: UNPRICED DUE TO SCARCITY		
*IMPERIAL RED/1: UNPRICED DUE TO SCARCITY		
*P.P.BLACK/1: UNPRICED DUE TO SCARCITY		
*P.P.CYAN/1: UNPRICED DUE TO SCARCITY		
*P.P.MAGENTA/1: UNPRICED DUE TO SCARCITY		
*P.P.YELLOW/1: UNPRICED DUE TO SCARCITY		
STATED ODDS 1:33		
AAF Anna Francolini	12.00	30.00
AAJ Andrew Jack	10.00	25.00
AAW Andrew Woodall	12.00	30.00
ADA Derek Arnold	12.00	30.00
ADT Dee Tails	10.00	25.00
AIK Ian Kenny	10.00	25.00

2018 Solo A Star Wars Story Autographs Pink

STATED ODDS 1:231		
STATED PRINT RUN 99 SER.#'d SETS		
AJS Joonas Suotamo	50.00	100.00
AWD Warwick Davis	20.00	50.00
AJSC Joonas Suotamo	50.00	100.00

2018 Solo A Star Wars Story Character Stickers

COMPLETE SET (7)	8.00	20.00
COMMON CARD (CS1-CS7)	2.00	5.00
STATED ODDS 1:12		

2018 Solo A Star Wars Story Icons

COMPLETE SET (7)	5.00	12.00
COMMON CARD (I1-I7)	1.00	2.50
*P.P.BLACK/1: UNPRICED DUE TO SCARCITY		
*P.P.CYAN/1: UNPRICED DUE TO SCARCITY		
*P.P.MAGENTA/1: UNPRICED DUE TO SCARCITY		
*P.P.YELLOW/1: UNPRICED DUE TO SCARCITY		
STATED ODDS 1:8		

2018 Solo A Star Wars Story Manufactured Patches

COMMON PATCH	3.00	8.00
*PINK/99: .5X TO 1.2X BASIC PATCHES		
*ORANGE/25: .6X TO 1.5X BASIC PATCHES		
*GOLD/10: UNPRICED DUE TO SCARCITY		
*IMPERIAL RED/1: UNPRICED DUE TO SCARCITY		
STATED ODDS 1:32		
MPCC Chewbacca	5.00	12.00
MPCH Chewbacca	5.00	12.00
MPHM Han Solo	6.00	15.00
MPIS Imperial Fleet Trooper	4.00	10.00
MPLH L3-37	5.00	12.00
MPLM Lando Calrissian	6.00	15.00
MPME Enfys Nest	5.00	12.00
MPMS Mimban Stormtrooper	6.00	15.00
MPQC Qi'ra	8.00	20.00
MPQH Qi'ra	8.00	20.00
MPRS R5-PHT	4.00	10.00
MPSS Stormtrooper	4.00	10.00
MPTS TIE Fighter Pilot	6.00	15.00
MPENH Enfys Nest	5.00	12.00
MPHSC Han Solo	6.00	15.00
MPHSH Han Solo	6.00	15.00
MPLCH Lando Calrissian	6.00	15.00

2018 Solo A Star Wars Story Ships and Vehicles

COMPLETE SET (9)	4.00	10.00
COMMON CARD (SV1-SV9)	.60	1.50
*P.P.BLACK/1: UNPRICED DUE TO SCARCITY		
*P.P.CYAN/1: UNPRICED DUE TO SCARCITY		
*P.P.MAGENTA/1: UNPRICED DUE TO SCARCITY		
*P.P.YELLOW/1: UNPRICED DUE TO SCARCITY		
STATED ODDS 1:4		

2018 Solo A Star Wars Story Silhouettes

COMPLETE SET (11)	6.00	15.00
COMMON CARD (SL1-SL11)	1.00	2.50
*P.P.BLACK/1: UNPRICED DUE TO SCARCITY		
*P.P.CYAN/1: UNPRICED DUE TO SCARCITY		
*P.P.MAGENTA/1: UNPRICED DUE TO SCARCITY		
*P.P.YELLOW/1: UNPRICED DUE TO SCARCITY		
STATED ODDS 1:2		

2018 Solo A Star Wars Story Smooth Sayings

COMPLETE SET (8)	8.00	20.00
COMMON CARD (SS1-SS8)	1.50	4.00
*P.P.BLACK/1: UNPRICED DUE TO SCARCITY		

*P.P.CYAN/1: UNPRICED DUE TO SCARCITY		
*P.P.MAGENTA/1: UNPRICED DUE TO SCARCITY		
*P.P.YELLOW/1: UNPRICED DUE TO SCARCITY		
STATED ODDS 1:6		
SS1 I Got This	1.50	4.00
SS2 Chewie Is My Copilot	1.50	4.00
SS3 Just Be Charming	1.50	4.00
SS4 We're Doing This My Way	1.50	4.00
SS5 Kessel Crew	1.50	4.00
SS6 Just Trust Us	1.50	4.00
SS7 Smooth & Sophisticated	1.50	4.00
SS8 Double-Crossing No-Good Swindler	1.50	4.00

2018 Solo A Star Wars Story Target Exclusive Manufactured Patches

COMMON PATCH	5.00	12.00
*PINK/99: .5X TO 1.2X BASIC PATCHES	6.00	15.00
*ORANGE/25: .6X TO 1.5X BASIC PATCHES	8.00	20.00
*GOLD/10: UNPRICED DUE TO SCARCITY		
*IMPERIAL RED/1: UNPRICED DUE TO SCARCITY		
STATED ODDS 1:TARGET BLASTER BOX		

2018 Solo A Star Wars Story Promo

P1 Han Solo	4.00	10.00

2018 Solo A Star Wars Story Denny's

COMPLETE SET (12)	20.00	50.00
UNOPENED PACK (2 CARDS+1 COUPON)	3.00	8.00
COMMON CARD (NNO)	2.00	5.00
*FOIL: 6X TO 15X	30.00	75.00

2018 Solo A Star Wars Story Odeon Cinemas

COMPLETE SET (4)	3.00	8.00
COMMON CARD (UNNUMBERED)	1.00	2.50

2009 Art of Star Wars Comics Postcards

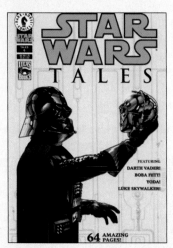

COMPLETE SET (100)	12.00	30.00
COMMON CARD (1-100)	.25	.60

2014 Disney Store Star Wars North America

COMPLETE SET (9)	10.00	25.00
COMMON CARD (1-10)	.75	2.00
US/CANADA EXCLUSIVE		
1 Luke Skywalker	2.00	5.00
4 Darth Vader	2.00	5.00
7 Princess Leia	2.00	5.00
9 Han Solo	2.00	5.00

2014 Disney Store Star Wars United Kingdom

COMPLETE SET (12)	15.00	40.00
COMMON CARD (1-12)	1.00	2.50
UK EXCLUSIVE		
1 Chewbacca	1.25	3.00
2 Darth Vader	4.00	10.00
4 Han Solo	4.00	10.00
6 Luke Skywalker	3.00	8.00
8 Obi-Wan Kenobi	1.25	3.00
9 Princess Leia Organa	3.00	8.00
10 R2-D2 and C-3PO	1.25	3.00
11 Stormtrooper	1.25	3.00

2008 Family Guy Episode IV A New Hope

COMPLETE SET (50)	5.00	12.00
COMMON CARD (1-50)	.15	.40
CL1 ISSUED AS CASE EXCLUSIVE		
CL1 Evil Empire CI	12.00	25.00

2008 Family Guy Episode IV A New Hope Droid Chat

COMPLETE SET (3)	5.00	12.00
COMMON CARD (DC1-DC3)	2.00	5.00
STATED ODDS 1:23		

2008 Family Guy Episode IV A New Hope Promos

P1 Left half w/Han	1.00	2.50
Pi Right half w/Leia	1.00	2.50

2008 Family Guy Episode IV A New Hope Puzzle

COMPLETE SET (9)	4.00	10.00
COMMON CARD (NH1-NH9)	.75	2.00
STATED ODDS 1:7		

2008 Family Guy Episode IV A New Hope Scenes from Space

COMPLETE SET (6)	4.00	10.00
COMMON CARD (S1-S6)	1.25	3.00
STATED ODDS 1:11		

2008 Family Guy Episode IV A New Hope Spaceships and Transports

COMPLETE SET (9)	4.00	10.00
COMMON CARD (ST1-ST9)	1.00	2.50
STATED ODDS 1:9		

2008 Family Guy Episode IV A New Hope What Happens Next?

COMPLETE SET (6)	4.00	10.00
COMMON CARD (WN1-WN6)	1.25	3.00
STATED ODDS 1:11		

2017 Funko Pop Buttons Star Wars

NNO Boba Fett	2.00	5.00
NNO C-3PO	2.00	5.00
NNO Chewbacca	2.00	5.00
NNO Darth Maul	2.00	5.00
NNO Darth Vader	4.00	10.00
NNO Ewok (Wicket)	2.00	5.00
NNO Greedo	2.00	5.00
NNO Han Solo HT		
NNO Jabba	2.00	5.00
NNO Jabba (vaping)		
(Hot Topic Exclusive)		
NNO Luke Skywalker		
(Hot Topic Exclusive)		
NNO Luke/Han/Leia	2.00	5.00
NNO Princess Leia	6.00	15.00
NNO R2-D2	2.00	5.00
NNO Stormtroopers	2.00	5.00

2015-17 Funko Star Wars Smuggler's Bounty Patches

COMPLETE SET (10)		
COMMON PATCH	2.00	5.00
SMUGGLER'S BOUNTY EXCLUSIVE		
NNO BB-8	2.50	6.00
NNO Boba Fett	2.00	5.00
NNO Boushh	2.00	5.00
NNO Cassian Andor	2.00	5.00
NNO Darth Vader	2.50	6.00
NNO Greedo	2.00	5.00
NNO TIE Fighter Pilot	2.00	5.00
NNO X-Wing Pilot	2.00	5.00
NNO Yoda	2.00	5.00
NNO Zeb	2.00	5.00

2015 Star Wars Original Trilogy Series Bikkuriman Stickers

COMPLETE SET (24)	30.00	80.00
COMMON CARD	2.00	5.00

2015 Star Wars Prequel Trilogy Series Bikkuriman Stickers

COMPLETE SET (24)	25.00	60.00
COMMON CARD	1.25	3.00

1996 Star Wars 3-Di Widevision

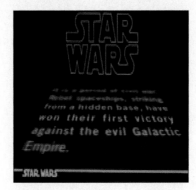

COMPLETE SET (63)	30.00	60.00
COMMON CARD (1-63)	.60	1.50
1M STATED ODDS 1:24		
1M Death Star Explosion	6.00	15.00

1996 Star Wars 3-Di Widevision Promos

3Di1 Darth Vader	2.50	6.00
3Di2 Luke Skywalker	12.00	30.00
Darth Vader/1000*		

2015 Star Wars Abrams Promos

COMPLETE SET (4)	10.00	25.00
COMMON CARD (1-4)	3.00	8.00
STATED ODDS 1:SET PER BOOK		

1997 Star Wars Adventure Journal

NNO One of a Kind by Doug Shuler
NNO To Fight Another Day by Mike Vilardi
NNO Mist Encounter by Doug Shuler

2018 Star Wars Archives Signature Series Adam Driver

62 Adam Driver 2016 TFA Chrome/2
65 Adam Driver 2016 TFA Chrome/2
66 Adam Driver 2016 TFA Chrome/1
92 Adam Driver 2016 Evolution/4
P1 Adam Driver 2015 Journey TFA Patches/1

2018 Star Wars Archives Signature Series Adrian Edmonson

52 Adrian Edmonson 2017 TLJ S1/86
52 Adrian Edmonson 2017 TLJ S1 Red/1
52 Adrian Edmonson 2017 TLJ S1 Purple/35
52 Adrian Edmonson 2017 TLJ S1 Green/50
52 Adrian Edmonson 2017 TLJ S1 Blue/65

2018 Star Wars Archives Signature Series Aidan Cook

16 Aidan Cook 2015 TFA S1/9
44 Aidan Cook 2015 TFA S1/9
44 Aidan Cook 2015 TFA S1 Green/2
64 Aidan Cook 2016 Rogue One S1 Blue/4
64 Aidan Cook 2016 Rogue One S1/28

2018 Star Wars Archives Signature Series Al Lampert

10 Al Lampert 1977 SW/4

468 Al Lampert 2013 GF2 Blue/56

2018 Star Wars Archives Signature Series Alan Harris

13 Alan Harris 2001 Evolution/31

31 Alan Harris 2016 Card Trader/28

31 Alan Harris 2016 Card Trader Blue/7

53 Alan Harris 2015 Journey TFA/51

53 Alan Harris 2015 Journey TFA Green/7

73 Alan Harris 1980 ESB/8

74 Alan Harris 1980 ESB/18

B2 Alan Harris 2016 Card Trader Bounty/6

TC6 Alan Harris 2016 Card Trader Choice/17

ESB4 Alan Harris 2017 GF Reborn/35

2018 Star Wars Archives Signature Series Alan Ruscoe

60 Alan Ruscoe 2001 Evolution/35

82 Alan Ruscoe 2012 Galactic Files/35

8J Alan Ruscoe 2015 Chrome JvS/40

8S Alan Ruscoe 2015 Chrome JvS Refractors/13

8S Alan Ruscoe 2015 Chrome JvS/54

426 Alan Ruscoe 2013 GF2/42

TPM21 Alan Ruscoe 2017 GF Reborn/27

2018 Star Wars Archives Signature Series Alan Tudyk

18 Alan Tudyk 2017 Rogue One S2 Black/2

19 Alan Tudyk 2017 Rogue One S2/21

29 Alan Tudyk 2017 Rogue One S2/20

51 Alan Tudyk 2017 Rogue One S2/16

56 Alan Tudyk 2017 Rogue One S2/20

57 Alan Tudyk 2017 Rogue One S2/10

71 Alan Tudyk 2017 Rogue One S2/20

76 Alan Tudyk 2017 Rogue One S2/20

C18 Alan Tudyk 2016 Rogue One S1 Icons/13

HR3 Alan Tudyk 2016 Rogue One S1 Heroes/5

HR4 Alan Tudyk 2017 Rogue One S2 Heroes/4

MP2 Alan Tudyk 2016 Rogue One MB Patches/7

PF7 Alan Tudyk 2017 Rogue One S2 PF/15

2018 Star Wars Archives Signature Series Alistaire Petrie

10 Alistaire Petrie 2016 Rogue One S1 Green/16

10 Alistaire Petrie 2016 Rogue One S1 Black/19

10 Alistaire Petrie 2016 Rogue One S1/77

2018 Star Wars Archives Signature Series Amanda Lawrence

47 Amanda Lawrence 2017 TLJ S1 Purple/35

47 Amanda Lawrence 2017 TLJ S1 Green/50

47 Amanda Lawrence 2017 TLJ S1 Blue/65

47 Amanda Lawrence 2017 TLJ S1/85

2018 Star Wars Archives Signature Series Amy Allen

81 Amy Allen 2012 Galactic Files/14

424 Amy Allen 2013 GF2/22

AOTC18 Amy Allen 2017 GF Reborn Orange/2

AOTC18 Amy Allen 2017 GF Reborn/37

2018 Star Wars Archives Signature Series Andrew Jack

12 Andrew Jack 2016 TFA S2 Heroes/2

17 Andrew Jack 2015 TFA S1 Blue/1

31 Andrew Jack 2017 TLJ S1 Purple/35

31 Andrew Jack 2017 TLJ S1 Green/50

31 Andrew Jack 2017 TLJ S1 Blue/66

31 Andrew Jack 2017 TLJ S1/85

49 Andrew Jack 2016 Card Trader Blue/8

49 Andrew Jack 2016 Card Trader/22

TFA21 Andrew Jack 2017 GF Reborn/22

2018 Star Wars Archives Signature Series Andy Serkis

1 Andy Serkis 2016 TFA Chrome Power of FO/11

10 Andy Serkis 2017 Journey TLJ/1

14 Andy Serkis 2017 Journey TLJ Characters/4

25 Andy Serkis 2017 TLJ S1/5

26 Andy Serkis 2016 Card Trader/26

30 Andy Serkis 2017 GF Reborn TFA10/30

60 Andy Serkis 2016 Card Trader Red/2

60 Andy Serkis 2016 Card Trader Blue/5

75 Andy Serkis 2016 TFA S2 Blue/4

75 Andy Serkis 2016 TFA S2 Green/5

75 Andy Serkis 2016 TFA Chrome Refractors/15

75 Andy Serkis 2016 TFA S2/16

2018 Star Wars Archives Signature Series Angus MacInnes

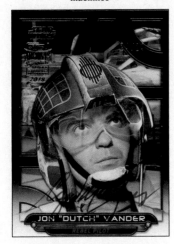

92 Angus MacInnes 2016 Rogue One MB Blue/1

92 Angus MacInnes 2016 Rogue One MB/47

476 Angus MacInnes 2013 GF 2/33

ANH28 Angus MacInnes 2017 GF Reborn/24

2018 Star Wars Archives Signature Series Anthony Forest

31 Anthony Forest 2016 Rogue One MB/36

94 Anthony Forest 1977 Star Wars/7

138 Anthony Forest 1977 Star Wars/9

223 Anthony Forest 2012 Galactic Files/45

WM1 Anthony Forest 2013 GF 2/17

2018 Star Wars Archives Signature Series Ashley Eckstein

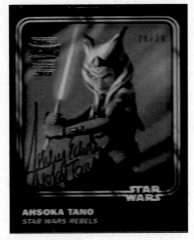

AHSOKA TANO
STAR WARS REBELS

7 Ashley Eckstein 2010 CW ROTBH/3

8 Ashley Eckstein 2017 Journey TLJ Red/1

8 Ashley Eckstein 2017 Journey TLJ Green/1

8 Ashley Eckstein 2017 Journey TLJ/6

10 Ashley Eckstein 2016 Evolution/59

11 Ashley Eckstein 2016 Evolution/39

12 Ashley Eckstein 2016 Evolution/36

36 Ashley Eckstein 2008 CW/9

42 Ashley Eckstein 2010 CW ROTBH/5

44 Ashley Eckstein 2010 CW ROTBH/5

62 Ashley Eckstein 2017 Journey TLJ/9

70 Ashley Eckstein 2008 CW/6

82 Ashley Eckstein 2008 CW/15

88 Ashley Eckstein 2010 CW ROTBH/5

98 Ashley Eckstein 2016 Card Trader/30

I4 Ashley Eckstein 2013 Jedi Legacy Influencers/24

13J Ashley Eckstein 2015 Chrome JvS Refractors/16

13J Ashley Eckstein 2015 Chrome JvS/55

13S Ashley Eckstein 2015 Chrome JvS/56

231 Ashley Eckstein 2012 Galactic Files/12

ACW1 Ashley Eckstein 2017 GF Reborn/34

2018 Star Wars Archives Signature Series Ben Daniels

9 Ben Daniels 2016 Rogue One S1 Black/18

9 Ben Daniels 2016 Rogue One S1/72

9 Ben Daniels 2016 Rogue One S1 Green/15

49 Ben Daniels 2016 Rogue One S1 Blue/8

49 Ben Daniels 2016 Rogue One S1 Green/9

49 Ben Daniels 2016 Rogue One S1/37

63 Ben Daniels 2017 Rogue One S2/10

2018 Star Wars Archives Signature Series Ben Mendelsohn

5 Ben Mendelsohn 2016 Rogue One MB Patches/6

13 Ben Mendelsohn 2016 Rogue One S1 Blue/8

13 Ben Mendelsohn 2016 Rogue One S1 Black/9

13 Ben Mendelsohn 2016 Rogue One S1/38

37 Ben Mendelsohn 2017 Rogue One S2 Blue/1

37 Ben Mendelsohn 2017 Rogue One S2/11

52 Ben Mendelsohn 2016 Rogue One S1 Blue/7

52 Ben Mendelsohn 2016 Rogue One S1 Black/10

52 Ben Mendelsohn 2016 Rogue One S1/36

66 Ben Mendelsohn 2016 Rogue One S1 Green/8

66 Ben Mendelsohn 2016 Rogue One S1 Gray/8

66 Ben Mendelsohn 2016 Rogue One S1/37

83 Ben Mendelsohn 2016 Rogue One S1 Black/7

83 Ben Mendelsohn 2016 Rogue One S1 Green/8

83 Ben Mendelsohn 2016 Rogue One S1 Blue/8

83 Ben Mendelsohn 2016 Rogue One S1/39

CI2 Ben Mendelsohn 2016 Rogue One S1 Characters/14

RO6 Ben Mendelsohn 2017 GF Reborn/23

VE3 Ben Mendelsohn 2016 Rogue One S1 Villains/6

2018 Star Wars Archives Signature Series Billy Dee Williams

8 Billy Dee Williams 1980 ESB/9

64 Billy Dee Williams 2016 Evolution/1

189 Billy Dee Williams 1980 ESB/2

198 Billy Dee Williams 1980 ESB/2

IL4 Billy Dee Williams 2013 Jedi Legacy Influencers I14/7

ESB3 Billy Dee Williams 2017 GF Reborn/1

2018 Star Wars Archives Signature Series Brian Herring

6 Brian Herring 2015 TFA S1/3

6 Brian Herring 2015 TFA S1 Blue/3

7 Brian Herring 2017 40th Ann./3

10 Brian Herring 2016 TFA Chrome Refractors/1

16 Brian Herring 2016 TFA S2 Heroes/6

26 Brian Herring 2016 TFA S2/8

27 Brian Herring 2016 TFA Chrome Refractors/1

27 Brian Herring 2016 TFA S2 Green/1

28 Brian Herring 2016 TFA S2/1

28 Brian Herring 2016 TFA S2 Green/2

30 Brian Herring 2016 TFA Chrome Wave Ref./1

48 Brian Herring 2016 Card Trader/8

78 Brian Herring 2015 TFA S1 Green/1

78 Brian Herring 2015 TFA S1 Blue/1

78 Brian Herring 2015 TFA S1/3

81 Brian Herring 2015 TFA S1 Purple/1

81 Brian Herring 2015 TFA S1/11

82 Brian Herring 2015 TFA S1/5

82 Brian Herring 2015 Journey TFA Green/10

82 Brian Herring 2015 Journey TFA/19

97 Brian Herring 2016 Journey TLJ Green/1

104 Brian Herring 2015 Journey TFA Pink/1

104 Brian Herring 2015 Journey TFA Green/7

104 Brian Herring 2015 Journey TFA/20

TFA4 Brian Herring 2017 GF Reborn/10

2018 Star Wars Archives Signature Series Caroline Blakiston

9 Caroline Blakiston 2016 Rogue One MB Heroes/6

30 Caroline Blakiston 2016 Card Trader Red/2

30 Caroline Blakiston 2016 Card Trader Blue/4

30 Caroline Blakiston 2016 Card Trader/25

63 Caroline Blakiston 1983 ROTJ/11

64 Caroline Blakiston 1983 ROTJ/38

85 Caroline Blakiston 2016 Evolution/47

174 Caroline Blakiston 2012 Galactic Files/14

B15 Caroline Blakiston 2016 Card Trader Bounty/5

ROTJ8 Caroline Blakiston 2017 GF Reborn/25

2018 Star Wars Archives Signature Series Cathy Munroe

37 Cathy Munroe 2016 Card Trader/29

37 Cathy Munroe 2016 Card Trader Blue/3

89 Cathy Munroe 2001 Evolution/33

B8 Cathy Munroe 2016 Card Trader Bounty/5

ESB6 Cathy Munroe 2017 GF Reborn Orange/3

ESB6 Cathy Munroe 2017 GF Reborn/25

2018 Star Wars Archives Signature Series Chris Parsons

1 Chris Parsons 2001 Evolution/34

38 Chris Parsons 2016 Card Trader Blue/8

38 Chris Parsons 2016 Card Trader/28

53 Chris Parsons 2015 Journey TLA/13

B7 Chris Parsons 2016 Card Trader Bounty/6

136 Chris Parsons 2012 Galactic Files/38

ESB5 Chris Parsons 2017 GF Reborn/24

2018 Star Wars Archives Signature Series Corey Dee Williams

40 Corey Dee Williams 2001 Star Wars Evolution/34

2018 Star Wars Archives Signature Series Daisy Ridley

23 Daisy Ridley 2016 TFA S2/1

P6 Daisy Ridley 2015 Journey TFA Patches/1

R1 Daisy Ridley 2015 Journey TFA Heroes/1

P15 Daisy Ridley 2015 Journey TFA Patches/1

2018 Star Wars Archives Signature Series Daniel Logan

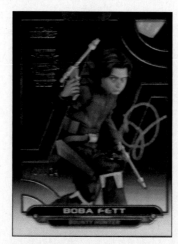

41 Daniel Logan 2012 Galactic Files/21

51 Daniel Logan 2016 Evolution Blue/4

51 Daniel Logan 2016 Evolution/48

78 Daniel Logan 2010 CW ROTBH/3

83 Daniel Logan 2010 CW ROTBH/4

408 Daniel Logan 2013 GF2/38

ACW7 Daniel Logan 2017 GF Reborn/24

AOTC5 Daniel Logan 2017 GF Reborn/28

2018 Star Wars Archives Signature Series Dave Chapman

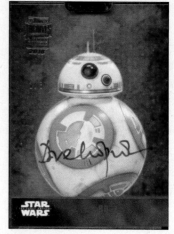

6 Dave Chapman 2015 TFA S1/20

6 Dave Chapman 2015 TFA S1 Blue/3

9 Dave Chapman 2016 TFA Chrome Heroes/10

16 Dave Chapman 2016 TFA S2 Heroes/4

19 Dave Chapman 2015 TFA S1 Movie Scenes/6

26 Dave Chapman 2016 TFA Chrome Refractors/3

26 Dave Chapman 2016 TFA S2/16

27 Dave Chapman 2016 TFA S2 Blue/1

28 Dave Chapman 2016 TFA Chrome Refractors/1

28 Dave Chapman 2016 TFA S2/5

30 Dave Chapman 2016 TFA S2/4

30 Dave Chapman 2016 TFA Chrome/7

39 Dave Chapman 2016 TFA Chrome/9

39 Dave Chapman 2016 TFA S2/14

40 Dave Chapman 2016 TFA Chrome/3

48 Dave Chapman 2016 Card Trader Blue/4

48 Dave Chapman 2016 Card Trader/16

49 Dave Chapman 2016 TFA S2/3

49 Dave Chapman 2016 TFA Chrome/5

63 Dave Chapman 2016 TFA S2 Green/3

63 Dave Chapman 2016 TFA S2 Blue/3

63 Dave Chapman 2016 TFA S2/7

63 Dave Chapman 2016 TFA Chrome/23

73 Dave Chapman 2016 TFA S2 Blue/3

73 Dave Chapman 2016 TFA Chrome/7

73 Dave Chapman 2016 TFA S2/14

76 Dave Chapman 2015 TFA S1/25

77 Dave Chapman 2015 TFA S1/12

78 Dave Chapman 2015 TFA S1/6

79 Dave Chapman 2015 TFA S1/7

80 Dave Chapman 2015 TFA S1/6

81 Dave Chapman 2015 TFA S1 Green/3

81 Dave Chapman 2015 TFA S1/23

82 Dave Chapman 2015 Journey TFA Black/3

82 Dave Chapman 2015 Journey TFA/48

83 Dave Chapman 2015 TFA S1/5

97 Dave Chapman 2017 Journey TLJ/1

R4 Dave Chapman 2015 Journey TFA Heroes/7

104 Dave Chapman 2015 Journey TFA Black/3

104 Dave Chapman 2015 Journey to TFA Green/20

104 Dave Chapman 2015 Journey TFA/48

P18 Dave Chapman 2015 Journey TFA Patches/3

TFA4 Dave Chapman 2017 GF Reborn/16

2018 Star Wars Archives Signature Series David Acord

7 David Acord 2016 TFA S2 Maz's Castle/2

8 David Acord 2015 TFA S1/13

11 David Acord 2015 TFA S1/10

20 David Acord 2015 TFA S1 Blue/11

20 David Acord 2015 TFA S1 Green/11

20 David Acord 2015 TFA S1/28

25   David Acord 2016 TFA Chrome/4
29   David Acord 2015 TFA S1/26
43   David Acord 2016 TFA Chrome/4
52   David Acord 2016 TFA Chrome Refractors/2
52   David Acord 2015 TFA S1/6
58   David Acord 2016 Card Trader/23
61   David Acord 2016 Card Trader/23
68   David Acord 2016 TFA S2 Blue/5
68   David Acord 2016 TFA S2 Green/10
68   David Acord 2016 TFA S2/25
68   David Acord 2016 TFA Chrome Refractors/30
68   David Acord 2016 TFA Chrome/38
75   David Acord 2015 TFA S1/11
TFA29   David Acord 2017 GF Reborn/22

2018 Star Wars Archives Signature Series David Ankrum

19   David Ankrum 2016 Card Trader/13
88   David Ankrum 2016 Rogue One MB Black/1
88   David Ankrum 2016 Rogue One MB/16
9R   David Ankrum 2014 Chrome 9R/11
118   David Ankrum 2012 Galactic Files/14
145   David Ankrum 2012 Galactic Files/13
175   David Ankrum 2012 Galactic Files/15
I12   David Ankrum 2013 Jedi Legacy Influencers/19
ANH23   David Ankrum 2017 GF Reborn/21

2018 Star Wars Archives Signature Series David Barclay

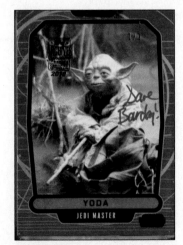

3   David Barclay 2017 40th Ann. Green/1
9   David Barclay 1980 ESB/10
9   David Barclay 2016 Card Trader/10
10   David Barclay 2016 Card Trader Blue/5
10   David Barclay 2016 Card Trader/19
13   David Barclay 1983 ROTJ/5

14   David Barclay 1983 ROTJ/18
15   David Barclay 1983 ROTJ/7
21   David Barclay 2012 Galactic Files/1
28   David Barclay 2017 40th Ann. Green/1
36   David Barclay 2001 Evolution/11
41   David Barclay 1999 Chrome Archives/1
46   David Barclay 1983 ROTJ/8
49   David Barclay 2015 Journey TFA Green/2
49   David Barclay 2015 Journey TFA/2
58   David Barclay 1980 ESB/7
63   David Barclay 1980 ESB/5
63   David Barclay Journey TFA/22
80   David Barclay 2015 Journey TFA Green/1
82   David Barclay 2016 Evolution/20
83   David Barclay 2016 Evolution Blue/19
83   David Barclay 2016 Evolution/19
163   David Barclay 2012 Galactic Files/11
172   David Barclay 1983 ROTJ/20
34L   David Barclay Jedi Legacy/30
35J   David Barclay 2015 Chrome JvS/19
35S   David Barclay Chrome JvS/31
490   David Barclay 2013 GF2/1
50E   David Barclay 2014 Chrome 50E/5
50R   David Barclay 2014 Chrome 50R/5
519   David Barclay 2013 GF2/15
C15   David Barclay 2013 Jedi Legacy Connections/10
ESB2   David Barclay 2017 GF Reborn/22

2018 Star Wars Archives Signature Series Dee Bradley Baker

6   Dee Baker 2008 CW/6
8   Dee Baker 2010 CW ROTBH/5
94   Dee Baker 2016 Card Trader Blue/7
94   Dee Baker 2016 Card Trader/26
233   Dee Baker 2012 Galactic Files/19
475   Dee Baker 2015 Chrome JvS/8
ACW9   Dee Baker 2017 GF Reborn/1
ACW9   Dee Baker 2017 GF Reborn/27

2018 Star Wars Archives Signature Series Deep Roy

21   Deep Roy 1983 ROTJ/14
183   Deep Roy 2012 Galactic Files/32
ROTJ16   Deep Roy 2017 GF Reborn/42

2018 Star Wars Archives Signature Series Denis Lawson

19   Denis Lawson 2016 Card Trader Red/1
19   Denis Lawson 2016 Card Trader Blue/4
19   Denis Lawson 2016 Card Trader/11
83   Denis Lawson 2001 Evolution/16
88   Denis Lawson 2016 Rogue One MB/27
9R   Denis Lawson 2014 Chrome Refractors/2
9R   Denis Lawson 2014 Chrome 9R/12
127   Denis Lawson 1983 ROTJ/9
145   Denis Lawson 2012 Galactic Files/16
175   Denis Lawson 2012 Galactic Files/16
I12   Denis Lawson 2013 Jedi Legacy Influencers/16
ANH23   Denis Lawson 2017 GF Reborn/13
ESB13   Denis Lawson 2017 GF Reborn/15

2018 Star Wars Archives Signature Series Derek Arnold

19   Derek Arnold 2016 Rogue One S1 Blue/7
19   Derek Arnold 2016 Rogue One S1/38
34   Derek Arnold 2017 Rogue One S2 Blue/2
34   Derek Arnold 2016 Rogue One S1 Green/8
34   Derek Arnold 2016 Rogue One S1/34
58   Derek Arnold 2017 Rogue One S2 Black/2
58   Derek Arnold 2017 Rogue One S2/10
87   Derek Arnold 2016 Rogue One S1 Green/8
87   Derek Arnold 2016 Rogue One S1/39
HR10   Derek Arnold 2016 Rogue One S1 Heroes/2

2018 Star Wars Archives Signature Series Dermot Crowley

39 Dermot Crowley 2016 Card Trader Blue/6

39 Dermot Crowley 2016 Card Trader/24

ROTJ9 Dermot Crowley 2017 GF Reborn/24

2018 Star Wars Archives Signature Series Dickey Beer

47 Dickey Beer 1983 ROTJ/7

25L Dickey Beer 2013 Jedi Legacy/14

32L Dickey Beer 2013 Jedi Legacy/20

379 Dickey Beer GF2/44

2018 Star Wars Archives Signature Series Felicity Jones

1 Felicity Jones 2016 Rogue One S1/6

21 Felicity Jones 2016 Rogue One S1/1

21 Felicity Jones 2016 Rogue One S1/4

24 Felicity Jones 2016 Rogue One S1/1

24 Felicity Jones 2016 Rogue One S1/6

46 Felicity Jones 2016 Rogue One S1/11

51 Felicity Jones 2016 Rogue One S1 Black/2

70 Felicity Jones 2016 Rogue One S1/1

70 Felicity Jones 2016 Rogue One S1/11

79 Felicity Jones 2016 Rogue One S1 Blue/1

79 Felicity Jones 2016 Rogue One S1/21

80 Felicity Jones 2016 Rogue One S1/11

84 Felicity Jones 2016 Rogue One S1/6

G1 Felicity Jones 2016 Rogue One S1 Gallery/1

RO1 Felicity Jones 2017 GF Reborn Blue/2

2018 Star Wars Archives Signature Series Femi Taylor

55 Femi Taylor 2001 Evolution/30

177 Femi Taylor 2012 Galactic Files/23

ROTJ5 Femi Taylor 2017 GF Reborn Blue/1

ROTJ5 Femi Taylor GF Reborn/30

2018 Star Wars Archives Signature Series Forest Whitaker

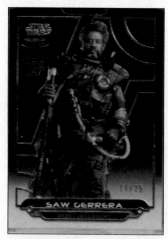

6 Forest Whitaker 2016 Rogue One S1 Green/16

6 Forest Whitaker 2016 Rogue One S1 Black/20

6 Forest Whitaker 2016 Rogue One S1/92

8 Forest Whitaker 2017 Rogue One S2 Posters/1

27 Forest Whitaker 2017 Rogue One S2/14

HR8 Forest Whitaker 2016 Rogue One S1 Heroes/4

RO7 Forest Whitaker 2017 GF Reborn/25

2018 Star Wars Archives Signature Series Garrick Hagon

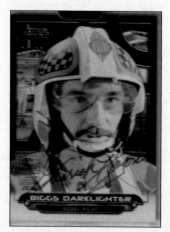

10 Garrick Hagon 2001 Evolution/33

36 Garrick Hagon 2016 Card Trader Blue/4

36 Garrick Hagon 2016 Card Trader/25

89 Garrick Hagon 2016 Rogue One MB/32

111 Garrick Hagon 2007 30th Ann./10

119 Garrick Hagon 2012 Galactic Files/32

16E Garrick Hagon 2014 Chrome/5

16R Garrick Hagon 2014 Chrome/8

243 Garrick Hagon 1977 Star Wars/12

I10 Garrick Hagon 2013 Jedi Legacy Influencers I10/37

ANH25 Garrick Hagon 2017 GF Reborn/39

2018 Star Wars Archives Signature Series Genevieve O'Reilly

8 Genevieve O'Reilly 2016 Rogue One S1 Blue/15

8 Genevieve O'Reilly 2016 Rogue One S1 Black/19

8 Genevieve O'Reilly 2016 Rogue One S1/99

9 Genevieve O'Reilly 2016 Rogue One MB Heroes/4

10 Genevieve O'Reilly 2017 Rogue One S2 Black/3

10 Genevieve O'Reilly 2017 Rogue One S2/15

41 Genevieve O'Reilly 2017 Rogue One S2/16

60 Genevieve O'Reilly 2017 40th Ann./3

73 Genevieve O'Reilly 2016 Rogue One S1 Green/8

73 Genevieve O'Reilly 2016 Rogue One S1/57

84 Genevieve O'Reilly 2016 Evolution/37

91 Genevieve O'Reilly 2012 Galactic Files/15

102 Genevieve O'Reilly 2016 Rogue One MB/1

102 Genevieve O'Reilly 2016 Rogue One MB/19

2018 Star Wars Archives Signature Series Gerald Home

ROTJ15 Gerald Home 2017 GF Reborn/23

2018 Star Wars Archives Signature Series Hayden Christensen

2 Hayden Christensen 2016 Evolution/8
3 Hayden Christensen 2017 Journey TLJ Red/1
3 Hayden Christensen 2016 Evolution/6
3 Hayden Christensen 2017 Journey TLJ/6
4 Hayden Christensen 2017 Journey TLJ/1
6 Hayden Christensen 2017 40th Ann./1
6 Hayden Christensen 2017 Journey TLJ/5
9 Hayden Christensen 2015 Journey TFA Black/1
9 Hayden Christensen 2015 Journey TFA Pink/1
9 Hayden Christensen 2017 Journey TLJ/4
12 Hayden Christensen 2017 Journey TLJ/3
13 Hayden Christensen 2010 CW ROTBH/8
14 Hayden Christensen 2016 Rogue One MB/4
15 Hayden Christensen 2016 Rogue One MB Black/1
17 Hayden Christensen 2015 Journey TFA Black/1
2J Hayden Christensen 2015 Chrome JvS Refractors/5
2J Hayden Christensen 2015 Chrome JvS/8
2S Hayden Christensen 2015 Chrome JvS/6
49 Hayden Christensen 2017 40th Ann. Blue/2
49 Hayden Christensen 2017 40th Ann./5
51 Hayden Christensen 2017 40th Ann./4
52 Hayden Christensen 2017 40th Ann./3
53 Hayden Christensen 2017 40th Ann./5
57 Hayden Christensen 2017 Journey TLJ Red/1
57 Hayden Christensen 2017 Journey TLJ/3
66 Hayden Christensen 2012 Galactic Files/10
71 Hayden Christensen 2016 Card Trader Blue/7
71 Hayden Christensen 2016 Card Trader/24
80 Hayden Christensen 2015 Journey TFA/6
89 Hayden Christensen 2017 40th Ann./1
93 Hayden Christensen 2004 Heritage/2
100 Hayden Christensen 2004 Heritage/1
17A Hayden Christensen 2013 Jedi Legacy/6
19A Hayden Christensen 2013 Jedi Legacy/8
21A Hayden Christensen 2013 Jedi Legacy/4
24A Hayden Christensen 2013 Jedi Legacy/6
27A Hayden Christensen 2013 Jedi Legacy/8
33A Hayden Christensen 2013 Jedi Legacy Blue/1
36A Hayden Christensen 2013 Jedi Legacy/8
38A Hayden Christensen 2013 Jedi Legacy/7
401 Hayden Christensen 2013 GF2/8
45A Hayden Christensen 2013 Jedi Legacy/5
CL7 Hayden Christensen 2012 Galactic Files Classic Lines/3
CL8 Hayden Christensen 2013 GF2/2
ROTS1 Hayden Christensen 2017 GF Reborn/24

2018 Star Wars Archives Signature Series Hermione Corfield

49 Hermione Corfield 2017 TLJ S1 Purple/36
49 Hermione Corfield 2017 TLJ S1 Green/50
49 Hermione Corfield 2017 TLJ S1 Blue/65
49 Hermione Corfield 2017 TLJ S1/85

2018 Star Wars Archives Signature Series Howie Weed

ESB15 Howie Weed 2017 GF Reborn/22

2018 Star Wars Archives Signature Series Ian McElhinney

17 Ian McElhinney 2016 Rogue One S1 Green/6
17 Ian McElhinney 2016 Rogue One S1 Black/9
17 Ian McElhinney 2016 Rogue One S1/39

2018 Star Wars Archives Signature Series Jack Klaff

90 Jack Klaff 2016 Rogue One MB/48
122 Jack Klaff 2012 Galactic Files/21

2018 Star Wars Archives Signature Series James Arnold Taylor

3 James Arnold Taylor CW ROTBH/1
19 James Arnold Taylor CW ROTBH/3

26 James Arnold Taylor CW ROTBH/4
40 James Arnold Taylor CW ROTBH/3

2018 Star Wars Archives Signature Series Jason Spisak

ACW15 Jason Spisak 2017 GF Reborn/24

2018 Star Wars Archives Signature Series Jeremy Bulloch

11 Jeremy Bulloch 2001 Evolution/19
12 Jeremy Bulloch 2016 Card Trader Blue/4
23 Jeremy Bulloch 1983 ROTJ/38
53 Jeremy Bulloch 2016 Evolution/14
53 Jeremy Bulloch 2016 Evolution/52
54 Jeremy Bulloch 2016 Evolution/48
73 Jeremy Bulloch 1980 ESB/13
75 Jeremy Bulloch 1980 ESB/22
162 Jeremy Bulloch 2012 Galactic Files/10
34J Jeremy Bulloch 2015 Chrome JvS/54
34S Jeremy Bulloch 2015 Chrome JvS/45
474 Jeremy Bulloch 2013 GF2/44
518 Jeremy Bulloch 2013 GF2/21
ESB1 Jeremy Bulloch GF Reborn/23

2018 Star Wars Archives Signature Series Jerome Blake

RUNE HAAKO
STAR WARS: THE PHANTOM MENACE

30 Jerome Blake 2012 Galactic Files/37
40 Jerome Blake 2006 Evolution Update/1
57 Jerome Blake 2001 Evolution/36
84 Jerome Blake 2016 Card Trader Blue/8
84 Jerome Blake 2016 Card Trader/25
382 Jerome Blake 2013 GF2/2
41J Jerome Blake 2015 Chrome JvS Refractors/6
41J Jerome Blake 2015 Chrome JvS/66
TPM15 Jerome Blake 2017 GF Reborn/23

2018 Star Wars Archives Signature Series Jimmy Vee

R2-D2

13 Jimmy Vee 2017 TLJ S1 Red/1
13 Jimmy Vee 2017 TLJ S1 Purple/35
13 Jimmy Vee 2017 TLJ S1 Green/50
13 Jimmy Vee 2017 TLJ S1 Blue/66
13 Jimmy Vee 2017 TLJ S1/85

2018 Star Wars Archives Signature Series John Boyega

2 John Boyega 2015 TFA S1 Montages/1
2 John Boyega 2015 TFA S1 Green/2
4 John Boyega 2015 Journey TFA Silhouette/3
9 John Boyega 2017 Journey TLJ Green/1
9 John Boyega 2016 TFA S2/1
13 John Boyega 2016 Evolution Stained/1
21 John Boyega 2016 TFA S2/1
29 John Boyega 2016 TFA S2/1
29 John Boyega 2016 TFA S2 Blue/2
32 John Boyega 2016 TFA S2/3
38 John Boyega 2016 TFA S2/5
39 John Boyega 2016 TFA S2 Purple/1
40 John Boyega 2015 TFA S1/1
45 John Boyega 2016 TFA S2/1
67 John Boyega 2016 TFA S2/1
70 John Boyega 2016 TFA S2 Blue/1
73 John Boyega 2017 Journey TLJ/28
75 John Boyega 2017 Journey TLJ/29
82 John Boyega 2017 Journey TLJ/26
85 John Boyega 2016 TFA S2/1
89 John Boyega 2016 Evolution/1
90 John Boyega 2016 TFA S1/1
90 John Boyega 2016 TFA S2 Green/3
96 John Boyega 2017 Journey TLJ/25
97 John Boyega 2015 TFA S1/1
99 John Boyega 2015 TFA S1/1
R9 John Boyega 2015 Journey TFA Heroes/1

2018 Star Wars Archives Signature Series John Morton

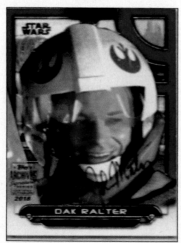

DAK RALTER

11 John Morton 1980 ESB/12
20 John Morton 2016 Card Trader Blue/6
20 John Morton 2016 Card Trader/33
37 John Morton 2004 Heritage/2
38 John Morton 1980 ESB/14
50 John Morton 1999 Chrome Archives/1
91 John Morton 1980 ESB/23
98 John Morton 1980 ESB/7
C8 John Morton 2013 Jedi Legacy Connections/29
131 John Morton 2012 Galactic Files /11
146 John Morton 2012 Galactic Files/31
210 John Morton 1980 ESB/8
220 John Morton 1980 ESB/38
489 John Morton 2013 GF2/23
FQ3 John Morton 2016 Card Trader Film Quotes/8
CL10 John Morton 2012 Galactic Files Classic Lines/1
ESB14 John Morton 2017 GF Reborn Blue/1
ESB14 John Morton 2017 GF Reborn/25

2018 Star Wars Archives Signature Series Joonas Suotamo

10 Joonas Suotamo 2015 TFA S1 Movie Scenes/3
25 Joonas Suotamo 2015 TFA S1/20
41 Joonas Suotamo 2016 TFA Chrome/3

44 Joonas Suotamo 2016 TFA Chrome/1
44 Joonas Suotamo 2016 TFA Chrome/3
59 Joonas Suotamo 2016 Evolution/20
70 Joonas Suotamo 2016 TFA S2 Green/3
70 Joonas Suotamo 2016 TFA Chrome Ref./8
70 Joonas Suotamo 2016 TFA S2/9
70 Joonas Suotamo 2016 TFA S1/11
76 Joonas Suotamo 2016 TFA Chrome Ref./3
76 Joonas Suotamo 2016 TFA S2/5
76 Joonas Suotamo 2016 TFA Chrome/7
P5 Joonas Suotamo 2015 Journey TFA Patches/5
100 Joonas Suotamo 2016 TFA Factory/1
100 Joonas Suotamo 2015 TFA S1/7
109 Joonas Suotamo 2015 Journey TFA Black/2
P13 Joonas Suotamo 2015 Journey TFA Patches/4
TFA11 Joonas Suotamo 2017 GF Reborn/24

2018 Star Wars Archives Signature Series Julian Glover

GENERAL VEERS
STAR WARS: THE EMPIRE STRIKES BACK

29 Julian Glover 2016 Card Trader/31
31 Julian Glover 2001 Evolution/31
140 Julian Glover 2012 Galactic Files/23
30R Julian Glover 2014 Chrome/7
ESB11 Julian Glover 2017 GF Reborn/36

2018 Star Wars Archives Signature Series Ken Leung

5 Ken Leung 2016 TFA Chrome Heroes/2
15 Ken Leung 2015 TFA S1 Movie Scenes/2
27 Ken Leung 2015 TFA S1/8
51 Ken Leung 2016 Card Trader Blue/7
51 Ken Leung 2016 Card Trader/22
TFA22 Ken Leung 2017 GF Reborn/24

2018 Star Wars Archives Signature Series Kenneth Colley

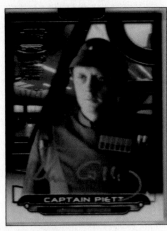

4 Ken Colley 2001 Evolution/38
16 Ken Colley 2016 Card Trader Blue/8
16 Ken Colley 2016 Card Trader/28
141 Ken Colley 2012 Galactic Files/24
29E Ken Colley 2014 Chrome/1
ESB9 Ken Colley 2017 GF Reborn/26
ROTJ7 Ken Colley 2017 GF Reborn/38

2018 Star Wars Archives Signature Series Kiran Shah

35 Kiran Shah 2017 TLJ S1 Purple/35
35 Kiran Shah 2017 TLJ S1 Green/50
35 Kiran Shah 2017 TLJ S1 Blue/65
35 Kiran Shah 2017 TLJ S1/85

2018 Star Wars Archives Signature Series Lily Cole

34 Lily Cole 2017 TLJ S1 Red/1
34 Lily Cole 2017 TLJ S1 Purple/34
34 Lily Cole 2017 TLJ S1 Green/50
34 Lily Cole 2017 TLJ S1 Blue/65
34 Lily Cole 2017 TLJ S1/85

2018 Star Wars Archives Signature Series Mads Mikkelsen

2 Mads Mikkelsen Rogue One S2 Green/1
2 Mads Mikkelsen Rogue One S2/8
38 Mads Mikkelsen Rogue One S1 Blue/7
38 Mads Mikkelsen Rogue One Black/9
38 Mads Mikkelsen Rogue One S1/33
RO8 Mads Mikkelsen GF Reborn/23

2018 Star Wars Archives Signature Series Mark Dodson

16 Mark Dodson 1983 ROTJ/40
34 Mark Dodson 2016 Card Trader Red/1
34 Mark Dodson 2016 Card Trader Blue/7
34 Mark Dodson 2016 Card Trader/29
71 Mark Dodson 2001 Evolution/34
181 Mark Dodson 2012 GF Reborn/28
ROTJ14 Mark Dodson 2017 GF Reborn/42

2018 Star Wars Archives Signature Series Matt Lanter

2 Matt Lanter 2008 CW/13
9 Matt Lanter 2016 Rogue One MB/33
10 Matt Lanter 2017 40th Ann./2
10 Matt Lanter 2017 40th Ann./4
10 Matt Lanter 2016 Rogue One MB/5
23 Matt Lanter 2010 CW ROTBH/3
36 Matt Lanter 2010 CW ROTBH/3
71 Matt Lanter 2010 CW ROTBH/4
84 Matt Lanter 2008 CW/5
22A Matt Lanter 2013 Jedi Legacy/2

2018 Star Wars Archives Signature Series Michaela Cottrell

25 Michaela Cottrell 2001 Evolution/39
28 Michaela Cottrell 2012 Galactic Files/29
17J Michaela Cottrell 2015 Chrome JvS Ref./24
17J Michaela Cottrell 2015 Chrome JvS/58
TPM22 Michaela Cottrell 2017 GF Reborn/31

2018 Star Wars Archives Signature Series Mike Edmonds

44 Mike Edmonds 2001 Evolution/34
82 Mike Edmonds 1983 ROTJ/8
84 Mike Edmonds 1983 ROTJ/16
85 Mike Edmonds 1983 ROTJ/33
92 Mike Edmonds 1983 ROTJ/14
103 Mike Edmonds 1983 ROTJ/4
171 Mike Edmonds 2012 Galactic Files/24

2018 Star Wars Archives Signature Series Mike Quinn

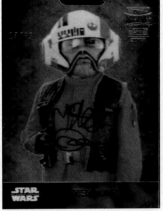

15 Mike Quinn 2016 Card Trader/29
16 Mike Quinn 2016 TFA Chrome Heroes/14
20 Mike Quinn 1983 ROTJ/41
22 Mike Quinn 1983 ROTJ/41
33 Mike Quinn 2016 Card Trader/25
39 Mike Quinn 2016 TFA Chrome Ref./4
39 Mike Quinn 2016 TFA Chrome/7
48 Mike Quinn 2016 TFA Factory/2
48 Mike Quinn 2016 TFA S1 Blue/4
48 Mike Quinn 2015 TFA S1 Green/7
48 Mike Quinn 2015 TFA S1/35

52 Mike Quinn 2001 Evolution/39
96 Mike Quinn 2016 TFA Green/4
96 Mike Quinn 2016 TFA Chrome/5
123 Mike Quinn 1983 ROTJ/28
182 Mike Quinn 2012 Galactic Files/12
184 Mike Quinn 1983 ROTJ/25
25R Mike Quinn 2014 Chrome Ref./1
25R Mike Quinn 2014 Chrome 25R/2
ROTJ12 Mike Quinn 2017 GF Reborn/25
ROTJ13 Mike Quinn 2017 GF Reborn/37

2018 Star Wars Archives Signature Series Nick Kellington

7 Nick Kellington 2016 Rogue One S1 Blue/15
7 Nick Kellington 2016 Rogue One S1 Black/17
7 Nick Kellington 2016 Rogue One S1/76
88 Nick Kellington 2016 Rogue One S1 Green/7
88 Nick Kellington 2016 Rogue One S1 Blue/8
88 Nick Kellington 2016 Rogue One S1/38
HR9 Nick Kellington 2016 Rogue One S1 Heroes/6

2018 Star Wars Archives Signature Series Nika Futterman

93 Nika Futterman 2016 Card Trader Blue/4
93 Nika Futterman 2016 Card Trader/21
30J Nika Futterman 2015 Chrome JvS/5
30S Nika Futterman 2015 Chrome JvS/4
ACW6 Nika Futterman 2017 GF Reborn/24

2018 Star Wars Archives Signature Series Oliver Ford Davies

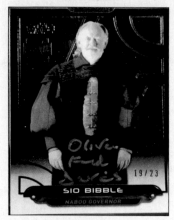

AOTC8 Oliver Ford Davies 2017 GF Reborn/24
TPM10 Oliver Ford Davies 2017 GF Reborn/23

2018 Star Wars Archives Signature Series Orli Shoshan

65 Orli Shoshan 2012 Galactic Files/31
6J Orli Shoshan 2015 Chrome JvS/59
6S Orli Shoshan 2015 Chrome JvS/61

2018 Star Wars Archives Signature Series Paul Blake

21 Paul Blake 2016 Card Trader Blue/8
21 Paul Blake 2016 Card Trader/26
33 Paul Blake 2001 Evolution/30
73 Paul Blake 2007 30th Ann./11
B1 Paul Blake 2016 Card Trader Bounty/9
104 Paul Blake 2012 Galactic Files/28
ANH19 Paul Blake 2017 GF Reborn Orange/1
ANH19 Paul Blake 2017 GF Reborn/36

2018 Star Wars Archives Signature Series Paul Brooke

371 Paul Brooke 2013 GF2/41
ROTJ11 Paul Brooke 2013 GF Reborn Orange/1
ROTJ11 Paul Brooke 2013 GF Reborn/24

2018 Star Wars Archives Signature Series Paul Kasey

20 Paul Kasey 2017 TLJ S1 Red/1
20 Paul Kasey 2017 TLJ S1 Purple/40
20 Paul Kasey 2017 TLJ S1 Green/50
20 Paul Kasey 2017 TLJ S1 Blue/67
20 Paul Kasey 2017 TLJ S1/85

2018 Star Wars Archives Signature Series Peter Mayhew

7 Peter Mayhew 1983 ROTJ/1
8 Peter Mayhew 2016 Card Trader Blue/7

8 Peter Mayhew 2016 Card Trader/22

33 Peter Mayhew 2015 Journey TFA Black/2

33 Peter Mayhew 2015 Journey TFA/3

40 Peter Mayhew Journey TFA/1

55 Peter Mayhew 2016 Evolution/25

56 Peter Mayhew 2016 Evolution/5

57 Peter Mayhew 2016 Evolution/4

58 Peter Mayhew 2016 Evolution/3

84 Peter Mayhew 1980 ESB/8

89 Peter Mayhew 1980 ESB/5

121 Peter Mayhew 1977 Star Wars/5

128 Peter Mayhew 1977 Star Wars/5

157 Peter Mayhew 2012 Galactic Files/3

217 Peter Mayhew 1980 ESB/2

24S Peter Mayhew 2015 Chrome JvS/8

24S Peter Mayhew 2015 Chrome JvS Ref./10

306 Peter Mayhew 1980 ESB/2

513 Peter Mayhew 2013 Galactic Files/2

FQ12 Peter Mayhew 2016 Card Trader Film Quotes/3

ROTS13 Peter Mayhew 2017 GF Reborn/24

2018 Star Wars Archives Signature Series Phil Eason

86 Phil Eason 2001 Evolution/35

393 Phil Eason 2013 GF2/48

2018 Star Wars Archives Signature Series Philip Anthony-Rodriguez

96 Philip Anthony-Rodriguez 2016 Card Trader Blue/4

96 Philip Anthony-Rodriguez 2016 Card Trader/22

2018 Star Wars Archives Signature Series Ralph Brown

TPM24 Ralph Brown 2017 GF Reborn/23

2018 Star Wars Archives Signature Series Ray Park

2 Ray Park 2016 Rogue One MB/6

4 Ray Park 2017 40th Ann./5

6 Ray Park 2012 Galactic Files/3

79 Ray Park 2004 Heritage/2

79 Ray Park 2016 Card Trader/22

94 Ray Park 2016 Evolution/30

B3 Ray Park 2016 Card Trader Bounty/5

285 Ray Park 2015 Chrome JvS/13

28J Ray Park 2015 Chrome JvS/4

FQ10 Ray Park 2016 Card Trader Film Quotes/7

TPM4 Ray Park 2017 GF Reborn/23

2018 Star Wars Archives Signature Series Robin Atkin Downes

ACW17 Robin Atkin Downes 2017 GF Reborn/24

2018 Star Wars Archives Signature Series Rusty Goffe

11 Rusty Goffe 1977 Star Wars/9

13 Rusty Goffe 1977 Star Wars/16

19 Rusty Goffe 1983 ROTJ/23

24 Rusty Goffe 2015 Journey TFA Green/15

24 Rusty Goffe 2015 Journey TFA/38

27 Rusty Goffe 2016 Card Trader Red/2

27 Rusty Goffe 2016 Card Trader Blue/7

27 Rusty Goffe 2016 Card Trader/25

38 Rusty Goffe 2001 Evolution/36

186 Rusty Goffe 1977 Star Wars/12

203 Rusty Goffe 1977 Star Wars/6

257 Rusty Goffe 1977 Star Wars/12

304 Rusty Goffe 1977 Star Wars/1

314 Rusty Goffe 1977 Star Wars/1

ANH8 Rusty Goffe 2017 GF Reborn Orange/2

ANH8 Rusty Goffe 2017 GF Reborn/25

2018 Star Wars Archives Signature Series Sam Witwer

TPM4 Sam Witwer 2017 GF Reborn/23

ACW13 Sam Witwer 2017 GF Reborn/23

2018 Star Wars Archives Signature Series Silas Carson

NUTE GUNRAY
TRADE FEDERATION VICEROY

82 Silas Carson 2016 Card Trader Red/1
82 Silas Carson 2016 Card Trader Blue/8
82 Silas Carson 2016 Card Trader/24
14J Silas Carson 2015 Chrome JvS Ref./7
14S Silas Carson 2015 Chrome JvS/7
TPM14 Silas Carson 2017 GF Reborn Orange/2
TPM14 Silas Carson 2017 GF Reborn/25
TPM19 Silas Carson 2017 GF Reborn/24

2018 Star Wars Archives Signature Series Simon Williamson

MAX REBO
STAR WARS: RETURN OF THE JEDI

40 Simon Williamson 2016 Card Trader Blue/7
40 Simon Williamson 2016 Card Trader/23

2018 Star Wars Archives Signature Series Stephen Stanton

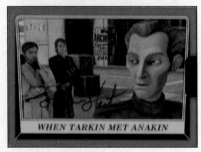

WHEN TARKIN MET ANAKIN

10 Stephen Stanton 2016 Rogue One MB/1
10 Stephen Stanton 2016 Rogue One MB/28
55 Stephen Stanton 2017 Journey TLJ Green/2
55 Stephen Stanton 2017 Journey TLJ/12
60 Stephen Stanton 2016 Evolution/34
42S Stephen Stanton 2015 Chrome JvS Ref./11

42S Stephen Stanton 2015 Chrome JvS/62
HR7 Stephen Stanton 2016 Rogue One S1 Heroes/8
MP4 Stephen Stanton 2016 Rogue One MB Patches/5

2018 Star Wars Archives Signature Series Steve Blum

ZEB ORRELIOS
STAR WARS REBELS

4 Steve Blum 2015 Rebels Foil/7
57 Steve Blum 2015 Rebels/57
74 Steve Blum 2015 Rebels Foil/5
81 Steve Blum 2015 Rebels Foil/7
85 Steve Blum 2015 Rebels/5
90 Steve Blum 2016 Card Trader Red/1
90 Steve Blum 2016 Card Trader Blue/8
90 Steve Blum 2016 Card Trader/26
REB4 Steve Blum 2017 GF Reborn/38

2018 Star Wars Archives Signature Series Taylor Gray

1 Taylor Gray 2015 Rebels/5
1 Taylor Gray 2015 Rebels Foil/6
15 Taylor Gray 2017 Journey TLJ Red/1
15 Taylor Gray 2017 Journey TLJ/6
16 Taylor Gray 2017 40th Ann./2
39 Taylor Gray 2015 Rebels/3
50 Taylor Gray 2015 Rebels Foil/5
50 Taylor Gray 2015 Rebels/6
54 Taylor Gray 2015 Rebels/6
61 Taylor Gray 2017 Journey TLJ Green/1
61 Taylor Gray 2015 Rebels/5
61 Taylor Gray 2015 Rebels Foil/7
62 Taylor Gray 2015 Rebels Foil/4
66 Taylor Gray 2015 Rebels/6
67 Taylor Gray 2015 Rebels/5
67 Taylor Gray 2015 Rebels/6
69 Taylor Gray 2015 Rebels Foil/7
69 Taylor Gray 2015 Rebels/8
73 Taylor Gray 2015 Rebels Foil/3
82 Taylor Gray 2015 Rebels Foil/6
86 Taylor Gray 2018 Card Trader Blue/6
86 Taylor Gray 2016 Card Trader/28
96 Taylor Gray 2015 Rebels Foil/6
96 Taylor Gray 2015 Rebels/6
98 Taylor Gray 2017 40th Ann./17
99 Taylor Gray 2015 Rebels/5
EL7 Taylor Gray 2016 Evolution EOTL/8
REB6 Taylor Gray 2017 GF Reborn/37

2018 Star Wars Archives Signature Series Temeura Morrison

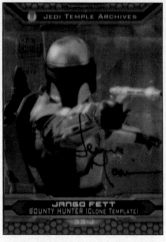

JEDI TEMPLE ARCHIVES

JANGO FETT
BOUNTY HUNTER (CLONE TEMPLATE)

95 Temuera Morrison 2004 Heritage/4
25A Temuera Morrison 2013 Jedi Legacy/1
25A Temuera Morrison 2013 Jedi Legacy/12
33J Temuera Morrison 2015 Chrome JvS Ref./12
33J Temuera Morrison 2015 Chrome JvS/42
33S Temuera Morrison 2015 Chrome JvS/49
AOTC4 Temuera Morrison 2017 GF Reborn/23

2018 Star Wars Archives Signature Series Tim Dry

FACE OF TERROR

164 Tim Dry 1983 ROTJ/43

2018 Star Wars Archives Signature Series Tim Rose

ADMIRAL ACKBAR
REBEL LEADER

2 Tim Rose 2016 TFA Chrome BTS/5
3 Tim Rose 2001 Evolution/37
7 Tim Rose 2016 TFA S2 Heroes/7
12 Tim Rose 2017 TLJ S1/35
14 Tim Rose 2016 Card Trader Blue/8
14 Tim Rose 2016 Card Trader/22
15 Tim Rose 2016 TFA Chrome Heroes/14
28 Tim Rose 2015 TFA S1 Blue/6
28 Tim Rose 2015 TFA S1 Green/12
28 Tim Rose 2015 TFA S1/28
35 Tim Rose 2017 Journey TLJ/6
37 Tim Rose 2017 Journey TLJ/7
10E Tim Rose 2015 Chrome/16
10R Tim Rose 2014 Chrome/24
124 Tim Rose 1983 ROTJ/33
167 Tim Rose 2012 Galactic Files/27
FQ16 Tim Rose 2016 Card Trader Film Quotes/8
ROTJ17 Tim Rose 2017 GF Reborn/24

2018 Star Wars Archives Signature Series Tiya Sircar

SABINE WREN
STAR WARS REBELS

3 Tiya Sircar 2015 Rebels Foil/6
3 Tiya Sircar 2015 Rebels/7
56 Tiya Sircar 2015 Rebels/6
88 Tiya Sircar 2016 Card Trader/25
REB3 Tiya Sircar 2017 GF Reborn/34

2018 Star Wars Archives Signature Series Toby Philpott

INTERGALACTIC GANGSTER

3 Toby Philpott 2017 40th Ann. Green/2
3 Toby Philpott 2017 40th Ann./5
9 Toby Philpott 2016 Card Trader Blue/4
9 Toby Philpott 2016 Card Trader/18

14 Toby Philpott 1983 ROTJ/20
15 Toby Philpott 1983 ROTJ/6
36 Toby Philpott 2001 Evolution/20
46 Toby Philpott 1983 ROTJ/15
62 Toby Philpott 1999 Chrome Archives/2
63 Toby Philpott 2015 Journey TFA Green/2
63 Toby Philpott 2015 Journey TFA/25
82 Toby Philpott 2016 Evolution/26
83 Toby Philpott 2016 Evolution/36
83 Toby Philpott 2016 EvolutionBlue /36
86 Toby Philpott 2007 30th Ann./3
163 Toby Philpott Galactic Files/17
172 Toby Philpott 1983 ROTJ/19
34L Toby Philpott 2013 Jedi Legacy/44
35J Toby Philpott 2015 Chrome JvS/29
35S Toby Philpott 2015 Chrome JvS/32
50R Toby Philpott 2014 Chrome/6
519 Toby Philpott 2013 GF2/25
C15 Toby Philpott 2013 Jedi Legacy Connections/26

2018 Star Wars Archives Signature Series Tom Kane

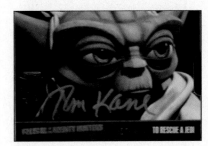

9 Tom Kane 2017 40th Ann./6
12 Tom Kane 2017 TLJ S1 Purple/15
12 Tom Kane 2017 TLJ S1 Green/25
12 Tom Kane 2017 TLJ S1 Blue/35
12 Tom Kane 2017 TLJ S1/49
15 Tom Kane 2017 40th Ann. Green/2
15 Tom Kane 2017 40th Ann./10
35 Tom Kane 2010 CW ROTBH/3
61 Tom Kane 2010 CW ROTBH/10
76 Tom Kane 2017 TLJ S1 Red/1
76 Tom Kane 2017 TLJ S1 Purple/15
76 Tom Kane 2017 TLJ S1 Green/25
76 Tom Kane 2017 TLJ S1 Blue/35
76 Tom Kane 2017 TLJ S1/49
92 Tom Kane 2017 40th Ann./2
92 Tom Kane 2017 40th Ann. Green/3

2018 Star Wars Archives Signature Series Tom Wilton

14 Tom Wilton 2015 TFA S1 Purple/5
14 Tom Wilton 2015 TFA S1 Blue/12
14 Tom Wilton 2015 TFA S1 Green/13
14 Tom Wilton 2015 TFA S1/36

2018 Star Wars Archives Signature Series Vanessa Marshall

HERA SYNDULLA
STAR WARS REBELS

6 Vanessa Marshall 2015 Rebels/5
6 Vanessa Marshall 2015 Rebels Foil/6
17 Vanessa Marshall 2016 Rogue One MB Black/1
17 Vanessa Marshall 2016 Rogue One MB/29
53 Vanessa Marshall 2015 Rebels Foil/6
59 Vanessa Marshall 2015 Rebels Foil/5
80 Vanessa Marshall 2015 Rebels/6
84 Vanessa Marshall 2015 Rebels Foil/6
89 Vanessa Marshall 2016 Card Trader Red/2
89 Vanessa Marshall 2016 Card Trader Blue/6
89 Vanessa Marshall 2016 Card Trader/27
97 Vanessa Marshall 2015 Rebels Foil/6
REB2 Vanessa Marshall 2017 GF Reborn Orange/4
REB2 Vanessa Marshall 2017 GF Reborn/39

2018 Star Wars Archives Signature Series Warwick Davis

PORTRAIT OF WICKET

2 Warwick Davis 2016 TFA S2 Maz's Castle/9
24 Warwick Davis 2016 Card Trader Red/2
24 Warwick Davis 2016 Card Trader Blue/5
24 Warwick Davis 2016 Card Trader/24
84 Warwick Davis 2001 Evolution/34
138 Warwick Davis 1983 ROTJ/40
142 Warwick Davis 1983 ROTJ/17
169 Warwick Davis 2012 Galactic Files/12
190 Warwick Davis 1983 ROTJ/22
ROTJ3 Warwick Davis 2017 GF Reborn/24

2018 Star Wars Archives Signature Series Zac Jensen

KIT FISTO
JEDI MASTER

6	Zac Jensen 2015 Chrome JvS/11	
58	Zac Jensen 2012 Galactic Files/25	
59	Zac Jensen 2017 Journey TLJ/4	
78	Zac Jensen 2012 Galactic Files/23	
11J	Zac Jensen 2015 Chrome JvS/53	
11S	Zac Jensen 2015 Chrome JvS Ref./12	
11S	Zac Jensen 2015 Chrome JvS/53	
AOTC17	Zac Jensen 2017 GF Reborn/24	

1984 Star Wars C-3PO's Cereal Masks

COMPLETE SET (6)	150.00	300.00
COMMON CARD	12.00	30.00
STATED ODDS 1:CEREAL BOX		

1	C-3PO	60.00	120.00
2	Chewbacca	25.00	60.00
5	Stormtrooper	15.00	40.00
6	Yoda	15.00	40.00

2016 Star Wars Card Trader

SAVAGE OPRESS
STAR WARS: THE CLONE WARS

COMPLETE SET (100)	6.00	15.00
UNOPENED BOX (24 PACKS)	35.00	50.00
UNOPENED PACK (6 CARDS)	2.00	3.00
COMMON CARD (1-100)	.12	.30
*BLUE: .6X TO 1.5X BASIC CARDS	.20	.50
*RED: 1.2X TO 3X BASIC CARDS	.40	1.00
*GREEN/99: 6X TO 15X BASIC CARDS	2.00	5.00

*ORANGE/50: 12X TO 30X BASIC CARDS	4.00	10.00
*BAT.DAM./10: 30X TO 80X BASIC CARDS	10.00	25.00
*SLAVE I/5: UNPRICED DUE TO SCARCITY		

2016 Star Wars Card Trader Actor Digital Autographs

COMPLETE SET (20)	150.00	300.00
COMMON CARD (DA1-DA20)	8.00	20.00
*RED/10: UNPRICED DUE TO SCARCITY		
*GOLD/5: UNPRICED DUE TO SCARCITY		
STATED ODDS 1:788		
STATED PRINT RUN 25 SER.#'d SETS		
UNPRICED DUE TO LACK OF MARKET INFO		

2016 Star Wars Card Trader Bounty

BULDUGA

BOUNTY

COMPLETE SET (20)	15.00	40.00
COMMON CARD (B1-B20)	1.25	3.00
STATED ODDS 1:5		

2016 Star Wars Card Trader Classic Artwork

CHEWBACCA

COMPLETE SET (20)	15.00	40.00
COMMON CARD (CA1-CA20))	1.25	3.00
STATED ODDS 1:5		

2016 Star Wars Card Trader Film Quotes

COMPLETE SET (20)	10.00	25.00
COMMON CARD (FQ1-FQ20)	1.00	2.50
STATED ODDS 1:4		

2016 Star Wars Card Trader Galactic Moments

GALACTIC MOMENTS
Lucas Begins
Filming Star Wars: A New Hope

COMPLETE SET (20)	15.00	40.00
COMMON CARD (GM1-GM20)	1.25	3.00
STATED ODDS 1:5		

2016 Star Wars Card Trader Reflections

REFLECTIONS

Darth Vader & Obi-Wan Kenobi

COMPLETE SET (7)	12.00	30.00
COMMON CARD (R1-R7)	2.50	6.00
STATED ODDS 1:8		

2016 Star Wars Card Trader Topps Choice

LAK
SIVRAK

COMPLETE SET (13)	15.00	40.00
COMMON CARD (TC1-TC13)	2.00	5.00
STATED ODDS 1:16		

TC4	Kabe	8.00	20.00
TC7	Lak Sivrak	3.00	8.00

TC10 Bo-Katan Kryze	3.00	8.00
TC13 Todo 360	2.50	6.00

2015 Star Wars Celebration VII Oversized Vintage Wrappers

COMPLETE SET (16)	50.00	100.00
COMMON CARD	3.00	8.00

2017 Star Wars Celebration Orlando Cartamundi Playing Card Promos

COMPLETE SET (4)	10.00	25.00
COMMON CARD (1-4)	3.00	8.00
2 Luke	4.00	10.00
3 Darth Vader	5.00	12.00
4 Boba Fett	4.00	10.00

1999 Star Wars Chrome Archives

COMPLETE SET (90)	10.00	25.00
UNOPENED BOX (36 PACKS)	65.00	80.00
UNOPENED PACK (5 CARDS)	2.00	2.50
COMMON CARD (1-90)	.20	.50

1999 Star Wars Chrome Archives Clearzone

COMPLETE SET (4)	7.50	20.00
COMMON CARD (C1-C4)	2.50	6.00

1999 Star Wars Chrome Archives Double Sided

COMPLETE SET (9)	40.00	100.00
COMMON CARD (C1-C9)	6.00	15.00

1999 Star Wars Chrome Archives Promos

P1 Hate me, Luke! Destroy me!	1.00	2.50
P2 Welcome, young Luke	1.00	2.50

2014 Star Wars Chrome Perspectives

COMPLETE SET (100)	30.00	60.00
UNOPENED BOX (24 PACKS)	175.00	200.00
UNOPENED PACK (6 CARDS)	8.00	10.00
COMMON CARD (1E-50E)	.40	1.00
COMMON CARD (1R-50R)	.40	1.00
*REFRACTOR: 1.2X TO 3X BASIC CARDS		
*PRISM: 1.5X TO 4X BASIC CARDS		
*X-FRACTOR/99: 3X TO 8X BASIC CARDS		
*GOLD REF./50: 6X TO 15X BASIC CARDS		
*SUPERFRACTOR/1: UNPRICED DUE TO SCARCITY		
*P.P.BLACK/1: UNPRICED DUE TO SCARCITY		
*P.P.CYAN/1: UNPRICED DUE TO SCARCITY		
*P.P.MAGENTA/1: UNPRICED DUE TO SCARCITY		
*P.P.YELLOW/1: UNPRICED DUE TO SCARCITY		

2014 Star Wars Chrome Perspectives Autographs

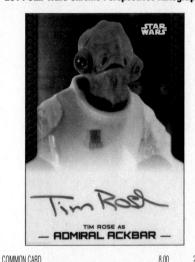

COMMON CARD	8.00	20.00
*GOLD REF./10: UNPRICED DUE TO SCARCITY		
*SUPERFRACTOR/1: UNPRICED DUE TO SCARCITY		
*P.P.BLACK/1: UNPRICED DUE TO SCARCITY		
*P.P.CYAN/1: UNPRICED DUE TO SCARCITY		
*P.P.MAGENTA/1: UNPRICED DUE TO SCARCITY		
*P.P.YELLOW/1: UNPRICED DUE TO SCARCITY		
STATED ODDS 1 PER BOX W/SKETCHES		
1 Angus MacInnes	15.00	40.00
2 Anthony Daniels		
3 Billy Dee Williams	50.00	100.00
4 Carrie Fisher	200.00	500.00
5 Harrison Ford EXCH	1000.00	4000.00
8 James Earl Jones	150.00	300.00
9 Jeremy Bulloch	30.00	60.00
11 Julian Glover	15.00	40.00
12 Kenneth Colley	12.00	25.00
13 Mark Capri	12.00	25.00
14 Mark Hamill		

2014 Star Wars Chrome Perspectives Empire Priority Targets

COMPLETE SET (10)	8.00	20.00
COMMON CARD (1-10)	1.25	3.00
*P.P.BLACK/1: UNPRICED DUE TO SCARCITY		
*P.P.CYAN/1: UNPRICED DUE TO SCARCITY		
*P.P.MAGENTA/1: UNPRICED DUE TO SCARCITY		
*P.P.YELLOW/1: UNPRICED DUE TO SCARCITY		
STATED ODDS 1:4		

2014 Star Wars Chrome Perspectives Empire Propaganda

COMPLETE SET (10)	15.00	40.00
COMMON CARD (1-10)	3.00	8.00

*P.P.BLACK/1: UNPRICED DUE TO SCARCITY

*P.P.CYAN/1: UNPRICED DUE TO SCARCITY

*P.P.MAGENTA/1: UNPRICED DUE TO SCARCITY

*P.P.YELLOW/1: UNPRICED DUE TO SCARCITY

STATED ODDS 1:24

2014 Star Wars Chrome Perspectives Helmet Medallions

COMPLETE SET (30)	75.00	200.00
COMMON CARD (1-30)	5.00	12.00

*GOLD/50: 1.2X TO 3X BASIC MEDALLIONS

STATED ODDS 1:24

2014 Star Wars Chrome Perspectives Rebel Propaganda

COMPLETE SET (10)	12.00	30.00
COMMON CARD (1-10)	2.00	5.00

*P.P.BLACK/1: UNPRICED DUE TO SCARCITY

*P.P.CYAN/1: UNPRICED DUE TO SCARCITY

*P.P.MAGENTA/1: UNPRICED DUE TO SCARCITY

*P.P.YELLOW/1: UNPRICED DUE TO SCARCITY

STATED ODDS 1:12

2014 Star Wars Chrome Perspectives Rebel Training

COMPLETE SET (10)	6.00	15.00
COMMON CARD (1-10)	1.25	3.00

*P.P.BLACK/1: UNPRICED DUE TO SCARCITY

*P.P.CYAN/1: UNPRICED DUE TO SCARCITY

*P.P.MAGENTA/1: UNPRICED DUE TO SCARCITY

*P.P.YELLOW/1: UNPRICED DUE TO SCARCITY

STATED ODDS 1:8

2014 Star Wars Chrome Perspectives Wanted Posters Rebellion

COMPLETE SET (10)	5.00	12.00
COMMON CARD (1-10)	.75	2.00

*P.P.BLACK/1: UNPRICED DUE TO SCARCITY

*P.P.CYAN/1: UNPRICED DUE TO SCARCITY

*P.P.MAGENTA/1: UNPRICED DUE TO SCARCITY

*P.P.YELLOW/1: UNPRICED DUE TO SCARCITY

STATED ODDS 1:2

2015 Star Wars Chrome Perspectives Jedi vs. Sith

COMPLETE SET (100)	25.00	60.00
UNOPENED BOX (24 PACKS)	60.00	70.00
UNOPENED PACK (6 CARDS)	3.00	4.00
COMMON CARD	.40	1.00

*REFRACTOR: 1.2X TO 3X BASIC CARDS

*PRISM REF/199: 1.5X TO 4X BASIC CARDS

*X-FRACTOR/99: 3X TO 8X BASIC CARDS

*GOLD REF/50: 6X TO 15X BASIC CARDS

*P.P.BLACK/1: UNPRICED DUE TO SCARCITY

*P.P.CYAN/1: UNPRICED DUE TO SCARCITY

*P.P.MAGENTA/1: UNPRICED DUE TO SCARCITY

*P.P.YELLOW/1: UNPRICED DUE TO SCARCITY

2015 Star Wars Chrome Perspectives Jedi vs. Sith Autographs

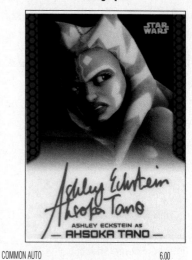

COMMON AUTO	6.00	15.00

*PRISM REF./50: .5X TO 1.2X BASIC AUTOS

* X-FRACTORS/25: .6X TO 1.5X BASIC AUTOS

*GOLD REF./10: UNPRICED DUE TO SCARCITY

*SUPERFRACTOR/1: UNPRICED DUE TO SCARCITY

*P.P.BLACK/1: UNPRICED DUE TO SCARCITY

*P.P.CYAN/1: UNPRICED DUE TO SCARCITY

*P.P.MAGENTA/1: UNPRICED DUE TO SCARCITY

*P.P.YELLOW/1: UNPRICED DUE TO SCARCITY

MARK HAMILL HAS NO BASE AUTO

NNO Ashley Eckstein	10.00	25.00
NNO Barbara Goodson	10.00	25.00
NNO Carrie Fisher	400.00	600.00
NNO David Prowse	50.00	100.00
NNO Jerome Blake	10.00	25.00
NNO Matthew Wood	10.00	25.00
NNO Michaela Cottrell	10.00	25.00
NNO Nalini Krishan	12.00	30.00
NNO Olivia D'Abo	10.00	25.00
NNO Peter Mayhew	25.00	60.00
NNO Ray Park	20.00	50.00
NNO Sam Witwer	10.00	25.00

2015 Star Wars Chrome Perspectives Jedi vs. Sith Jedi Hunt

COMPLETE SET (10)	10.00	25.00
COMMON CARD (1-10)	2.00	5.00

*P.P.BLACK/1: UNPRICED DUE TO SCARCITY

*P.P.CYAN/1: UNPRICED DUE TO SCARCITY

*P.P.MAGENTA/1: UNPRICED DUE TO SCARCITY

*P.P.YELLOW/1: UNPRICED DUE TO SCARCITY

STATED ODDS 1:4

2015 Star Wars Chrome Perspectives Jedi vs. Sith
Jedi Information Guide

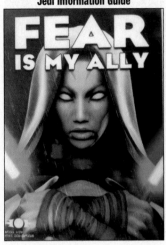

COMPLETE SET (10)	20.00	50.00
COMMON CARD (1-10)	4.00	10.00

*P.P.BLACK/1: UNPRICED DUE TO SCARCITY

*P.P.CYAN/1: UNPRICED DUE TO SCARCITY

*P.P.MAGENTA/1: UNPRICED DUE TO SCARCITY

*P.P.YELLOW/1: UNPRICED DUE TO SCARCITY

STATED ODDS 1:12

2015 Star Wars Chrome Perspectives Jedi vs. Sith
Jedi Training

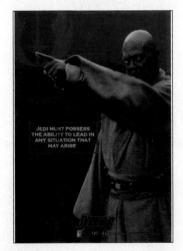

COMPLETE SET (10)	12.00	30.00
COMMON CARD (1-10)	2.50	6.00

*P.P.BLACK/1: UNPRICED DUE TO SCARCITY

*P.P.CYAN/1: UNPRICED DUE TO SCARCITY

*P.P.MAGENTA/1: UNPRICED DUE TO SCARCITY

*P.P.YELLOW/1: UNPRICED DUE TO SCARCITY

STATED ODDS 1:24

2015 Star Wars Chrome Perspectives Jedi vs. Sith
Medallions

COMPLETE SET (36)	120.00	250.00
COMMON MEDALLION (1-36)	5.00	10.00
*SILVER/150: .6X TO 1.5X BASIC MEDALLIONS	6.00	15.00
*GOLD/50: .75X TO 2X BASIC MEDALLIONS	8.00	20.00
OVERALL MEDALLION ODDS 1:BOX		

2015 Star Wars Chrome Perspectives Jedi vs. Sith
Rare Dual Autographs

COMMON AUTO	25.00	60.00

*P.P.BLACK/1: UNPRICED DUE TO SCARCITY

*P.P.CYAN/1: UNPRICED DUE TO SCARCITY

*P.P.MAGENTA/1: UNPRICED DUE TO SCARCITY

*P.P.YELLOW/1: UNPRICED DUE TO SCARCITY

STATED PRINT RUN 200 SER.#'d SETS

NNO A.Allen/O.Shoshan	50.00	100.00
NNO A.Eckstein/N.Futterman	30.00	75.00
NNO A.Eckstein/O.D'Abo	50.00	100.00
NNO M.Cottrell/Z.Jensen	50.00	100.00

2015 Star Wars Chrome Perspectives Jedi vs. Sith
Sith Fugitives

COMPLETE SET (10)	8.00	20.00
COMMON CARD (1-10)	1.50	4.00

*P.P.BLACK/1: UNPRICED DUE TO SCARCITY

*P.P.CYAN/1: UNPRICED DUE TO SCARCITY

*P.P.MAGENTA/1: UNPRICED DUE TO SCARCITY

*P.P.YELLOW/1: UNPRICED DUE TO SCARCITY

STATED ODDS 1:2

2015 Star Wars Chrome Perspectives Jedi vs. Sith
Sith Propaganda

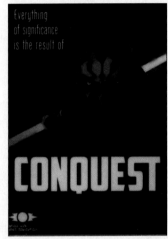

COMPLETE SET (10)	12.00	30.00
COMMON CARD (1-10)	2.50	6.00

*P.P.BLACK/1: UNPRICED DUE TO SCARCITY

*P.P.CYAN/1: UNPRICED DUE TO SCARCITY

*P.P.MAGENTA/1: UNPRICED DUE TO SCARCITY

*P.P.YELLOW/1: UNPRICED DUE TO SCARCITY

STATED ODDS 1:8

2015 Star Wars Chrome Perspectives Jedi vs. Sith
The Force Awakens

COMPLETE SET (8)	20.00	50.00
COMMON CARD	4.00	10.00

*MATTE BACK: .6X TO1.5X BASIC CARDS

STATED ODDS 1:24

2004 Star Wars Clone Wars Cartoon

COMPLETE SET (90)	5.00	12.00
UNOPENED HOBBY BOX (36 PACKS)	50.00	60.00
UNOPENED HOBBY PACK (7 CARDS)	1.50	2.00
UNOPENED RETAIL BOX (36 PACKS)	55.00	65.00
UNOPENED RETAIL PACK (7 CARDS)	1.75	2.25
COMMON CARD (1-90)	.15	.40

2004 Star Wars Clone Wars Cartoon Autographs

COMMON CARD	12.00	30.00

2004 Star Wars Clone Wars Cartoon Battle Motion

COMPLETE SET (10)	15.00	40.00
COMMON CARD (B1-B10)	2.00	5.00

2004 Star Wars Clone Wars Cartoon Stickers

COMPLETE SET (10)	3.00	8.00
COMMON CARD (1-10)	.40	1.00

2008 Star Wars Clone Wars

ROTTA THE HUTTLET

COMPLETE SET (90)	5.00	12.00
UNOPENED BOX (36 PACKS)	40.00	50.00
UNOPENED PACK (7 CARDS)	1.50	2.00

COMMON CARD (1-90)	.15	.40
*GOLD: 8X TO 20X BASIC CARD		

2008 Star Wars Clone Wars Foil

COMPLETE SET (10)	12.00	25.00
COMMON CARD (1-10)	2.00	5.00
STATED ODDS 1:3 RETAIL		

2008 Star Wars Clone Wars Animation Cels

COMPLETE SET (10)	7.50	15.00
COMMON CARD (1-10)	1.25	3.00
STATED ODDS 1:6		
ALSO KNOWN AS THE WHITE CELS		

2008 Star Wars Clone Wars Blue Animation Cels

COMPLETE SET (5)	15.00	40.00
COMMON CARD	4.00	10.00
STATED ODDS 1:6 WALMART PACKS		

2008 Star Wars Clone Wars Red Animation Cels

COMPLETE SET (5)	20.00	50.00
COMMON CARD	5.00	12.00
STATED ODDS 1:6 TARGET PACKS		

2008 Star Wars Clone Wars Coins Purple

COMPLETE SET (12)	15.00	40.00
COMMON CARD (1-12)	2.50	6.00
*RED: SAME VALUE		
*YELLOW: SAME VALUE		
PURPLE ODDS 2:WALMART/MEIER BONUS BOX		
RED ODDS 2:TARGET BONUS BOX		
YELLOW ODDS 2:TRU BONUS BOX		

2008 Star Wars Clone Wars Motion

COMPLETE SET (5)	4.00	8.00
COMMON CARD (1-5)	1.25	3.00
STATED ODDS 1:8 RETAIL		

2008 Star Wars Clone Wars Promos

COMPLETE SET (2)	2.50	6.00
COMMON CARD (P1-P2)	1.50	4.00

2008 Star Wars Clone Wars Stickers

COMPLETE SET (90)	15.00	40.00
COMMON CARD (1-90)	.40	1.00

2008 Star Wars Clone Wars Stickers Die-Cut Magnets

COMPLETE SET (9)	10.00	25.00
COMMON CARD (1-9)	2.00	5.00
STATED ODDS 1:12		

2008 Star Wars Clone Wars Stickers Die-Cut Pop-Ups

YODA

COMPLETE SET (10)	3.00	8.00
COMMON CARD (1-10)	.60	1.50
STATED ODDS 1:3		

2008 Star Wars Clone Wars Stickers Foil

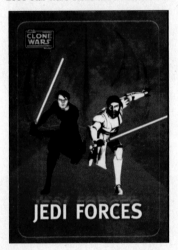

JEDI FORCES

COMPLETE SET (10)	5.00	12.00
COMMON CARD (1-10)	.75	2.00
STATED ODDS 1:3		

2008 Star Wars Clone Wars Stickers Temporary Tattoos

COMPLETE SET (10)	6.00	15.00
COMMON CARD (1-10)	1.00	2.50
STATED ODDS 1:4		

2008 Star Wars Clone Wars Stickers Tin Lid Stickers

COMPLETE SET (6)	12.00	30.00
STATED ODDS 1 PER TIN		
1 Anakin	3.00	8.00
2 Obi-Wan	3.00	8.00
3 Anakin and Obi-Wan	3.00	8.00
4 Clone Troopers	3.00	8.00
5 Yoda	3.00	8.00
6 Anakin and Ahsoka	3.00	8.00

2010 Star Wars Clone Wars Rise of the Bounty Hunters

COMPLETE SET (90)	4.00	10.00
UNOPENED BOX (24 PACKS)	15.00	20.00
UNOPENED PACK (7 CARDS)	.75	1.00
COMMON CARD (1-90)	.10	.30
*SILVER/100: 20X TO 50X BASIC CARDS		
*GOLD/1: UNPRICED DUE TO SCARCITY		

2010 Star Wars Clone Wars Rise of the Bounty Hunters Cels Red

OBI-WAN AND CAD BANE

COMPLETE SET (5)	8.00	20.00
COMMON CARD (1-5)	3.00	8.00

2010 Star Wars Clone Wars Rise of the Bounty Hunters Cels Yellow

COMPLETE SET (5)	6.00	15.00
COMMON CARD (1-5)	2.50	6.00

2010 Star Wars Clone Wars Rise of the Bounty Hunters Foil

CODY

COMPLETE SET (20)	8.00	20.00
COMMON CARD (1-20)	.60	1.50
STATED ODDS 1:3		

2010 Star Wars Clone Wars Rise of the Bounty Hunters Motion

COMPLETE SET (5)	6.00	15.00
COMMON CARD (1-5)	1.50	4.00
STATED ODDS 1:6		

2010 Star Wars Clone Wars Rise of the Bounty Hunters Promos

P1 Cad Bane and Others	1.25	3.00
P3 Pre Vizsla and Mandalorian Death Watch	1.25	3.00

2009 Star Wars Clone Wars Widevision

ATTACK ON THE SENATE

COMPLETE SET (80)	5.00	12.00
UNOPENED BOX (24 PACKS)	60.00	70.00
UNOPENED PACK (7 CARDS)	2.50	3.00
COMMON CARD (1-80)	.15	.40
*SILVER: 5X TO 12X BASIC CARDS		

2009 Star Wars Clone Wars Widevision Animation Cels

THREEPIO AND JAR JAR

COMPLETE SET (10)	6.00	15.00
COMMON CARD (1-10)	.75	2.00
STATED ODDS 1:4		

2009 Star Wars Clone Wars Widevision Autographs

MATT LANTER
ANAKIN SKYWALKER

COMMON AUTO	8.00	20.00
STATED ODDS 1:67 HOBBY; 1:174 RETAIL		
NNO Anthony Daniels		
NNO Matthew Wood/Droids	15.00	40.00
NNO Matthew Wood/Grievous	10.00	25.00
NNO Nika Futterman	12.00	30.00
NNO Tom Kane	12.00	30.00

2009 Star Wars Clone Wars Widevision Foil Characters

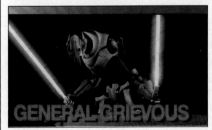

GENERAL GRIEVOUS

COMPLETE SET (20)	15.00	40.00
COMMON CARD (1-20)	1.00	2.50
STATED ODDS 1:3		

2009 Star Wars Clone Wars Widevision Motion

COMPLETE SET (5)	6.00	15.00
COMMON CARD (1-5)	1.50	4.00
STATED ODDS 1:8		

2009 Star Wars Clone Wars Widevision Season Two Previews

COMPLETE SET (8)	3.00	8.00
COMMON CARD (PV1-PV8)	.50	1.25
STATED ODDS 1:2		

1994 Star Wars Day

COMPLETE SET (2)	6.00	15.00
COMMON CARD (SD1-SD2)	4.00	10.00

1995 Star Wars Day

NNO Millennium Falcon w/X-Wings and TIE Fighters	5.00	12.00

1999 Star Wars Defeat the Dark Side and Win Medallions

COMPLETE SET W/O SP (16)	12.00	30.00
COMMON MEDALLION	1.00	2.50
2 Daultay Dofine/50*		
4 Yoda/1500*		
10 Shmi Skywalker/1*		
13 Battle Droid/1*		
20 Chancellor Valorum/1*		

2015 Star Wars Disney Pixar Cars Promos

COMPLETE SET (5)	30.00	80.00
COMMON CARD	10.00	25.00

2015 Star Wars Disney Store The Force Awakens Promos

Finn on the run!

COMPLETE SET (8)	20.00	50.00
COMMON CARD (SKIP #'d)	4.00	10.00
11 BB-8 on the move!	6.00	15.00
67 Kylo Ren ignites his Lightsaber!	5.00	12.00
96 The Millennium Falcon	5.00	12.00

2011 Star Wars Dog Tags

COMPLETE SET (24)	25.00	60.00
UNOPENED BOX (PACKS)		
UNOPENED PACK (1 TAG+1 CARD)		
COMMON TAG (1-24)	2.00	5.00
*SILVER: .5X TO 1.2X BASIC TAGS	2.50	6.00
*RAINBOW: 1.2X TO 3X BASIC TAGS	6.00	15.00

2001 Star Wars Evolution

COMPLETE SET (93)	5.00	12.00
UNOPENED BOX (36 PACKS)	45.00	60.00
UNOPENED PACK (8 CARDS)	1.50	2.00
COMMON CARD (1-93)	.15	.40

2001 Star Wars Evolution Autographs

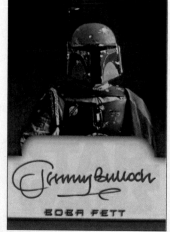

BOBA FETT

COMMON AUTO	15.00	40.00
GROUP A/1000* STATED ODDS 1:37		
GROUP B/400* STATED ODDS 1:919		
GROUP C/300* STATED ODDS 1:2450		

GROUP D/100* STATED ODDS 1:3677

NNO Anthony Daniels/100*	1000.00	1500.00
NNO Billy Dee Williams/300*	200.00	400.00
NNO Carrie Fisher/100*	1000.00	1500.00
NNO Ian McDiarmid/400*	250.00	500.00
NNO James Earl Jones/1000*	200.00	350.00
NNO Jeremy Bulloch/1000*	75.00	150.00
NNO Kenny Baker/1000*	125.00	200.00
NNO Lewis MacLeod	20.00	50.00
NNO Michael Culver/1000*	20.00	50.00
NNO Michonne Bourriague/1000*	20.00	50.00
NNO Peter Mayhew/400*	100.00	200.00
NNO Phil Brown/1000*	25.00	60.00
NNO Warwick Davis/1000*	20.00	50.00

2001 Star Wars Evolution Insert A

COMPLETE SET (12)	15.00	30.00
COMMON CARD (1A-12A)	1.50	4.00
STATED ODDS 1:6		

2001 Star Wars Evolution Insert B

COMPLETE SET (8)	20.00	40.00
COMMON CARD (1B-8B)	2.50	6.00
STATED ODDS 1:12		

2001 Star Wars Evolution Promos

COMMON CARD	1.00	2.50
P3 Nien Nunb ALPHA CON	3.00	8.00
P4 Anakin Skywalker SDCC	2.00	5.00

2006 Star Wars Evolution Update

COMPLETE SET (90)	5.00	12.00
UNOPENED BOX (24 PACKS)	40.00	50.00
UNOPENED PACK (6 CARDS)	2.00	2.25
COMMON CARD (1-90)	.15	.40
1D ISSUED AS DAMAGED AUTO REPLACEMENT		
CL1 Luke Connections CL	.40	1.00
CL2 Leia Connections CL	.40	1.00
1D Luke Skywalker SP	2.00	5.00
P1 Obi-Wan Kenobi PROMO	1.00	2.50
P2 Darth Vader PROMO	1.00	2.50

2006 Star Wars Evolution Update Autographs

COMMON AUTO (UNNUMBERED)	6.00	15.00
STATED ODDS 1:24 HOBBY		
GROUP A ODDS 1:2,005		
GROUP B ODDS 1:231		
GROUP C ODDS 1:81		
GROUP D ODDS 1:259		
GROUP E ODDS 1:48		
NNO Alec Guinness		
NNO Bob Keen B	25.00	50.00
NNO David Barclay B	25.00	50.00
NNO Garrick Hagon E	10.00	25.00
NNO George Lucas		
NNO Hayden Christensen A	600.00	1000.00
NNO James Earl Jones A	200.00	400.00
NNO John Coppinger B	15.00	40.00
NNO Maria De Aragon C	10.00	25.00
NNO Matt Sloan E	8.00	20.00
NNO Michonne Bourriague C	10.00	25.00
NNO Mike Edmonds B	15.00	40.00
NNO Mike Quinn B	25.00	50.00
NNO Nalini Krishan D	8.00	20.00
NNO Peter Cushing		
NNO Richard LeParmentier C	10.00	25.00
NNO Sandi Finlay C	8.00	20.00
NNO Toby Philpott B	25.00	50.00
NNO Wayne Pygram B	90.00	175.00

2006 Star Wars Evolution Update Etched Foil Puzzle

COMPLETE SET (6)	6.00	15.00
COMMON CARD (1-6)	1.25	3.00
STATED ODDS 1:6		

2006 Star Wars Evolution Update Galaxy Crystals

Yoda & Mace Windu

COMPLETE SET (10)	12.50	30.00
COMMON CARD (G1-G10)	1.50	4.00
STATED ODDS 1:4 RETAIL		

2006 Star Wars Evolution Update Insert A

COMPLETE SET (20)	20.00	40.00
COMMON CARD (1A-20A)	1.50	4.00
STATED ODDS 1:6		

2006 Star Wars Evolution Update Insert B

COMPLETE SET (15)	20.00	40.00
COMMON CARD (1B-15B)	2.00	5.00
STATED ODDS 1:12		

2006 Star Wars Evolution Update Luke and Leia

COMPLETE SET (2)	1000.00	2000.00
COMMON CARD (1-2)	600.00	1200.00
STATED ODDS 1:1975 HOBBY		
STATED PRINT RUN 100 SER. #'d SETS		

2016 Star Wars Evolution

LUKE SKYWALKER

COMPLETE SET (100)	8.00	20.00
UNOPENED BOX (24 PACKS)	60.00	75.00
UNOPENED PACK (8 CARDS)	2.50	3.00
COMMON CARD (1-100)	.15	.40
*LTSBR BLUE: 4X TO 10X BASIC CARDS		
*LTSBR PURPLE: 8X TO 20X BASIC CARDS		
*GOLD/50: 15X TO 40X BASIC CARDS		
*IMP.RED/1: UNPRICED DUE TO SCARCITY		
*P.P.BLACK/1: UNPRICED DUE TO SCARCITY		
*P.P.CYAN/1: UNPRICED DUE TO SCARCITY		
*P.P.MAGENTA/1: UNPRICED DUE TO SCARCITY		
*P.P.YELLOW/1: UNPRICED DUE TO SCARCITY		

2016 Star Wars Evolution Autographs

JOHN BOYEGA AS FINN

COMMON AUTO	6.00	15.00
*PURPLE/25: .6X TO 1.5X BASIC AUTOS		
*GOLD/10: UNPRICED DUE TO SCARCITY		
*IMP.RED/1: UNPRICED DUE TO SCARCITY		
*P.P.BLACK/1: UNPRICED DUE TO SCARCITY		
*P.P.CYAN/1: UNPRICED DUE TO SCARCITY		
*P.P.MAGENTA/1: UNPRICED DUE TO SCARCITY		
*P.P.YELLOW/1: UNPRICED DUE TO SCARCITY		
RANDOMLY INSERTED INTO PACKS		
NNO Alan Harris	8.00	20.00
NNO Amy Allen	10.00	25.00
NNO Andy Serkis	100.00	200.00
NNO Angus MacInnes	12.00	30.00
NNO Ashley Eckstein	20.00	50.00
NNO Clive Revill	25.00	60.00
NNO Dee Bradley Baker	8.00	20.00
NNO Deep Roy	10.00	25.00
NNO Denis Lawson	15.00	40.00
NNO Dickey Beer	12.00	30.00
NNO Freddie Prinze Jr.	60.00	120.00
NNO George Takei	15.00	40.00

NNO	Greg Grunberg	15.00	40.00
NNO	Harriet Walter	12.00	30.00
NNO	Hugh Quarshie	20.00	50.00
NNO	Jeremy Bulloch	15.00	40.00
NNO	Jerome Blake	10.00	25.00
NNO	John Boyega	75.00	150.00
NNO	John Ratzenberger	8.00	20.00
NNO	Keisha Castle-Hughes	10.00	25.00
NNO	Kenneth Colley	12.00	30.00
NNO	Matthew Wood	12.00	30.00
NNO	Mercedes Ngoh	20.00	50.00
NNO	Michael Carter	20.00	50.00
NNO	Mike Quinn	8.00	20.00
NNO	Orli Shoshan	8.00	20.00
NNO	Paul Blake	8.00	20.00
NNO	Phil Lamarr	15.00	40.00
NNO	Ray Park	25.00	60.00
NNO	Sam Witwer	8.00	20.00
NNO	Stephen Stanton	10.00	25.00
NNO	Taylor Gray	10.00	25.00
NNO	Tim Dry	12.00	30.00
NNO	Tiya Sircar	8.00	20.00
NNO	Tom Kane	10.00	25.00
NNO	Vanessa Marshall	8.00	20.00
NNO	Warwick Davis	12.00	30.00

2016 Star Wars Evolution Evolution of the Lightsaber

COMPLETE SET (9)	12.00	30.00
COMMON CARD (EL1-EL9)	2.00	5.00
*P.P.BLACK/1: UNPRICED DUE TO SCARCITY		
*P.P.CYAN/1: UNPRICED DUE TO SCARCITY		
*P.P.MAGENTA/1: UNPRICED DUE TO SCARCITY		
*P.P.YELLOW/1: UNPRICED DUE TO SCARCITY		
STATED ODDS 1:8		

2016 Star Wars Evolution Evolution of Vehicles and Ships

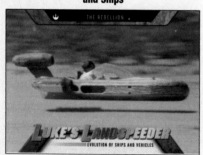

COMPLETE SET (18)	8.00	20.00
COMMON CARD (EV1-EV18)	.75	2.00
*P.P.BLACK/1: UNPRICED DUE TO SCARCITY		
*P.P.CYAN/1: UNPRICED DUE TO SCARCITY		
*P.P.MAGENTA/1: UNPRICED DUE TO SCARCITY		
*P.P.YELLOW/1: UNPRICED DUE TO SCARCITY		
STATED ODDS 1:2		

2016 Star Wars Evolution Lenticular Morph

COMPLETE SET (9)	60.00	120.00
COMMON CARD (1-9)	6.00	15.00
STATED ODDS 1:72		
1 Darth Vader	10.00	25.00
2 Luke Skywalker	10.00	25.00
3 Leia Organa	8.00	20.00
4 Han Solo	10.00	25.00
9 Chewbacca	8.00	20.00

2016 Star Wars Evolution Marvel Star Wars Comics

COMPLETE SET (17)	12.00	30.00
COMMON CARD (EC1-EC17)	1.50	4.00
*P.P.BLACK/1: UNPRICED DUE TO SCARCITY		
*P.P.CYAN/1: UNPRICED DUE TO SCARCITY		
*P.P.MAGENTA/1: UNPRICED DUE TO SCARCITY		
*P.P.YELLOW/1: UNPRICED DUE TO SCARCITY		
STATED ODDS 1:4		

2016 Star Wars Evolution Patches

COMMON CARD	5.00	12.00
*SILVER/50: 5X TO 1.2X BASIC CARDS		
*GOLD/25: .6X TO 1.5X BASIC CARDS		
*IMP.RED/1: UNPRICED DUE TO SCARCITY		
*PLATINUM/10: UNPRICED DUE TO SCARCITY		
NNO Admiral Ackbar	6.00	15.00
NNO Ahsoka Tano	6.00	15.00
NNO BB-8	8.00	20.00
NNO Chancellor Palpatine	6.00	15.00

NNO	Clone Trooper	6.00	15.00
NNO	Darth Vader	6.00	15.00
NNO	Ezra Bridger	6.00	15.00
NNO	General Hux	6.00	15.00
NNO	Grand Moff Tarkin	8.00	20.00
NNO	Han Solo	8.00	20.00
NNO	Kylo Ren	8.00	20.00
NNO	Luke Skywalker	6.00	15.00
NNO	Mon Mothma	6.00	15.00
NNO	Poe Dameron	6.00	15.00
NNO	Princess Leia Organa	6.00	15.00
NNO	Qui-Gon Jinn	6.00	15.00
NNO	Rey	10.00	25.00
NNO	Senator Amidala	6.00	15.00
NNO	Supreme Leader Snoke	6.00	15.00

2016 Star Wars Evolution SP Inserts

COMPLETE SET (9)	250.00	500.00
COMMON CARD (1-9)	25.00	60.00
STATED PRINT RUN 100 SER.#'d SETS		
1 Luke Stormtrooper Disguise	30.00	80.00
2 Leia Boussh Disguise	30.00	80.00
5 Vader Birth of the Dark Lord	50.00	100.00
6 Boba Fett Skiff Battle	30.00	80.00

2016 Star Wars Evolution Stained Glass Pairings

COMPLETE SET (9)	20.00	50.00
COMMON CARD (1-9)	2.50	6.00
STATED ODDS 1:24		
1 Luke Skywalker Princess Leia	5.00	12.00
2 Han Solo Lando Calrissian	4.00	10.00
4 Darth Sidious Darth Maul	4.00	10.00
5 Darth Vader Grand Moff Tarkin	3.00	8.00
6 Kylo Ren Captain Phasma	3.00	8.00
7 Chewbacca C-3PO	3.00	8.00
9 Rey Finn	6.00	15.00

2007 Star Wars Family Guy Blue Harvest DVD Promos

COMPLETE SET (12)	5.00	12.00
COMMON CARD (UNNUMBERED)	.75	2.00

1996 Star Wars Finest

COMPLETE SET (90)	10.00	25.00
UNOPENED BOX (36 PACKS)	45.00	60.00
UNOPENED PACK (5 CARDS)	1.50	2.00
COMMON CARD (1-90)	.20	.50
*REF.: 5X TO 12X BASIC CARDS		

1996 Star Wars Finest Embossed

COMPLETE SET (6)	10.00	25.00
COMMON CARD (F1-F6)	2.00	5.00

1996 Star Wars Finest Matrix

COMPLETE SET (4)	6.00	15.00
COMMON CARD (M1-M4)	2.00	5.00
NNO Exchange Card		

1996 Star Wars Finest Promos

COMPLETE SET (3)	2.50	6.00
COMMON CARD (SWF1-SWF3)	1.00	2.50
B1 Han Solo & Chewbacca (Album Exclusive)	3.00	8.00
NNO 1-Card Sheet		
NNO 1-Card Sheet Refractor		
NNO Star Wars Goes Split Level	200.00	400.00

2015 Star Wars Galactic Connexions

COMPLETE SET (75)	8.00	20.00
COMMON DISC	.20	.50
*FOIL: .6X TO 1.5X BASIC DISCS		
*BLK: .75X TO 2X BASIC DISCS		
*HOLOFOIL: .75X TO 2X BASIC DISCS		
*BLK FOIL: 1.5X TO 4X BASIC DISCS		
*CLR: 1.5X TO 4X BASIC DISCS		
*PATTERN FOIL: 2X TO 5X BASIC DISCS		
*BLK PATTERN FOIL: 2.5X TO 6X BASIC DISCS		
*JABBA SLIME GREEN: 3X TO 8X BASIC DISCS		
*CLR FOIL: 4X TO 10X BASIC DISCS		
*LTSABER RED: 4X TO 10X BASIC DISCS		
*CLR PATTERN FOIL: 8X TO 20X BASIC DISCS		
*C-3PO GOLD: 10X TO 25X BASIC DISCS		
*DEATH STAR SILVER: 12X TO 30X BASIC DISCS		
*SOLID GOLD: 20X TO 50X BASIC DISCS		

2015 Star Wars Galactic Connexions Battle Damaged Border

COMPLETE SET (5)		
*BATTLE DAMAGED: X TO X BASIC CARDS		
STATED ODDS 1:		
1 Darth Vader Red	250.00	500.00
2 Han Solo Red	150.00	300.00
3 Luke Skywalker Red	120.00	250.00
4 Obi-Wan Kenobi Red		
5 Princess Leia Organa Red		

2015 Star Wars Galactic Connexions Blue Starfield Exclusives

COMPLETE SET (10)	10.00	25.00
COMMON DISC	1.50	4.00

2015 Star Wars Galactic Connexions SDCC Promos

COMPLETE SET (6)	100.00	200.00

COMMON DISC	12.00	30.00
4 Stormtrooper Red	30.00	80.00
5 Stormtrooper Gold	20.00	50.00

2015 Star Wars Galactic Connexions Series 2

COMPLETE SET (75)	8.00	20.00
COMMON DISC	.20	.50
*GRAY FOIL: .6X TO 1.5X BASIC DISCS		
*BLK: .75X TO 2X BASIC DISCS		
*GRAY: .75X TO 2X BASIC DISCS		
*BLK FOIL: 1.5X TO 4X BASIC DISCS		
*CLR: 1.5X TO 4X BASIC DISCS		
*GRAY PATTERN FOIL: 2X TO 5X BASIC DISCS		
*BLK PATTERN FOIL: 2.5X TO 6X BASIC DISCS		
*JABBA SLIME GREEN: 3X TO 8X BASIC DISCS		
*CLR FOIL: 4X TO 10X BASIC DISCS		
*LTSABER PURPLE: 4X TO 10X BASIC DISCS		
*LTSABER RED: 4X TO 10X BASIC DISCS		
*CLR PATTERN FOIL: 8X TO 20X BASIC DISCS		
*C-3PO GOLD: 10X TO 25X BASIC DISCS		
*DEATH STAR SILVER: 12X TO 30X BASIC DISCS		
*SOLID GOLD: 20X TO 50X BASIC DISCS		

2012 Star Wars Galactic Files

COMPLETE SET (350)	25.00	50.00
UNOPENED BOX (24 PACKS)	80.00	100.00
UNOPENED PACK (12 CARDS)	4.00	5.00
COMMON CARD (1-350)	.15	.40
*BLUE: 8X TO 20X BASIC CARDS	3.00	8.00
*RED: 20X TO 50X BASIC CARDS	8.00	20.00
*GOLD/1: UNPRICED DUE TO SCARCITY		
*P.P.BLACK/1: UNPRICED DUE TO SCARCITY		
*P.P.CYAN/1: UNPRICED DUE TO SCARCITY		
*P.P.MAGENTA/1: UNPRICED DUE TO SCARCITY		
*P.P.YELLOW/1: UNPRICED DUE TO SCARCITY		
76 Darth Vader (Jedi Purge) SP	12.00	30.00
96 Luke Skywalker (Stormtrooper) SP	12.00	30.00
125B Princess Leia (Despair) SP	12.00	30.00

2012 Star Wars Galactic Files Autographs

COMMON AUTO		10.00	25.00
STATED ODDS ONE AUTO OR PATCH PER HOBBY BOX			
NNO	Carrie Fisher	200.00	350.00
NNO	Daniel Logan	12.00	30.00
NNO	Felix Silla	12.00	30.00
NNO	Harrison Ford	2500.00	4000.00
NNO	Irvin Kershner	600.00	1000.00
NNO	Jake Lloyd	25.00	60.00
NNO	James Earl Jones	200.00	350.00
NNO	Jeremy Bulloch	20.00	50.00
NNO	Mark Hamill	300.00	500.00
NNO	Matthew Wood	15.00	40.00
NNO	Michonne Bourrigue	12.00	30.00
NNO	Peter Mayhew	30.00	75.00
NNO	Ray Park	15.00	40.00

2012 Star Wars Galactic Files Classic Lines

COMPLETE SET (10)	3.00	8.00
COMMON CARD (CL1-CL10)	.75	2.00
STATED ODDS 1:4		

2012 Star Wars Galactic Files Duels of Fate

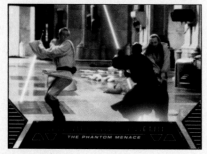

COMPLETE SET (10)	4.00	10.00
COMMON CARD (DF1-DF10)	1.00	2.50
STATED ODDS 1:6		

2012 Star Wars Galactic Files Galactic Moments

COMPLETE SET (20)	20.00	40.00
COMMON CARD (GM1-GM20)	1.50	4.00
STATED ODDS 1:6		

2012 Star Wars Galactic Files Heroes on Both Sides

COMPLETE SET (10)	4.00	10.00
COMMON CARD (HB1-HB10)	1.00	2.50
STATED ODDS 1:6		

2012 Star Wars Galactic Files I Have a Bad Feeling About This

COMPLETE SET (8)	3.00	8.00
COMMON CARD (BF1-BF8)	.75	2.00
STATED ODDS 1:4		

2012 Star Wars Galactic Files Patches

COMMON CARD	8.00	20.00
STATED ODDS ONE AUTO OR PATCH PER HOBBY BOX		
PR1 X-Wing Fighter Pilots: Red Leader	50.00	100.00
Garven Dreis		
PR2 X-Wing Fighter Pilots: Red Two	50.00	100.00
Wedge Antilles		
PR3 X-Wing Fighter Pilots: Red Three	50.00	100.00

Biggs Darklighter		
PR4 X-Wing Fighter Pilots: Red Four	50.00	100.00
John D. Branon		
PR5 X-Wing Fighter Pilots: Red Five	100.00	200.00
Luke Skywalker		
PR6 X-Wing Fighter Pilots: Red Six	50.00	100.00
Jek Porkins		
PR12 Jedi Starfighter Pilots	12.00	30.00
Obi-Wan Kenobi		
PR13 Jedi Starfighter Pilots	15.00	40.00
Anakin Skywalker		
PR14 Jedi Starfighter Pilots	12.00	30.00
Plo Koon		
PR17 Snowspeeder Pilots: Rogue Leader	75.00	150.00
Luke Skywalker		
PR18 Snowspeeder Pilots: Rogue Two	40.00	80.00
Zev Senesca		
PR19 Snowspeeder Pilots: Rogue Three	40.00	80.00
Wedge Antilles		
PR20 Snowspeeder Pilots: Rogue Four	30.00	60.00
Derek Hobbie Kuvian		
PR21 Snowspeeder Pilots: Rogue Leader	30.00	60.00
(Gunner) Dak Ralter		
PR23 Death Star Command	15.00	40.00
Grand Moff Tarkin		
PR24 Death Star Command	15.00	40.00
Darth Vader		
PR25 Millennium Falcon Pilots	35.00	70.00
Han Solo		
PR26 Millennium Falcon Pilots	15.00	40.00
Chewbacca		
PR27 Millennium Falcon Pilots: Gold Leader	25.00	50.00
Lando Calrissian		
PR28 Millennium Falcon Pilots: Gold Leader	15.00	40.00
Nien Numb		

2013 Star Wars Galactic Files 2

COMPLETE SET (353)	20.00	50.00
COMP.SET W/O SP (350)	12.00	30.00
UNOPENED BOX (24 PACKS)	70.00	80.00
UNOPENED PACK (12 CARDS)	3.00	4.00
COMMON CARD (351-699)	.15	.40
COMMON SP	4.00	10.00
*BLUE/350: 2X TO 5X BASIC CARDS		
*RED/35: 15X TO 40X BASIC CARDS		
*GOLD/10: 50X TO 120X BASIC CARDS		
*P.P.BLACK/1: UNPRICED DUE TO SCARCITY		
*P.P.CYAN/1: UNPRICED DUE TO SCARCITY		
*P.P.MAGENTA/1: UNPRICED DUE TO SCARCITY		
*P.P.YELLOW/1: UNPRICED DUE TO SCARCITY		
463b Han Solo Stormtrooper SP	4.00	10.00
481b Luke Skywalker Bacta Tank SP	4.00	10.00
510b Princess Leia Slave Girl SP	4.00	10.00

2013 Star Wars Galactic Files 2 Autographs

COMMON AUTO	12.00	30.00
STATED ODDS 1:55		
NNO Billy Dee Williams	50.00	100.00
NNO Carrie Fisher	200.00	350.00
NNO Ian McDiarmid	400.00	600.00
NNO James Earl Jones	200.00	350.00
NNO Jeremy Bulloch	15.00	40.00
NNO Mark Hamill	350.00	500.00
NNO Peter Mayhew	30.00	75.00

2013 Star Wars Galactic Files 2 Dual Autographs

ANNOUNCED COMBINED PRINT RUN 200		
NNO A.Eckstein/T.Kane	100.00	200.00
NNO J.Bulloch/A.Harris	100.00	200.00
NNO J.Jones/I.McDiarmid		
NNO C.Fisher/M.Hamill		
NNO H.Ford/P.Mayhew		

2013 Star Wars Galactic Files 2 Classic Lines

COMPLETE SET (10)	3.00	8.00
COMMON CARD (CL1-CL10)	.60	1.50
*P.P.BLACK/1: UNPRICED DUE TO SCARCITY		
*P.P.CYAN/1: UNPRICED DUE TO SCARCITY		
*P.P.MAGENTA/1: UNPRICED DUE TO SCARCITY		
*P.P.YELLOW/1: UNPRICED DUE TO SCARCITY		
STATED ODDS 1:4		

2013 Star Wars Galactic Files 2 Galactic Moments

COMPLETE SET (20)	30.00	60.00
COMMON CARD (GM1-GM20)	2.00	5.00
*P.P.BLACK/1: UNPRICED DUE TO SCARCITY		
*P.P.CYAN/1: UNPRICED DUE TO SCARCITY		
*P.P.MAGENTA/1: UNPRICED DUE TO SCARCITY		
*P.P.YELLOW/1: UNPRICED DUE TO SCARCITY		
STATED ODDS 1:12		

2013 Star Wars Galactic Files 2 Honor the Fallen

COMPLETE SET (10)	4.00	10.00
COMMON CARD (HF1-HF10)	.75	2.00
*P.P.BLACK/1: UNPRICED DUE TO SCARCITY		
*P.P.CYAN/1: UNPRICED DUE TO SCARCITY		
*P.P.MAGENTA/1: UNPRICED DUE TO SCARCITY		
*P.P.YELLOW/1: UNPRICED DUE TO SCARCITY		
STATED ODDS 1:6		

2013 Star Wars Galactic Files 2 Medallions

COMMON MEDALLION (MD1-MD30)	8.00	20.00
STATED ODDS 1:55		
MD1 Luke Skywalker	12.00	30.00
MD3 Han Solo	20.00	50.00
MD5 Lando Calrissian	12.00	30.00
MD6 Han Solo	150.00	250.00
MD7 Boba Fett	30.00	75.00
MD9 Princess Leia Organa	15.00	40.00
MD10 Bail Organa	10.00	25.00
MD12 General Veers	20.00	50.00
MD13 Jawa	20.00	50.00
MD14 C-3PO	30.00	75.00
MD15 R2-D2	15.00	40.00
MD16 R5-D4	12.00	30.00
MD19 Luke Skywalker	30.00	75.00
MD20 Obi-Wan Kenobi	12.00	30.00
MD21 C-3PO & R2-D2	30.00	75.00
MD22 TIE Fighter Pilot	10.00	25.00
MD23 Darth Vader	15.00	40.00
MD24 Stormtrooper	12.00	30.00
MD25 Obi-Wan Kenobi	12.00	30.00
MD26 Plo Koon	12.00	30.00
MD27 Captain Panaka	12.00	30.00
MD28 Qui-Gon Jinn	12.00	30.00
MD29 Obi-Wan Kenobi	15.00	40.00
MD30 Queen Amidala	50.00	100.00

2013 Star Wars Galactic Files 2 Ripples in the Galaxy

COMPLETE SET (10)	4.00	10.00
COMMON CARD (RG1-RG10)	.75	2.00
*P.P.BLACK/1: UNPRICED DUE TO SCARCITY		
*P.P.CYAN/1: UNPRICED DUE TO SCARCITY		
*P.P.MAGENTA/1: UNPRICED DUE TO SCARCITY		
*P.P.YELLOW/1: UNPRICED DUE TO SCARCITY		
STATED ODDS 1:6		

2013 Star Wars Galactic Files 2 The Weak Minded

COMPLETE SET (7)	2.50	6.00
COMMON CARD (WM1-WM7)	.60	1.50
*P.P.BLACK/1: UNPRICED DUE TO SCARCITY		
*P.P.CYAN/1: UNPRICED DUE TO SCARCITY		
*P.P.MAGENTA/1: UNPRICED DUE TO SCARCITY		
*P.P.YELLOW/1: UNPRICED DUE TO SCARCITY		
STATED ODDS 1:3		

2017 Star Wars Galactic Files Reborn

COMPLETE SET (200)	10.00	25.00
UNOPENED BOX (24 PACKS)	80.00	100.00
UNOPENED PACK (6 CARDS)	4.00	5.00
COMMON CARD	.15	.40

*ORANGE: .75X TO 2X BASIC CARDS
*BLUE: 1.2X TO 3X BASIC CARDS
*GREEN/199: 4X TO 10X BASIC CARDS
*PURPLE/99: 8X TO 20X BASIC CARDS
*GOLD/10: 20X TO 50X BASIC CARDS
*RED/1: UNPRICED DUE TO SCARCITY
*P.P.BLACK/1: UNPRICED DUE TO SCARCITY
*P.P.CYAN/1: UNPRICED DUE TO SCARCITY
*P.P.MAGENTA/1: UNPRICED DUE TO SCARCITY
*P.P.YELLOW/1: UNPRICED DUE TO SCARCITY

2017 Star Wars Galactic Files Reborn Autographs

COMMON AUTO	5.00	12.00

*GOLD/5-25: UNPRICED DUE TO SCARCITY
*RED/1: UNPRICED DUE TO SCARCITY
*P.P.BLACK/1: UNPRICED DUE TO SCARCITY
*P.P.CYAN/1: UNPRICED DUE TO SCARCITY
*P.P.MAGENTA/1: UNPRICED DUE TO SCARCITY
*P.P.YELLOW/1: UNPRICED DUE TO SCARCITY

NNO Adrienne Wilkinson	6.00	15.00
NNO Alan Tudyk	100.00	200.00
NNO Anna Graves	8.00	20.00
NNO Ashley Eckstein	12.00	30.00
NNO Bruce Spence	5.00	12.00
NNO Catherine Taber	15.00	40.00
NNO Dave Barclay	10.00	25.00
NNO David Bowers	6.00	15.00
NNO Dee Bradley	12.00	30.00
NNO Denis Lawson	10.00	25.00
NNO Freddie Prinze		
NNO George Takei	12.00	30.00
NNO Hassani Shapi	8.00	20.00
NNO Jeremy Bulloch	20.00	50.00
NNO Jerome Blake	6.00	15.00
NNO Jesse Jensen	6.00	15.00
NNO Jim Cummings	6.00	15.00
NNO Julian Glover	6.00	15.00
NNO Kath Soucie	8.00	20.00
NNO Keone Young	20.00	50.00
NNO Lewis MacLeod	5.00	12.00
NNO Mary Oyaya	12.00	30.00
NNO Megan Udall	6.00	15.00
NNO Michael Carter	8.00	20.00
NNO Michonne Bourriague	6.00	15.00
NNO Nika Futterman	12.00	30.00
NNO Oliver Ford	8.00	20.00
NNO Oliver Walpole	10.00	25.00
NNO Olivia D'Abo	8.00	20.00
NNO Phil Eason	6.00	15.00
NNO Phil LaMarr	10.00	25.00
NNO Rajia Baroudi	8.00	20.00
NNO Rena Owen	6.00	15.00

NNO Rohan Nichol	10.00	25.00
NNO Sam Witwer	15.00	40.00
NNO Stephen Stanton	25.00	60.00
NNO Tom Kenny	6.00	15.00
NNO Wayne Pygram	8.00	20.00
NNO Zac Jensen	8.00	20.00

2017 Star Wars Galactic Files Reborn Dual Autographs

COMMON CARD	15.00	40.00

STATED PRINT RUN 5-50 SER.#'d SETS

NNO Blakiston/Rose/50	20.00	50.00
NNO Fisher/Blakiston/5		
NNO McDiarmid/Carson/5		

2017 Star Wars Galactic Files Reborn Famous Quotes

COMPLETE SET (15)	8.00	20.00
COMMON CARD (MQ1-MQ15)	1.00	2.50

*GOLD/10: UNPRICED DUE TO SCARCITY
*RED/1: UNPRICED DUE TO SCARCITY
*P.P.BLACK/1: UNPRICED DUE TO SCARCITY
*P.P.CYAN/1: UNPRICED DUE TO SCARCITY
*P.P.MAGENTA/1: UNPRICED DUE TO SCARCITY
*P.P.YELLOW/1: UNPRICED DUE TO SCARCITY

2017 Star Wars Galactic Files Reborn Galactic Moments

COMPLETE SET (9)	8.00	20.00
COMMON CARD (GM1-GM9)	1.25	3.00

*GOLD/10: UNPRICED DUE TO SCARCITY
*RED/1: UNPRICED DUE TO SCARCITY
*P.P.BLACK/1: UNPRICED DUE TO SCARCITY

*P.P.CYAN/1: UNPRICED DUE TO SCARCITY
*P.P.MAGENTA/1: UNPRICED DUE TO SCARCITY
*P.P.YELLOW/1: UNPRICED DUE TO SCARCITY

2017 Star Wars Galactic Files Reborn Locations

COMPLETE SET (10)	6.00	15.00
COMMON CARD (L1-L10)	1.00	2.50

*GOLD/10: UNPRICED DUE TO SCARCITY
*RED/1: UNPRICED DUE TO SCARCITY
*P.P.BLACK/1: UNPRICED DUE TO SCARCITY
*P.P.CYAN/1: UNPRICED DUE TO SCARCITY
*P.P.MAGENTA/1: UNPRICED DUE TO SCARCITY
*P.P.YELLOW/1: UNPRICED DUE TO SCARCITY

2017 Star Wars Galactic Files Reborn Vehicle Medallions

COMMON CARD	5.00	12.00

*SILVER/99: .6X TO 1.5X BASIC CARDS
*GOLD/50: 1.2X TO 3X BASIC CARDS
*RED/1: UNPRICED DUE TO SCARCITY

2017 Star Wars Galactic Files Reborn Vehicles

COMPLETE SET (20)	10.00	25.00
COMMON CARD (V1-V20)	.75	2.00

*PURPLE/99: 1.5X TO 4X BASIC CARDS
*GOLD/10: UNPRICED DUE TO SCARCITY
*RED/1: UNPRICED DUE TO SCARCITY
*P.P.BLACK/1: UNPRICED DUE TO SCARCITY
*P.P.CYAN/1: UNPRICED DUE TO SCARCITY
*P.P.MAGENTA/1: UNPRICED DUE TO SCARCITY
*P.P.YELLOW/1: UNPRICED DUE TO SCARCITY

2017 Star Wars Galactic Files Reborn Weapons

CHEWBACCA'S BOWCASTER

COMPLETE SET (10)	6.00	15.00
COMMON CARD (W1-W10)	1.00	2.50

*PURPLE/99: 1.2X TO 3X BASIC CARDS

*GOLD/10: UNPRICED DUE TO SCARCITY

*RED/1: UNPRICED DUE TO SCARCITY

*P.P.BLACK/1: UNPRICED DUE TO SCARCITY

*P.P.CYAN/1: UNPRICED DUE TO SCARCITY

*P.P.MAGENTA/1: UNPRICED DUE TO SCARCITY

*P.P.YELLOW/1: UNPRICED DUE TO SCARCITY

2018 Star Wars Galactic Files

ANAKIN SKYWALKER

COMPLETE SET (200)	12.00	30.00
UNOPENED BOX (24 PACKS)	60.00	90.00
UNOPENED PACK (8 CARDS)	3.00	4.00
COMMON CARD (RO9-ROTS23)	.20	.50

*ORANGE: .6X TO 1.5X BASIC CARDS

*BLUE: .75X TO 2X BASIC CARDS

*GREEN/199: 4X TO 10X BASIC CARDS

*PURPLE/99: 6X TO 15X BASIC CARDS

*GOLD/10: UNPRICED DUE TO SCARCITY

*WHITE/5: UNPRICED DUE TO SCARCITY

*RED/1: UNPRICED DUE TO SCARCITY

*P.P.BLACK/1: UNPRICED DUE TO SCARCITY

*P.P.CYAN/1: UNPRICED DUE TO SCARCITY

*P.P.MAGENTA/1: UNPRICED DUE TO SCARCITY

*P.P.YELLOW/1: UNPRICED DUE TO SCARCITY

2018 Star Wars Galactic Files Autographs

HAN SOLO

AUTHENTIC AUTOGRAPH

COMMON AUTO

*GOLD/10: UNPRICED DUE TO SCARCITY

*WHITE/5: UNPRICED DUE TO SCARCITY

*RED/1: UNPRICED DUE TO SCARCITY

*P.P.BLACK/1: UNPRICED DUE TO SCARCITY

*P.P.CYAN/1: UNPRICED DUE TO SCARCITY

*P.P.MAGENTA/1: UNPRICED DUE TO SCARCITY

*P.P.YELLOW/1: UNPRICED DUE TO SCARCITY

NNO Adam Driver		
NNO Alan Tudyk		
NNO Alistair Petrie		
NNO Andy De La Tour	12.00	30.00
NNO Anna Graves	5.00	12.00
NNO Anthony Daniels		
NNO Ariyon Bakare	6.00	15.00
NNO Ashley Eckstein		
NNO Barbara Goodson		
NNO Billy Dee Williams		
NNO Bonnie Piesse	5.00	12.00
NNO Carrie Fisher		
NNO Cas Anvar	10.00	25.00
NNO Clive Revill		
NNO Daisy Ridley		
NNO Daniel Mays	6.00	15.00
NNO David Tennant		
NNO Donnie Yen		
NNO Felicity Jones		
NNO Forest Whitaker		
NNO Freddie Prinze Jr.		
NNO George Takei		
NNO Greg Grunberg		
NNO Gwendoline Christie		
NNO Harrison Ford		
NNO Hayden Christensen		
NNO Hugh Skinner	8.00	20.00
NNO Ian McDiarmid		
NNO Jett Lucas	6.00	15.00
NNO John Boyega		
NNO Jordan Stephens	5.00	12.00
NNO Kate Fleetwood	5.00	12.00
NNO Kenny Baker		
NNO Kipsang Rotich	5.00	12.00
NNO Laura Dern		
NNO Marc Silk	5.00	12.00
NNO Meredith Salenger	6.00	15.00
NNO Ray Park		
NNO Riz Ahmed		
NNO Robbie Daymond	5.00	12.00

NNO Robert Nairne	10.00	25.00
NNO Sarah Michelle Gellar		
NNO Temuera Morrison		
NNO Valene Kane	6.00	15.00

2018 Star Wars Galactic Files Band of Heroes

THE RESISTANCE

COMPLETE SET (7)	5.00	12.00
COMMON CARD (BH1-BH7)	1.25	3.00

*PURPLE/99: X TO 1.5X BASIC CARDS

*GOLD/10: UNPRICED DUE TO SCARCITY

*WHITE/5: UNPRICED DUE TO SCARCITY

*P.P.BLACK/1: UNPRICED DUE TO SCARCITY

*P.P.CYAN/1: UNPRICED DUE TO SCARCITY

*P.P.MAGENTA/1: UNPRICED DUE TO SCARCITY

*P.P.YELLOW/1: UNPRICED DUE TO SCARCITY

2018 Star Wars Galactic Files Galactic Moments

MEETING HAN SOLO

COMPLETE SET (10)	6.00	15.00
COMMON CARD (GM1-GM10)	1.00	2.50

*PURPLE/99: .75X TO 2X BASIC CARDS

*GOLD/10: UNPRICED DUE TO SCARCITY

*WHITE/5: UNPRICED DUE TO SCARCITY

*P.P.BLACK/1: UNPRICED DUE TO SCARCITY

*P.P.CYAN/1: UNPRICED DUE TO SCARCITY

*P.P.MAGENTA/1: UNPRICED DUE TO SCARCITY

*P.P.YELLOW/1: UNPRICED DUE TO SCARCITY

2018 Star Wars Galactic Files Locations

CLOUD CITY GANTRY

COMPLETE SET (10)	8.00	20.00
COMMON CARD (L1-L10)	1.25	3.00

*PURPLE/99: .75X TO 2X BASIC CARDS

*GOLD/10: UNPRICED DUE TO SCARCITY

*WHITE/5: UNPRICED DUE TO SCARCITY

*P.P.BLACK/1: UNPRICED DUE TO SCARCITY

*P.P.CYAN/1: UNPRICED DUE TO SCARCITY

*P.P.MAGENTA/1: UNPRICED DUE TO SCARCITY

*P.P.YELLOW/1: UNPRICED DUE TO SCARCITY

2018 Star Wars Galactic Files Manufactured Movie Poster Patches

DARTH MAUL

*BLUE/99: .5X TO 1.2X BASIC PATCHES
*GREEN/50: .6X TO 1.5X BASIC PATCHES
*PURPLE/25: .75X TO 2X BASIC PATCHES
*GOLD/10: UNPRICED DUE TO SCARCITY
*WHITE/5: UNPRICED DUE TO SCARCITY
*RED/1: UNPRICED DUE TO SCARCITY

NNO Admiral Ackbar - Return of the Jedi		
NNO Anakin Skywalker - Attack of the Clones	8.00	20.00
NNO Anakin Skywalker - Revenge of the Sith	8.00	20.00
NNO Anakin Skywalker - The Phantom Menace	8.00	20.00
NNO Baze Malbus - Rogue One		
NNO Boba Fett - The Empire Strikes Back	10.00	25.00
NNO Bodhi Rook - Rogue One	15.00	40.00
NNO C-3PO - A New Hope	10.00	25.00
NNO Captain Phasma - The Force Awakens		
NNO Cassian Andor - Rogue One		
NNO Chirrut Imwe - Rogue One	10.00	25.00
NNO Count Dooku - Attack of the Clones		
NNO Darth Maul - The Phantom Menace	10.00	25.00
NNO Darth Sidious - Revenge of the Sith		
NNO Darth Vader - Revenge of the Sith		
NNO Darth Vader - The Empire Strikes Back		
NNO Director Krennic - Rogue One	8.00	20.00
NNO Finn - The Force Awakens		
NNO Finn - The Last Jedi		
NNO General Grievous - Revenge of the Sith	6.00	15.00
NNO General Hux - The Last Jedi	6.00	15.00
NNO General Leia Organa - The Force Awakens	12.00	30.00
NNO Grand Moff Tarkin - A New Hope	8.00	20.00
NNO Han Solo - A New Hope	12.00	30.00
NNO Han Solo - Return of the Jedi	12.00	30.00
NNO Han Solo - The Empire Strikes Back	12.00	30.00
NNO Han Solo - The Force Awakens	12.00	30.00
NNO Jabba The Hutt - Return of the Jedi	6.00	15.00
NNO Jango Fett - Attack of the Clones	6.00	15.00
NNO Jyn Erso - Rogue One		
NNO Kylo Ren - The Force Awakens		
NNO Kylo Ren - The Last Jedi		
NNO Lando Calrissian - The Empire Strikes Back	8.00	20.00
NNO Luke Skywalker - A New Hope	10.00	25.00
NNO Luke Skywalker - Return of the Jedi	10.00	25.00
NNO Luke Skywalker - The Empire Strikes Back	10.00	25.00
NNO Luke Skywalker - The Last Jedi	10.00	25.00
NNO Obi-Wan Kenobi - A New Hope	6.00	15.00
NNO Obi-Wan Kenobi - Attack of the Clones	6.00	15.00
NNO Obi-Wan Kenobi - Revenge of the Sith	12.00	30.00
NNO Obi-Wan Kenobi - The Phantom Menace	6.00	15.00
NNO Padme Amidala - Attack of the Clones	12.00	30.00
NNO Poe Dameron - The Force Awakens		
NNO Poe Dameron - The Last Jedi		
NNO Princess Leia - The Empire Strikes Back	15.00	40.00
NNO Princess Leia Organa - A New Hope	10.00	25.00
NNO Princess Leia Organa - Return of the Jedi	10.00	25.00
NNO Queen Amidala - The Phantom Menace	12.00	30.00
NNO Qui-Gon Jinn - The Phantom Menace	15.00	40.00
NNO R2-D2 - A New Hope	8.00	20.00
NNO Rey - The Force Awakens	10.00	25.00
NNO Rey - The Last Jedi	15.00	40.00
NNO Saw Gerrera - Rogue One	15.00	40.00
NNO Supreme Leader Snoke - The Last Jedi		
NNO The Emperor - Return of the Jedi	15.00	40.00
NNO Yoda - The Empire Strikes Back		

2018 Star Wars Galactic Files Memorable Quotes

"SEE YOU AROUND, KID"

COMPLETE SET (10)	6.00	15.00
COMMON CARD (MQ1-MQ10)	1.00	2.50

*PURPLE/99: .75X TO 2X BASIC CARDS
*GOLD/10: UNPRICED DUE TO SCARCITY
*WHITE/5: UNPRICED DUE TO SCARCITY
*P.P.BLACK/1: UNPRICED DUE TO SCARCITY
*P.P.CYAN/1: UNPRICED DUE TO SCARCITY
*P.P.MAGENTA/1: UNPRICED DUE TO SCARCITY
*P.P.YELLOW/1: UNPRICED DUE TO SCARCITY

2018 Star Wars Galactic Files Sinister Syndicates

BLACK SUN

COMPLETE SET (15)	10.00	25.00
COMMON CARD (SS1-SS15)	1.25	3.00

*PURPLE/99: .75X TO 2X BASIC CARDS
*GOLD/10: UNPRICED DUE TO SCARCITY
*WHITE/5: UNPRICED DUE TO SCARCITY
*P.P.BLACK/1: UNPRICED DUE TO SCARCITY
*P.P.CYAN/1: UNPRICED DUE TO SCARCITY
*P.P.MAGENTA/1: UNPRICED DUE TO SCARCITY
*P.P.YELLOW/1: UNPRICED DUE TO SCARCITY

2018 Star Wars Galactic Files Source Material Fabric Swatches

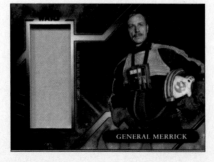

GENERAL MERRICK

COMMON SWATCH	20.00	50.00

*PURPLE/25: UNPRICED DUE TO SCARCITY
*GOLD/10: UNPRICED DUE TO SCARCITY
*WHITE/5: UNPRICED DUE TO SCARCITY
*RED/1: UNPRICED DUE TO SCARCITY

NNO Galen Erso's Jacket	25.00	60.00
NNO Jyn Erso's Poncho	50.00	100.00
NNO Poe Dameron's Shirt	25.00	60.00
NNO Praetorian Guard's Uniform	30.00	75.00
NNO Rey's Head Wrap	60.00	120.00
NNO Rey's Jacket	100.00	200.00

2018 Star Wars Galactic Files Vehicles

COUNT DOOKU'S SOLAR SAILER

COMPLETE SET (10)	6.00	15.00
COMMON CARD (V1-V10)	1.00	2.50

*NO FOIL: .5X TO 1.2X BASIC CARDS
*PURPLE/99: .75X TO 2X BASIC CARDS
*GOLD/10: UNPRICED DUE TO SCARCITY
*WHITE/5: UNPRICED DUE TO SCARCITY
*P.P.BLACK/1: UNPRICED DUE TO SCARCITY
*P.P.CYAN/1: UNPRICED DUE TO SCARCITY
*P.P.MAGENTA/1: UNPRICED DUE TO SCARCITY
*P.P.YELLOW/1: UNPRICED DUE TO SCARCITY

2018 Star Wars Galactic Files Weapons

CHIRRUT ÎMWE'S STAFF

COMPLETE SET (10)	6.00	15.00
COMMON CARD (W1-W10)	1.00	2.50

*PURPLE/99: .75X TO 2X BASIC CARDS
*GOLD/10: UNPRICED DUE TO SCARCITY
*WHITE/5: UNPRICED DUE TO SCARCITY
*P.P.BLACK/1: UNPRICED DUE TO SCARCITY
*P.P.CYAN/1: UNPRICED DUE TO SCARCITY
*P.P.MAGENTA/1: UNPRICED DUE TO SCARCITY
*P.P.YELLOW/1: UNPRICED DUE TO SCARCITY

1993-95 Star Wars Galaxy

COMPLETE SET (365)	15.00	40.00
COMP.SER 1 SET (140)	6.00	15.00
COMP.SER 2 SET (135)	6.00	15.00
COMP.SER 3 SET (90)	6.00	15.00
UNOPENED SER.1 BOX (36 PACKS)	30.00	40.00
UNOPENED SER.1 PACK (8 CARDS)	1.00	1.25
UNOPENED SER.2 BOX (36 PACKS)	20.00	30.00
UNOPENED SER.2 PACK (8 CARDS)	.75	1.00
UNOPENED SER.3 BOX (36 PACKS)	20.00	30.00
UNOPENED SER.3 PACK (7 CARDS)	.75	1.00
COMMON CARD (1-365)	.15	.40
*MIL.FALCON FOIL: .8X TO 2X BASIC CARDS		
*FIRST DAY: 1X TO 2.5X BASIC CARDS		
DARTH VADER FOIL UNNUMBERED	4.00	10.00

1993-95 Star Wars Galaxy Clearzone

COMPLETE SET (6)	15.00	40.00
COMMON CARD (E1-E6)	3.00	8.00

1993-95 Star Wars Galaxy Etched Foil

COMPLETE SET (18)	60.00	120.00
COMMON CARD (1-18)	3.00	8.00

1993-95 Star Wars Galaxy LucasArts

COMPLETE SET (12)	6.00	15.00
COMMON CARD (L1-L12)	.60	1.50

1993-95 Star Wars Galaxy Promos

0 Ralph McQuarrie (Darth Vader)	2.50	6.00
0 Drew Sturzan artwork (SW Galaxy Magazine)	1.25	3.00
0 Ken Steacy Art		
P1 Jae Lee/Rancor Monster(dealer cello pack)	1.25	4.00
P1 Jae Lee/Rancor Monster/AT-AT		
P1 Rancor Card		
AT-AT/Yoda 5X7		
P2 Chris Sprouse/Luke building lightsaber (NSU)	2.00	5.00
P2 Snowtrooper (Convention exclusive)	1.50	4.00
P3 Yoda Shrine SP	250.00	400.00
P3 Darth Vader on Hoth (NSU)	1.25	3.00
P4 Dave Gibbons/C-3PO and Jawas (SW Galaxy 1 Tin Set)		
P4 Luke on Dagobah/Art Suydam	.60	1.50
P5 Joe Phillips/Han and Chewbacca (Cards Illustrated)	2.00	5.00
P5 AT-AT	.75	2.00
P6 Tom Taggart/Boba Fett (Hero)	2.50	6.00
P6 Luke with lightsaber (SW Galaxy Magazine)		
P7 Leia with Jacen and Jania (Wizard Magazine)	2.00	5.00
P8 Boba Fett and Darth Vader (Cards Illustrated)	4.00	10.00
140 Look for Series Two (Bend Ems Toys)		
DH2 Cam Kennedy artwork/BobaFett	2.00	5.00
DH3 Cam Kennedy artwork/Millennium Falcon	2.00	5.00
NNO Jim Starlin/Stormtrooper and Ewoks (Triton #3)	1.50	4.00
NNO Tim Truman/Tuskan Raiders	3.00	8.00
NNO Boba Fett	3.00	8.00
NNO AT-AT 5 x 7 (Previews)		
NNO Boba Fett/Dengar (Classic Star Wars)	2.00	5.00
NNO Jabba the Hutt (NSU/Starlog/Wizard)	1.25	3.00
NNO Princess Leia (NSU)	1.50	4.00
NNO Sandtrooper (Wizard Magazine)	1.50	4.00

NNO Truce at Bakura (Bantam exclusive)	4.00	10.00
NNO Princess Leia/Sandtrooper 2-Card Panel (Advance exclusive)		
NNO Jabba the Hutt, Obi-Wan/Darth Vader 5X7 (Previews exclusive)		
DH1A Cam Kennedy artwork/Battling Robots	2.00	5.00
(Dark Lords of the Sith comic)		
Series at line 8		
DH1B Cam Kennedy artwork/Battling Robots	2.00	5.00
(Dark Lords of the Sith comic)		
Series at line 9		
SWB1 Grand Moff Tarkin (album exclusive)	4.00	10.00

1999 Star Wars Galaxy Collector

COMPLETE SET W/O SP (9)	6.00	15.00
COMMON CARD (SW0-SW9)	1.25	3.00
SW0 Episode I	30.00	75.00
(Non-Sport Update Gummie Award Exclusive)		

1996 Star Wars Galaxy Magazine Cover Gallery

COMPLETE SET (4)	3.00	8.00
COMMON CARD (C1-C4)	1.00	2.50

1995 Star Wars Galaxy Magazine Finest Promos

COMPLETE SET (4)	3.00	8.00
COMMON CARD (SWGM1-SWGM4)	1.50	4.00

2009 Star Wars Galaxy Series 4

COMPLETE SET (120)	5.00	12.00
UNOPENED BOX (24 PACKS)	70.00	80.00
UNOPENED PACK (7 CARDS)	3.00	4.00
UNOPENED BOX (24 PACKS)	100.00	120.00
UNOPENED PACK (7 CARDS)	5.00	6.00
COMMON CARD (1-120)	.15	.40
*P.P.BLACK/1: UNPRICED DUE TO SCARCITY		
*P.P.CYAN/1: UNPRICED DUE TO SCARCITY		
*P.P.MAGENTA/1: UNPRICED DUE TO SCARCITY		
*P.P.YELLOW/1: UNPRICED DUE TO SCARCITY		

2009 Star Wars Galaxy Series 4 Silver Foil

COMPLETE SET (15)	5.00	12.00
COMMON CARD (1-15)	.60	1.50
*BRONZE: 2X TO 5X BASIC CARDS		
*GOLD: .8X TO 2X BASIC CARDS		
*SILVER REF./1: UNPRICED DUE TO SCARCITY		
STATED ODDS 1:3		

2009 Star Wars Galaxy Series 4 Etched Foil

COMPLETE SET (6)	6.00	12.00
COMMON CARD (1-6)	1.50	4.00
STATED ODDS 1:6		

2009 Star Wars Galaxy Series 4 Galaxy Evolutions

COMPLETE SET (6)	30.00	80.00
COMMON CARD (1-6)	8.00	20.00
STATED ODDS 1:24 RETAIL		

2009 Star Wars Galaxy Series 4 Lost Galaxy

COMPLETE SET (5)	12.00	25.00
COMMON CARD (1-5)	3.00	8.00
STATED ODDS 1:24		
YODA'S WORLD/999 STATED ODDS 1:277		
JOHN RHEAUME AUTO STATED ODDS 1:2,789		
NNO Yoda's World/999	15.00	30.00
NNOAU Yoda's World		
Rheaume AU		

2009 Star Wars Galaxy Series 4 Promos

COMPLETE SET (4)	8.00	20.00
COMMON CARD (P1A-P3)	.75	2.00
P1A Ventress	1.50	4.00
Dooku GEN		
P1B Starcruiser crash/ (Fan Club Excl.)	6.00	15.00
P3 Group shot WW	2.00	5.00

2010 Star Wars Galaxy Series 5

COMPLETE SET (120)	8.00	20.00
COMMON CARD (1-120)	.15	.40
*P.P.BLACK/1: UNPRICED DUE TO SCARCITY		
*P.P.CYAN/1: UNPRICED DUE TO SCARCITY		
*P.P.MAGENTA/1: UNPRICED DUE TO SCARCITY		
*P.P.YELLOW/1: UNPRICED DUE TO SCARCITY		

2010 Star Wars Galaxy Series 5 Etched Foil

COMPLETE SET (6)	4.00	10.00
COMMON CARD (1-6)	1.25	3.00
STATED ODDS 1:6 H/R		

2010 Star Wars Galaxy Series 5 Silver Foil

COMPLETE SET (15)	6.00	15.00
COMMON CARD (1-15)	.60	1.50
*BRONZE FOIL: 1.2X TO 3X BASIC CARDS		
*GOLD FOIL/770: 6X TO 15X BASIC CARDS		
*SILVER REFR./1: UNPRICED DUE TO SCARCITY		
STATED ODDS 1:3 H/R		

2010 Star Wars Galaxy Series 5 Autographs

COMMON AUTO	30.00	80.00
STATED ODDS 1:274 HOBBY		
DP David Prowse	60.00	120.00
JB Jeremy Bulloch	50.00	100.00
JJ James Earl Jones	120.00	250.00
KB Kenny Baker	50.00	100.00
MH Mark Hamill	300.00	450.00

2010 Star Wars Galaxy Series 5 Lost Galaxy

COMPLETE SET (5)	10.00	25.00
COMMON CARD (1-5)	3.00	8.00
STATED ODDS 1:24 HOBBY		

2011 Star Wars Galaxy Series 6

COMPLETE SET (120)	8.00	20.00
COMMON CARD (1-120)	.15	.40

*P.P.BLACK/1: UNPRICED DUE TO SCARCITY
*P.P.CYAN/1: UNPRICED DUE TO SCARCITY
*P.P.MAGENTA/1: UNPRICED DUE TO SCARCITY
*P.P.YELLOW/1: UNPRICED DUE TO SCARCITY

2011 Star Wars Galaxy Series 6 Silver Foil

COMPLETE SET (10)	6.00	15.00
COMMON CARD (1-10)	1.00	2.50

*BRONZE: 1.2X TO 3X BASIC CARDS
*GOLD/600: 4X TO 10X BASIC CARDS
UNPRICED REFR. PRINT RUN 1
STATED ODDS 1:3

2011 Star Wars Galaxy Series 6 Animation Cels

COMPLETE SET (9)	20.00	40.00
COMMON CARD (1-9)	3.00	8.00

STATED ODDS 1:4 RETAIL

2011 Star Wars Galaxy Series 6 Etched Foil

COMPLETE SET (6)	5.00	12.00
COMMON CARD (1-6)	1.25	3.00

STATED ODDS 1:6

2012 Star Wars Galaxy Series 7

COMPLETE SET (110)	8.00	20.00
UNOPENED BOX (24 PACKS)	60.00	70.00
UNOPENED PACK (7 CARDS)	2.50	3.00
COMMON CARD (1-110)	.15	.40

*P.P.BLACK/1: UNPRICED DUE TO SCARCITY
*P.P.CYAN/1: UNPRICED DUE TO SCARCITY
*P.P.MAGENTA/1: UNPRICED DUE TO SCARCITY
*P.P.YELLOW/1: UNPRICED DUE TO SCARCITY

2012 Star Wars Galaxy Series 7 Silver Foil

COMPLETE SET (15)	6.00	15.00
COMMON CARD (1-15)	.75	2.00

*BRONZE: 1.5X TO 4X SILVER
*GOLD: 3X TO 8X SILVER
*SILVER REF./1: UNPRICED DUE TO SCARCITY
STATED ODDS 1:3

2012 Star Wars Galaxy Series 7 Cels

COMPLETE SET (9)	35.00	70.00
COMMON CARD (1-9)	4.00	10.00

2012 Star Wars Galaxy Series 7 Etched Foil

COMPLETE SET (6)	5.00	12.00
COMMON CARD (1-6)	1.50	4.00

*ORIG.ART./1: UNPRICED DUE TO SCARCITY
STATED ODDS 1:6

2004 Star Wars Heritage

BLESSINGS FROM BEYOND

COMPLETE SET (120)	8.00	20.00
UNOPENED BOX (36 PACKS)	65.00	70.00
UNOPENED PACK (5 CARDS)	2.00	2.50
COMMON CARD (1-120)	.15	.40

2004 Star Wars Heritage Alphabet Stickers

| COMPLETE SET (30) | 12.00 | 30.00 |
| STATED ODDS 1:3 RETAIL | | |

2004 Star Wars Heritage Autographs

STATED ODDS 1:578

NNO Carrie Fisher	300.00	500.00
NNO James Earl Jones	150.00	300.00
NNO Mark Hamill	600.00	1000.00

2004 Star Wars Heritage Etched Wave One

COMPLETE SET (6)	6.00	15.00
COMMON CARD (1-6)	1.25	3.00
STATED ODDS 1:9		

2004 Star Wars Heritage Etched Wave Two

COMPLETE SET (6)	6.00	15.00
COMMON CARD (1-6)	1.25	3.00
STATED ODDS 1:9		

2004 Star Wars Heritage Promos

Return of the Jedi

COMMON CARD (P1-P6, S1)	.75	2.00
P1 The Phantom Menace	2.00	5.00
P2 Attack of the Clones	6.00	15.00
P6 Return of the Jedi	2.00	5.00
S1 Empire Strikes Back CT UK	2.50	6.00

2015 Star Wars High Tek

COMPLETE SET w/o SP (112)	60.00	120.00
COMPLETE SET w/SP (127)	250.00	500.00
UNOPENED BOX (8 CARDS)	100.00	120.00
COMMON CARD (1-112)	.40	1.00
*DS CORE: .5X TO 1.2X BASIC CARDS		
*HOTH TAC.: .5X TO 1.2X BASIC CARDS		
*TIE FRONT: .6X TO 1.5X BASIC CARDS		
*VADER TIE: .6X TO 1.5X BASIC CARDS		
*MIL.FALCON: .75X TO 2X BASIC CARDS		
*STAR DEST.: .75X TO 2X BASIC CARDS		
*CARBON: 1X TO 2.5X BASIC CARDS		
*EMP.THRONE: 1X TO 2.5X BASIC CARDS		
*DS EXT.: 2X TO 5X BASIC CARDS		
*TIE WING: 2X TO 5X BASIC CARDS		
TIDAL/99: 1.2X TO 3X BASIC CARDS		
GOLD RAINBOW/50: 1.5X TO 4X BASIC CARDS		
CLOUDS/25: 2X TO 5X BASIC CARDS		
RED ORBIT/5: UNPRICED DUE TO SCARCITY		
BLACK GALACTIC/1: UNPRICED DUE TO SCARCITY		
*P.P.BLACK/1: UNPRICED DUE TO SCARCITY		
*P.P.CYAN/1: UNPRICED DUE TO SCARCITY		
*P.P.MAGENTA/1: UNPRICED DUE TO SCARCITY		
*P.P.YELLOW/1: UNPRICED DUE TO SCARCITY		
1A Luke	3.00	8.00
lightsaber		
1B Luke	10.00	25.00
blaster SP		
1C Luke	12.00	30.00
Jedi Knight SP		
2A Leia	3.00	8.00
A New Hope		
2B Leia	15.00	40.00

COMPLETE SET (6)	6.00	15.00
COMMON CARD (1-6)	1.25	3.00
STATED ODDS 1:9		

Bespin uniform SP		
2C Leia	120.00	200.00
Slave SP		
3A Han Solo	4.00	10.00
blaster		
3B Han Solo	20.00	50.00
Bespin SP		
3C Han Solo	12.00	30.00
Endor SP		
4 Darth Vader	5.00	12.00
5A The Emperor	2.00	5.00
5B Sheev Palpatine SP	4.00	10.00
5C Darth Sidious SP	12.00	30.00
6 Yoda	1.25	3.00
7A C-3PO	4.00	10.00
shiny chrome		
7B C-3PO	8.00	20.00
dirty chrome SP		
8 R2-D2	1.25	3.00
9 Chewbacca	1.25	3.00
10A Lando	2.00	5.00
cape		
10B Lando	8.00	20.00
blaster SP		
11 Boba Fett	2.00	5.00
36A Anakin Skywalker	1.25	3.00
36B Anakin	6.00	15.00
two lightsabers SP		
37A Obi-Wan Kenobi	1.25	3.00
37B Obi-Wan	12.00	30.00
young SP		
37C Obi-Wan	8.00	20.00
old SP		
40A Padme	1.25	3.00
dark dress		
40B Padme Amidala	10.00	25.00
white outfit SP		
42 Darth Maul	1.25	3.00
44B Boba Fett	25.00	60.00
armor SP		
88 Anakin Skywalker	1.25	3.00
94 The Inquisitor	.75	2.00
106 Finn	3.00	8.00
107 Kylo Ren	3.00	8.00
108 Rey	5.00	12.00
109 Poe Dameron	3.00	8.00
110 BB-8	4.00	10.00
111 Captain Phasma	3.00	8.00
112 Flametrooper	2.00	5.00

2015 Star Wars High Tek Armor Tek

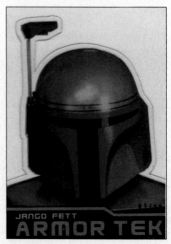

COMPLETE SET (10)	120.00	250.00
COMMON CARD (AT1-AT10)	8.00	20.00
STATED PRINT RUN 50 SER.#'d SETS		
AT1 Boba Fett	15.00	40.00
AT3 Commander Cody	15.00	40.00
AT4 Darth Vader	20.00	50.00
AT5 Jango Fett	12.00	30.00
AT7 Luke Skywalker	12.00	30.00
AT8 Sabine Wren	10.00	25.00
AT9 Poe Dameron	15.00	40.00
AT10 Kylo Ren	15.00	40.00

2015 Star Wars High Tek Autographs

COMMON AUTO (SKIP #'d)	6.00	15.00
*TIDAL/75: .5X TO 1.2X BASIC AUTOS		
*GOLD RAINBOW/50: .6X TO 1.5X BASIC AUTOS		
*CLOUDS/25: .75X TO 2X BASIC AUTOS		
*RED ORBIT/5: UNPRICED DUE TO SCARCITY		
*P.P.BLACK/1: UNPRICED DUE TO SCARCITY		
*P.P.CYAN/1: UNPRICED DUE TO SCARCITY		
*P.P.MAGENTA/1: UNPRICED DUE TO SCARCITY		
*P.P.YELLOW/1: UNPRICED DUE TO SCARCITY		
2 Carrie Fisher	200.00	400.00
4 David Prowse	120.00	250.00
6 Deep Roy	20.00	50.00
7 Anthony Daniels	80.00	150.00
9 Peter Mayhew	25.00	60.00
11 Jeremy Bulloch	15.00	40.00
12 Paul Blake	10.00	25.00
14 Alan Harris	8.00	20.00
16 Tim Rose	10.00	25.00
20 Warwick Davis	12.00	30.00
23 Dickey Beer	10.00	25.00
27 John Ratzenberger	10.00	25.00
28 Pam Rose	30.00	80.00
29 Dickey Beer	15.00	40.00
30 Paul Brooke	10.00	25.00
42 Ray Park	20.00	50.00
49 Bai Ling	8.00	20.00
57 Amy Allen	10.00	25.00
61 Silas Carson	10.00	25.00
78 Bruce Spence	8.00	20.00
79 Wayne Pygram	10.00	25.00
80 Silas Carson	10.00	25.00
90 Andy Secombe	8.00	20.00
96 Taylor Gray	10.00	25.00
97 Vanessa Marshall	8.00	20.00

100 Tiya Sircar	12.00	30.00
102 Ashley Eckstein	10.00	25.00
104 George Takei	20.00	50.00
105 Dee Bradley Baker	12.00	30.00

2015 Star Wars High Tek Moments of Power

COMPLETE SET (15)	175.00	350.00
COMMON CARD (MP1-MP15)	8.00	20.00
STATED PRINT RUN 50 SER.#'d SETS		
MP1 Anakin Skywalker	10.00	25.00
MP2 Darth Maul	12.00	30.00
MP3 Obi-Wan Kenobi	15.00	40.00
MP4 Padme Amidala	12.00	30.00
MP6 Yoda	12.00	30.00
MP7 The Emperor	10.00	25.00
MP8 Han Solo	20.00	50.00
MP9 Luke Skywalker	15.00	40.00
MP10 Boba Fett	15.00	40.00
MP11 Chewbacca	10.00	25.00
MP13 Princess Leia Organa	15.00	40.00
MP15 Darth Vader	20.00	50.00

2015 Star Wars High Tek Tek Heads

COMPLETE SET (15)	150.00	275.00
COMMON CARD (TH1-TH15)	6.00	15.00
STATED PRINT RUN 50 SER.#'d SETS		
TH1 Darth Vader	20.00	50.00
TH2 C-3PO	10.00	25.00
TH3 Luke Skywalker	10.00	25.00
TH4 R2-D2	8.00	20.00
TH5 IG-88	8.00	20.00
TH7 BB-8	12.00	30.00
TH8 FX-7	8.00	20.00
TH10 2-1B	10.00	25.00
TH12 R7-A7	10.00	25.00
TH13 General Grievous	8.00	20.00
TH14 Chopper	10.00	25.00

2016 Star Wars High Tek

COMPLETE SET W/O SP (112)	100.00	200.00
COMPLETE SET W/SP (127)	300.00	600.00
UNOPENED BOX (1 PACK/8 CARDS)	50.00	60.00
COMMON CARD (SW1-SW112)	1.25	3.00
*F1P1: SAME VALUE AS BASIC		
*F1P2: SAME VALUE AS BASIC		
*F1P3: .75X TO 2X BASIC CARDS		
*F1P4: .75X TO 2X BASIC CARDS		
*F1P5: 1.5X TO 4X BASIC CARDS		
*F2P1: SAME VALUE AS BASIC		
*F2P2: SAME VALUE AS BASIC		
*F2P3: .75X TO 2X BASIC CARDS		
*F2P4: 1X TO 2.5X BASIC CARDS		
*F2P5: 1.50X TO 4X BASIC CARDS		
*BLUE RAIN/99: .75X TO 2X BASIC CARDS		
*GOLD RAIN/50: 1.5X TO 4X BASIC CARDS		
*ORANGE MAGMA/25: 3X TO 6X BASIC CARDS		
*GREEN CUBE/10: 4X TO 10X BASIC CARDS		
*RED ORBIT/5: 6X TO 15X BASIC CARDS		
*BLACK GALACTIC/1: UNPRICED DUE TO SCARCITY		
*P.P.BLACK/1: UNPRICED DUE TO SCARCITY		
*P.P.CYAN/1: UNPRICED DUE TO SCARCITY		
*P.P.MAGENTA/1: UNPRICED DUE TO SCARCITY		
*P.P.YELLOW/1: UNPRICED DUE TO SCARCITY		
SW60A Kylo Ren	15.00	40.00
Dark Side Disciple SP		
SW72A General Leia Organa	25.00	60.00
Resistance Leader SP		
SW75A Rey	15.00	40.00
Jakku Scavenger SP		
SW75B Rey	80.00	150.00
Force Sensitive SP		
SW75C Rey	60.00	120.00
Starkiller Base Duel SP		
SW76A FN-2187	30.00	80.00
First Order Stormtrooper SP		
SW76B Flametrooper	12.00	30.00
First Order Infantry SP		
SW76C Snowtrooper	12.00	30.00
First Order Infantry SP		
SW76D TIE Pilot	12.00	30.00
First Order Pilot SP		
SW84A Han Solo	50.00	100.00
Smuggler SP		
SW87A Finn	30.00	80.00
Resistance Warrior SP		
SW87B Finn	20.00	50.00
Resistance Fighter SP		
SW88A Chewbacca	30.00	80.00
Millennium Falcon Co-Pilot SP		

SW100A Poe Dameron	25.00	60.00
Resistance Messenger SP		
SW100B Poe Dameron	15.00	40.00
Resistance Pilot SP		

2016 Star Wars High Tek Armor Tek

COMMON CARD (AT1-AT11)	8.00	20.00
STATED PRINT RUN 50 SER.#'d SETS		
AT1 Kylo Ren	15.00	40.00
AT2 Captain Phasma	12.00	30.00
AT3 Poe Dameron	10.00	25.00
AT6 First Order Tie Fighter Pilot	12.00	30.00
AT7 First Order Stormtrooper	12.00	30.00
AT8 Rey	20.00	50.00
AT9 Stormtrooper (Heavy Gunner)	10.00	25.00
AT11 Sidon Ithano	12.00	30.00

2016 Star Wars High Tek Autographs

COMMON CARD	5.00	12.00
*BLUE RAIN/75: .5X TO 1.2X BASIC CARDS		
*GOLD RAIN/50: .6X TO 1.5X BASIC CARDS		
*ORANGE MAGMA/25: .75X TO 2X BASIC CARDS		
*GREEN CUBE/10: UNPRICED DUE TO SCARCITY		
*RED ORBIT/5: UNPRICED DUE TO SCARCITY		
*BLACK GALACTIC: UNPRICED DUE TO SCARCITY		
*P.P.BLACK/1: UNPRICED DUE TO SCARCITY		
*P.P.CYAN/1: UNPRICED DUE TO SCARCITY		
*P.P.MAGENTA/1: UNPRICED DUE TO SCARCITY		
*P.P.YELLOW/1: UNPRICED DUE TO SCARCITY		
STATED ODDS 1:		
3 Aidan Cook/Cookie Tuggs	8.00	20.00
4 Alan Ruscoe/Bib Fortuna	6.00	15.00
6 Amy Allen	8.00	20.00
8 Anna Brewster	8.00	20.00
10 Ashley Eckstein	10.00	25.00

13 Brian Vernel	6.00	15.00
15 Catherine Taber	6.00	15.00
17 Cristina da Silva	8.00	20.00
20 Dave Barclay	8.00	20.00
21 David Acord/Med.Droid	6.00	15.00
22 David Acord/Voiceover	6.00	15.00
23 David Bowers	6.00	15.00
24 Dee Bradley Baker	6.00	15.00
26 Dickey Beer		
30 Harriet Walter	6.00	15.00
33 Jeremy Bulloch	12.00	30.00
38 Julie Dolan	8.00	20.00
39 Kiran Shah	6.00	15.00
40 Marc Silk	6.00	15.00
42 Mark Dodson/S.Crumb	6.00	15.00
45 Michael Kingma	6.00	15.00
47 Mike Edmonds	6.00	15.00
48 Mike Quinn	8.00	20.00
50 Paul Blake	6.00	15.00
51 Paul Springer	6.00	15.00
57 Sam Witwer	8.00	20.00
59 Sebastian Armesto	6.00	15.00
60 Silas Carson	8.00	20.00
62 Taylor Gray	6.00	15.00
63 Tim Rose	6.00	15.00
64 Tiya Sircar	6.00	15.00
66 Tosin Cole	10.00	25.00

2016 Star Wars High Tek Autographs Gold Rainbow

*GOLD RAINBOW/50: .6X TO 1.5X BASIC CARDS		
12 Brian Herring	25.00	60.00
25 Denis Lawson	15.00	40.00
67 Warwick Davis	12.00	30.00

2016 Star Wars High Tek Autographs Orange Magma Diffractor

*ORANGE MAGMA/25: .75X TO 2X BASIC CARDS		
14 Carrie Fisher	250.00	500.00
28 Freddie Prinze Jr.	30.00	80.00
37 John Boyega	120.00	250.00

2016 Star Wars High Tek Living Tek

COMMON CARD (LT1-LT13)	6.00	15.00
STATED PRINT RUN 50 SER.#'d SETS		
LT1 Crusher Roodown	10.00	25.00
LT2 Luke Skywalker	15.00	40.00
LT3 C-3PO	8.00	20.00
LT4 BB-8	12.00	30.00
LT5 GA-97	8.00	20.00
LT6 Luggabeast	8.00	20.00
LT7 PZ-4CO	8.00	20.00
LT9 B-U4D	12.00	30.00
LT11 Sidon Ithano	12.00	30.00
LT12 HURID-327	8.00	20.00
LT13 R2-D2	8.00	20.00

2017 Star Wars High Tek

UNOPENED BOX (1 PACK OF 8 CARDS)	50.00	80.00
COMMON FORM 1 (1-56)	1.00	2.50
COMMON FORM 2 (57-112)	1.50	4.00
*F1P1: .75X TO 2X BASIC CARDS	2.00	5.00
*F1P2: .75X TO 2X BASIC CARDS	2.00	5.00
*F1P3: 1X TO 2.5X BASIC CARDS	2.50	6.00
*F2P1: .6X TO 1.5X BASIC CARDS	2.50	6.00
*F2P3: .6X TO 1.5X BASIC CARDS	2.50	6.00
*TIDAL DIFF./99: 1X TO 2.5X BASIC CARDS	2.50	6.00
*F2P2: .75X TO 2X BASIC CARDS	3.00	8.00
*GOLD R.F./50: 1.2X TO 3X BASIC CARDS	3.00	8.00
*F1P4: 2X TO 5X BASIC CARDS	5.00	12.00
*F2P4: 1.2X TO 3X BASIC CARDS	5.00	12.00
*F1P5: 3X TO 8X BASIC CARDS	8.00	20.00
*F2P5: UNPRICED DUE TO SCARCITY		
*ORANGE DIFF./25: UNPRICED DUE TO SCARCITY		
*GREEN DIFF./10: UNPRICED DUE TO SCARCITY		
*RED DIFF./5: UNPRICED DUE TO SCARCITY		
*BLACK DIFF./1: UNPRICED DUE TO SCARCITY		
*P.P.BLACK/1: UNPRICED DUE TO SCARCITY		
*P.P.CYAN/1: UNPRICED DUE TO SCARCITY		
*P.P.MAGENTA/1: UNPRICED DUE TO SCARCITY		
*P.P.YELLOW/1: UNPRICED DUE TO SCARCITY		
7 Rey	2.50	6.00
14 Han Solo	1.50	4.00
15 Luke Skywalker	1.50	4.00
16 Princess Leia Organa	3.00	8.00
20 Jango Fett	2.00	5.00
36 Boba Fett	1.50	4.00
53 Kylo Ren	1.25	3.00
56 Yoda	1.25	3.00
57 Jyn Erso	4.00	10.00
62 Chirrut Imwe	2.00	5.00
68 Darth Vader	2.00	5.00

2017 Star Wars High Tek Autographs

*GREEN DIFF./10: UNPRICED DUE TO SCARCITY
*RED DIFF./5: UNPRICED DUE TO SCARCITY
*BLACK DIFF./1: UNPRICED DUE TO SCARCITY
*P.P.BLACK/1: UNPRICED DUE TO SCARCITY
*P.P.CYAN/1: UNPRICED DUE TO SCARCITY
*P.P.MAGENTA/1: UNPRICED DUE TO SCARCITY
*P.P.YELLOW/1: UNPRICED DUE TO SCARCITY
RANDOMLY INSERTED INTO PACKS

NNO	Adrienne Wilkinson	6.00	15.00
NNO	Alistair Petrie	6.00	15.00
NNO	Angus MacInnes	6.00	15.00
NNO	Anthony Forest	6.00	15.00
NNO	Ariyon Bakare	10.00	25.00
NNO	Ashley Eckstein	10.00	25.00
NNO	Ben Daniels	6.00	15.00
NNO	Brian Herring	15.00	40.00
NNO	Cathy Munroe	12.00	30.00
NNO	Chris Parsons	8.00	20.00
NNO	Daniel Mays	15.00	40.00
NNO	David Acord	6.00	15.00
NNO	Derek Arnold	6.00	15.00
NNO	Duncan Pow	6.00	15.00
NNO	Guy Henry	20.00	50.00
NNO	Ian McElhinney	6.00	15.00
NNO	Ian Whyte	6.00	15.00
NNO	Jeremy Bulloch	15.00	40.00
NNO	Jordan Stephens	10.00	25.00
NNO	Lars Mikkelsen	10.00	25.00
NNO	Lloyd Sherr	6.00	15.00
NNO	Matthew Wood	6.00	15.00
NNO	Olivia d'Abo	6.00	15.00
NNO	Stephen Stanton		
NNO	Valene Kane	10.00	25.00
NNO	Zarene Dallas	6.00	15.00

2017 Star Wars High Tek Heroes and Villains of The Force Awakens

C-3PO

COMPLETE SET (20)	150.00	300.00
COMMON CARD (HV1-HV20)	6.00	15.00
STATED PRINT RUN 50 SER.#'d SETS		
HV1 Han Solo	10.00	25.00
HV2 Luke Skywalker	10.00	25.00
HV4 Kylo Ren	8.00	20.00
HV5 Rey	20.00	50.00
HV6 Finn	12.00	30.00
HV8 Supreme Leader Snoke	8.00	20.00
HV9 R2-D2	10.00	25.00
HV12 Snap Wexley	10.00	25.00
HV13 Captain Phasma	8.00	20.00
HV14 General Hux	8.00	20.00
HV17 Ello Asty	8.00	20.00
HV18 Unkar Plutt	8.00	20.00
HV19 Chewbacca	10.00	25.00
HV20 Riot Control Stormtrooper	12.00	30.00

2017 Star Wars High Tek A More Elegant Weapon

COMMON CARD (MW1-MW10)	10.00	25.00
STATED PRINT RUN 50 SER.#'d SETS		
MW1 Yoda	15.00	40.00
MW2 Ahsoka Tano	12.00	30.00
MW3 Anakin Skywalker	12.00	30.00
MW5 Rey	30.00	75.00
MW6 Luke Skywalker	15.00	40.00
MW7 Darth Vader	15.00	40.00
MW8 Obi-Wan Kenobi	12.00	30.00
MW10 Mace Windu	12.00	30.00

2017 Star Wars High Tek Rogue One Vehicles

STATED PRINT RUN 50 SER.#'d SETS		
RV1 Jyn Erso/U-wing	10.00	25.00
RV2 Gunner/Death Star	6.00	15.00
RV3 Krennic/Krennic's Shuttle	12.00	30.00
RV4 Tank Commander/Combat Assault Tank	6.00	15.00
RV5 Tarkin/Imperial Star Destroyer	8.00	20.00
RV6 Merrick/X-wing	12.00	30.00
RV7 TIE Striker Pilot/TIE Striker		
RV8 Cassian Andor/U-wing		
RV9 K-2SO/U-wing		
RV10 Bohdi Rook/Imperial Zeta-Class Transport	6.00	15.00

2017 Star Wars High Tek Troopers

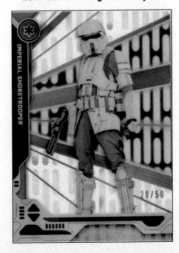

IMPERIAL SHORETROOPER

2017 Star Wars High Tek Troopers

COMMON CARD (TR1-TR16)	6.00	15.00
STATED PRINT RUN 50 SER.#'d SETS		
TR1 First Order TIE Fighter Pilot	10.00	25.00
TR2 First Order Stormtrooper	8.00	20.00
TR3 First Order Riot Control Stormtrooper	10.00	25.00
TR9 Imperial Death Trooper	15.00	40.00
TR12 Imperial Sandtrooper	10.00	25.00
TR14 Imperial TIE Fighter Pilot	8.00	20.00
TR15 Galactic Republic Clone Trooper	8.00	20.00
TR16 Galactic Marine	10.00	25.00

2015 Star Wars Honey Maid

COMPLETE SET (12)	3.00	8.00
COMMON CARD	.40	1.00
PAN1 Obi-Wan Kenobi	2.00	5.00
Darth Vader		
Han Solo		
Chewbacca		
Storm Trooper		
C-3PO		
PAN2 R2-D2	2.00	5.00
The Emperor		
Yoda		
Luke Skywalker		
Boba Fett		
Princess Leia Organa		

2013 Star Wars Jedi Legacy

COMPLETE SET (90)	6.00	15.00
UNOPENED BOX (24 PACKS)	60.00	70.00
UNOPENED PACK (8 CARDS)	2.50	3.00
COMMON CARD (1A-45L)	.20	.50
*BLUE: 1.2X TO 3X BASIC CARDS		
*MAGENTA: 4X TO 10X BASIC CARDS		
*GREEN: X TO X BASIC CARDS		
*GOLD/10: 50X TO 120X BASIC CARDS		
*P.P.BLACK/1: UNPRICED DUE TO SCARCITY		
*P.P.CYAN/1: UNPRICED DUE TO SCARCITY		
*P.P.MAGENTA/1: UNPRICED DUE TO SCARCITY		
*P.P.YELLOW/1: UNPRICED DUE TO SCARCITY		

2013 Star Wars Jedi Legacy Autographs

COMMON CARD (UNNUMBERED)	10.00	25.00

STATED ODDS 1:72

NNO	Alan Harris	20.00	50.00
NNO	Anthony Daniels	200.00	400.00
NNO	Billy Dee Williams	125.00	250.00
NNO	Carrie Fisher	300.00	500.00
NNO	Harrison Ford	1750.00	2500.00
NNO	Ian McDiarmid	300.00	500.00
NNO	James Earl Jones	150.00	300.00
NNO	Jeremy Bulloch	30.00	60.00
NNO	John Morton	15.00	40.00
NNO	Kenneth Colley	15.00	40.00
NNO	Kenny Baker	30.00	60.00
NNO	Mark Hamill	400.00	600.00
NNO	Tim Rose	15.00	40.00

2013 Star Wars Jedi Legacy Chewbacca Fur Relics

COMMON CARD (CR1-CR4)	75.00	150.00

STATED ODDS 1:720

2013 Star Wars Jedi Legacy Connections

COMPLETE SET (15)	5.00	12.00
COMMON CARD (C1-C15)	.60	1.50

*P.P.BLACK/1: UNPRICED DUE TO SCARCITY

*P.P.CYAN/1: UNPRICED DUE TO SCARCITY

*P.P.MAGENTA/1: UNPRICED DUE TO SCARCITY

*P.P.YELLOW/1: UNPRICED DUE TO SCARCITY

STATED ODDS 1:2

2013 Star Wars Jedi Legacy Ewok Fur Relics

COMMON CARD (ER1-ER4)	20.00	50.00

STATED ODDS 1:120

ER1	Wicket W. Warrick	35.00	70.00
ER4	Widdle Warrick	50.00	100.00

2013 Star Wars Jedi Legacy Film Cels

COMMON CARD (FR1-FR30)	10.00	25.00

STATED ODDS 1:BOX

FR6	Darth Vader	20.00	50.00

2013 Star Wars Jedi Legacy Dual Film Cels

COMPLETE SET (6)	120.00	250.00
COMMON CARD (DFR1-DFR6)	20.00	50.00

STATED ODDS 1:144

DFR1	Darth Vader/Luke Skywalker	30.00	60.00

2013 Star Wars Jedi Legacy Triple Film Cels

COMPLETE SET (10)	250.00	500.00
COMMON CARD (TFR1-TFR10)	30.00	60.00

STATED ODDS 1:144

2013 Star Wars Jedi Legacy Influencers

COMPLETE SET (18)	5.00	12.00
COMMON CARD (I1-I18)	.50	1.25

*P.P.BLACK/1: UNPRICED DUE TO SCARCITY

*P.P.CYAN/1: UNPRICED DUE TO SCARCITY

*P.P.MAGENTA/1: UNPRICED DUE TO SCARCITY

*P.P.YELLOW/1: UNPRICED DUE TO SCARCITY

STATED ODDS 1:2

2013 Star Wars Jedi Legacy Jabba's Sail Barge Relics

COMPLETE SET (5)	300.00	600.00
COMMON CARD (JR1-JR5)	50.00	100.00

STATED ODDS 1:336

JR1	Luke Skywalker	125.00	200.00

JR2 Leia Organa	100.00	175.00
JR3 Boba Fett	75.00	150.00

2013 Star Wars Jedi Legacy The Circle is Now Complete

COMPLETE SET (12)	35.00	70.00
COMMON CARD (CC1-CC12)	4.00	10.00
*P.P.BLACK/1: UNPRICED DUE TO SCARCITY		
*P.P.CYAN/1: UNPRICED DUE TO SCARCITY		
*P.P.MAGENTA/1: UNPRICED DUE TO SCARCITY		
*P.P.YELLOW/1: UNPRICED DUE TO SCARCITY		
STATED ODDS 1:12		
NNO1 Luke Skywalker PROMO		

2013 Star Wars Jedi Legacy Promos

COMMON CARD	3.00	8.00
P1 Battle Through Blood	8.00	20.00
(Darth Vader)		
P2 Battle Through Blood	8.00	20.00
(Luke Skywalker)		
P3 Challenge of a Fallen Jedi	8.00	20.00
(Anakin vs. Count Dooku)		
P4 Challenge of a Fallen Jedi	8.00	20.00
(Luke vs. Vader)		
P5 Death of a Mentor	3.00	8.00
(Qui Gon vs. Darth Maul)		
(Philly Non-Sports Show Exclusive)		
NNO Darth Vader Disc	1.50	4.00
NNO Luke Skywalker Disc	1.50	4.00
NNO Two Paths. Two Journeys. One Destiny		
(5 X 7 Jumbo)		

2015 Star Wars Journey to The Force Awakens

COMPLETE SET (110)	10.00	25.00
COMMON CARD (1-110)	.20	.50
*JABBA SLIME GREEN: .5X TO 1.2X BASIC CARDS		
*BLACK: .6X TO 1.5X BASIC CARDS		
*DEATH STAR SILVER: .75X TO 2X BASIC CARDS		
*LTSBR. NEON PINK: 1.5X TO 4X BASIC CARDS		
*PURPLE: 4X TO 10X BASIC CARDS		

*HOTH ICE/150: 6X TO 15X BASIC CARDS		
*GOLD/50: 10X TO 25X BASIC CARDS		
*HOLOGRAM/25: 15X TO 40X BASIC CARDS		
*RED IMPERIAL/1: UNPRICED DUE TO SCARCITY		
*P.P. BLACK/1: UNPRICED DUE TO SCARCITY		
*P.P. CYAN/1: UNPRICED DUE TO SCARCITY		
*P.P. MAGENTA/1: UNPRICED DUE TO SCARCITY		
*P.P. YELLOW/1: UNPRICED DUE TO SCARCITY		

2015 Star Wars Journey to The Force Awakens Autographs

COMMON CARD	8.00	20.00
*SILVER/50: .75X TO 2X BASIC AUTOS		
*GOLD/10: UNPRICED DUE TO SCARCITY		
*RED/1: UNPRICED DUE TO SCARCITY		
*P.P.BLACK/1: UNPRICED DUE TO SCARCITY		
*P.P.CYAN/1: UNPRICED DUE TO SCARCITY		
*P.P.MAGENTA/1: UNPRICED DUE TO SCARCITY		
*P.P.YELLOW/1: UNPRICED DUE TO SCARCITY		
NNO Alan Harris	12.00	30.00
NNO Amy Allen	25.00	60.00
NNO Angus MacInnes	10.00	25.00
NNO Anthony Daniels	200.00	400.00
NNO Ashley Eckstein	15.00	40.00
NNO Bai Ling	15.00	40.00
NNO Billy Dee Williams	50.00	100.00
NNO Caroline Blakiston	10.00	25.00
NNO Carrie Fisher	120.00	250.00
NNO David Prowse	80.00	150.00
NNO Dickey Beer	10.00	25.00
NNO Femi Taylor	12.00	30.00
NNO Hassani Shapi	12.00	30.00
NNO Jeremy Bulloch	50.00	100.00
NNO Jerome Blake	10.00	25.00
NNO John Ratzenberger	12.00	30.00
NNO Kenji Oates	10.00	25.00
NNO Kenneth Colley	10.00	25.00
NNO Kenny Baker	60.00	120.00
NNO Mark Hamill	225.00	350.00
NNO Michonne Bourriague	12.00	30.00
NNO Mike Quinn	25.00	60.00
NNO Nika Futterman	10.00	25.00
NNO Olivia d'Abo	80.00	150.00
NNO Orli Shoshan	10.00	25.00
NNO Pam Rose	10.00	25.00
NNO Peter Mayhew	30.00	80.00
NNO Ray Park	25.00	60.00
NNO Rohan Nichol	12.00	30.00
NNO Steven Blum	10.00	25.00
NNO Taylor Gray	12.00	30.00
NNO Tiya Sircar	25.00	60.00
NNO Vanessa Marshall	15.00	40.00
NNO Wayne Pygram	12.00	30.00

2015 Star Wars Journey to The Force Awakens Behind-the-Scenes

The Birth of 2-1B

COMPLETE SET (9)	5.00	12.00
COMMON CARD (BTS1-BTS9)	1.00	2.50
*P.P.BLACK/1: UNPRICED DUE TO SCARCITY		
*P.P.CYAN/1: UNPRICED DUE TO SCARCITY		
*P.P.MAGENTA/1: UNPRICED DUE TO SCARCITY		
*P.P.YELLOW/1: UNPRICED DUE TO SCARCITY		

2015 Star Wars Journey to The Force Awakens Blueprints

COMPLETE SET (8)	15.00	40.00
COMMON CARD (BP1-BP8)	3.00	8.00
BP1 BB-8	6.00	15.00
BP3 Millennium Falcon	5.00	12.00
BP4 X-Wing Fighter	4.00	10.00

2015 Star Wars Journey to The Force Awakens Character Stickers

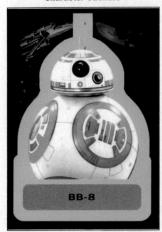

BB-8

| COMPLETE SET (18) | 15.00 | 40.00 |
| COMMON CARD (S1-S18) | 1.25 | 3.00 |

*P.P.BLACK/1: UNPRICED DUE TO SCARCITY

*P.P.CYAN/1: UNPRICED DUE TO SCARCITY

*P.P.MAGENTA/1: UNPRICED DUE TO SCARCITY

*P.P.YELLOW/1: UNPRICED DUE TO SCARCITY

S1 Luke Skywalker	1.50	4.00
S2 Han Solo	2.00	5.00
S9 BB-8	2.50	6.00
S10 Captain Phasma	1.50	4.00
S11 Kylo Ren	2.00	5.00
S14 Darth Vader	2.00	5.00
S15 Boba Fett	1.50	4.00
S17 Kylo Ren	2.00	5.00
S18 Yoda	1.50	4.00

2015 Star Wars Journey to The Force Awakens
Choose Your Destiny

| COMPLETE SET (9) | 12.00 | 30.00 |
| COMMON CARD (CD1-CD9) | 2.50 | 6.00 |

2015 Star Wars Journey to The Force Awakens
Classic Captions

| COMPLETE SET (8) | 15.00 | 40.00 |
| COMMON CARD (CC1-CC8) | 4.00 | 10.00 |

2015 Star Wars Journey to The Force Awakens
Cloth Stickers

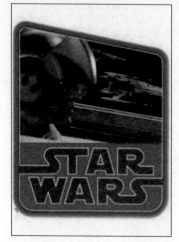

COMPLETE SET (9)	8.00	20.00
COMMON CARD (CS1-CS9)	1.50	4.00
CS6 Kylo Ren	2.00	5.00
CS9 Kylo Ren (w/TIE Fighters)	2.00	5.00

2015 Star Wars Journey to The Force Awakens
Concept Art

| COMPLETE SET (9) | 5.00 | 12.00 |
| COMMON CARD (CA1-CA9) | 1.00 | 2.50 |

*P.P.BLACK/1: UNPRICED DUE TO SCARCITY

*P.P.CYAN/1: UNPRICED DUE TO SCARCITY

*P.P.MAGENTA/1: UNPRICED DUE TO SCARCITY

*P.P.YELLOW/1: UNPRICED DUE TO SCARCITY

2015 Star Wars Journey to The Force Awakens
Dual Autographs

STATED PRINT RUN 3 SER.#'d SETS

UNPRICED DUE TO SCARCITY

1 Mark Hamill/Kenny Baker

2 Ian McDiarmid/Wayne Pygram

3 Peter Mayhew/Anthony Daniels

4 Mark Hamill/David Prowse

2015 Star Wars Journey to The Force Awakens
Family Legacy Matte Backs

SATINE KRYZE   BO-KATAN KRYZE

| COMPLETE SET (8) | 10.00 | 25.00 |
| COMMON CARD (FL1-FL8) | 1.50 | 4.00 |

*GLOSSY: .5X TO 1.2X BASIC CARDS

*P.P.BLACK/1: UNPRICED DUE TO SCARCITY

*P.P.CYAN/1: UNPRICED DUE TO SCARCITY

*P.P.MAGENTA/1: UNPRICED DUE TO SCARCITY

*P.P.YELLOW/1: UNPRICED DUE TO SCARCITY

FL1 Boba Fett and Jango Fett	2.00	5.00
FL2 Anakin Skywalker and Luke Skywalker	2.00	5.00
FL3 Padme Amidala and Leia Organa	2.00	5.00

2015 Star Wars Journey to The Force Awakens
Heroes of the Resistance

BB-8

HEROES OF THE RESISTANCE

| COMPLETE SET (9) | 6.00 | 15.00 |
| COMMON CARD (R1-R9) | 1.25 | 3.00 |

*P.P.BLACK/1: UNPRICED DUE TO SCARCITY

*P.P.CYAN/1: UNPRICED DUE TO SCARCITY

*P.P.MAGENTA/1: UNPRICED DUE TO SCARCITY

*P.P.YELLOW/1: UNPRICED DUE TO SCARCITY

| R4 BB-8 | 2.00 | 5.00 |
| R8 The Millennium Falcon | 1.50 | 4.00 |

2015 Star Wars Journey to The Force Awakens
Patches

COMPLETE SET (20)	150.00	300.00
COMMON CARD (P1-P20)	8.00	20.00
P1 First Order Kylo Ren	12.00	30.00
P3 First Order Captain Phasma	12.00	30.00
P9 X-Wing Fighter BB-8	12.00	30.00
P18 BB-8 BB-8	12.00	30.00

2015 Star Wars Journey to The Force Awakens
Power of the First Order

COMPLETE SET (8)	6.00	15.00
COMMON CARD (FD1-FD8)	1.25	3.00
*P.P.BLACK/1: UNPRICED DUE TO SCARCITY		
*P.P.CYAN/1: UNPRICED DUE TO SCARCITY		
*P.P.MAGENTA/1: UNPRICED DUE TO SCARCITY		
*P.P.YELLOW/1: UNPRICED DUE TO SCARCITY		
FD1 Kylo Ren	2.00	5.00
FD2 Captain Phasma	1.50	4.00

2015 Star Wars Journey to The Force Awakens
Silhouette Foil

COMPLETE SET (8)	4.00	10.00
COMMON CARD (1-8)	.75	2.00
*P.P.BLACK/1: UNPRICED DUE TO SCARCITY		
*P.P.CYAN/1: UNPRICED DUE TO SCARCITY		
*P.P.MAGENTA/1: UNPRICED DUE TO SCARCITY		
*P.P.YELLOW/1: UNPRICED DUE TO SCARCITY		
ERRONEOUSLY LISTED AS A 9-CARD SET		
ON THE CARD BACKS		
5 Kylo Ren	1.50	4.00
7 Captain Phasma	1.25	3.00

2015 Star Wars Journey to The Force Awakens
Promos

COMPLETE SET (6)	10.00	25.00
COMMON CARD (P1-P6)	2.00	5.00
P1 Luke Skywalker	6.00	15.00
(SDCC Marvel Star Wars Lando exclusive)		
P6 Kanan Jarrus	5.00	12.00
(NYCC exclusive)		

2015 Star Wars Journey to The Force Awakens UK

COMPLETE SET (208)	30.00	80.00
COMMON CARD	.30	.75
LEY Yoda		
LEBF Boba Fett		
LECH Chewbacca		
LEHS Han Solo		
LELC Lando Calrissian		
LELS Luke Skywalker		
LEPL Princess Leia		
LER2 R2-D2		
LEST Stormtrooper		
LETE The Emperor		

2017 Star Wars Journey to The Last Jedi

COMPLETE SET (110)	12.00	30.00
UNOPENED BOX (24 PACKS)	85.00	100.00
UNOPENED PACK (8 CARDS)	3.00	4.00
COMMON CARD (1-110)	.20	.50
*GREEN STAR.: .5X TO 1.2X BASIC CARDS	.25	.60
*PINK STAR.: .6X TO 1.5X BASIC CARDS	.30	.75
*BLACK STAR.: .75X TO 2X BASIC CARDS	.40	1.00
*SILVER STAR.: 1.2X TO 3X BASIC CARDS	.60	1.50
*PURPLE STAR.: 2X TO 5X BASIC CARDS	1.00	2.50
*WHITE STAR./199: 12X TO 30X BASIC CARDS	6.00	15.00
*ORANGE STAR./50: 15X TO 40X BASIC CARDS	8.00	20.00

*GOLD STAR./25: 25X TO 60X BASIC CARDS	12.00	30.00
*IMP. RED/1: UNPRICED DUE TO SCARCITY		
*P.P.BLACK/1: UNPRICED DUE TO SCARCITY		
*P.P.CYAN/1: UNPRICED DUE TO SCARCITY		
*P.P.MAGENTA/1: UNPRICED DUE TO SCARCITY		
*P.P.YELLOW/1: UNPRICED DUE TO SCARCITY		

2017 Star Wars Journey to The Last Jedi Allies

HAN SOLO — CHEWBACCA

COMPLETE SET (5)	50.00	100.00
COMMON CARD (1-5)	10.00	25.00
*P.P.BLACK/1: UNPRICED DUE TO SCARCITY		
*P.P.CYAN/1: UNPRICED DUE TO SCARCITY		
*P.P.MAGENTA/1: UNPRICED DUE TO SCARCITY		
*P.P.YELLOW/1: UNPRICED DUE TO SCARCITY		
STATED ODDS 1:		
GAMESTOP EXCLUSIVE		

2017 Star Wars Journey to The Last Jedi
Autographs

LANDO CALRISSIAN
AUTHENTIC AUTOGRAPH

*GOLD/10: UNPRICED DUE TO SCARCITY		
*IMP. RED/1: UNPRICED DUE TO SCARCITY		
*P.P.BLACK/1: UNPRICED DUE TO SCARCITY		
*P.P.CYAN/1: UNPRICED DUE TO SCARCITY		
*P.P.MAGENTA/1: UNPRICED DUE TO SCARCITY		
*P.P.YELLOW/1: UNPRICED DUE TO SCARCITY		
AAD Adam Driver		
AAE Ashley Eckstein		
AAP Alistair Petrie		
AAS Andy Serkis		
AAT Alan Tudyk		
ABD Ben Daniels	20.00	50.00
ABH Brian Herring	12.00	30.00
ABL Billie Lourd		
ABW Billy Dee Williams		
ACD Cristina da Silva	12.00	30.00
ACF Carrie Fisher		
ACR Clive Revill		
ACT Catherine Taber	15.00	40.00
ADB Dee Bradley Baker	12.00	30.00
ADC Dave Chapman	20.00	50.00
ADL Daniel Logan	12.00	30.00
ADP Duncan Pow	8.00	20.00
ADR Daisy Ridley		
ADY Donnie Yen		

AFJ Felicity Jones		
AFP Freddie Prinze Jr.		
AFW Forest Whitaker		
AGC Gwendoline Christie		
AGT George Takei		
AHC Hayden Christensen		
AHF Harrison Ford		
AIU Iko Uwais		
AIW Ian Whyte	10.00	25.00
AJB John Boyega		
AJC Jim Cummings	10.00	25.00
AJD Julie Dolan	10.00	25.00
AJI Jason Isaacs		
AKB Kenny Baker		
AKF Kate Fleetwood		
AKY Keone Young	15.00	40.00
AMH Mark Hamill		
APB Paul Blake	15.00	40.00
APM Peter Mayhew		
APW Paul Warren	10.00	25.00
ARA Riz Ahmed		
ARC Richard Cunningham	12.00	30.00
ARP Ray Park		
ASG Stefan Grube	12.00	30.00
ASR Scott Richardson	15.00	40.00
ASW Sam Witwer		
ATB Thomas Brodie-Sangster		
ATC Tosin Cole		
ATK Tom Kane		
ATW Tom Wilton	12.00	30.00
AWP Wayne Pygram	10.00	25.00
AYR Yayan Ruhian		
AZD Zarene Dallas	12.00	30.00
AADA Anthony Daniels		
AADX Adam Driver Unmasked		
ACAR Cecp Arif Rahman	15.00	40.00
ADAR Derek Arnold		
ADBA Dave Barclay	10.00	25.00
ADRX Daisy Ridley Scavenger		
AGGA Gloria Garcia	12.00	30.00
AGGA Greg Grunberg		
AIMD Ian McDiarmid		
AIME Ian McElhinney	12.00	30.00
AJBL Jerome Blake	10.00	25.00
AJBU Jeremy Bulloch		
ASDB Sharon Duncan-Brewster	15.00	40.00

2017 Star Wars Journey to The Last Jedi Blueprints

COMPLETE SET (7)	8.00	20.00
COMMON CARD (1-7)	2.00	5.00
*P.P.BLACK/1: UNPRICED DUE TO SCARCITY		
*P.P.CYAN/1: UNPRICED DUE TO SCARCITY		
*P.P.MAGENTA/1: UNPRICED DUE TO SCARCITY		
*P.P.YELLOW/1: UNPRICED DUE TO SCARCITY		

2017 Star Wars Journey to The Last Jedi Character Retro Stickers

COMPLETE SET (18)	100.00	200.00
COMMON CARD (1-18)	6.00	15.00
*P.P.BLACK/1: UNPRICED DUE TO SCARCITY		
*P.P.CYAN/1: UNPRICED DUE TO SCARCITY		
*P.P.MAGENTA/1: UNPRICED DUE TO SCARCITY		
*P.P.YELLOW/1: UNPRICED DUE TO SCARCITY		

2017 Star Wars Journey to The Last Jedi Characters

COMPLETE SET (16)	12.00	30.00
COMMON CARD (1-16)	1.25	3.00
*P.P.BLACK/1: UNPRICED DUE TO SCARCITY		
*P.P.CYAN/1: UNPRICED DUE TO SCARCITY		
*P.P.MAGENTA/1: UNPRICED DUE TO SCARCITY		
*P.P.YELLOW/1: UNPRICED DUE TO SCARCITY		

2017 Star Wars Journey to The Last Jedi Choose Your Destiny

COMPLETE SET (10)	8.00	20.00
COMMON CARD (1-10)	1.25	3.00
*P.P.BLACK/1: UNPRICED DUE TO SCARCITY		
*P.P.CYAN/1: UNPRICED DUE TO SCARCITY		
*P.P.MAGENTA/1: UNPRICED DUE TO SCARCITY		
*P.P.YELLOW/1: UNPRICED DUE TO SCARCITY		

2017 Star Wars Journey to The Last Jedi Darkness Rises

COMPLETE SET (6)	6.00	15.00
COMMON CARD (1-6)	1.50	4.00

2017 Star Wars Journey to The Last Jedi Family Legacy

COMPLETE SET (6)	5.00	12.00
COMMON CARD (1-6)	1.25	3.00
*P.P.BLACK/1: UNPRICED DUE TO SCARCITY		
*P.P.CYAN/1: UNPRICED DUE TO SCARCITY		
*P.P.MAGENTA/1: UNPRICED DUE TO SCARCITY		
*P.P.YELLOW/1: UNPRICED DUE TO SCARCITY		

2017 Star Wars Journey to The Last Jedi Illustrated Characters

COMPLETE SET (14)	10.00	25.00
COMMON CARD (1-14)	1.00	2.50
*P.P.BLACK/1: UNPRICED DUE TO SCARCITY		

*P.P.CYAN/1: UNPRICED DUE TO SCARCITY
*P.P.MAGENTA/1: UNPRICED DUE TO SCARCITY
*P.P.YELLOW/1: UNPRICED DUE TO SCARCITY

2017 Star Wars Journey to The Last Jedi Patches

COMMON CARD (UNNUMBERED)	5.00	12.00
*ORANGE/99: .75X TO 2X BASIC CARDS	10.00	25.00
*GOLD/25: 1.2X TO 3X BASIC CARDS	15.00	40.00
*IMP. RED/1: UNPRICED DUE TO SCARCITY		
STATED ODDS 1:		

2017 Star Wars Journey to The Last Jedi Rey Continuity

COMPLETE SET (10)	12.00	30.00
COMMON CARD (1-5)	1.25	3.00
COMMON CARD (6-10)	2.00	5.00
*P.P.BLACK/1: UNPRICED DUE TO SCARCITY		
*P.P.CYAN/1: UNPRICED DUE TO SCARCITY		
*P.P.MAGENTA/1: UNPRICED DUE TO SCARCITY		
*P.P.YELLOW/1: UNPRICED DUE TO SCARCITY		
RANDOMLY INSERTED INTO PACKS		
1-5 JOURNEY TO THE LAST JEDI EXCLUSIVE		
6-10 THE LAST JEDI SER.1 EXCLUSIVE		
11-15 THE LAST JEDI SER.2 EXCLUSIVE		

1996 Star Wars Laser

0 Star Wars 20th Anniversary Commemorative Magazine	3.00	8.00

2016 Star Wars LEGO Droid Tales

COMPLETE SET (9)	15.00	40.00
UNOPENED PACK (3 CARDS)	6.00	8.00
COMMON CARD (DT1-DT9)		

ONE PACK INSERTED INTO
STAR WARS LEGO DROID TALES DVD

1995 Star Wars Mastervisions

COMPLETE BOXED SET (36)	10.00	25.00
COMMON CARD (1-36)	.30	.75

1995 Star Wars Mastervisions Promos

COMMON CARD	.75	2.00
P2 Luke on Hoth	1.25	3.00
(Star Wars Galaxy Magazine Exclusive)		

2015 Star Wars Masterwork

COMPLETE SET w/o SP (50)	60.00	120.00
UNOPENED BOX (4 MINIBOXES)	300.00	350.00
UNOPENED MINIBOX (5 CARDS)	80.00	95.00
COMMON CARD (1-50)	2.00	5.00
COMMON CARD (51-75)	5.00	12.00
*BLUE/299: .5X TO 1.2X BASIC CARDS		
*BLUE SP/299: .2X TO .50X BASIC CARDS		
*SILVER/99: .75X TO 2X BASIC CARDS		
*SILVER SP/99: .3X TO .80X BASIC CARDS		
*GREEN/50: 1.2X TO 3X BASIC CARDS		
*GREEN SP/50: .5X TO 1.2X BASIC CARDS		
*P.P.BLACK/1: UNPRICED DUE TO SCARCITY		
*P.P.CYAN/1: UNPRICED DUE TO SCARCITY		
*P.P.MAGENTA./1: UNPRICED DUE TO SCARCITY		
*P.P.YELLOW/1: UNPRICED DUE TO SCARCITY		

2015 Star Wars Masterwork Autographs

COMMON CARD	10.00	25.00
*FRAMED/28: X TO X BASIC CARDS		
*FOIL/25: X TO X BASIC CARDS		
*CANVAS/10: UNPRICED DUE TO SCARCITY		
*WOOD/1: UNPRICED DUE TO SCARCITY		
STATED ODDS 1:4		
NNO Alan Harris	12.00	30.00
NNO Amy Allen	12.00	30.00
NNO Angus MacInnes	12.00	30.00
NNO Anthony Daniels	120.00	250.00
NNO Ashley Eckstein	20.00	50.00
NNO Billy Dee Williams	120.00	250.00
NNO Carrie Fisher	500.00	800.00
NNO Dickey Beer	12.00	30.00
NNO Gerald Home	15.00	40.00
NNO Harrison Ford	1800.00	3000.00
NNO James Earl Jones	150.00	300.00
NNO Jeremy Bulloch	25.00	60.00
NNO Jerome Blake	12.00	30.00
NNO John Morton	20.00	50.00
NNO John Ratzenberger	15.00	40.00
NNO Kenneth Colley	12.00	30.00
NNO Kenny Baker	120.00	250.00
NNO Mark Hamill	350.00	600.00
NNO Mike Quinn	12.00	30.00
NNO Oliver Ford Davies	15.00	40.00
NNO Pam Rose	12.00	30.00
NNO Paul Brooke	25.00	60.00
NNO Peter Mayhew	50.00	100.00
NNO Phil Eason	15.00	40.00
NNO Rusty Goffe	15.00	40.00
NNO Tim Rose	25.00	60.00
NNO Wayne Pygram	15.00	40.00
NNO Zachariah Jensen	15.00	40.00

2015 Star Wars Masterwork Companions

COMPLETE SET (10)	25.00	60.00
COMMON CARD (C1-C10)	10.00	10.00
*RAINBOW/299: .6X TO 1.5X BASIC CARDS		
*CANVAS/99: 1X TO 2.5X BASIC CARDS		
*WOOD/50: 1.2X TO 3X BASIC CARDS		
*CLEAR ACE./25: 1.5X TO 4X BASIC CARDS		
*METAL/10: UNPRICED DUE TO SCARCITY		

*GOLDEN METAL/1: UNPRICED DUE TO SCARCITY
*P.P.BLACK/1: UNPRICED DUE TO SCARCITY
*P.P.CYAN/1: UNPRICED DUE TO SCARCITY
*P.P.MAGENTA/1: UNPRICED DUE TO SCARCITY
*P.P.YELLOW/1: UNPRICED DUE TO SCARCITY

C1 Han Solo and Chewbacca	6.00	15.00
C2 Luke and Leia	6.00	15.00
C3 Vader and Palpatine	5.00	12.00
C5 C-3PO and R2-D2	5.00	12.00
C8 R2-D2 and Luke Skywalker	5.00	12.00
C10 Boba Fett and Jango Fett	5.00	12.00

2015 Star Wars Masterwork Defining Moments

COMPLETE SET (10)	25.00	60.00
COMMON CARD (DM1-DM10)	4.00	10.00

*RAINBOW/299: .6X TO 1.5X BASIC CARDS
*CANVAS/99: 1X TO 2.5X BASIC CARDS
*WOOD/50: 1.2X TO 3X BASIC CARDS
*CLEAR ACE./25: 1.5X TO 4X BASIC CARDS
*METAL/10: UNPRICED DUE TO SCARCITY
*GOLDEN METAL/1: UNPRICED DUE TO SCARCITY
*P.P.BLACK/1: UNPRICED DUE TO SCARCITY
*P.P.CYAN/1: UNPRICED DUE TO SCARCITY
*P.P.MAGENTA/1: UNPRICED DUE TO SCARCITY
*P.P.YELLOW/1: UNPRICED DUE TO SCARCITY

DM1 Darth Vader	5.00	12.00
DM2 Luke Skywalker	5.00	12.00
DM3 Han Solo	8.00	20.00
DM4 Princess Leia Organa	5.00	12.00
DM7 Anakin Skywalker	5.00	12.00
DM8 Obi-Wan Kenobi	5.00	12.00
DM10 Chewbacca	5.00	12.00

2015 Star Wars Masterwork Return of the Jedi Bunker Relics Bronze

COMMON CARD	12.00	30.00

*SILVER/77: .75X TO 2X BASIC CARDS
CARDS 1, 2, 3, 4, 10, 12 SER.#'d TO 155
CARDS 5, 6, 7, 8, 9, 11 SER.#'d TO 255

1 Han Solo/155	20.00	50.00
2 Princess Leia Organa/155	20.00	50.00
3 Chewbacca/155	15.00	40.00

4 Luke Skywalker/155	25.00	60.00
10 Ewok (frame)/155	15.00	40.00
12 Han, Leia & Luke/155	20.00	50.00

2015 Star Wars Masterwork Scum and Villainy

COMPLETE SET (10)	25.00	60.00
COMMON CARD (SV1-SV10)	4.00	10.00

*RAINBOW/299: 1.5X TO 6X BASIC CARDS
*CANVAS/99: 1X TO 2.5X BASIC CARDS
*WOOD/50: 1.2X TO 3X BASIC CARDS
*CLEAR ACE./25: 1.5X TO 4X BASIC CARDS
*METAL/10: UNPRICED DUE TO SCARCITY
*GOLDEN METAL/1: UNPRICED DUE TO SCARCITY
*P.P.BLACK/1: UNPRICED DUE TO SCARCITY
*P.P.CYAN/1: UNPRICED DUE TO SCARCITY
*P.P.MAGENTA/1: UNPRICED DUE TO SCARCITY
*P.P.YELLOW/1: UNPRICED DUE TO SCARCITY

SV1 Boba Fett	6.00	15.00
SV2 Jabba the Hutt	5.00	12.00
SV4 General Grievous	6.00	15.00
SV5 Jango Fett	5.00	12.00
SV8 Ponda Baba	6.00	15.00
SV9 Bossk	5.00	12.00
SV10 Tusken Raider	6.00	15.00

2015 Star Wars Masterwork Stamp Relics

COMMON CARD	20.00	50.00

STATED ODDS 1:CASE

NNO Anakin vs. Obi-Wan	50.00	100.00
NNO Ben (Obi-Wan) Kenobi	30.00	80.00
NNO Boba Fett	60.00	120.00
NNO C-3PO	25.00	60.00
NNO Darth Maul	50.00	100.00
NNO Darth Vader	30.00	80.00
NNO Emperor Palpatine	30.00	80.00

NNO Han Solo and Chewbacca	50.00	100.00
NNO Luke Skywalker	30.00	80.00
NNO The Millennium Falcon	50.00	100.00
NNO X-Wing Fighter	30.00	80.00

2015 Star Wars Masterwork Triple Autograph

STATED PRINT RUN 2 SER. #'d SETS
UNPRICED DUE TO SCARCITY

1 Mark Hamill
Harrison Ford
Carrie Fisher

2015 Star Wars Masterwork Weapons Lineage Medallions

COMPLETE SET (30)	250.00	500.00
COMMON CARD	8.00	20.00

*SILVER/50: 1.2X TO 3X BASIC CARDS
*GOLD/10: UNPRICED DUE TO SCARCITY
STATED ODDS 1:6

NNO Anakin Skywalker	10.00	25.00
Mace Windu's Lightsaber		
NNO Anakin Skywalker	12.00	30.00
Anakin Skywalker's Lightsaber		
NNO B. Fett's Blaster	10.00	25.00
NNO B. Fett's Blaster	12.00	30.00
NNO Darth Maul's Lightsaber	10.00	25.00
NNO Vader	10.00	25.00
Vader's Lightsaber		
NNO Vader	10.00	25.00
Vader's Lightsaber		
NNO Vader	10.00	25.00
Vader's Lightsaber		
NNO Vader Solo's Blaster	12.00	30.00
NNO Darth Vader	15.00	40.00
Luke Skywalker's Lightsaber		
NNO Han Solo	12.00	30.00
Han Solo's Blaster		
NNO Han Solo	12.00	30.00
Han Solo's Blaster		

NNO Han Solo		15.00	40.00
Luke Skywalker's Lightsaber			
NNO Luke Skywalker		10.00	25.00
Luke Skywalker's Lightsaber			
NNO Luke Skywalker		10.00	25.00
Luke Skywalker's Lightsaber			
NNO Mace Windu		10.00	25.00
Mace Windu's Lightsaber			
NNO Princess Leia Organa		10.00	25.00
Stormtrooper Blaster Rifle			
NNO Leia		12.00	30.00
Leia's Blaster			
NNO R2-D2		10.00	25.00
Luke's Lightsaber			
NNO Stormtrooper		12.00	30.00
Stormtrooper Blaster Rifle			
NNO Yoda		15.00	40.00
Yoda's Lightsaber			

2016 Star Wars Masterwork

COMPLETE SET W/SP (75)		200.00	400.00
COMPLETE SET W/O SP (50)		30.00	80.00
UNOPENED BOX (4 PACKS)		150.00	200.00
UNOPENED PACK (5 CARDS)		50.00	60.00
COMMON CARD (1-75)		2.00	5.00
COMMON SP (51-75)		4.00	10.00
*BLUE MET.: SAME VALUE		2.00	5.00
*BLUE MET.SP: SAME VALUE		4.00	10.00
*SILVER MET./99: .75X TO 1.5X BASIC CARDS		3.00	8.00
*SILVER MET.SP/99: .30X TO .75X BASIC CARDS		3.00	8.00
*GREEN MET./50: 1.2X TO 3X BASIC CARDS		6.00	15.00
*GREEN MET.SP/50: .6X TO 1.5X BASIC CARDS		6.00	15.00
*LTSBR PURP./25: 1.5X TO 4X BASIC CARDS		8.00	20.00
*LTSBR PURP.SP/25: .75X TO 2X BASIC CARDS		8.00	20.00
*GOLD/1: UNPRICED DUE TO SCARCITY			
*P.P.BLACK/1: UNPRICED DUE TO SCARCITY			
*P.P.CYAN/1: UNPRICED DUE TO SCARCITY			
*P.P.MAGENTA/1: UNPRICED DUE TO SCARCITY			
*P.P.YELLOW/1: UNPRICED DUE TO SCARCITY			
66 Han Solo SP		6.00	15.00
71 Rey SP		8.00	20.00

2016 Star Wars Masterwork Alien Identification Guide

COMPLETE SET (10)		20.00	50.00
COMMON CARD (AI1-AI10)		2.50	6.00
*FOIL/299: .6X TO 1.5X BASIC CARDS		3.00	8.00
*CANVAS/99: .75X TO 2X BASIC CARDS		5.00	12.00
*WOOD/50: 1X TO 2.5X BASIC CARDS		6.00	15.00
*SILVER/10: UNPRICED DUE TO SCARCITY			
*GOLD/1: UNPRICED DUE TO SCARCITY			
*P.P.BLACK/1: UNPRICED DUE TO SCARCITY			
*P.P.CYAN/1: UNPRICED DUE TO SCARCITY			
*P.P.MAGENTA/1: UNPRICED DUE TO SCARCITY			
*P.P.YELLOW/1: UNPRICED DUE TO SCARCITY			
STATED ODDS 1:4			

2016 Star Wars Masterwork Autographs

COMMON CARD		6.00	15.00
*FOIL/50: .6X TO 1.5X BASIC CARDS			
*CANVAS/25: .75X TO 2X BASIC CARDS			
*WOOD/10: UNPRICED DUE TO SCARCITY			
*SILVER/10: UNPRICED DUE TO SCARCITY			
*GOLD/1: UNPRICED DUE TO SCARCITY			
*P.P.BLACK/1: UNPRICED DUE TO SCARCITY			
*P.P.CYAN/1: UNPRICED DUE TO SCARCITY			
*P.P.MAGENTA/1: UNPRICED DUE TO SCARCITY			
*P.P.YELLOW/1: UNPRICED DUE TO SCARCITY			
5 Andy Serkis		80.00	150.00
8 Ashley Eckstein		12.00	30.00
11 Caroline Blakiston		8.00	20.00
14 Clive Revill		12.00	30.00
15 Corey Dee Williams		8.00	20.00
19 David Ankrum		8.00	20.00
20 David Barclay		8.00	20.00
24 Dickey Beer		10.00	25.00
34 Jeremy Bulloch		15.00	40.00
39 John Coppinger		8.00	20.00
47 Mark Dodson		10.00	25.00
50 Matthew Wood		8.00	20.00
55 Mike Edmonds		8.00	20.00
56 Mike Quinn		8.00	20.00
65 Sam Witwer		8.00	20.00
73 Tim Dry		8.00	20.00
74 Tim Rose		8.00	20.00
75 Tiya Sircar		8.00	20.00

2016 Star Wars Masterwork Autographs Canvas

*CANVAS/25: .75X TO 2X BASIC CARDS
STATED ODDS 1:25
STATED PRINT RUN 25 SER.#'d SETS

1 Adam Driver		800.00	1200.00
5 Andy Serkis		150.00	300.00
7 Anthony Daniels		80.00	150.00
10 Billy Dee Williams			
12 Carrie Fisher		300.00	600.00
16 Daisy Ridley		1200.00	2000.00
23 Denis Lawson		25.00	60.00
26 Freddie Prinze Jr.		30.00	80.00
29 Greg Grunberg		12.00	30.00
31 Harrison Ford/1			
32 Hugh Quarshie			
38 John Boyega			
42 Julian Glover			
43 Keisha Castle-Hughes			
48 Mark Hamill		250.00	500.00
52 Michael Carter		12.00	30.00
60 Peter Mayhew			
61 Ray Park			
79 Warwick Davis		15.00	40.00

2016 Star Wars Masterwork Autographs Foil

*FOIL/50: .6X TO 1.5X BASIC CARDS
STATED ODDS 1:30
STATED PRINT RUN 50 SER.#'d SETS

3 Alan Harris			
7 Anthony Daniels		50.00	100.00
12 Carrie Fisher			
14 Clive Revill			
15 Corey Dee Williams			
19 David Ankrum			
20 David Barclay			
23 Denis Lawson			
25 Femi Taylor			
26 Freddie Prinze Jr.			
27 Garrick Hagon			
28 George Takei		15.00	40.00
29 Greg Grunberg		10.00	25.00
32 Hugh Quarshie		10.00	25.00
33 Jack Klaff			
38 John Boyega		120.00	250.00
40 John Morton			
41 John Ratzenberger			
43 Keisha Castle-Hughes			
44 Kenneth Colley			
47 Mark Dodson			
51 Mercedes Ngoh			
52 Michael Carter			
59 Paul Blake			
60 Peter Mayhew		30.00	80.00
61 Ray Park			
67 Sean Crawford			
76 Toby Philpott			
79 Warwick Davis			

2016 Star Wars Masterwork Dual Autographs

STATED ODDS 1:4,658

NNO Fisher/Baker		
NNO Barclay/Philpott	25.00	60.00
NNO McDiarmid/Revil		
NNO Blake/Bowers	20.00	50.00
NNO Hamill/Ridley		
NNO Hamill/Baker		
NNO Pygram/Stanton	15.00	40.00

2016 Star Wars Masterwork Great Rivalries

COMPLETE SET (10)	15.00	40.00
COMMON CARD (GR1-GR10)	2.50	6.00
*FOIL/299: .6X TO 1.5X BASIC CARDS		
*CANVAS/99: .75X TO 2X BASIC CARDS		
*WOOD/50: 1X TO 2.5X BASIC CARDS		
*SILVER/10: UNPRICED DUE TO SCARCITY		
*GOLD/1: UNPRICED DUE TO SCARCITY		
*P.P.BLACK/1: UNPRICED DUE TO SCARCITY		
*P.P.CYAN/1: UNPRICED DUE TO SCARCITY		
*P.P.MAGENTA/1: UNPRICED DUE TO SCARCITY		
*P.P.YELLOW/1: UNPRICED DUE TO SCARCITY		
STATED ODDS 1:2		

2016 Star Wars Masterwork Medallion Relics

COMMON CARD	5.00	12.00
*SILVER/99: .6X TO 1.5X BASIC CARDS	8.00	20.00
*GOLD/10: 1.5X TO 4X BASIC CARDS	20.00	50.00
*PLATINUM/1: UNPRICED DUE TO SCARCITY		
STATED ODDS 1:7		
NNO Han Solo Hoth	6.00	15.00
NNO Han Solo Starkiller Base	6.00	15.00
NNO Han Solo Yavin	6.00	15.00
NNO Kylo Ren Starkiller Base		
NNO Rey Starkiller Base	6.00	15.00

2016 Star Wars Masterwork Show of Force

COMPLETE SET (10)	25.00	60.00
COMMON CARD (SF1-SF10)	3.00	8.00
*FOIL/299: .6X TO 1.5X BASIC CARDS	5.00	12.00
*CANVAS/99: .75X TO 2X BASIC CARDS	6.00	15.00
*WOOD/50: 1X TO 2.5X BASIC CARDS	8.00	20.00
*SILVER/10: UNPRICED DUE TO SCARCITY		
*GOLD/1: UNPRICED DUE TO SCARCITY		
*P.P.BLACK/1: UNPRICED DUE TO SCARCITY		
*P.P.CYAN/1: UNPRICED DUE TO SCARCITY		
*P.P.MAGENTA/1: UNPRICED DUE TO SCARCITY		
*P.P.YELLOW/1: UNPRICED DUE TO SCARCITY		
STATED ODDS 1:4		
SF10 Rey	4.00	10.00

2016 Star Wars Masterwork Stamp Relics

COMPLETE SET (12)	100.00	200.00
COMMON CARD	8.00	20.00
*BRONZE/99: .6X TO 1.5X BASIC CARDS	12.00	30.00
*SILVER/50: .75X TO 2X BASIC CARDS	15.00	40.00
*GOLD/10: UNPRICED DUE TO SCARCITY		
*PLATINUM/1: UNPRICED DUE TO SCARCITY		
STATED ODDS 1:13		
STATED PRINT RUN 249 SER.#'d SETS		
NNO Han Solo	10.00	25.00
NNO Rey	12.00	30.00

2017 Star Wars Masterwork

COMPLETE SET (100)		
COMPLETE SET W/O SP (75)		
UNOPENED BOX (4 MINIBOXES)		
UNOPENED MINIBOX (5 CARDS)		
COMMON CARD (1-75)	2.50	6.00
COMMON SP (76-100)	5.00	12.00
*BLUE: .5X TO 1.25X BASIC CARDS	3.00	8.00
*GREEN/99: .6X TO 1.5X BASIC CARDS	4.00	10.00
*PURPLE/50: .75X TO 2X BASIC CARDS	5.00	12.00
*GOLD/25: 1X TO 2.5X BASIC CARDS	6.00	15.00
*RED/1: UNPRICED DUE TO SCARCITY		
*P.P.BLACK/1: UNPRICED DUE TO SCARCITY		
*P.P.CYAN/1: UNPRICED DUE TO SCARCITY		
*P.P.MAGENTA/1: UNPRICED DUE TO SCARCITY		
*P.P.YELLOW/1: UNPRICED DUE TO SCARCITY		

2017 Star Wars Masterwork Adventures of R2-D2

COMMON CARD (AR1-AR10)	2.50	6.00
*RAINBOW FOIL: .5X TO 1.25X BASIC CARDS	3.00	8.00
*CANVAS: .6X TO 1.5X BASIC CARDS	4.00	10.00
*WOOD/50: .75X TO 2X BASIC CARDS	5.00	12.00
*METAL/10: UNPRICED DUE TO SCARCITY		
*GOLD TINTED/1: UNPRICED DUE TO SCARCITY		
*P.P.BLACK/1: UNPRICED DUE TO SCARCITY		
*P.P.CYAN/1: UNPRICED DUE TO SCARCITY		
*P.P.MAGENTA/1: UNPRICED DUE TO SCARCITY		
*P.P.YELLOW/1: UNPRICED DUE TO SCARCITY		

2017 Star Wars Masterwork Autographs

COMMON CARD	6.00	15.00

*WOOD/10: UNPRICED DUE TO SCARCITY
SILVER FRAMED/10>: UNPRICED DUE TO SCARCITY
*GOLD TINTED/1: UNPRICED DUE TO SCARCITY

NNO Adam Driver (horizontal)		
NNO Adam Driver (vertical)		
NNO Alan Tudyk	50.00	100.00
NNO Andy Serkis		
NNO Ashley Eckstein	15.00	40.00
NNO Ben Daniels	8.00	20.00
NNO Billy Dee Williams		
NNO Brian Herring	15.00	40.00
NNO Clive Revill	8.00	20.00
NNO Daisy Ridley		
NNO Dee Bradley Baker	10.00	25.00
NNO Derek Arnold	8.00	20.00
NNO Donnie Yen	60.00	120.00
NNO Felicity Jones (horizontal)		
NNO Felicity Jones (vertical)		
NNO Forest Whitaker (horizontal)		
NNO Forest Whitaker (vertical)		
NNO Freddie Prinze Jr.		
NNO Gwendoline Christie		
NNO Harrison Ford		
NNO Hayden Christensen	150.00	300.00
NNO Ian McDiarmid		
NNO Ian Whyte	10.00	25.00
NNO Jeremy Bulloch	15.00	40.00
NNO John Boyega (horizontal)		
NNO John Boyega (vertical)	60.00	120.00
NNO Julian Glover	12.00	30.00
NNO Lars Mikkelsen	25.00	60.00
NNO Mark Hamill		
NNO Mary Elizabeth McGlynn	12.00	30.00
NNO Matt Lanter	15.00	40.00
NNO Matthew Wood		
NNO Phil LaMarr	8.00	20.00
NNO Ray Park		
NNO Riz Ahmed		
NNO Robbie Daymond	10.00	25.00
NNO Sam Witwer	10.00	25.00
NNO Sarah Michelle Gellar		
NNO Temuera Morrison	25.00	60.00
NNO Tiya Sircar	8.00	20.00
NNO Tom Baker		
NNO Valene Kane	25.00	60.00
NNO Warwick Davis	10.00	25.00
NNO Zarene Dallas	8.00	20.00

2017 Star Wars Masterwork Droid Medallion Relics

COMMON CARD	5.00	12.00
*SILVER/40: .5X TO 1.2X BASIC RELICS	6.00	15.00
*GOLD/25: .6X TO 1.5X BASIC RELICS	8.00	20.00
*BLACK/1: UNPRICED DUE TO SCARCITY		
STATED PRINT RUN 150 SER.#'d SETS		

2017 Star Wars Masterwork Dual Autographs

*PURPLE/10: UNPRICED DUE TO SCARCITY
*GOLD/5: UNPRICED DUE TO SCARCITY
*RED/1: UNPRICED DUE TO SCARCITY

NNO Graves/Taber	20.00	50.00
NNO Daniels/Baker		
NNO Herring/Baker		
NNO Fisher/Baker		
NNO Barclay/Taylor	15.00	40.00
NNO Jones/Tudyk		
NNO Whitaker/Ahmed		
NNO Prinze Jr./Gellar		
NNO Christie/Boyega		
NNO Christensen/Baker		
NNO Christensen/Wood		
NNO McDiarmid/Christensen		
NNO Uwais/Qin-Fee	12.00	30.00
NNO Isaccs/Gray	20.00	50.00
NNO Ratzenberger/MacInnes	12.00	30.00
NNO Hamill/Christensen		
NNO Hamill/Baker		
NNO Salenger/Futterman	12.00	30.00
NNO Kasey/Stanton	12.00	30.00
NNO Marshall/Fleetwood		
NNO Witwer/Wilkinson	15.00	40.00
NNO Morrison/Logan	20.00	50.00
NNO Cole/Grube		

2017 Star Wars Masterwork Evolution of the Rebel Alliance

COMMON CARD (LP1-LP10)	2.50	6.00
*RAINBOW FOIL/249: .5X TO 1.25X BASIC CARDS	3.00	8.00
*CANVAS/99: .6X TO 1.5X BASIC CARDS	4.00	10.00
*WOOD/50: .75X TO 2X BASIC CARDS	5.00	12.00
*METAL/10: UNPRICED DUE TO SCARCITY		
*GOLD TINTED/1: UNPRICED DUE TO SCARCITY		
*P.P.BLACK/1: UNPRICED DUE TO SCARCITY		
*P.P.CYAN/1: UNPRICED DUE TO SCARCITY		
*P.P.MAGENTA/1: UNPRICED DUE TO SCARCITY		
*P.P.YELLOW/1: UNPRICED DUE TO SCARCITY		
LP1 A Meeting of Necessity	2.50	6.00
LP2 Fulcrum's crucial role	2.50	6.00
LP3 The Rebellion engages	2.50	6.00
LP4 The Rebellion's First Victory	2.50	6.00
LP5 The Rebellion's bright new hope	2.50	6.00
LP6 The Death Star destroyed	2.50	6.00
LP7 Bitter defeat on Hoth	2.50	6.00
LP8 The Rebellion Triumphant	2.50	6.00
LP9 Against the First Order	2.50	6.00
LP10 A Resistance left standing	2.50	6.00

2017 Star Wars Masterwork Film Strips

COMMON CARD (FCR1-FCR40)	10.00	25.00

2017 Star Wars Masterwork Hall of Heroes

COMPLETE SET (10)	12.00	30.00
COMMON CARD (HH1-HH10)	3.00	8.00
*RAINBOW FOIL: .5X TO 1.2X BASIC CARDS	4.00	10.00
*CANVAS: .6X TO 1.5X BASIC CARDS	5.00	12.00
*WOOD: UNPRICED DUE TO SCARCITY		
*METAL: UNPRICED DUE TO SCARCITY		
*GOLD TINTED: UNPRICED DUE TO SCARCITY		

*P.P.BLACK/1: UNPRICED DUE TO SCARCITY
*P.P.CYAN/1: UNPRICED DUE TO SCARCITY
*P.P.MAGENTA/1: UNPRICED DUE TO SCARCITY
*P.P.YELLOW/1: UNPRICED DUE TO SCARCITY

2017 Star Wars Masterwork Source Material Jumbo Swatch Relics

COMMON CARD		25.00	60.00
JRCAR	Admiral Ackbar Resistance Uniform	30.00	75.00
JRCGE	Galen Erso Farmer Disguise	60.00	120.00
JRCGF	General Hux First Order Uniform	50.00	100.00
JRCRD	Rey Desert Tunic	200.00	400.00
JRCRO	Rey Outer Garment	150.00	300.00

2018 Star Wars Masterwork

GENERAL HUX

COMPLETE SET W/SP (125)		
COMPLETE SET W/O SP (100)		
UNOPENED BOX (4 PACKS)	150.00	200.00
UNOPENED PACK (5 CARDS)	40.00	50.00
COMMON CARD (1-100)	2.50	6.00
COMMON SP (101-125)	6.00	15.00

*BLUE: .5X TO 1.2X BASIC CARDS
*GREEN/99: .6X TO 1.5X BASIC CARDS
*PURPLE/50: .75X TO 2X BASIC CARDS
*ORANGE/10: UNPRICED DUE TO SCARCITY
*BLACK/5: UNPRICED DUE TO SCARCITY
*GOLD/1: UNPRICED DUE TO SCARCITY
*P.P.BLACK/1: UNPRICED DUE TO SCARCITY
*P.P.CYAN/1: UNPRICED DUE TO SCARCITY
*P.P.MAGENTA/1: UNPRICED DUE TO SCARCITY
*P.P.YELLOW/1: UNPRICED DUE TO SCARCITY

101	Luke Skywalker SP	8.00	20.00
102	Princess Leia Organa SP	12.00	30.00
103	Rey SP	15.00	40.00
104	Finn SP	10.00	25.00
105	Obi-Wan Kenobi SP	10.00	25.00
106	Anakin Skywalker SP	10.00	25.00
108	Darth Vader SP	8.00	20.00
109	Darth Maul SP	8.00	20.00
110	Boba Fett SP	12.00	30.00
111	Han Solo SP	12.00	30.00
113	Lando Calrissian SP	10.00	25.00
114	Saw Gerrera SP	10.00	25.00
115	Jyn Erso SP	12.00	30.00
116	Captain Cassian Andor SP	10.00	25.00
119	Kylo Ren SP	10.00	25.00
121	Ahsoka Tano SP	8.00	20.00
124	Bo-Katan Kryze SP	8.00	20.00

2018 Star Wars Masterwork Autographed Commemorative Vehicle Patches

COMPLETE SET (20)
*BLACK/5: UNPRICED DUE TO SCARCITY
*GOLD/1: UNPRICED DUE TO SCARCITY

STATED PRINT RUN SER.#'d SETS
UNPRICED DUE TO SCARCITY

MPAAD	Anthony Daniels
MPABH	Brian Herring
MPABM	Ben Mendelsohn
MPAFJ	Felicity Jones
MPAGO	Genevieve O'Reilly
MPAHC	Hayden Christensen
MPAHQ	Hugh Quarshie
MPAIM	Ian McDiarmid
MPAJB	John Boyega
MPALM	Lars Mikkelsen
MPAMQ	Mike Quinn
MPARA	Riz Ahmed
MPASB	Steve Blum
MPATG	Taylor Gray
MPATS	Tiya Sircar
MPAVM	Vanessa Marshall
MPADBB	Dee Bradley Baker
MPAFPJ	Freddie Prinze Jr.
MPAGMT	Guy Henry
MPAMEM	Mary Elizabeth McGlynn

2018 Star Wars Masterwork Autographs

COMMON AUTO		6.00	15.00

*BLUE FOIL/99: .5X TO 1.2X BASIC AUTOS
*RAINBOW/50: X TO X BASIC AUTOS
*CANVAS/25: X TO X BASIC AUTOS
*WOOD/10: UNPRICED DUE TO SCARCITY
*SILVER FR./5: UNPRICED DUE TO SCARCITY
*GOLD FR./1: UNPRICED DUE TO SCARCITY
*P.P.BLACK/1: UNPRICED DUE TO SCARCITY
*P.P.CYAN/1: UNPRICED DUE TO SCARCITY
*P.P.MAGENTA/1: UNPRICED DUE TO SCARCITY
*P.P.YELLOW/1: UNPRICED DUE TO SCARCITY

NNO	Andrew Kishino	8.00	20.00
NNO	Ashley Eckstein	12.00	30.00
NNO	Brent Spiner	12.00	30.00
NNO	Cavin Cornwall	12.00	30.00
NNO	Daniel Mays	8.00	20.00
NNO	David Barclay	10.00	25.00
NNO	Denis Lawson	8.00	20.00
NNO	Guy Henry	8.00	20.00
NNO	Howie Weed	12.00	30.00
NNO	James Arnold Taylor	10.00	25.00
NNO	Jason Spisak	8.00	20.00
NNO	Jeremy Bulloch	15.00	40.00
NNO	Jimmy Vee	10.00	25.00
NNO	Lars Mikkelsen	10.00	25.00
NNO	Laura Dern	100.00	200.00
NNO	Matt Lanter	8.00	20.00
NNO	Matthew Wood	10.00	25.00
NNO	Nathalie Cuzner	8.00	20.00
NNO	Robert Nairne	8.00	20.00

NNO	Sam Witwer	12.00	30.00
NNO	Simon Williamson	12.00	30.00
NNO	Tom Wilton	8.00	20.00

2018 Star Wars Masterwork Commemorative Vehicle Patches

QUI-GON JINN

COMMON PATCH		4.00	10.00

*PURPLE/50: .6X TO 1.5X BASIC PATCHES
*BLACK/5: UNPRICED DUE TO SCARCITY
*GOLD/1: UNPRICED DUE TO SCARCITY
RANDOMLY INSERTED INTO PACKS

MPBHF	Slave I/Boba Fett	8.00	20.00
MPGEA	Chimaera/Grand Admiral Thrawn	6.00	15.00
MPGEK	Chimaera/Kassius Konstantine	6.00	15.00
MPGEM	Krennic's Shuttle/Grand Moff Tarkin	6.00	15.00
MPGEP	Chimaera/Governor Arihnda Pryce	5.00	12.00
MPGEV	Star Destroyer/Darth Vader	5.00	12.00
MPGRB	Radiant VII/Bail Organa	6.00	15.00
MPGRP	Radiant VII/PadmÈ Amidala	8.00	20.00
MPJOA	Anakin's Fighter/Anakin Skywalker	5.00	12.00
MPJOO	Anakin's Fighter/Obi-Wan Kenobi	6.00	15.00
MPJOQ	Anakin's Fighter/Qui-Gon Jinn	5.00	12.00
MPPSA	The Ghost/Ahsoka Tano	5.00	12.00
MPPSE	The Ghost/Ezra Bridger	5.00	12.00
MPPSH	The Ghost/Hera Syndulla	5.00	12.00
MPPSZ	The Ghost/Zeb Orrelios	6.00	15.00
MPRAB	U-Wing/Bodhi Rook	5.00	12.00
MPRAH	Y-Wing/Han Solo	12.00	30.00
MPRAJ	U-Wing/Jyn Erso	5.00	12.00
MPRAK	U-Wing/K-2SO	5.00	12.00
MPRAM	U-Wing/Baze Malbus	6.00	15.00
MPRAP	Y-Wing/Princess Leia Organa	8.00	20.00
MPRAR	Y-Wing/R2-D2	5.00	12.00
MPRAS	Y-Wing/Luke Skywalker	6.00	15.00
MPRMH	The Millennium Falcon/Han Solo	10.00	25.00
MPRML	The Millennium Falcon/Lando Calrissian	5.00	12.00
MPRMN	The Millennium Falcon/Nien Nunb	5.00	12.00
MPRMP	The Millennium Falcon/Princess Leia Organa	8.00	20.00
MPRMS	The Millennium Falcon/Luke Skywalker	6.00	15.00
MPTRF	Black One/Finn	6.00	15.00
MPTRL	Black One/General Leia Organa	8.00	20.00
MPTRR	Black One/Rey	8.00	20.00

2018 Star Wars Masterwork Dual Autographs

*WOOD/10: UNPRICED DUE TO SCARCITY
*BLACK/5: UNPRICED DUE TO SCARCITY
GOLD/1: UNPRICED DUE TO SCARCITY

NNO	A.Cook/I.Whyte		
NNO	B.Mendelsohn/G.Henry		
NNO	B.Williams/M.Quinn		
NNO	C.Blakiston/G.O'Reilly		
NNO	D.Ridley/J.Boyega		
NNO	E.Bauersfeld/K.Rotich	20.00	50.00

TRADING CARDS

NNO F.Jones/B.Mendelsohn		
NNO G.Takei/M.Lanter		
NNO H.Christensen/R.Park		
NNO J.Taylor/N.Futterman		
NNO J.Boyega/B.Herring	75.00	150.00
NNO J.Boyega/J.Suotamo	75.00	150.00
NNO K.Leung/G.Grunberg	15.00	40.00
NNO K.Baker/D.Barclay		
NNO L.Mikkelsen/M.McGlynn	20.00	50.00
NNO M.Salenger/O.D'Abo	30.00	75.00
NNO R.Park/M.Wood		
NNO R.Ahmed/A.Tudyk		
NNO S.Witwer/S.Stanton		
NNO S.Gellar/P.Anthony-Rodriguez		

2018 Star Wars Masterwork History of the Jedi

COMPLETE SET (10)	10.00	25.00
COMMON CARD (HJ1-HJ10)	1.50	4.00

*RAINBOW/299: SAME VALUE AS BASIC
*CANVAS/25: 1.2X TO 3X BASIC CARDS
*WOOD/10: UNPRICED DUE TO SCARCITY
*METAL/5: UNPRICED DUE TO SCARCITY
*GOLD METAL/1: UNPRICED DUE TO SCARCITY
*P.P.BLACK/1: UNPRICED DUE TO SCARCITY
*P.P.CYAN/1: UNPRICED DUE TO SCARCITY
*P.P.MAGENTA/1: UNPRICED DUE TO SCARCITY
*P.P.YELLOW/1: UNPRICED DUE TO SCARCITY

HJ1 Yoda	2.50	6.00
HJ2 Mace Windu	2.50	6.00
HJ4 Qui-Gon Jinn	2.00	5.00
HJ5 Obi-Wan Kenobi	2.00	5.00
HJ6 Anakin Skywalker	2.00	5.00
HJ9 Luke Skywalker	2.00	5.00
HJ10 Rey	3.00	8.00

2018 Star Wars Masterwork Powerful Partners

COMPLETE SET (8)	10.00	25.00
COMMON CARD (PP1-PP8)	1.50	4.00

*RAINBOW/299: SAME VALUE AS BASIC
*CANVAS/25: X TO X BASIC CARDS
*WOOD/10: UNPRICED DUE TO SCARCITY
*METAL/5: UNPRICED DUE TO SCARCITY
*GOLD METAL/1: UNPRICED DUE TO SCARCITY
*P.P.BLACK/1: UNPRICED DUE TO SCARCITY

*P.P.CYAN/1: UNPRICED DUE TO SCARCITY
*P.P.MAGENTA/1: UNPRICED DUE TO SCARCITY
*P.P.YELLOW/1: UNPRICED DUE TO SCARCITY

PP1 Han Solo & Chewbacca	2.50	6.00
PP3 Luke Skywalker & Princess Leia Organa	2.50	6.00
PP4 Darth Vader & Grand Moff Tarkin	2.50	6.00
PP6 Jyn Erso & Captain Cassian Andor	3.00	8.00
PP7 Rey & Finn	3.00	8.00
PP8 Finn & Rose Tico	2.00	5.00

2018 Star Wars Masterwork Source Material Fabric Swatches

JRGH General Hux Jacket Lining		
JRLP Luke Skywalker Pants		
JRLT Luke Skywalker Tunic	75.00	150.00
JRPD Poe Dameron Jacket Lining	100.00	200.00
JRRG Poe Dameron Shirt	50.00	100.00
JRRS Jyn Erso Poncho		
JRRT Rey Desert Tunic Sleeves	150.00	300.00
JRCRT Rose Tico Ground Crew Flightsuit Lining	100.00	200.00

2018 Star Wars Masterwork Stamp Relics

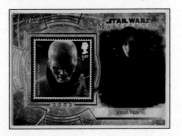

COMMON MEM	6.00	15.00

*BLACK/5: UNPRICED DUE TO SCARCITY
*GOLD/1: UNPRICED DUE TO SCARCITY
RANDOMLY INSERTED INTO PACKS

SBF Finn	8.00	20.00
BB-8!		
SBP Poe Dameron	8.00	20.00
BB-8!		
SBR Rey	10.00	25.00
BB-8!		
SCC Chewbacca	8.00	20.00
Chewbacca!		
SCH Han Solo	8.00	20.00
Chewbacca!		
SCL Lando Calrissian	6.00	15.00
Chewbacca!		
SCP Princess Leia Organa	12.00	30.00
C-3PO and Jabba the Hutt's Palace		
SCR R2-D2	6.00	15.00
C-3PO and Jabba the Hutt's Palace		
SCS Luke Skywalker	6.00	15.00
C-3PO and Jabba the Hutt's Palace		
SKC Captain Cassian Andor	6.00	15.00
K-2SO on Scarif!		
SKJ Jyn Erso	10.00	25.00
K-2SO on Scarif!		
SKK K-2SO	12.00	30.00
K-2SO on Scarif!		
SMF Finn	6.00	15.00
Maz Kanata's Castle!		
SMH Han Solo	8.00	20.00
Maz Kanata's Castle!		
SMR Rey	8.00	20.00
Maz Kanata's Castle!		
SPC Chewbacca	6.00	15.00
Ahch-To Island Porgs!		
SPL Luke Skywalker	6.00	15.00
Ahch-To Island Porgs!		
SPR Rey	12.00	30.00
Ahch-To Island Porgs!		
SRA Anakin Skywalker	6.00	15.00
R2-D2!		
SRO Obi-Wan Kenobi	8.00	20.00
R2-D2!		
SRP PadmÈ Amidala	8.00	20.00
R2-D2!		
SSH General Hux	6.00	15.00
Supreme Leader Snoke and the First Order		
SSK Kylo Ren	10.00	25.00
Supreme Leader Snoke and the First Order		
SSP Captain Phasma	6.00	15.00
Supreme Leader Snoke and the First Order		

2018 Star Wars Masterwork Super Weapons

COMMON CARD (SW1-SW7)	2.00	5.00

*RAINBOW/299: .5X TO 1.2X BASIC CARDS
*CANVAS/25: 1.2X TO 3X BASIC CARDS
*WOOD/10: UNPRICED DUE TO SCARCITY
*METAL/5: UNPRICED DUE TO SCARCITY
*GOLD METAL/1: UNPRICED DUE TO SCARCITY
*P.P.BLACK/1: UNPRICED DUE TO SCARCITY
*P.P.CYAN/1: UNPRICED DUE TO SCARCITY
*P.P.MAGENTA/1: UNPRICED DUE TO SCARCITY
*P.P.YELLOW/1: UNPRICED DUE TO SCARCITY

2017 Star Wars May the 4th Be with You

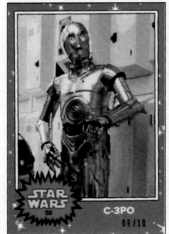

COMPLETE SET (20)	12.00	30.00
COMPLETE FACTORY SET (21)	40.00	80.00
COMMON CARD (1-20)	1.00	2.50
*SILVER/10: 6X TO 15X BASIC CARDS	15.00	40.00

*GOLD/1: UNPRICED DUE TO SCARCITY
RELEASED 5/4/2017

2017 Star Wars May the 4th Be with You Autographs

COMMON CARD	10.00	25.00

*SILVER/10: .6X TO 1.5X BASIC AUTOS
*GOLD/1: UNPRICED DUE TO SCARCITY
STATED ODDS 1:SET

1A Harrison Ford		
2A Mark Hamill	400.00	600.00
3A Carrie Fisher		
4A Kenny Baker		
5A Anthony Daniels	175.00	300.00
7A Jeremy Bulloch	25.00	60.00
8A Ian McDiarmid	250.00	400.00
10A Billy Dee Williams		
14A Kenneth Colley	12.00	30.00
16A Erik Bauersfeld	25.00	60.00
16A Tim Rose	15.00	40.00
19A Paul Blake		

1997-98 Star Wars Men Behind the Masks

COMPLETE SET (4)		
COMMON CARD (P1-P4)		
P1 Darth Vader & Boba Fett	10.00	25.00
(Given to Auction Seat Holders)		
P2 Darth Vader & Boba Fett	10.00	25.00
(Given as Admission Ticket)		
P3 Peter Mayhew as Chewbacca	8.00	20.00
(Given to Auction Reserve Seat Holders)/1000*		
P4 Maria de Aragon as Greedo	10.00	25.00
(Show Exclusive)/800*		

1997-98 Star Wars Men Behind the Masks Test Issue

NNO Chewbacca	125.00	250.00
(prismatic foil/triangles)		
NNO Chewbacca	125.00	250.00
(prismatic foil/vertical lines)		
NNO Chewbacca	125.00	250.00
(refractor foil)		
NNO Greedo	125.00	250.00
(prismatic foil/spotted)		
NNO Greedo	125.00	250.00
(prismatic foil/traingles)		
NNO Greedo	125.00	250.00
(prismatic foil/vertical lines)		
NNO Greedo	125.00	250.00
(refractor foil)		

1994-96 Star Wars Metal

COMPLETE SET (60)	30.00	75.00
COMMON CARD (1-60)	1.00	2.50

1994-96 Star Wars Metal Promos

COMPLETE SET (3)	12.00	30.00
COMMON CARD (P1-P3)	6.00	15.00
P1 Star Wars Episode IV	6.00	15.00
P2 The Empire Strikes Back	6.00	15.00
P3 Return of the Jedi	6.00	15.00

1996 Star Wars Metal Art of Ralph McQuarrie

COMPLETE SET (20)	10.00	25.00
COMMON CARD (1-20)	1.00	2.50
COA Certificate of Authenticity		

1998 Star Wars Metal Bounty Hunters

COMPLETE SET (5)	2.50	6.00
COMMON CARD (1-5)	1.00	2.50
HSJH Han Solo and Jabba the Hutt SE		

1995 Star Wars Metal Dark Empire I

COMPLETE SET (6)	3.00	8.00
COMMON CARD (1-6)	1.00	2.50

1996 Star Wars Metal Dark Empire II

COMPLETE SET (6)	3.00	8.00
COMMON CARD (1-6)	1.00	2.50

1998 Star Wars Metal Jedi Knights

COMPLETE SET (5)	3.00	8.00
COMMON CARD (1-5)	1.00	2.50
MES Mos Eisley Spaceport SE	1.50	4.00

1998 Star Wars Metal Jedi Knights Avon

COMPLETE SET (4)	3.00	8.00
COMMON CARD (1-4)	1.00	2.50
WIC Wampa Ice Creature SE	1.50	4.00

1997 Star Wars Metal Shadows of the Empire

COMPLETE SET (6)	4.00	10.00
COMMON CARD (1-6)	1.00	2.50

2015 Star Wars Micro Collector Packs

COMPLETE SET (36)	60.00	120.00
COMMON CARD (1-36)	1.50	4.00
NNO 3-D Glasses	.40	1.00

2015 Star Wars Micro Collector Packs 3-D Posters

COMPLETE SET (6)	3.00	8.00
COMMON CARD	.60	1.50
STATED ODDS 1:1		

2015 Star Wars Micro Collector Packs Micro-Comics

COMPLETE SET (6)	4.00	10.00
COMMON CARD	.75	2.00
STATED ODDS 1:1		

1996 Star Wars Multimotion

2M Star Wars 20th Anniversary Commemorative Magazine	2.50	6.00

1999 Star Wars The New Jedi Order

NNO SDCC Exclusive	2.00	5.00

2015 Star Wars NYCC Oversized Exclusives

COMPLETE SET (70)	75.00	150.00
COMMON CARD (1-70)	2.00	5.00

2018 Star Wars On-Demand The Last Jedi

COMPLETE SET (20)	15.00	40.00
COMMON CARD (1-20)	1.25	3.00
*PURPLE: .75X TO 2X BASIC CARDS	2.50	6.00

2018 Star Wars On-Demand The Last Jedi Autographs

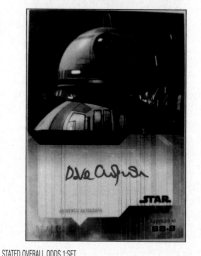

STATED OVERALL ODDS 1:SET

NNO Adam Driver		
NNO Andrew Jack	10.00	25.00
NNO Andy Serkis		
NNO Anthony Daniels		
NNO Billie Lourd		
NNO Brian Herring	8.00	20.00
NNO Daisy Ridley		
NNO Dave Chapman	8.00	20.00
NNO Gwendoline Christie		
NNO Jimmy Vee	10.00	25.00
NNO John Boyega	50.00	100.00
NNO Mike Quinn	15.00	40.00
NNO Paul Kasey	8.00	20.00
NNO Tim Rose	15.00	40.00
NNO Tom Kane	8.00	20.00

2018 Star Wars On-Demand Rebels Series Finale

COMPLETE SET (20)	15.00	40.00
COMMON CARD (1-20)	1.25	3.00

*BLUE: 1X TO 2.5X BASIC CARDS
*PURPLE/10: UNPRICED DUE TO SCARCITY
*RED/5: UNPRICED DUE TO SCARCITY
*GOLD/1: UNPRICED DUE TO SCARCITY
STATED PRINT RUN 461 SETS

2018 Star Wars On-Demand Rebels Series Finale Autographs

*PURPLE/10: UNPRICED DUE TO SCARCITY
*RED/5: UNPRICED DUE TO SCARCITY

*GOLD/1: UNPRICED DUE TO SCARCITY
STATED OVERALL ODDS 1:SET

NNO	Ashley Eckstein		
NNO	Dee Bradley Baker	12.00	30.00
NNO	Forest Whitaker		
NNO	Freddie Prinze Jr.		
NNO	Genevieve O'Reilly	10.00	25.00
NNO	Ian McDiarmid	60.00	120.00
NNO	Lars Mikkelsen	30.00	75.00
NNO	Mary Elizabeth McGlynn	15.00	40.00
NNO	Stephen Stanton	12.00	30.00
NNO	Steve Blum	15.00	40.00
NNO	Taylor Gray		
NNO	Tom Baker		
NNO	Vanessa Marshall		
NNO	Warwick Davis		

1995 Star Wars The Power of the Force

NNO	Luke Skywalker	2.00	5.00

2011 Star Wars Power Plates

COMPLETE SET W/SP (30)	75.00	150.00
COMP.SET W/O SP (24)	50.00	100.00
UNOPENED BOX (48 PACKS)	120.00	150.00
UNOPENED PACK (1 PLATE)	2.50	3.00
COMMON PLATE	3.00	8.00
COMMON PLATE SP	5.00	12.00
SP STATED ODDS 1:8		

1999 Star Wars Preview Guide

NNO	Pod Racers		5.00

(Orange County Register Exclusive)

1997 Star Wars Quality Bakers

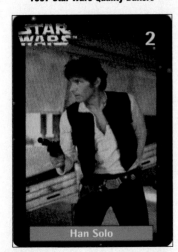

COMPLETE SET (10)	12.00	30.00
COMMON CARD (1-10)	2.00	5.00

2016 Star Wars Rancho Obi-Wan Little Debbie

COMPLETE SET (12)	20.00	50.00
COMMON CARD (1-12)	2.50	6.00
STATED ODDS 1:1 BOXES OF STAR CRUNCH		

2015 Star Wars Rebels

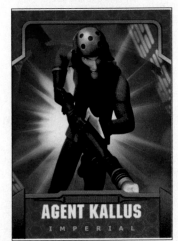

COMPLETE SET (100)	6.00	15.00
UNOPENED BOX (24 PACKS)	40.00	50.00
UNOPENED PACK (6 CARDS)	2.00	2.50
COMMON CARD (1-100)	.12	.30
*FOIL: 2X TO 5X BASIC CARDS		

2015 Star Wars Rebels Stickers

COMPLETE SET (20)	5.00	12.00
COMMON CARD (1-20)	.40	1.00

2015 Star Wars Rebels Tattoos

COMPLETE SET (10)	6.00	15.00
COMMON CARD (1-10)	1.00	2.50
STATED ODDS 1:8		

2017 Star Wars Rebels Season 4 Preview Set

COMPLETE SET (25)	30.00	80.00
UNOPENED BOXED SET (27 CARDS)		
COMMON CARD	2.00	5.00
*PURPLE/25: 1.2X TO 3X BASIC CARDS	6.00	15.00
*SILVER/10: UNPRICED DUE TO SCARCITY		
*GOLD/5: UNPRICED DUE TO SCARCITY		
*RED/1: UNPRICED DUE TO SCARCITY		
RELEASED 10/17/2017		

2017 Star Wars Rebels Season 4 Preview Set Autographs

*GOLD/5: UNPRICED DUE TO SCARCITY
*RED/1: UNPRICED DUE TO SCARCITY

STATED ODDS 1:1 PER BOX SET

NNO	Freddie Prinze Jr.		
NNO	Taylor Gray		
NNO	Vanessa Marshall		
NNO	Tiya Sircar		
NNO	Steve Blum		
NNO	Ashley Eckstein		
NNO	Sam Witwer		
NNO	Jason Isaacs		
NNO	Philip Anthony Rodriguez		
NNO	Sarah Michelle Gellar		
NNO	Stephen Stanton	12.00	30.00
NNO	Billy Dee Williams		
NNO	Forest Whitaker		
NNO	Stephen Stanton		
NNO	Genevieve OiReilly		
NNO	Mary Elizabeth McGlynn	12.00	30.00
NNO	Phil Lamarr		
NNO	Tom Baker		
NNO	Jim Cummings		

2014 Star Wars Rebels Subway Promos

COMPLETE SET (6)	6.00	15.00
COMMON CARD	1.50	4.00

2016 Star Wars Rogue One Mission Briefing

COMPLETE SET (110)	8.00	20.00
UNOPENED BOX (24 PACKS)	85.00	100.00
UNOPENED PACK (8 CARDS)	4.00	5.00
COMMON CARD (1-110)	.20	.50
*BLACK: .75X TO 2X BASIC CARDS	.40	1.00
*GREEN: 1.2X TO 3X BASIC CARDS	.60	1.50
*BLUE: 1.5X TO 4X BASIC CARDS	.75	2.00
*GRAY/100: 8X TO 20X BASIC CARDS	4.00	10.00
*GOLD/50: 12X TO 30X BASIC CARDS	6.00	15.00
*ORANGE;/1: UNPRICED DUE TO SCARCITY		
*P.P.BLACK/1: UNPRICED DUE TO SCARCITY		
*P.P.CYAN/1: UNPRICED DUE TO SCARCITY		
*P.P.MAGENTA/1: UNPRICED DUE TO SCARCITY		
*P.P.YELLOW/1: UNPRICED DUE TO SCARCITY		

2016 Star Wars Rogue One Mission Briefing Autographs

COMMON CARD	6.00	15.00
*BLACK/50: .6X TO 1.5X BASIC AUTOS		
*BLUE/25: 1.2X TO 3X BASIC AUTOS		
*GOLD/10: UNPRICED DUE TO SCARCITY		
*ORANGE/1: UNPRICED DUE TO SCARCITY		
*P.P.BLACK/1: UNPRICED DUE TO SCARCITY		
*P.P.CYAN/1: UNPRICED DUE TO SCARCITY		
*P.P.MAGENTA/1: UNPRICED DUE TO SCARCITY		
*P.P.YELLOW/1: UNPRICED DUE TO SCARCITY		
RANDOMLY INSERTED INTO PACKS		

NNO	Adrienne Wilkinson	12.00	30.00
NNO	Al Lampert	10.00	25.00
NNO	Anna Graves	15.00	40.00
NNO	Barbara Frankland	10.00	25.00
NNO	Brian Blessed	8.00	20.00
NNO	Candice Orwell	12.00	30.00
NNO	Catherine Taber		
NNO	Clive Revill	12.00	30.00
NNO	Corey Dee Williams	10.00	25.00
NNO	Dave Barclay		
NNO	David Ankrum	10.00	25.00

NNO	Eric Lopez	10.00	25.00
NNO	Femi Taylor	8.00	20.00
NNO	Garrick Hagon	10.00	25.00
NNO	George Roubicek	10.00	25.00
NNO	Glyn Baker	10.00	25.00
NNO	Ian Liston	10.00	25.00
NNO	Jack Klaff	8.00	20.00
NNO	Jim Cummings	12.00	30.00
NNO	John Coppinger	15.00	40.00
NNO	Kenneth Colley	8.00	20.00
NNO	Lloyd Sherr	10.00	25.00
NNO	Megan Udall	10.00	25.00
NNO	Mercedes Ngoh	8.00	20.00
NNO	Michaela Cottrell	8.00	20.00
NNO	Mike Edmonds	12.00	30.00
NNO	Oliver Walpole	10.00	25.00
NNO	Paul Springer	12.00	30.00
NNO	Rajia Baroudi	12.00	30.00
NNO	Rich Oldfield	15.00	40.00
NNO	Rusty Goffe	10.00	25.00
NNO	Sam Witwer	15.00	40.00
NNO	Scott Capurro	12.00	30.00
NNO	Sean Crawford	10.00	25.00
NNO	Stephen Stanton	8.00	20.00
NNO	Tom Kane	8.00	20.00
NNO	Wayne Pygram	10.00	25.00

2016 Star Wars Rogue One Mission Briefing Character Foil

COMPLETE SET (9)	12.00	20.00
COMMON CARD (1-9)	2.00	5.00
*P.P.BLACK/1: UNPRICED DUE TO SCARCITY		
*P.P.CYAN/1: UNPRICED DUE TO SCARCITY		
*P.P.MAGENTA/1: UNPRICED DUE TO SCARCITY		
*P.P.YELLOW/1: UNPRICED DUE TO SCARCITY		
STATED ODDS 1:8		

2016 Star Wars Rogue One Mission Briefing Comic Strips Inserts

COMPLETE SET (12)	8.00	20.00
COMMON CARD (1-12)	1.25	3.00
*P.P.BLACK/1: UNPRICED DUE TO SCARCITY		
*P.P.CYAN/1: UNPRICED DUE TO SCARCITY		
*P.P.MAGENTA/1: UNPRICED DUE TO SCARCITY		
*P.P.YELLOW/1: UNPRICED DUE TO SCARCITY		

2016-17 Star Wars Rogue One Darth Vader Continuity

COMPLETE SET (15)	20.00	50.00
COMMON CARD (1-15)	2.50	6.00
MISSION BRIEFING (1-5)		
SERIES ONE (6-10)		
SERIES TWO (11-15)		
*P.P.BLACK/1: UNPRICED DUE TO SCARCITY		
*P.P.CYAN/1: UNPRICED DUE TO SCARCITY		
*P.P.MAGENTA/1: UNPRICED DUE TO SCARCITY		
*P.P.YELLOW/1: UNPRICED DUE TO SCARCITY		
STATED ODDS 1:12		

2016 Star Wars Rogue One Mission Briefing The Death Star

SUPERLASER

COMPLETE SET (9)	6.00	15.00
COMMON CARD (1-9)	.75	2.00

*P.P.BLACK/1: UNPRICED DUE TO SCARCITY		
*P.P.CYAN/1: UNPRICED DUE TO SCARCITY		
*P.P.MAGENTA/1: UNPRICED DUE TO SCARCITY		
*P.P.YELLOW/1: UNPRICED DUE TO SCARCITY		
STATED ODDS 1:4		

2016 Star Wars Rogue One Mission Briefing Heroes of the Rebel Alliance

COMPLETE SET (9)	10.00	25.00
COMMON CARD (1-9)	1.50	3.00
*P.P.BLACK/1: UNPRICED DUE TO SCARCITY		
*P.P.CYAN/1: UNPRICED DUE TO SCARCITY		
*P.P.MAGENTA/1: UNPRICED DUE TO SCARCITY		
*P.P.YELLOW/1: UNPRICED DUE TO SCARCITY		
STATED ODDS 1:8		
1 Luke Skywalker	2.00	5.00
2 Princess Leia	2.00	5.00
3 Han Solo	2.00	5.00
4 Chewbacca	1.50	4.00
6 Obi-Wan Kenobi	1.50	4.00
7 R2-D2	1.50	4.00

2016 Star Wars Rogue One Mission Briefing Mission Briefing Monday

COMPLETE SET (36)	150.00	300.00
COMMON CARD	6.00	15.00
NOV.7, 2016 (MBME1-MBME6)/206*		
NOV.14, 2016 (MBM1-MBM5)/226*		
NOV.21, 2016 (MBM6-MBM10)/218*		
NOV.28, 2016 (MBM11-MBM15)/212*		
DEC.5, 2016 (MBM16-MBM20)/224*		
DEC.12, 2016 (MBM21-MBM25)/234*		
DEC.19, 2016 (MBM26-MBM30)/252*		

2016 Star Wars Rogue One Mission Briefing Montages

COMPLETE SET (9)	15.00	40.00
COMMON CARD (1-9)	3.00	8.00
*P.P.BLACK/1: UNPRICED DUE TO SCARCITY		
*P.P.CYAN/1: UNPRICED DUE TO SCARCITY		
*P.P.MAGENTA/1: UNPRICED DUE TO SCARCITY		
*P.P.YELLOW/1: UNPRICED DUE TO SCARCITY		
STATED ODDS 1:24		
1 Storming the Beach	3.00	8.00
2 Imperial Assault	3.00	8.00
3 Jyn Erso	5.00	12.00
4 Within Rebel Base	3.00	8.00
5 Patrol of the Empire	3.00	8.00
6 Fearsome Death Trooper	3.00	8.00
7 Director Krennic	3.00	8.00
8 In Flames	3.00	8.00
9 Rebel Ensemble	3.00	8.00

2016 Star Wars Rogue One Mission Briefing NYCC Exclusives

COMPLETE SET (10)	12.00	30.00
COMMON CARD (E1-E10)	2.00	5.00
2016 NYCC EXCLUSIVE		

2016 Star Wars Rogue One Mission Briefing Patches

DIRECTOR KRENNIC

COMPLETE SET (12)	50.00	100.00
COMMON CARD (M1-M12)	3.00	8.00

*GRAY/100: .75X TO 2X BASIC CARDS		
*GOLD/50: 1.5X TO 4X BASIC CARDS		
*RED/10: 3X TO 8X BASIC CARDS		
STATED ODDS 1:26		
1 Jyn Erso	6.00	15.00
3 L-1 Droid	5.00	12.00
4 Admiral Raddus	4.00	10.00
6 TIE Fighter Pilot	4.00	10.00
7 Shoretrooper	4.00	10.00
10 Captain Cassian Andor	5.00	12.00
11 Bistan	4.00	10.00

2016 Star Wars Rogue One Mission Briefing Stickers

COMPLETE SET (18)	10.00	25.00
COMMON CARD (1-18)	1.00	2.50
*P.P.BLACK/1: UNPRICED DUE TO SCARCITY		
*P.P.CYAN/1: UNPRICED DUE TO SCARCITY		
*P.P.MAGENTA/1: UNPRICED DUE TO SCARCITY		
*P.P.YELLOW/1: UNPRICED DUE TO SCARCITY		
STATED ODDS 1:12		
1 Jyn Erso	1.50	4.00
13 Darth Vader	2.00	5.00

2016 Star Wars Rogue One Mission Briefing Villains of the Galactic Empire

COMPLETE SET (8)	8.00	20.00
COMMON CARD (1-8)	1.25	3.00
*P.P.BLACK/1: UNPRICED DUE TO SCARCITY		
*P.P.CYAN/1: UNPRICED DUE TO SCARCITY		
*P.P.MAGENTA/1: UNPRICED DUE TO SCARCITY		
*P.P.YELLOW/1: UNPRICED DUE TO SCARCITY		
STATED ODDS 1:8		
1 Darth Vader	1.25	5.00

1999 Star Wars Sci-Fi Expo Celebrity Promos

P1 Garrick Hagon	8.00	20.00
(Biggs Darklighter)		
P2 Peter Mayhew	8.00	20.00
(Chewbacca)		

2015 Star Wars SDCC Oversized Exclusives

COMPLETE SET (100)	120.00	250.00
COMMON CARD (1-100)	2.00	5.00

1997 Star Wars SE Trilogy 3-D Doritos Discs

COMPLETE SET (20)	5.00	12.00
COMMON CARD	.40	1.00

1997 Star Wars SE Trilogy 3-D Doritos-Cheetos

COMPLETE SET (6)	3.00	8.00
COMMON CARD (1-6)	.75	2.00

1996 Star Wars Shadows of the Empire

COMPLETE SET (100) 15.00 40.00
COMMON CARD (1-72, 83-100) .15 .40
COMMON ETCHED (73-78) 2.00 5.00
COMMON EMBOSSED (79-82) 3.00 8.00
73-78 STATED ODDS 1:9
79-82 STATED ODDS 1:18

1996 Star Wars Shadows of the Empire Promos

COMMON CARD 1.00 2.50
SOTE1 Xizor 2.00 5.00
SOTE2 Darth Vader 2.00 5.00
SOTE3 Luke Skywalker 2.00 5.00
SOTE4 Dash Rendar & Leebo 2.00 5.00
SOTE5 Boba Fett 8.00 15.00
(Convention Exclusive)
SOTE6 Guri 2.00 5.00
SOTE7 C-3PO & R2-D2 2.00 5.00
NNO SOTE3-SOTE1 (Luke Skywalker/Darth Vader)

1978 Star Wars Spaceship Hang Gliders

COMPLETE SET (4) 75.00 150.00
COMMON CARD 20.00 50.00

2017 Star Wars Stellar Signatures

COMMON AUTOS 25.00 60.00
*BLUE/25: .5X TO 1.2X BASIC AUTOS 30.00 75.00
*GREEN/20: UNPRICED DUE TO SCARCITY
*PURPLE/10: UNPRICED DUE TO SCARCITY
*GOLD/5: UNPRICED DUE TO SCARCITY
*GALACTIC BLACK/1: UNPRICED DUE TO SCARCITY
*IMPERIAL RED/1: UNPRICED DUE TO SCARCITY
*REB.ALL.ORANGE/1: UNPRICED DUE TO SCARCITY
STATED PRINT RUN 40 SER.#'d SETS
100 TOTAL BOXES PRODUCED
NNO Adam Driver 400.00 650.00
NNO Forest Whitaker 75.00 150.00
NNO Freddie Prinze Jr. 50.00 100.00
NNO Genevieve O'Reilly 50.00 100.00
NNO Gwendoline Christie 250.00 400.00
NNO Harrison Ford 2500.00 4000.00
NNO Hayden Christensen 250.00 400.00
NNO Ian McDiarmid 250.00 400.00
NNO Jeremy Bulloch 30.00 75.00
NNO John Boyega 120.00 250.00
NNO Joonas Suotamo 30.00 75.00
NNO Kenny Baker 75.00 150.00
NNO Lars Mikkelsen 75.00 150.00
NNO Mark Hamill EXCH
NNO Matthew Wood 30.00 75.00
NNO Peter Mayhew 75.00 150.00
NNO Ray Park 60.00 120.00
NNO Riz Ahmed 50.00 100.00
NNO Sarah Michelle Gellar 120.00 250.00
NNO Stephen Stanton EXCH
NNO Temuera Morrison 30.00 75.00
NNO Tim Curry 100.00 175.00

NNO Tom Baker 100.00 200.00
NNO Warwick Davis 50.00 100.00
NNO Alan Tudyk 100.00 175.00
NNO Andy Serkis 75.00 150.00
NNO Ashley Eckstein 60.00 120.00
NNO Ben Mendelsohn EXCH
NNO Billy Dee Williams 75.00 150.00
NNO Brian Herring 30.00 75.00
NNO Carrie Fisher 300.00 500.00
NNO Daisy Ridley 800.00 1200.00
NNO Donnie Yen 75.00 150.00
NNO Felicity Jones 300.00 500.00

1997 Star Wars Stickers US

COMPLETE SET (66) 7.50 20.00
COMMON CARD (1-66) .20 .50
PRODUCED BY PANINI

1997 Star Wars Trilogy The Complete Story

COMPLETE SET (72) 6.00 15.00
COMMON CARD (1-72) .25 .60
0 Promo 1.00 2.00

1997 Star Wars Trilogy The Complete Story Laser

COMPLETE SET (6) 6.00 15.00
COMMON CARD (LC1-LC6) 1.25 3.00
STATED ODDS 1:9

1997 Star Wars Trilogy Merlin

COMPLETE SET (125) 10.00 25.00
UNOPENED BOX (48 PACKS) 25.00 40.00
UNOPENED PACK (5 CARDS) 1.00 1.25
COMMON CARD (1-125) .15 .40

1997 Star Wars Trilogy Merlin Case-Toppers

COMPLETE SET (3) 20.00 50.00
COMMON CARD (P1-P3) 8.00 20.00
STATED ODDS 1:CASE

1997 Star Wars Trilogy Special Edition

COMPLETE SET (72) 6.00 15.00
UNOPENED BOX (36 PACKS) 80.00 100.00
UNOPENED PACK (9 CARDS) 2.50 3.00
COMMON CARD (1-72) .15 .40
13D ISSUED AS BOX TOPPER
13D X-Wings Departing 6.00 15.00

1997 Star Wars Trilogy Special Edition Holograms

COMPLETE SET (2) 10.00 25.00
COMMON CARD (1-2) 6.00 15.00
STATED ODDS 1:18

1997 Star Wars Trilogy Special Edition Laser

COMPLETE SET (6) 6.00 15.00
COMMON CARD (LC1-LC6) 1.25 3.00
STATED ODDS 1:9

1997 Star Wars Trilogy Special Edition Promos

COMPLETE SET (8) 10.00 25.00
COMMON CARD (P1-P8) 1.25 3.00
P1 Three Stormtroopers 4.00 10.00
P4 Sandcrawler 3.00 8.00
P5 Jawa and Landspeeder 3.00 8.00
P6 Millennium Falcon 3.00 8.00

1997 Star Wars Trilogy Special Edition Kenner Promos

COMPLETE SET (4) 10.00 25.00
COMMON CARD (H1-H4) 4.00 10.00

1997 Star Wars Trilogy Special Edition Micro Machine Promos

COMPLETE SET (5) 12.00 30.00
COMMON CARD (G1-G5) 4.00 10.00

1997 Star Wars Vehicles

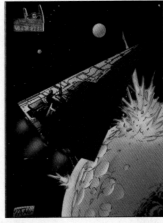

COMPLETE SET (72) 5.00 12.00
UNOPENED BOX (36 PACKS) 40.00 50.00
UNOPENED PACK (5 CARDS) 1.25 1.50
COMMON CARD (1-72) .15 .40

1997 Star Wars Vehicles 3-D

COMPLETE SET (3) 25.00 60.00
COMMON CARD 8.00 20.00
STATED ODDS 1:36
3 Princess Leia 15.00 40.00
Luke Skywalker

1997 Star Wars Vehicles Cut-Away

COMPLETE SET (4) 7.50 20.00
COMMON CARD (C1-C4) 2.50 6.00
STATED ODDS 1:18

1997 Star Wars Vehicles Promos

P1A Darth Vader & Stormtroopers on Speeder Bikes 12.00 30.00
chromium)/3200*
P1B Darth Vader & Stormtroopers on Speeder Bikes 30.00 75.00
(refractor)/320*
P2A Stormtroopers on Speeder Bikes 20.00 50.00
(chromium)/1600*
P2B Stormtroopers on Speeder Bikes 50.00 100.00
(refractor)/160*
NNO 2-Card Sheet

TCG

1995 Star Wars Premiere

COMPLETE SET (324)	75.00	150.00
BOOSTER BOX (36 PACKS)	75.00	150.00
BOOSTER PACK (15 CARDS)	3.00	6.00
RELEASED IN DECEMBER 1995		

1 5D6-RA-7 (Fivedesix) R1	1.25	3.00
2 Admiral Motti R2	.75	2.00
3 Chief Bast U1	.30	.75
4 Colonel Wullf Yularen U1	.30	.75
5 Commander Praji U2	.30	.75
6 Darth Vader R1	.30	.75
7 Dathcha U1	3.00	8.00
8 Death Star Trooper C2	10.00	25.00
9 Djas Puhr R2	.30	.75
10 Dr. Evazan R2	.12	.30
11 DS-61-2 U1	.75	2.00
12 DS-61-3 R1	.75	2.00
13 EG-6 (Eegee-Six) U2	.30	.75
14 Feltipern Trevagg U1	.30	.75
15 Garindan R2	.75	2.00
16 General Tagge R2	.75	2.00
17 Grand Moff Tarkin R1	3.00	8.00
18 Imperial Pilot C2	.12	.30
19 Imperial Trooper Guard C2	.12	.30
20 Jawa DARK C2	.12	.30
21 Kitik Keed'kak R1	1.25	3.00
22 Labria R2	.12	.30
23 Lieutenant Tanbris U2	.75	2.00
24 LIN-V8M (Elleyein-Veeateemm) C1	.30	.75
25 Miiiyoom Onith U2	.30	.75
26 MSE-6 ëMouseí Droid U1	.30	.75
27 Myo R2	.75	2.00
28 Ponda Baba U1	.30	.75
29 Prophetess U1	.30	.75
30 R1-G4 (Arone-Geefour) C2	.12	.30
31 R4-M9 (Arfour-Emmnine) C2	.12	.30
32 Stormtrooper C3	.12	.30
33 Tonnika Sisters R1	1.25	3.00
34 Tusken Raider C2	.12	.30
35 WED-9-M1 ëBanthaí Droid R2	.75	2.00
36 Wuher U2	.30	.75
37 Blaster Scope U1	.30	.75
38 Caller DARK U2	.30	.75
39 Comlink C1	.12	.30
40 Droid Detector C2	.12	.30
41 Fusion Generator Supply Tanks DARK C2	.12	.30

42 Observation Holocam U2	.30	.75
43 Restraining Bolt DARK C2	.12	.30
44 Stormtrooper Backpack C2	.12	.30
45 Stormtrooper Utility Belt C2	.12	.30
46 A Disturbance In The Force U1	.30	.75
47 Baniss Keeg C2	.12	.30
48 Blast Door Controls U2	.30	.75
49 Blaster Rack U1	.30	.75
50 Dark Hours U2	.30	.75
51 Death Star Sentry U1	.30	.75
52 Disarmed DARK R1	1.25	3.00
53 Expand The Empire R1	1.25	3.00
54 Fear Will Keep Them In Line R2	.75	2.00
55 I Find Your Lack Of Faith Disturbing R1	1.25	3.00
56 íive Lost Artoo! U1	.30	.75
57 Jawa Pack U1	.30	.75
58 Juri Juice R2	.75	2.00
59 Ket Maliss C2	.12	.30
60 Lateral Damage R2	.75	2.00
61 Luke? Luuuuke! U1	.30	.75
62 Macroscan C2	.12	.30
63 Molator R1	1.25	3.00
64 Organaís Ceremonial Necklace R1	1.25	3.00
65 Presence Of The Force R1	1.25	3.00
66 Reactor Terminal U2	.30	.75
67 Send A Detachment Down R1	1.25	3.00
68 Sunsdown U1	.30	.75
69 Tactical Re-Call R2	.75	2.00
70 Wrong Turn U1	.30	.75
71 Your Eyes Can Deceive You U1	1.25	3.00
72 Alter DARK U1	.30	.75
73 Boring Conversation Anyway R1	1.25	3.00
74 Charming To The Last R2	.75	2.00
75 Collateral Damage C2	.12	.30
76 Counter Assault C1	.12	.30
77 Dark Collaboration R1	1.25	3.00
78 Dark Jedi Presence R1	4.00	10.00
79 Dark Maneuvers C2	.12	.30
80 Dead Jawa C2	.12	.30
81 Elis Helrot U2	.30	.75
82 Emergency Deployment U1	.30	.75
83 Evacuate? U2	.30	.75
84 Full Scale Alert U2	.30	.75
85 Gravel Storm U2	.30	.75
86 I Have You Now R2	.75	2.00
87 Imperial Barrier DARK C2	.12	.30
88 Imperial Code Cylinder C2	.12	.30
89 Imperial Reinforcements C1	.12	.30
90 It's Worse C2	.12	.30
91 I've Got A Problem Here C2	.12	.30
92 Kintan Strider C1	.30	.75
93 Limited Resources U2	.30	.75
94 Local Trouble R1	1.25	3.00
95 Lone Pilot R2	.75	2.00
96 Lone Warrior R2	.75	2.00
97 Look Sir, Droids R1	1.25	3.00
98 Moment Of Triumph R2	.75	2.00
99 Nevar Yalnal R2	.75	2.00
100 Ommni Box C2	.12	.30
101 Overload C2	.12	.30
102 Physical Choke R1	1.25	3.00
103 Precise Attack C2	.12	.30
104 Scanning Crew C2	.12	.30
105 Sense DARK U1	.30	.75
106 Set For Stun C2	.12	.30
107 Takeel C2	.12	.30
108 Tallon Roll C2	.12	.30
109 The Circle Is Now Complete R1	1.25	3.00
110 The Empireís Back U1	.30	.75
111 Trinto Duaba U1	.30	.75
112 Trooper Charge U2	.30	.75

113 Tusken Scavengers C2	.12	.30
114 Utinni! DARK R1	1.25	3.00
115 Vaderís Eye R1	1.25	3.00
116 Weíre All Gonna Be A Lot Thinner! R1	1.25	3.00
117 You Overestimate Their Chances C1	.30	.75
118 Your Powers Are Weak, Old Man R1	.12	.30
119 Alderaan DARK R1	1.25	3.00
120 Dantooine DARK U1	.30	.75
121 Death Star: Central Core U2	.30	.75
122 Death Star: Detention Block Corridor C1	.12	.30
123 Death Star: Docking Bay 327 DARK C2	.12	.30
124 Death Star: Level 4 Military Corridor U1	.30	.75
125 Death Star: War Room U2	.30	.75
126 Kessel U2	.75	2.00
127 Tatooine DARK C2	.12	.30
128 Tatooine: Cantina DARK R2	.75	2.00
129 Tatooine: Docking Bay 94 DARK C2	.12	.30
130 Tatooine: Jawa Camp DARK C1	.12	.30
131 Tatooine: Jundland Wastes C1	.12	.30
132 Tatooine: Larsi Moisture Farm DARK C1	.12	.30
133 Tatooine: Mos Eisley DARK C1	.12	.30
134 Yavin 4 DARK C2	.12	.30
135 Yavin 4: Docking Bay DARK C2	.12	.30
136 Yavin 4: Jungle DARK U2	.30	.75
137 Black 2 R1	2.50	6.00
138 Black 3 U1	.30	.75
139 Devastator R1	2.50	6.00
140 Imperial-Class Star Destroyer U1	.75	2.00
141 TIE Advanced x1 U2	.30	.75
142 TIE Fighter C2	.12	.30
143 TIE Scout C2	.12	.30
144 Vaderís Custom TIE R1	4.00	10.00
145 Bantha U2	.30	.75
146 Lift Tube DARK C2	.12	.30
147 Sandcrawler DARK R2	.75	2.00
148 Ubrikkian 9000 Z001 C2	.12	.30
149 Assault Rifle R2	.75	2.00
150 Blaster Rifle DARK C1	.12	.30
151 Boosted TIE Cannon U1	.30	.75
152 Dark Jedi Lightsaber U1	.40	1.00
153 Gaderffii Stick C2	.12	.30
154 Han Seeker R2	.75	2.00
155 Imperial Blaster DARK C2	.12	.30
156 Ion Cannon U1	.30	.75
157 Laser Projector U2	.30	.75
158 Light Repeating Blaster Rifle R1	1.25	3.00
159 Luke Seeker R2	.75	2.00
160 Timer Mine DARK C2	.12	.30
161 Turbolaser Battery R2	.75	2.00
162 Vaderís Lightsaber R1	3.00	8.00
163 2X-3KPR (Tooex) U1	.30	.75
164 Beru Lars U2	.30	.75
165 Biggs Darklighter R2	.75	2.00
166 BoShek U1	.30	.75
167 C-3PO (See-Threepio) R1	3.00	8.00
168 CZ-3 (Seezee-Three) C1	.12	.30
169 Dice Ibegon R2	.75	2.00
170 Dutch R1	2.50	6.00
171 Figrin Dían U2	.30	.75
172 General Dodonna U2	.30	.75
173 Han Solo R1	5.00	12.00
174 Jawa LIGHT C2	.12	.30
175 Jek Porkins U1	.30	.75
176 Kabe U1	.30	.75
177 KalíFalnl Cindros R1	1.25	3.00
178 Leesub Sirln R2	.12	.30
179 Leia Organa R1	.75	2.00
180 LIN-V8K (Elleyein-Veeatekay) C1	4.00	10.00
181 Luke Skywalker R1	6.00	15.00
182 Momaw Nadon U2	.30	.75
183 Obi-Wan Kenobi R1	4.00	10.00

184	Owen Lars U1	.30	.75
185	Pops U1	.30	.75
186	R2-X2 (Artoo-Extoo) C2	.12	.30
187	R4-E1 (Arfour-Eeone) C2	.12	.30
188	Rebel Guard C2	.12	.30
189	Rebel Pilot C2	.12	.30
190	Rebel Trooper C3	.12	.30
191	Red Leader R1	2.50	6.00
192	Shistavanen Wolfman C2	.12	.30
193	Talz C2	.12	.30
194	WED-9-M1 'Bantha' Droid R2	.75	2.00
195	Wioslea U1	.30	.75
196	Caller LIGHT U2	.30	.75
197	Electrobinoculars C2	.12	.30
198	Fusion Generator Supply Tanks LIGHT C2	.12	.30
199	Hydroponics Station U2	.30	.75
200	Restraining Bolt LIGHT C2	.12	.30
201	Targeting Computer U1	.30	.75
202	Tatooine Utility Belt C2	.12	.30
203	Vaporator C2	.12	.30
204	A Tremor In The Force U1	.30	.75
205	Affect Mind R1	1.25	3.00
206	Beggar R1	1.25	3.00
207	Crash Site Memorial U1	.30	.75
208	Death Star Plans R1	1.25	3.00
209	Demotion R2	.75	2.00
210	Disarmed Light R1	1.25	3.00
211	Ellorrs Madak C2	.12	.30
212	Eyes In The Dark U1	.30	.75
213	Jawa Siesta U1	.30	.75
214	Kessel LIGHT U2	1.25	3.00
215	K'lor'slug R1	.30	.75
216	Lightsaber Proficiency R1	1.25	3.00
217	Mantellian Savrip R2	.75	2.00
218	Nightfall U1	.30	.75
219	Obi-Wan's Cape R1	1.25	3.00
220	Our Most Desperate Hour R1	1.25	3.00
221	Plastoid Armor U2	.30	.75
222	Rebel Planners R2	.75	2.00
223	Restricted Deployment U1	.30	.75
224	Revolution R1	1.25	3.00
225	Rycar Ryjerd U1	.30	.75
226	Sai'torr Kal Fas C2	.12	.30
227	Special Modifications U1	.30	.75
228	Traffic Control U2	.30	.75
229	Tusken Breath Mask U1	.30	.75
230	Yavin Sentry U2	.30	.75
231	Yerka Mig U1	.12	.30
232	A Few Maneuvers C2	.12	.30
233	Alter LIGHT U1	.30	.75
234	Beru Stew U2	.30	.75
235	Cantina Brawl R1	1.25	3.00
236	Collision! C2	.12	.30
237	Combined Attack C2	.12	.30
238	Don't Get Cocky R1	1.25	3.00
239	Don't Underestimate Our Chances C1	.12	.30
240	Droid Shutdown C2	.12	.30
241	Escape Pod U2	.30	.75
242	Friendly Fire C2	.12	.30
243	Full Throttle R2	.75	2.00
244	Gift Of The Mentor R1	1.25	3.00
245	Han's Back U2	.30	.75
246	Han's Dice C2	.12	.30
247	Hear Me Baby, Hold Together C2	.12	.30
248	Help Me Obi-Wan Kenobi R1	1.25	3.00
249	How Did We Get Into This Mess? U2	.30	.75
250	Hyper Escape C2	.12	.30
251	Into The Garbage Chute, Flyboy R2	.12	.30
252	It Could Be Worse C2	.75	2.00
253	I've Got A Bad Feeling About This C2	.12	.30
254	Jedi Presence R1	1.25	3.00
255	Krayt Dragon Howl R1	1.25	3.00
256	Leia's Back U2	.30	.75
257	Luke's Back U2	.30	.75
258	Move Along... R1	1.25	3.00
259	Nabrun Leids U1	.30	.75
260	Narrow Escape C2	.12	.30
261	Noble Sacrifice R2	.75	2.00
262	Old Ben C2	.12	.30
263	On The Edge R2	.75	2.00
264	Out Of Nowhere U2	.30	.75
265	Panic U1	.30	.75
266	Radar Scanner C2	.12	.30
267	Rebel Barrier C2	.12	.30
268	Rebel Reinforcements C1	.12	.30
269	Return Of A Jedi U2	.30	.75
270	Scomp Link Access C2	.12	.30
271	Sense LIGHT U1	.30	.75
272	Skywalkers R1	1.25	3.00
273	Solo Han R2	.75	2.00
274	Spaceport Speeders U2	.30	.75

275	Surprise Assault C1	.12	.30
276	Thank The Maker R2	.75	2.00
277	The Bith Shuffle C2	.12	.30
278	The Force Is Strong With This One R2	.75	2.00
279	This Is All Your Fault U1	.30	.75
280	Utinni! LIGHT R1	1.25	3.00
281	Warrior's Courage R2	.75	2.00
282	We're Doomed C2	.12	.30
283	Alderaan LIGHT U2	.75	2.00
284	Dantooine LIGHT U1	.30	.75
285	Death Star: Detention Block Control Room U2	.30	.75
286	Death Star: Docking Bay 327 LIGHT C2	.12	.30
287	Death Star: Trash Compactor U1	.30	.75
288	Kessel LIGHT U2	.30	.75
289	Tatooine LIGHT C2	.12	.30
290	Tatooine: Cantina LIGHT R2	.75	2.00
291	Tatooine: Docking Bay 94 LIGHT C2	.12	.30
292	Tatooine: Dune Sea C1	.12	.30
293	Tatooine: Jawa Camp LIGHTC1	.12	.30
294	Tatooine: Larsi Moisture Farm LIGHT U2	.30	.75
295	Tatooine: Mos Eisley LIGHT U2	.30	.75
296	Tatooine: Obi-Wan's Hut R1	1.25	3.00
297	Yavin 4 C2	.12	.30
298	Yavin 4: Docking Bay LIGHT C1	.12	.30
299	Yavin 4: Jungle LIGHT C2	1.25	3.00
300	Yavin 4: Massassi Throne Room R1	.30	.75
301	Yavin 4: Massassi War Room U2	.30	.75
302	Corellian Corvette U2	.40	1.00
303	Gold 1 R2	.75	2.00
304	Gold 5 R2	.75	2.00
305	Millenium Falcon R1	3.00	8.00
306	Red 1 U1	.30	.75
307	Red 3 R2	.75	2.00
308	X-wing C2	.12	.30
309	Y-wing C2	.12	.30
310	Lift Tube LIGHT C2	.12	.30
311	Luke's X-34 Landspeeder U2	.30	.75
312	Sandcrawler LIGHT R2	.75	2.00
313	SoroSuub V-35 Landspeeder C2	.12	.30
314	Blaster C2	.12	.30
315	Blaster Rifle LIGHT C2	.12	.30
316	Han's Heavy Blaster Pistol R2	.75	2.00
317	Jedi Lightsaber U1	.30	.75
318	Leia's Sporting Blaster U1	.30	.75
319	Obi-Wan's Lightsaber R1	2.50	6.00
320	Proton Torpedoes C2	.12	.30
321	Quad Laser Cannon U1	.30	.75
322	Tagge Seeker R2	.75	2.00
323	Tarkin Seeker R2	.75	2.00
324	Timer Mine LIGHT C2	.12	.30

1996 Star Wars Hoth

COMPLETE SET (163)	50.00	100.00
BOOSTER BOX (36 PACKS)	50.00	100.00
BOOSTER PACK (15 CARDS)	2.00	4.00
RELEASED IN NOVEMBER 1996		

1	AT-AT Driver C2	.12	.30
2	Admiral Ozzel R1	1.25	3.00
3	Captain Lennox U1	.40	1.00
4	Captain Piett R2	1.25	3.00
5	FX-10 (Effex-ten) C2	.12	.30
6	General Veers R1	3.00	8.00
7	Imperial Gunner C2	.12	.30
8	Lieutenant Cabbel U2	.40	1.00
9	Probe Droid C2	.12	.30
10	Snowtrooper C3	.12	.30
11	Snowtrooper Officer C1	.12	.30

12	Wampa R2	1.25	3.00
13	Deflector Shield Generators U2	.40	1.00
14	Evacuation Control U1	.40	1.00
15	Portable Fusion Generator C2	.12	.30
16	Probe Antennae U2	.40	1.00
17	Breached Defenses U2	.40	1.00
18	Death Mark R1	1.25	3.00
19	Death Squadron U1	.40	1.00
20	Frostbite LIGHT C2	.12	.30
21	Frozen Dinner R1	1.25	3.00
22	High Anxiety R1	1.25	3.00
23	Ice Storm LIGHT U1	.40	1.00
24	Image Of The Dark Lord R2	1.25	3.00
25	Imperial Domination U1	.40	1.00
26	Meteor Impact? R1	1.25	3.00
27	Mournful Roar R1	1.25	3.00
28	Responsibility Of Command R1	1.25	3.00
29	Silence Is Golden U2	.40	1.00
30	The Shield Doors Must Be Closed U1	.40	1.00
31	This Is Just Wrong R1	1.25	3.00
32	Too Cold For Speeders U1	.40	1.00
33	Weapon Malfunction R1	1.25	3.00
34	Target The Main Generator R2	1.25	3.00
35	A Dark Time For The Rebellion C1	.12	.30
36	Cold Feet C2	.12	.30
37	Collapsing Corridor R2	1.25	3.00
38	ComScan Detection C2	.12	.30
39	Crash Landing U1	.40	1.00
40	Debris Zone R2	1.25	3.00
41	Direct Hit U1	.40	1.00
42	Exhaustion U2	.40	1.00
43	Exposure U1	.40	1.00
44	Furry Fury R2	1.25	3.00
45	He Hasn't Come Back Yet C2	.12	.30
46	I'd Just As Soon Kiss A Wookiee C2	.12	.30
47	Imperial Supply C1	.12	.30
48	Lightsaber Deficiency U1	.40	1.00
49	Oh, Switch Off C2	.12	.30
50	Our First Catch Of The Day C2	.12	.30
51	Probe Telemetry C2	.12	.30
52	Scruffy-Looking Nerf Herder R2	1.25	3.00
53	Self-Destruct Mechanism U1	.40	1.00
54	Stop Motion C2	.12	.30
55	Tactical Support R2	1.25	3.00
56	That's It, The Rebels Are There! U2	.40	1.00
57	Trample R1	1.25	3.00
58	Turn It Off! Turn It Off! C1	.12	.30
59	Walker Barrage U1	.40	1.00
60	Wall Of Fire U1	.40	1.00
61	Yaggle Gakkle R2	1.25	3.00
62	Hoth DARK U2	.40	1.00
63	Hoth: Defensive Perimeter LIGHT C2	.12	.30
64	Hoth: Echo Command Center (War Room) LIGHT U2	.40	1.00
65	Hoth: Echo Corridor DARK U2	.40	1.00
66	Hoth: Echo Docking Bay LIGHT C2	.12	.30
67	Hoth: Ice Plains C2	.12	.30
68	Hoth: North Ridge LIGHT C2	.12	.30
69	Hoth: Wampa Cave R2	1.25	3.00
70	Ord Mantell LIGHT U2	.40	1.00
71	Stalker R1	4.00	10.00
72	Tyrant R1	3.00	8.00
73	Blizzard 1 R1	2.50	6.00
74	Blizzard 2 R2	1.25	3.00
75	Blizzard Scout 1 R1	2.50	6.00
76	Blizzard Walker U2	.40	1.00
77	AT-AT Cannon U1	.40	1.00
78	Echo Base Operations R2	1.25	3.00
79	Infantry Mine LIGHT C2	.12	.30
80	Probe Droid Laser U2	.40	1.00
81	Vehicle Mine LIGHT C2	.12	.30
82	2-1B (Too-Onebee) R1	1.25	3.00
83	Cal Alder U2	.40	1.00
84	Commander Luke Skywalker R1	6.00	15.00
85	Dack Ralter R2	1.25	3.00
86	Derek ëHobbieí Klivian U1	.40	1.00
87	Electro-Rangefinder U1	.40	1.00
88	Echo Base Trooper Officer C1	.12	.30
89	Echo Trooper Backpack C2	.12	.30
90	FX-7 (Effex-Seven) C2	.12	.30
91	General Carlist Rieekan R2	1.25	3.00
92	Jeroen Webb U1	.40	1.00
93	K-3PO (Kay-Threepio) R1	1.25	3.00
94	Major Bren Derlin R2	1.25	3.00
95	R2 Sensor Array C2	.12	.30
96	R5-M2 (Arfive-Emmtoo) C2	.12	.30
97	Rebel Scout C1	.12	.30
98	Rogue Gunner C2	.12	.30
99	Romas Lock Navander U2	.40	1.00
100	Shawn Valdez U1	.40	1.00
101	Tamizander Rey U2	.40	1.00

102	Tauntaun Handler C2	.12	.30
103	Tigran Jamiro U1	.40	1.00
104	Toryn Farr U1	.40	1.00
105	WED-1016 ëTechieí Droid C1	.12	.30
106	Wes Janson R2	1.25	3.00
107	Wyron Serper U2	.40	1.00
108	Zev Senesca R2	1.25	3.00
109	Artillery Remote R2	1.25	3.00
110	EG-4 (Eegee-Four) C1	.12	.30
111	Hoth LIGHT U2	.40	1.00
112	R-3PO (Ar-Threepio) DARK R2	1.25	3.00
112	R-3PO (Ar-Threepio) LIGHT R2	1.25	3.00
113	Bacta Tank R2	2.00	5.00
114	Disarming Creature R1	1.25	3.00
115	Echo Base Trooper C3	.12	.30
116	E-web Blaster C1	.12	.30
117	Frostbite DARK C2	.12	.30
118	Ice Storm DARK U1	.40	1.00
119	Tauntaun Bones U1	.40	1.00
120	The First Transport Is Away! R1	1.25	3.00
121	Attack Pattern Delta U1	.40	1.00
122	Dark Dissension R1	1.25	3.00
123	Fall Back! C2	.12	.30
124	I Thought They Smelled Bad On The Outside R1	1.25	3.00
125	It Can Wait C2	.12	.30
126	Lucky Shot U1	.40	1.00
127	Nice Of You Guys To Drop By C2	.12	.30
128	One More Pass U1	.40	1.00
129	Perimeter Scan C2	.12	.30
130	Rug Hug R1	1.25	3.00
131	Under Attack U1	.40	1.00
132	Walker Sighting U2	.40	1.00
133	Whoís Scruffy-Looking? R1	1.25	3.00
134	You Have Failed Me For The Last Time R1	1.25	3.00
135	You Will Go To The Dagobah System R1	1.25	3.00
136	Hoth Survival Gear C2	.12	.30
137	Hoth: Defensive Perimeter DARK C2	.12	.30
138	Hoth: Echo Command Center (War Room) DARK U2	.40	1.00
139	Hoth: Echo Corridor LIGHT C2	.12	.30
140	Hoth: Echo Docking Bay DARK C2	.12	.30
141	Hoth: Echo Med Lab C2	.12	.30
142	Hoth: Main Power Generators U2	.40	1.00
143	Hoth: North Ridge DARK C2	.12	.30
144	Hoth: Snow Trench C2	.12	.30
145	Ord Mantell DARK C2	.12	.30
146	Medium Transport U2	.40	1.00
147	Rogue 1 R1	2.50	6.00
148	Rogue 2 R2	1.25	3.00
149	Rogue 3 R1	2.50	6.00
150	Snowspeeder U2	.40	1.00
151	Tauntaun C2	.12	.30
152	Anakinís Lightsaber R1	6.00	15.00
153	Atgar Laser Cannon U2	.40	1.00
154	Concussion Grenade R1	1.25	3.00
155	Dual Laser Cannon U1	.40	1.00
156	Golan Laser Battery U1	.40	1.00
157	Infantry Mine DARK C2	.12	.30
158	Medium Repeating Blaster Cannon C1	.12	.30
159	Planet Defender Ion Cannon R2	1.25	3.00
160	Power Harpoon U1	.40	1.00
161	Surface Defense Cannon R2	1.25	3.00
162	Vehicle Mine DARK C2	.12	.30

1996 Star Wars Jedi Pack

COMPLETE SET (11)		3.00	8.00
RELEASED IN 1996			
1	Hyperoute Navigation Chart PM	.40	1.00
2	Dark Forces PM	.40	1.00
3	Eriadu PM	.40	1.00
4	For Luck PM	.40	1.00
5	Gravity Shadow PM	.40	1.00
6	Han PM	.40	1.00
7	Leia PM	.40	1.00
8	Lukeís T-16 Skyhopper PM	.40	1.00
9	Motti PM	.40	1.00
10	Tarkin PM	.40	1.00
11	Tedn Dahai PM	.40	1.00

1996 Star Wars A New Hope

COMPLETE SET (162)		50.00	100.00
BOOSTER BOX (36 PACKS)		50.00	100.00
BOOSTER PACK (15 CARDS)		2.00	4.00
RELEASED IN JULY 1996			
1	Advosze C2	.12	.30
2	Captain Khurgee U1	.40	1.00
3	DS-61-4 R2	1.25	3.00
4	Dannik Jerriko R1	1.25	3.00
5	Danz Borin U2	.40	1.00
6	Death Star R2	4.00	10.00
7	Defel C2	.12	.30
8	Greedo R1	3.00	8.00
9	Hem Dazon R1	1.25	3.00
10	IT-O (Eyetee-Oh) R1	1.25	3.00
11	Imperial Commander C2	.12	.30
12	Imperial Squad Leader C3	.12	.30
13	Lirin Carín U2	.40	1.00
14	Lt. Pol Treidum C1	.12	.30
15	Lt. Shann Childsen U1	.40	1.00
16	Mosep U2	.40	1.00
17	Officer Evax C1	.12	.30
18	R2-Q2 (Artoo-Kyootoo) C2	.12	.30
19	R3-T6 (Arthree-Teesix) R1	1.25	3.00
20	R5-A2 (Arfive-Aytoo) C2	.12	.30
21	Reegesk U2	.40	1.00
22	Reserve Pilot U1	.40	1.00
23	Rodian C2	.12	.30
24	Tech Moír U2	.40	1.00
25	Trooper Davin Felth R2	1.25	3.00
26	U-3PO (Yoo-Threepio) R1	1.25	3.00
27	URoRRuRíRíR U2	.40	1.00
28	WED15-I7 ëSeptoidí Droid U2	.40	1.00
29	Dianoga C2	1.25	3.00
30	Death Star Tractor Beam R2	1.25	3.00
31	Hypo R1	1.25	3.00
32	Laser Gate U2	.40	1.00
33	Maneuver Check R2	1.25	3.00
34	Tractor Beam U1	.40	1.00
35	Astromech Shortage U2	.40	1.00
36	Besieged R2	1.25	3.00
37	Come With Me C2	.12	.30
38	Dark Waters R2	1.25	3.00
39	Hyperwave Scan U1	.40	1.00
40	Imperial Justice C2	.12	.30
41	Krayt Dragon Bones U1	.40	1.00
42	Merc Sunlet C2	.12	.30
43	Program Trap U1	.40	1.00
44	Spice Mines Of Kessel R1	1.25	3.00
45	Swilla Corey C2	.12	.30
46	Tentacle C2	.12	.30
47	Thereíll Be Hell To Pay U2	.40	1.00

48	Undercover LIGHT U2	.40	1.00
49	Commence Primary Ignition R2	1.25	3.00
50	Evader U1	.40	1.00
51	Ghhhk C2	.12	.30
52	Iím On The Leader R1	1.25	3.00
53	Informant U1	.40	1.00
54	Monnok C2	.12	.30
55	Ngiok C2	.12	.30
56	Oo-ta Goo-ta, Solo? C2	.12	.30
57	Retract the Bridge R1	1.25	3.00
58	Sniper U1	.40	1.00
59	Stunning Leader C2	.12	.30
60	This Is Some Rescue! U1	.40	1.00
61	We Have A Prisoner C2	.12	.30
62	Death Star Gunner C1	.12	.30
63	Death Star: Conference Room U1	.40	1.00
64	Imperial Holotable R1	1.25	3.00
65	Kashyyyk LIGHTC1	.12	.30
66	Kiffex R1	1.25	3.00
67	Ralltiir LIGHT C1	.12	.30
68	Sandcrawler: Droid Junkheap R1	1.25	3.00
69	Tatooine: Bluffs R1	1.25	3.00
70	Black 4 U2	.40	1.00
71	Conquest R1	4.00	10.00
72	TIE Assault Squadron U1	.40	1.00
73	TIE Vanguard C2	.12	.30
74	Victory-Class Star Destroyer U1	.40	1.00
75	Bespin Motors Void Spider THX 1138 C2	.12	.30
76	Mobquet A-1 Deluxe Floater C2	.12	.30
77	Enhanced TIE Laser Cannon C2	.12	.30
78	Jawa Blaster C2	.12	.30
79	Leia Seeker R2	1.25	3.00
80	Superlaser R2	2.00	5.00
81	URoRRuRíRíRís Hunting Rifle U1	.40	1.00
82	Arcona C2	.12	.30
83	Brainiac R1	2.50	6.00
84	Chewbacca R2	6.00	15.00
85	Commander Evram Lajaie C1	.12	.30
86	Commander Vanden Willard U2	.40	1.00
87	Corellian C2	.12	.30
88	Doikk Naíts U2	.40	1.00
89	Garouf Lafoe U2	.40	1.00
90	Het Nkik U2	.40	1.00
91	Hunchback R1	1.25	3.00
92	Ickabel Gíont U2	.40	1.00
93	Magnetic Suction Tube DARK R2	1.25	3.00
94	Nalan Cheel U2	.40	1.00
95	R2-D2 (Artoo-Detoo) R2	6.00	15.00
96	R5-D4 (Arfive-Defour) C2	.12	.30
97	RA-7 (Aray-Seven) C2	.12	.30
98	Rebel Commander C2	.12	.30
99	Rebel Squad Leader C3	.12	.30
100	Rebel Tech C1	.12	.30
101	Saurin C2	.12	.30
102	Tiree U2	.40	1.00
103	Tzizvvt R2	1.25	3.00
104	Wedge Antilles R1	6.00	15.00
105	Zutton C1	.12	.30
106	Fire Extinguisher U2	.40	1.00
107	Magnetic Suction Tube LIGHT R2	1.25	3.00
108	Rectenna C2	.12	.30
109	Remote C2	.12	.30
110	Sensor Panel U1	.40	1.00
111	Cell 2187 R1	1.25	3.00
112	Commence Recharging R2	1.25	3.00
113	Eject! Eject! C2	.12	.30
114	Grappling Hook C2	.12	.30
115	Logistical Delay U2	.40	1.00
116	Lukeís Cape R1	1.25	3.00
117	M-HYD ëBinaryí Droid U1	.40	1.00
118	Scanner Techs U1	.40	1.00
119	Solomahal C2	.12	.30
120	Theyíre On Dantooine R1	1.25	3.00
121	Undercover DARK U2	.40	1.00
122	Whatíre You Tryiní To Push On Us? U2	.40	1.00
123	Attack Run R2	1.25	3.00
124	Advance Preparation U1	.40	1.00
125	Alternatives To Fighting U1	.40	1.00
126	Blast The Door, Kid! C2	.12	.30
127	Blue Milk C2	.12	.30
128	Corellian Slip C2	.12	.30
129	Double Agent R2	1.25	3.00
130	Grimtaash C2	.12	.30
131	Houjix C2	.12	.30
132	I Have A Very Bad Feeling About This C2	.12	.30
133	Iím Here To Rescue You U1	.40	1.00
134	Let The Wookiee Win R1	5.00	12.00
135	Out Of Commission U2	.40	1.00
136	Quite A Mercenary C2	.12	.30
137	Sabotage U1	.40	1.00
138	Sorry About The Mess U1	.40	1.00

139 Wookiee Roar R1	1.25	3.00
140 Y-wing Assault Squadron U1	.40	1.00
141 Clakdor VII R2	1.25	3.00
142 Corellia R1	1.25	3.00
143 Death Star: Trench R2	1.25	3.00
144 Dejarik Hologameboard R1	1.25	3.00
145 Kashyyyk DARK C1	.12	.30
146 Ralltiir DARK C1	.12	.30
147 Sandcrawler: Loading Bay R1	1.25	3.00
148 Yavin 4: Massassi Ruins U1	.40	1.00
149 Youíre All Clear Kid! R1	1.25	3.00
150 Gold 2 U1	.40	1.00
151 Red 2 R1	1.25	3.00
152 Red 5 R1	3.00	8.00
153 Red 6 U1	.40	1.00
154 Tantive IV R1	4.00	10.00
155 Yavin 4: Briefing Room U1	.40	1.00
156 Incom T-16 Skyhopper C2	.12	.30
157 Rogue Bantha U1	.40	1.00
158 Bowcaster R2	1.25	3.00
159 Jawa Ion Gun C2	.12	.30
160 Lukeís Hunting Rifle U1	.40	1.00
161 Motti Seeker R2	1.25	3.00
162 SW-4 Ion Cannon R2	1.25	3.00

1997 Star Wars Cloud City

COMPLETE SET (180)	50.00	100.00
BOOSTER BOX (60 PACKS)	50.00	100.00
BOOSTER PACK (9 CARDS)	2.00	4.00
RELEASED IN NOVEMBER 1997		
1 Ability, Ability, Ability C	.12	.30
2 Abyss U	.40	1.00
3 Access Denied C	.12	.30
4 Advantage R	1.25	3.00
5 Aiiii! Aaa! Agggggggggg! R	1.25	3.00
6 All My Urchins R	1.25	3.00
7 All Too Easy R	1.25	3.00
8 Ambush R	1.25	3.00
9 Armed And Dangerous U	.40	1.00
10 Artoo, Come Back At Once! R	1.25	3.00
11 As Good As Gone C	.12	.30
12 Atmospheric Assault R	1.25	3.00
13 Beldonís Eye R	1.25	3.00
14 Bespin DARK U	.40	1.00
15 Bespin LIGHT U	.40	1.00
16 Bespin: Cloud City DARK U	.40	1.00
17 Bespin: Cloud City LIGHT U	.40	1.00
18 Binders C	.12	.30
19 Bionic Hand R	1.25	3.00
20 Blasted Droid C	.12	.30
21 Blaster Proficiency C	.12	.30
22 Boba Fett R	8.00	20.00
23 Boba Fettís Blaster Rifle R	3.00	8.00
24 Bounty C	.12	.30
25 Brief Loss Of Control R	1.25	3.00
26 Bright Hope R	1.25	3.00
27 Captain Bewil R	1.25	3.00
28 Captain Han Solo R	8.00	20.00
29 Captive Fury U	.40	1.00
30 Captive Pursuit C	.12	.30
31 Carbon-Freezing U	.40	1.00
32 Carbonite Chamber Console U	.40	1.00
33 Chasm U	.40	1.00
34 Chief Retwin R	1.25	3.00
35 Civil Disorder C	.12	.30
36 Clash Of Sabers U	.40	1.00
37 Cloud Car DARK C	.12	.30

38 Cloud Car LIGHT C	.12	.30
39 Cloud City Blaster DARK C	.12	.30
40 Cloud City Blaster LIGHT C	.12	.30
41 Cloud City Engineer C	.12	.30
42 Cloud City Sabacc DARK U	.40	1.00
43 Cloud City Sabacc LIGHT U	.40	1.00
44 Cloud City Technician C	.12	.30
45 Cloud City Trooper DARK C	.12	.30
46 Cloud City Trooper LIGHT C	.12	.30
47 Cloud City: Carbonite Chamber DARK U	.40	1.00
48 Cloud City: Carbonite Chamber LIGHT U	.40	1.00
49 Cloud City: Chasm Walkway DARK C	.12	.30
50 Cloud City: Chasm Walkway LIGHT C	.12	.30
51 Cloud City: Dining Room R	1.25	3.00
52 Cloud City: East Platform (Docking Bay) C	.12	.30
53 Cloud City: Guest Quarters R	1.25	3.00
54 Cloud City: Incinerator DARK C	.12	.30
55 Cloud City: Incinerator LIGHT C	.12	.30
56 Cloud City: Lower Corridor DARK U	.40	1.00
57 Cloud City: Lower Corridor LIGHT U	.40	1.00
58 Cloud City: Platform 327 (Docking Bay) C	.12	.30
59 Cloud City: Security Tower C	.12	.30
60 Cloud City: Upper Plaza Corridor DARK C	.12	.30
61 Cloud City: Upper Plaza Corridor LIGHT U	.40	1.00
62 Clouds DARK C	.12	.30
63 Clouds LIGHT C	.12	.30
64 Commander Desanne U	.40	1.00
65 Computer Interface C	.12	.30
66 Courage Of A Skywalker R	1.25	3.00
67 Crack Shot U	.40	1.00
68 Cyborg Construct U	.40	1.00
69 Dark Approach R	1.25	3.00
70 Dark Deal R	1.25	3.00
71 Dark Strike C	.12	.30
72 Dash C	.12	.30
73 Despair R	1.25	3.00
74 Desperate Reach U	.40	1.00
75 Dismantle On Sight R	1.25	3.00
76 Dodge C	.12	.30
77 Double Back U	.40	1.00
78 Double-Crossing, No-Good Swindler C	.12	.30
79 E Chu Ta C	.12	.30
80 E-3PO R	1.25	3.00
81 End This Destructive Conflict R	1.25	3.00
82 Epic Duel R	2.00	5.00
83 Fall Of The Empire U	.40	1.00
84 Fall Of The Legend U	.40	1.00
85 Flight Escort R	1.25	3.00
86 Focused Attack R	1.25	3.00
87 Force Field R	1.25	3.00
88 Forced Landing R	1.25	3.00
89 Frozen Assets R	1.25	3.00
90 Gamblerís Luck R	1.25	3.00
91 Glancing Blow R	1.25	3.00
92 Haven R	1.25	3.00
93 Heís All Yours, Bounty Hunter R	1.25	3.00
94 Heart Of The Chasm U	.40	1.00
95 Hero Of A Thousand Devices U	.40	1.00
96 Higher Ground R	1.25	3.00
97 Hindsight R	1.25	3.00
98 Hopping Mad R	1.25	3.00
99 Human Shield C	.12	.30
100 I Am Your Father R	1.25	3.00
101 I Donít Need Their Scum, Either R	1.25	3.00
102 I Had No Choice R	1.25	3.00
103 Imperial Decree U	.40	1.00
104 Imperial Trooper Guard Dainsom U	.40	1.00
105 Impressive, Most Impressive R	1.25	3.00
106 Innocent Scoundrel U	.40	1.00
107 Interrogation Array R	1.25	3.00
108 Into The Ventilation Shaft, Lefty R	1.25	3.00
109 Itís A Trap! U	.40	1.00
110 Kebyc U	.40	1.00
111 Keep Your Eyes Open C	.12	.30
112 Lando Calrissian DARK R	5.00	12.00
113 Lando Calrissian LIGHT R	5.00	12.00
114 Landoís Wrist Comlink U	.40	1.00
115 Leia Of Alderaan R	2.00	5.00
116 Levitation Attack U	.40	1.00
117 Lieutenant Cecius U	.40	1.00
118 Lieutenant Sheckil R	1.25	3.00
119 Lift Tube Escape C	.12	.30
120 Lobot R	2.50	6.00
121 Lukeís Blaster Pistol R	1.25	3.00
122 Mandalorian Armor R	2.00	5.00
123 Mostly Armless R	1.25	3.00
124 NOOOOOOOOOOOO! R	1.25	3.00

125 Obsidian 7 R	2.00	5.00
126 Obsidian 8 R	2.00	5.00
127 Off The Edge R	1.25	3.00
128 Old Pirates R	1.25	3.00
129 Out Of Somewhere U	.40	1.00
130 Path Of Least Resistance C	.12	.30
131 Point Man R	1.25	3.00
132 Prepare The Chamber U	.40	1.00
133 Princess Leia R	4.00	10.00
134 Projective Telepathy U	.40	1.00
135 Protector R	1.25	3.00
136 Punch It! R	1.25	3.00
137 Put That Down C	.12	.30
138 Redemption R	2.50	6.00
139 Release Your Anger R	1.25	3.00
140 Rendezvous Point On Tatooine R	1.25	3.00
141 Rescue In The Clouds C	.12	.30
142 Restricted Access C	.12	.30
143 Rite Of Passage C	.12	.30
144 Shattered Hope U	.40	1.00
145 Shocking Information C	.12	.30
146 Shocking Revelation C	.12	.30
147 Slave I R	4.00	10.00
148 Slip Sliding Away R	1.25	3.00
149 Smoke Screen R	1.25	3.00
150 Somersault C	.12	.30
151 Sonic Bombardment U	.40	1.00
152 Special Delivery C	.12	.30
153 Surprise R	1.25	3.00
154 Surreptitious Glance R	1.25	3.00
155 Swing-And-A-Miss U	.40	1.00
156 The Emperoris Prize R	1.25	3.00
157 This Is Even Better R	1.25	3.00
158 This Is Still Wrong R	1.25	3.00
159 Tibanna Gas Miner DARK C	.12	.30
160 Tibanna Gas Miner LIGHT C	.12	.30
161 TIE Sentry Ships C	.12	.30
162 Treva Horme U	.40	1.00
163 Trooper Assault C	.12	.30
164 Trooper Jerrol Blendin U	.40	1.00
165 Trooper Utris Mitoc U	.40	1.00
166 Ugloste R	1.25	3.00
167 Ugnaught C	.12	.30
168 Uncontrollable Fury R	1.25	3.00
169 Vaderís Bounty R	1.25	3.00
170 Vaderís Cape R	1.25	3.00
171 Weíll Find Han R	1.25	3.00
172 Weíre The Bait R	1.25	3.00
173 Weapon Levitation U	.40	1.00
174 Weapon Of An Ungrateful Son U	.40	1.00
175 Weather Vane DARK U	.40	1.00
176 Weather Vane LIGHT U	.40	1.00
177 Why Didnít You Tell Me? R	1.25	3.00
178 Wiorkettle U	.40	1.00
179 Wookiee Strangle R	1.25	3.00
180 You Are Beaten U	.40	1.00

1997 Star Wars Dagobah

COMPLETE SET (181)	50.00	100.00
BOOSTER BOX (60 PACKS)	50.00	100.00
BOOSTER PACK (9 CARDS)	1.50	3.00
RELEASED ON APRIL 23, 1997		
1 3,720 To 1 C	.12	.30
2 4-LOM R	2.50	6.00
3 4-LOMís Concussion Rifle R	2.00	5.00
4 A Dangerous Time C	.12	.30
5 A Jediís Strength U	.40	1.00

6 Anger, Fear, Aggression C	.12	.30
7 Anoat DARK U	.40	1.00
8 Anoat LIGHT U	.40	1.00
9 Apology Accepted C	.12	.30
10 Asteroid Field DARK C	.12	.30
11 Asteroid Field LIGHT C	.12	.30
12 Asteroid Sanctuary C	.12	.30
13 Asteroids Do Not Concern Me R	1.25	3.00
14 Astroid Sanctuary C	.12	.30
15 Astromech Translator C	.12	.30
16 At Peace R	1.25	3.00
17 Avenger R	4.00	10.00
18 Away Put Your Weapon U	.40	1.00
19 Awwww, Cannot Get Your Ship Out C	.12	.30
20 Bad Feeling Have I R	1.25	3.00
21 Big One DARK U	.40	1.00
22 Big One LIGHT U	.40	1.00
23 Big One: Asteroid Cave	.40	1.00
or Space Slug Belly DARK U		
24 Big One: Asteroid Cave	.40	1.00
or Space Slug Belly LIGHT U		
25 Blasted Varmints C	.12	.30
26 Bog-wing DARK C	.12	.30
27 Bog-wing LIGHT C	.12	.30
28 Bombing Run R	1.25	3.00
29 Bossk R	3.00	8.00
30 Bosskís Mortar Gun R	2.00	5.00
31 Broken Concentration R	1.25	3.00
32 Captain Needa R	2.00	5.00
33 Close Call C	.12	.30
34 Closer?! U	.40	1.00
35 Comm Chief C	.12	.30
36 Commander Brandei U	.40	1.00
37 Commander Gherant U	.40	1.00
38 Commander Nemet U	.40	1.00
39 Control DARK U	.40	1.00
40 Control LIGHT U	.40	1.00
41 Corporal Derdram U	.40	1.00
42 Corporal Vandolay U	.40	1.00
43 Corrosive Damage R	1.25	3.00
44 Dagobah U	.40	1.00
45 Dagobah: Bog Clearing R	1.25	3.00
46 Dagobah: Cave R	1.25	3.00
47 Dagobah: Jungle U	.40	1.00
48 Dagobah: Swamp U	.40	1.00
49 Dagobah: Training Area C	.12	.30
50 Dagobah: Yodaís Hut R	2.00	5.00
51 Defensive Fire C	.12	.30
52 Dengar R	1.25	3.00
53 Dengarís Blaster Carbine R	1.25	3.00
54 Descent Into The Dark R	1.25	3.00
55 Do, Or Do Not C	.12	.30
56 Domain Of Evil U	.40	1.00
57 Dragonsnake R	1.25	3.00
58 Droid Sensorscope C	.12	.30
59 Effective Repairs R	1.25	3.00
60 Egregious Pilot Error R	1.25	3.00
61 Encampment C	.12	.30
62 Executor R	8.00	20.00
63 Executor: Comm Station U	.40	1.00
64 Executor: Control Station U	.40	1.00
65 Executor: Holotheatre R	1.25	3.00
66 Executor: Main Corridor C	.12	.30
67 Executor: Meditation Chamber R	1.25	3.00
68 Failure At The Cave R	1.25	3.00
69 Fear C	.12	.30
70 Field Promotion R	1.25	3.00
71 Flagship R	1.25	3.00
72 Flash Of Insight U	.40	1.00
73 Found Someone You Have U	.40	1.00
74 Frustration R	1.25	3.00
75 Great Warrior C	.12	.30
76 Grounded Starfighter U	.40	1.00
77 Hanís Toolkit R	1.25	3.00
78 He Is Not Ready C	.12	.30
79 Hiding In The Garbage R	1.25	3.00
80 HoloNet Transmission U	.40	1.00
81 Houndís Tooth R	2.50	6.00
82 I Have A Bad Feeling About This R	1.25	3.00
83 I Want That Ship R	1.25	3.00
84 IG-2000 R	2.00	5.00
85 IG-88 R	4.00	10.00
86 IG-88ís Neural Inhibitor R	2.00	5.00
87 IG-88ís Pulse Cannon R	2.00	5.00
88 Imbalance U	.40	1.00
89 Imperial Helmsman C	.12	.30
90 Ineffective Maneuver U	.40	1.00
91 It Is The Future You See R	1.25	3.00
92 Jedi Levitation R	1.25	3.00
93 Knowledge And Defense C	.12	.30
94 Landing Claw C	1.25	3.00

95 Lando System? R	1.25	3.00
96 Levitation U	.40	1.00
97 Lieutenant Commander Ardan U	.40	1.00
98 Lieutenant Suba U	1.25	3.00
99 Lieutenant Venka U	.40	1.00
100 Light Maneuvers R	1.25	3.00
101 Location, Location, Location R	1.25	3.00
102 Lost In Space R	1.25	3.00
103 Lost Relay C	.12	.30
104 Lukeís Backpack R	1.25	3.00
105 Mist Hunter R	2.00	5.00
106 Moving To Attack Position C	.12	.30
107 Much Anger In Him R	1.25	3.00
108 Mynock DARK C	.12	.30
109 Mynock LIGHT C	.12	.30
110 Never Tell Me The Odds C	.12	.30
111 No Disintegrations! R	1.25	3.00
112 Nudj C	.12	.30
113 Obi-Wanís Apparition R	1.25	3.00
114 Order To Engage R	1.25	3.00
115 Polarized Negative Power Coupling R	1.25	3.00
116 Portable Fusion Generator C	.12	.30
117 Precision Targeting U	.40	1.00
118 Proton Bombs U	.40	1.00
119 Punishing One R	2.00	5.00
120 Quick Draw C	.12	.30
121 Raithal DARK R	1.25	3.00
122 Raithal LIGHT U	.40	1.00
123 Rebel Flight Suit C	.12	.30
124 Recoil In Fear C	.12	.30
125 Reflection R	1.25	3.00
126 Report To Lord Vader R	1.25	3.00
127 Res Luk Raíauf R	1.25	3.00
128 Retractable Arm C	.12	.30
129 Rogue Asteroid DARK C	.12	.30
130 Rogue Asteroid LIGHT C	.12	.30
131 Rycarís Run R	1.25	3.00
132 Scramble U	.40	1.00
133 Shoo! Shoo! U	.40	1.00
134 Shot In The Dark U	.40	1.00
135 Shut Him Up Or Shut Him Down U	.40	1.00
136 Size Matters Not R	1.25	3.00
137 Sleen C	.12	.30
138 Smuggleris Blues R	1.25	3.00
139 Something Hit Us! U	.40	1.00
140 Son of Skywalker R	8.00	20.00
141 Space Slug DARK R	1.25	3.00
142 Space Slug LIGHT U	.40	1.00
143 Star Destroyer: Launch Bay C	.12	.30
144 Starship Levitation U	.40	1.00
145 Stone Pile R	1.25	3.00
146 Sudden Impact U	.40	1.00
147 Take Evasive Action C	.12	.30
148 The Dark Path R	1.25	3.00
149 The Professor R	1.25	3.00
150 There Is No Try C	.12	.30
151 Theyíd Be Crazy To Follow Us C	.12	.30
152 This Is More Like It R	1.25	3.00
153 This Is No Cave R	1.25	3.00
154 Those Rebels Wonít Escape Us C	.12	.30
155 Through The Force Things	1.25	3.00
You Will See R		
156 TIE Avenger C	.12	.30
157 TIE Bomber U	.40	1.00
158 Tight Squeeze R	1.25	3.00
159 Transmission Terminated U	.40	1.00
160 Tunnel Vision U	.40	1.00
161 Uncertain Is The Future C	.12	.30
162 Unexpected Interruption R	1.25	3.00
163 Vine Snake DARK C	.12	.30
164 Vine Snake LIGHT C	.12	.30
165 Visage Of The Emperor R	1.25	3.00
166 Visored Vision C	.12	.30
167 Voyeur C	.12	.30
168 Warrant Officer MiKae U	.40	1.00
169 Wars Not Make One Great U	.40	1.00
170 We Can Still Outmaneuver Them R	1.25	3.00
171 We Donít Need Their Scum R	1.25	3.00
172 WHAAAAAAAAAOOOOW! R	1.25	3.00
173 What Is Thy Bidding, My Master? R	1.25	3.00
174 Yoda R	8.00	20.00
175 Yoda Stew U	.40	1.00
176 Yoda, You Seek Yoda R	1.25	3.00
177 Yodaís Gimer Stick R	1.25	3.00
178 Yodaís Hope U	.40	1.00
179 You Do Have Your Moments U	.40	1.00
180 Zuckuss R	2.00	5.00
181 Zuckussí Snare Rifle R	1.25	3.00

1997 Star Wars First Anthology

COMPLETE SET (6)	3.00	8.00
RELEASED IN 1997		
1 Boba Fett PV	.75	2.00
2 Commander Wedge Antilles PV	.75	2.00
3 Death Star Assault Squadron PV	.75	2.00
4 Hit And Run PV	.75	2.00
5 Jabbaís Influence PV	.75	2.00
6 X-wing Assault Squadron PV	.75	2.00

1997 Star Wars Rebel Leaders

COMPLETE SET (2)	1.25	3.00
RELEASED IN 1997		
1 Gold Leader In Gold 1 PM	1.00	2.50
2 Red Leader In Red 1 PM	1.00	2.50

1998 Star Wars Enhanced Premiere

COMPLETE SET (6)	3.00	8.00
RELEASED IN 1998		
1 Boba Fett With Blaster Rifle PM	.75	2.00
2 Darth Vader With Lightsaber PM	.75	2.00
3 Han With Heavy Blaster Pistol PM	.75	2.00
4 Leia With Blaster Rifle PM	.75	2.00
5 Luke With Lightsaber PM	.75	2.00
6 Obi-Wan With Lightsaber PM	.75	2.00

1998 Star Wars Jabba's Palace

COMPLETE SET (180)	40.00	80.00
BOOSTER BOX (60 PACKS)	40.00	80.00
BOOSTER PACK (9 CARDS)	1.00	2.00
RELEASED IN MAY 1998		
1 8D8 R	1.25	3.00
2 A Gift U	.40	1.00
3 Abyssin C	.12	.30
4 Abyssin Ornament U	.40	1.00
5 All Wrapped Up U	.40	1.00
6 Amanaman R	1.25	3.00
7 Amanin C	.12	.30
8 Antipersonnel Laser Cannon U	.40	1.00
9 Aqualish C	.12	.30
10 Arc Welder U	.40	1.00
11 Ardon Vapor Crell R	1.25	3.00
12 Artoo R	3.00	8.00
13 Artoo, I Have A Bad Feeling About This U	.40	1.00
14 Attark R	1.25	3.00
15 Aved Luun R	1.25	3.00
16 Biomarr Monk C	.12	.30
17 Bane Malar R	1.25	3.00
18 Bantha Fodder C	.12	.30
19 Barada R	1.25	3.00
20 Baragwin C	.12	.30
21 Bargaining Table U	.40	1.00
22 Beedo R	1.25	3.00
23 BG-J38 R	1.25	3.00
24 Bib Fortuna R	1.25	3.00
25 Blaster Deflection R	1.25	3.00
26 Bo Shuda U	.40	1.00
27 Bubo U	.40	1.00
28 Cane Adiss U	.40	1.00
29 Chadra-Fan C	.12	.30
30 Chevin C	.12	.30
31 Choke C	.12	.30
32 Corellian Retort U	.40	1.00
33 CZ-4 C	.12	.30
34 Den Of Thieves U	.40	1.00
35 Dengaris Modified Riot Gun R	1.25	3.00
36 Devaronian C	.12	.30
37 Donit Forget The Droids C	.12	.30
38 Double Laser Cannon R	1.25	3.00
39 Droopy McCool R	1.25	3.00
40 Dune Sea Sabacc DARK U	.40	1.00
41 Dune Sea Sabacc LIGHT U	.40	1.00
42 Elom C	.12	.30
43 Ephant Mon R	1.25	3.00
44 EV-9D9 R	1.25	3.00
45 Fallen Portal U	.40	1.00
46 Florn Lamproid C	.12	.30
47 Fozec R	1.25	3.00
48 Gailid R	1.25	3.00
49 Gamorrean Ax C	.12	.30
50 Gamorrean Guard C	.12	.30
51 Garon Nas Tal R	1.25	3.00

52 Geezum R	1.25	3.00
53 Ghoel R	1.25	3.00
54 Giran R	1.25	3.00
55 Gran C	.12	.30
56 Hinemthe C	.12	.30
57 Herat R	1.25	3.00
58 Hermi Odle R	1.25	3.00
59 Hidden Compartment U	.40	1.00
60 Hidden Weapons U	.40	1.00
61 Holoprojector U	.40	1.00
62 Hutt Bounty R	1.25	3.00
63 Hutt Smooch U	.40	1.00
64 I Must Be Allowed To Speak R	1.25	3.00
65 Information Exchange U	.40	1.00
66 Ishi Tib C	.12	.30
67 Ithorian C	.12	.30
68 JiQuille R	1.25	3.00
69 Jabba the Hutt R	4.00	10.00
70 Jabbaís Palace Sabacc DARK U	.40	1.00
71 Jabbaís Palace Sabacc LIGHT U	.40	1.00
72 Jabbaís Palace: Audience Chamber DARK U	.40	1.00
73 Jabbaís Palace: Audience Chamber LIGHT U	.40	1.00
74 Jabbaís Palace: Droid Workshop U	.40	1.00
75 Jabbaís Palace: Dungeon U	.40	1.00
76 Jabbaís Palace: Entrance Cavern DARK U	.40	1.00
77 Jabbaís Palace: Entrance Cavern LIGHT U	.40	1.00
78 Jabbaís Palace: Rancor Pit U	.40	1.00
79 Jabbaís Sail Barge R	2.50	6.00
80 Jabbaís Sail Barge: Passenger Deck R	1.25	3.00
81 Jedi Mind Trick R	1.25	3.00
82 Jess R	1.25	3.00
83 Jet Pack U	.40	1.00
84 Kalit R	1.25	3.00
85 Ke Chu Ke Kakuta? C	.12	.30
86 Kiffex R	1.25	3.00
87 Kirdo III R	1.25	3.00
88 Kithaba R	1.25	3.00
89 Kitonak C	.12	.30
90 Klaatu R	1.25	3.00
91 Klatooinian Revolutionary C	.12	.30
92 Laudica R	1.25	3.00
93 Leslomy Tacema R	1.25	3.00
94 Life Debt R	1.25	3.00
95 Loje Nella R	1.25	3.00
96 Malakili R	1.25	3.00
97 Mandalorian Mishap U	.40	1.00
98 Max Rebo R	1.25	3.00
99 Mos Eisley Blaster DARK C	.12	.30
100 Mos Eisley Blaster LIGHT C	.12	.30
101 Murttoc Yine R	1.25	3.00
102 Nal Hutta R	1.25	3.00
103 Nar Shaddaa Wind Chimes U	.40	1.00
104 Nikto C	.12	.30
105 Nizuc Bek R	1.25	3.00
106 None Shall Pass C	.12	.30
107 Nysad R	1.25	3.00
108 Oola R	1.25	3.00
109 Ortolan C	.12	.30
110 Ortugg R	1.25	3.00
111 Palejo Reshad R	1.25	3.00
112 Pote Snitkin R	1.25	3.00
113 Princess Leia Organa R	3.00	8.00
114 Projection Of A Skywalker U	.40	1.00
115 Pucumir Thryss R	1.25	3.00
116 Quarren C	.12	.30
117 Quick Reflexes C	.12	.30
118 Rikik Dinec, Hero Of The Dune Sea R	1.25	3.00
119 Rancor R	2.50	6.00
120 Rayc Ryjerd R	1.25	3.00
121 Ree-Yees R	1.25	3.00
122 Rennek R	1.25	3.00
123 Resistance U	.40	1.00
124 Revealed U	.40	1.00
125 Saelt-Marae R	1.25	3.00
126 Salacious Crumb R	1.25	3.00
127 Sandwhirl DARK U	.40	1.00
128 Sandwhirl LIGHT U	.40	1.00
129 Scum And Villainy R	1.25	3.00
130 Sergeant Doallyn R	1.25	3.00
131 Shasa Tiel R	1.25	3.00
132 Sic-Six C	.12	.30
133 Skiff DARK C	.12	.30
134 Skiff LIGHT C	.12	.30
135 Skrilling C	.12	.30
136 Skull U	.40	1.00
137 Snivvian C	.12	.30
138 Someone Who Loves You U	.40	1.00

139 Strangle R	1.25	3.00
140 Tamtel Skreej R	2.50	6.00
141 Tanus Spijek R	1.25	3.00
142 Tatooine: Desert DARK C	.12	.30
143 Tatooine: Desert LIGHT C	.12	.30
144 Tatooine: Great Pit Of Carkoon U	.40	1.00
145 Tatooine: Hutt Canyon U	.40	1.00
146 Tatooine: Jabbaís Palace U	.40	1.00
147 Taym Dren-garen R	1.25	3.00
148 Tessek R	1.25	3.00
149 The Signal C	.12	.30
150 Thermal Detonator R	2.00	5.00
151 Thul Fain R	1.25	3.00
152 Tibrin R	1.25	3.00
153 Torture C	.12	.30
154 Trandoshan C	.12	.30
155 Trap Door U	.40	1.00
156 Twilek Advisor C	.12	.30
157 Ultimatum U	.40	1.00
158 Unfriendly Fire R	1.25	3.00
159 Vedain R	1.25	3.00
160 Velken Tezeri R	1.25	3.00
161 Vibro-Ax DARK C	.12	.30
162 Vibro-Ax LIGHT C	.12	.30
163 Vizam R	1.25	3.00
164 Vul Tazaene R	1.25	3.00
165 Weapon Levitation U	.40	1.00
166 Weequay Guard C	.12	.30
167 Weequay Hunter C	.12	.30
168 Weequay Marksman U	.40	1.00
169 Weequay Skiff Master C	.12	.30
170 Well Guarded U	.40	1.00
171 Whiphid C	.12	.30
172 Wittin R	1.25	3.00
173 Wooof R	1.25	3.00
174 Worrt U	.40	1.00
175 Wounded Wookiee U	.40	1.00
176 Yarkora C	.12	.30
177 Yarna díal Gargan U	.40	1.00
178 You Will Take Me To Jabba Now C	.12	.30
179 Yoxgit R	1.25	3.00
180 Yuzzum C	.12	.30

1998 Star Wars Official Tournament Sealed Deck

COMPLETE SET (18)	4.00	10.00
RELEASED IN 1998		
1 Arleil Schous PM	.40	1.00
2 Black Squadron TIE PM	.40	1.00
3 Chall Bekan PM	.40	1.00
4 Corulag DARK PM	.40	1.00
5 Corulag LIGHT PM	.40	1.00
6 Dreadnaught-Class Heavy Cruiser PM	.40	1.00
7 Faithful Service PM	.40	1.00
8 Forced Servitude PM	.40	1.00
9 Gold Squadron Y-wing PM	.40	1.00
10 Itis a Hit! PM	.40	1.00
11 Obsidian Squadron TIE PM	.40	1.00
12 Rebel Trooper Recruit PM	.40	1.00
13 Red Squadron X-wing PM	.40	1.00
14 Stormtrooper Cadet PM	.40	1.00
15 Tarkinis Orders PM	.40	1.00
16 Tatooine: Jundland Wastes PM	.40	1.00
17 Tatooine: Tusken Canyon PM	.40	1.00
18 Z-95 Headhunter PM	.40	1.00

1998 Star Wars Second Anthology

1998 Star Wars Special Edition

COMPLETE SET (6)	4.00	10.00
RELEASED IN 1998		
1 Flagship Operations PV	1.00	2.50
2 Mon Calamari Star Cruiser PV	1.00	2.50
3 Mon Mothma PV	1.00	2.50
4 Rapid Deployment PV	1.00	2.50
5 Sarlacc PV	1.00	2.50
6 Thunderflare PV	1.00	2.50

COMPLETE SET (324)	75.00	150.00
BOOSTER BOX (30 PACKS)	60.00	120.00
BOOSTER PACK (9 CARDS)	3.00	6.00
RELEASED IN NOVEMBER 1998		
1 ISB Operations / Empireís Sinister Agents R	1.00	2.50
2 2X-7KPR (Tooex) C	.12	.30
3 A Bright Center To The Universe U	.40	1.00
4 A Day Long Remembered U	.40	1.00
5 A Real Hero R	1.00	2.50
6 Air-2 Racing Swoop C	.12	.30
7 Ak-rev U	.40	1.00
8 Alderaan Operative C	.12	.30
9 Alert My Star Destroyer! C	.12	.30
10 All Power To Weapons C	.12	.30
11 All Wings Report In R	1.00	2.50
12 Anoat Operative DARK C	.12	.30
13 Anoat Operative LIGHT C	.12	.30
14 Antilles Maneuver C	.12	.30
15 ASP-707 (Ayesspee) F	.60	1.50
16 Balanced Attack U	.40	1.00
17 Bantha Herd R	.75	2.00
18 Barquin Dían U	.40	1.00
19 Ben Kenobi R	2.00	5.00
20 Blast Points C	.12	.30
21 Blown Clear U	.40	1.00
22 Boba Fett R	1.50	4.00
23 Boelo R	1.00	2.50
24 Bossk In Houndís Tooth R	1.00	2.50
25 Bothan Spy C	.12	.30
26 Bothawui F	.60	1.50
27 Bothawui Operative C	.12	.30
28 Brangus Glee R	.75	2.00
29 Bren Quersey U	.40	1.00
30 Bron Burs R	.75	2.00
31 B-wing Attack Fighter F	.60	1.50
32 Camie R	1.00	2.50
33 Carbon Chamber Testing	1.00	2.50
My Favorite Decoration R		
34 Chyler U	.40	1.00
35 Clakidor VII Operative U	.40	1.00
36 Cloud City Celebration R	1.00	2.50
37 Cloud City Occupation R	1.25	3.00
38 Cloud City: Casino DARK U	.40	1.00
39 Cloud City: Casino LIGHT U	.40	1.00
40 Cloud City: Core Tunnel U	.40	1.00
41 Cloud City: Downtown Plaza DARK R	1.00	2.50
42 Cloud City: Downtown Plaza LIGHT R	1.00	2.50
43 Cloud City: Interrogation Room C	.12	.30
44 Cloud City: North Corridor C	.12	.30
45 Cloud City: Port Town District U	.40	1.00
46 Cloud City: Upper Walkway C	.12	.30
47 Cloud City: West Gallery DARK C	.12	.30
48 Cloud City: West Gallery LIGHT C	.12	.30
49 Colonel Feyn Gospic R	1.00	2.50
50 Combat Cloud Car F	.60	1.50
51 Come Here You Big Coward! C	.12	.30

52 Commander Wedge Antilles R	1.00	2.50
53 Coordinated Attack C	.12	.30
54 Corellia Operative U	.40	1.00
55 Corellian Engineering Corporation R	1.00	2.50
56 Corporal Grenwick R	.75	2.00
57 Corporal Prescott U	.40	1.00
58 Corulag Operative C	.12	.30
59 Coruscant Celebration R	.75	2.00
60 Coruscant DARK R	2.50	6.00
61 Coruscant LIGHT R	1.00	2.50
62 Coruscant: Docking Bay C	.12	.30
63 Coruscant: Imperial City U	.40	1.00
64 Coruscant: Imperial Square R	1.25	3.00
65 Counter Surprise Assault R	1.00	2.50
66 Dagobah U	.40	1.00
67 Dantooine Base Operations	.75	2.00
More Dangerous Than You Realize R		
68 Dantooine Operative C	.12	.30
69 Darklighter Spin C	.12	.30
70 Darth Vader, Dark Lord Of The Sith R	6.00	15.00
71 Death Squadron Star Destroyer R	1.00	2.50
72 Death Star Assault Squadron R	1.00	2.50
73 Death Star R	1.25	3.00
74 Death Star: Detention Block Control Room C	.12	.30
75 Death Star: Detention Block Corridor C	.12	.30
76 Debnoli R	1.00	2.50
77 Desert DARK F	.60	1.50
78 Desert LIGHT F	.60	1.50
79 Desilijic Tattoo U	.40	1.00
80 Desperate Tactics C	.12	.30
81 Destroyed Homestead R	1.00	2.50
82 Dewback C	.12	.30
83 Direct Assault C	.12	.30
84 Disruptor Pistol DARK F	.60	1.50
85 Disruptor Pistol LIGHT F	.60	1.50
86 Docking And Repair Facilities R	1.00	2.50
87 Dodo Bodonawieedo U	.40	1.00
88 Donít Tread On Me R	1.00	2.50
89 Down With The Emperor! U	.40	1.00
90 Dr. Evazanís Sawed-off Blaster U	.40	1.00
91 Draw Their Fire U	.40	1.00
92 Dreaded Imperial Starfleet R	1.25	3.00
93 Droid Merchant C	.12	.30
94 Dune Walker R	1.25	3.00
95 Echo Base Trooper Rifle C	.12	.30
96 Elyhek Rue U	.40	1.00
97 Entrenchment R	.75	2.00
98 Eriadu Operative C	.12	.30
99 Executor: Docking Bay U	.40	1.00
100 Farm F	.60	1.50
101 Feltipern Trevaggís Stun Rifle U	.40	1.00
102 Firepower C	.12	.30
103 Firin Morett U	.40	1.00
104 First Aid F	.60	1.50
105 First Strike U	.40	1.00
106 Flare-S Racing Swoop C	.12	.30
107 Flawless Marksmanship C	.12	.30
108 Floating Refinery C	.12	.30
109 Fondor U	.40	1.00
110 Forest DARK F	.60	1.50
111 Forest LIGHT F	.60	1.50
112 Gela Yeens U	.40	1.00
113 General McQuarrie R	.75	2.00
114 Gold 3 U	.40	1.00
115 Gold 4 U	.40	1.00
116 Gold 6 U	.40	1.00
117 Goo Nee Tay R	1.00	2.50
118 Greeata U	.40	1.00
119 Grondorn Muse R	.75	2.00
120 Harc Seff U	.40	1.00
121 Harvest R	1.25	3.00
122 Heavy Fire Zone C	.12	.30
123 Heroes Of Yavin R	.75	2.00
124 Heroic Sacrifice U	.40	1.00
125 Hidden Base	1.50	4.00
Systems Will Slip Through Your Fingers R		
126 Hit And Run R	.75	2.00
127 Hol Okand U	.40	1.00
128 Homing Beacon R	1.00	2.50
129 Hoth Sentry U	.40	1.00
130 Hunt Down And Destroy The Jedi	1.50	4.00
Their Fire Has Gone Out Of The Universe R		
131 Hunting Party R	1.00	2.50
132 I Canít Shake Him! C	.12	.30
133 Iasa, The Traitor Of Jawa Canyon R	.75	2.00
134 IM4-099 F	.60	1.50
135 Imperial Atrocity R	3.00	8.00
136 Imperial Occupation / Imperial Control R	1.00	2.50
137 Imperial Propaganda R	3.00	8.00
138 In Range C	.12	.30
139 Incom Corporation R	.75	2.00

140 InCom Engineer C	.12	.30
141 Intruder Missile DARK F	.60	1.50
142 Intruder Missile LIGHT F	.60	1.50
143 Itís Not My Fault! F	.60	1.50
144 Jabba R	1.00	2.50
145 Jabbaís Influence R	.75	2.00
146 Jabbaís Space Cruiser R	1.25	3.00
147 Jabbaís Through With You U	.40	1.00
148 Jabbaís Twerps U	.40	1.00
149 Joh Yowza R	.75	2.00
150 Jungle DARK F	.60	1.50
151 Jungle LIGHT F	.60	1.50
152 Kalitis Sandcrawler R	1.00	2.50
153 Kashyyyk Operative DARK U	.40	1.00
154 Kashyyyk Operative LIGHT U	.40	1.00
155 Kessel Operative U	.40	1.00
156 Ketwol R	.75	2.00
157 Kiffex Operative DARK U	.40	1.00
158 Kiffex Operative LIGHT U	.40	1.00
159 Kirdo III Operative C	.12	.30
160 Koensayr Manufacturing R	1.00	2.50
161 Krayt Dragon R	1.00	2.50
162 Kuat Drive Yards R	1.25	3.00
163 Kuat U	.40	1.00
164 Landois Blaster Rifle R	1.00	2.50
165 Legendary Starfighter C	.12	.30
166 Leiaís Blaster Rifle R	1.00	2.50
167 Lieutenant Lepira U	.40	1.00
168 Lieutenant Naytaan U	.40	1.00
169 Lieutenant Tarn Mison R	1.00	2.50
170 Lobel C	.12	.30
171 Lobot R	1.00	2.50
172 Local Defense U	.40	1.00
173 Local Uprising / Liberation R	1.00	2.50
174 Lyn Me U	.40	1.00
175 Major Palo Torshan R	1.00	2.50
176 Makurth F	.60	1.50
177 Maneuvering Flaps C	.12	.30
178 Masterful Move C	.12	.30
179 Mechanical Failure R	.75	2.00
180 Meditation R	1.25	3.00
181 Medium Bulk Freighter U	.40	1.00
182 Melas R	1.00	2.50
183 Mind What You Have Learned	1.25	3.00
Save You It Can R		
184 Moisture Farmer C	.12	.30
185 Nal Hutta Operative C	.12	.30
186 Neb Dulo U	.40	1.00
187 Nebit R	1.00	2.50
188 Niado Duegad U	.40	1.00
189 Nick Of Time U	.40	1.00
190 No Bargain U	.40	1.00
191 Old Times R	.75	2.00
192 On Target C	.12	.30
193 One-Arm R	1.00	2.50
194 Oppressive Enforcement U	.40	1.00
195 Ord Mantell Operative C	.12	.30
196 Organized Attack C	.12	.30
197 OS-72-1 In Obsidian 1 R	1.00	2.50
198 OS-72-10 R	1.00	2.50
199 OS-72-2 In Obsidian 2 R	1.00	2.50
200 Outer Rim Scout R	1.50	4.00
201 Overwhelmed C	.12	.30
202 Patrol Craft DARK C	.12	.30
203 Patrol Craft LIGHT C	.12	.30
204 Planetary Subjugation U	.40	1.00
205 Ponda Babaís Hold-out Blaster U	.40	1.00
206 Portable Scanner C	.12	.30
207 Power Pivot C	.12	.30
208 Precise Hit C	.12	.30
209 Pride Of The Empire C	.12	.30
210 Princess Organa R	1.25	3.00
211 Put All Sections On Alert C	.12	.30
212 R2-A5 (Artoo-Ayfive) U	.40	1.00
213 R3-A2 (Arthree-Aytoo) U	.40	1.00
214 R3-T2 (Arthree-Teetoo) R	1.00	2.50
215 Raithal Operative C	.12	.30
216 Ralltiir Freighter Captain F	.60	1.50
217 Ralltiir Operations	1.50	4.00
In The Hands Of The Empire R		
218 Ralltiir Operative C	.12	.30
219 Rapid Fire C	.12	.30
220 Rappertunie U	.40	1.00
221 Rebel Ambush C	.12	.30
222 Rebel Base Occupation R	.75	2.00
223 Rebel Fleet R	1.00	2.50
224 Red 10 U	.40	1.00
225 Red 7 U	.40	1.00
226 Red 8 U	.40	1.00
227 Red 9 U	.40	1.00
228 Relentless Pursuit C	.12	.30

TRADING CARD GAMES AND MINIATURES

229	Rendezvous Point R	1.00	2.50
230	Rendili F	.60	1.50
231	Rendili StarDrive R	.75	2.00
232	Rescue The Princess	1.00	2.50
	Sometimes I Amaze Even Myself R		
233	Return To Base R	1.00	2.50
234	Roche F	.40	1.00
235	Rock Wart F	.60	1.50
236	Rogue 4 R	1.50	4.00
237	Ronto DARK C	.12	.30
238	Ronto LIGHT C	.12	.30
239	RRiururrrr R	1.00	2.50
240	Ryle Torsyn U	.40	1.00
241	Rystall R	1.50	4.00
242	Sacrifice F	.60	1.50
243	Sandspeeder F	.60	1.50
244	Sandtrooper F	.60	1.50
245	Sarlacc R	1.00	2.50
246	Scrambled Transmission U	.40	1.00
247	Scurrier F	.60	1.50
248	Secret Plans U	.40	1.00
249	Sentinel-Class Landing Craft F	.60	1.50
250	Sergeant Edian U	.40	1.00
251	Sergeant Hollis R	1.00	2.50
252	Sergeant Major Bursk U	.40	1.00
253	Sergeant Major Enfield R	.75	2.00
254	Sergeant Merril U	.40	1.00
255	Sergeant Narthax R	1.00	2.50
256	Sergeant Torent R	1.00	2.50
257	S-Foils C	.12	.30
258	SFS L-s9.3 Laser Cannons C	.12	.30
259	Short-Range Fighters R	1.00	2.50
260	Sienar Fleet Systems R	1.00	2.50
261	Slayn and Korpil Facilities R	.75	2.00
262	Slight Weapons Malfunction C	.12	.30
263	Soth Petikkin R	.75	2.00
264	Spaceport City DARK F	.60	1.50
265	Spaceport City LIGHT F	.60	1.50
266	Spaceport Docking Bay DARK F	.60	1.50
267	Spaceport Docking Bay LIGHT F	.60	1.50
268	Spaceport Prefectís Office F	.60	1.50
269	Spaceport Street DARK F	.60	1.50
270	Spaceport Street LIGHT F	.60	1.50
271	Spiral R	1.25	3.00
272	Star Destroyer! R	1.00	2.50
273	Stay Sharp! U	.40	1.00
274	Steady Aim C	.12	.30
275	Strategic Reserves R	1.00	2.50
276	Suppressive Fire C	.12	.30
277	Surface Defense R	1.00	2.50
278	Swamp DARK F	.60	1.50
279	Swamp LIGHT F	.60	1.50
280	Swoop Mercenary F	.60	1.50
281	Sy Snootles R	1.00	2.50
282	T-47 Battle Formation R	1.00	2.50
283	Tarkinís Bounty U	.40	1.00
284	Tatooine Celebration R	1.25	3.00
285	Tatooine Occupation R	1.50	4.00
286	Tatooine: Anchorhead F	.60	1.50
287	Tatooine: Beggarís Canyon R	.75	2.00
288	Tatooine: Jabbaís Palace C	.12	.30
289	Tatooine: Jawa Canyon DARK U	.40	1.00
290	Tatooine: Jawa Canyon LIGHT U	.40	1.00
291	Tatooine: Krayt Dragon Pass F	.60	1.50
292	Tatooine: Tosche Station C	.12	.30
293	Tauntaun Skull C	.12	.30
294	Tawss Khaa R	.75	2.00
295	The Planet That Itís Farthest From U	.40	1.00
296	Thedit R	1.00	2.50
297	Theron Nett U	.40	1.00
298	Theyíre Coming In Too Fast! C	.12	.30
299	Theyíre Tracking Us C	.12	.30
300	Theyíve Shut Down The Main Reactor C	.12	.30
301	Tibrin Operative C	.12	.30
302	TIE Defender Mark I F	.60	1.50
303	TK-422 R	1.00	2.50
304	Trooper Sabacc DARK F	.60	1.50
305	Trooper Sabacc LIGHT F	.60	1.50
306	Uh-oh! U	.40	1.00
307	Umpass-stay R	.75	2.00
308	UriíRuír R	1.00	2.50
309	URoRRuRiRiRís Bantha R	1.00	2.50
310	Uutkik R	1.00	2.50
311	Vaderís Personal Shuttle R	1.00	2.50
312	Vengeance R	1.00	2.50
313	Wakeelmui U	.40	1.00
314	Watch Your Back! C	.12	.30
315	Weapons Display C	.12	.30
316	Wise Advice U	.40	1.00
317	Wittinís Sandcrawler R	1.00	2.50
318	Womp Rat C	.12	.30

319	Wookiee F	.60	1.50
320	Wrist Comlink C	.12	.30
321	X-wing Assault Squadron R	1.00	2.50
322	X-wing Laser Cannon C	.12	.30
323	Yavin 4 Trooper F	.60	1.50
324	Yavin 4: Massassi Headquarters R	1.00	2.50

1999 Star Wars Endor

COMPLETE SET (180)		75.00	150.00
BOOSTER BOX (30 PACKS)		75.00	150.00
BOOSTER PACK (9 CARDS)		3.50	7.00
RELEASED IN JUNE 1999			
1	AT-ST Pilot C	.12	.30
2	Biker Scout Trooper C	.12	.30
3	Colonel Dyer R	1.25	3.00
4	Commander Igar R	1.25	3.00
5	Corporal Avarik U	.40	1.00
6	Corporal Drazin U	.40	1.00
7	Corporal Drelosyn R	1.25	3.00
8	Corporal Misik R	1.00	2.50
9	Corporal Oberk R	1.25	3.00
10	Elite Squadron Stormtrooper C	.12	.30
11	Lieutenant Arnet U	.40	1.00
12	Lieutenant Grond U	.40	1.00
13	Lieutenant Renz R	.75	2.00
14	Lieutenant Watts R	1.25	3.00
15	Major Hewex R	.75	2.00
16	Major Marquand R	1.50	4.00
17	Navy Trooper C	.12	.30
18	Navy Trooper Fenson R	1.00	2.50
19	Navy Trooper Shield Technician C	.12	.30
20	Navy Trooper Vesden U	.40	1.00
21	Sergeant Barich R	2.00	5.00
22	Sergeant Elsek U	.40	1.00
23	Sergeant Irol R	1.50	4.00
24	Sergeant Tarl U	.40	1.00
25	Sergeant Wallen R	1.50	4.00
26	An Entire Legion Of My Best Troops U	.40	1.00
27	Aratech Corporation R	1.00	2.50
28	Battle Order U	.40	1.00
29	Biker Scout Gear U	.40	1.00
30	Closed Door R	.75	2.00
31	Crossfire R	3.00	8.00
32	Early Warning Network R	.75	2.00
33	Empireís New Order R	.75	2.00
34	Establish Secret Base R	1.50	4.00
35	Imperial Academy Training C	.12	.30
36	Imperial Arrest Order U	.40	1.00
37	Ominous Rumors R	.75	2.00
38	Perimeter Patrol R	1.00	2.50
39	Pinned Down U	.40	1.00
40	Relentless Tracking R	.75	2.00
41	Search And Destroy U	.40	1.00
42	Security Precautions R	2.50	6.00
43	Well-earned Command R	.75	2.00
44	Accelerate C	.12	.30
45	Always Thinking With Your Stomach R	2.50	6.00
46	Combat Readiness C	.12	.30
47	Compact Firepower C	.12	.30
48	Counterattack R	.75	2.00
49	Dead Ewok C	.12	.30
50	Donít Move! C	.12	.30
51	Eee Chu Wawa! C	.12	.30
52	Endor Scout Trooper C	.12	.30
53	Freeze! U	.40	1.00
54	Go For Help! C	.12	.30
55	High-speed Tactics U	.40	1.00

56	Hot Pursuit C	.12	.30
57	Imperial Tyranny C	.12	.30
58	Itís An Older Code R	.75	2.00
59	Main Course U	.40	1.00
60	Outflank C	.12	.30
61	Pitiful Little Band C	.12	.30
62	Scout Recon C	.12	.30
63	Sneak Attack C	.12	.30
64	Wounded Warrior R	1.50	4.00
65	You Rebel Scum R	1.00	2.50
66	Carida U	.40	1.00
67	Endor Occupation R	.75	2.00
68	Endor: Ancient Forest U	.40	1.00
69	Endor: Back Door LIGHT U	.40	1.00
70	Endor: Bunker LIGHT U	.40	1.00
71	Endor: Dark Forest R	2.50	6.00
72	Endor: Dense Forest LIGHT C	.12	.30
73	Endor: Ewok Village LIGHT U	.40	1.00
74	Endor: Forest Clearing U	.40	1.00
75	Endor: Great Forest LIGHT C	.12	.30
76	Endor: Landing Platform	.12	.30
	(Docking Bay) LIGHT C		
77	Endor DARK U	.40	1.00
78	Lambda-class Shuttle C	.12	.30
79	Speeder Bike LIGHT C	.12	.30
80	Tempest 1 R	.75	2.00
81	Tempest Scout 1 R	1.00	2.50
82	Tempest Scout 2 R	2.00	5.00
83	Tempest Scout 3 R	.75	2.00
84	Tempest Scout 4 R	2.50	6.00
85	Tempest Scout 5 R	2.00	5.00
86	Tempest Scout 6 R	2.50	6.00
87	Tempest Scout U	.40	1.00
88	AT-ST Dual Cannon R	6.00	15.00
89	Scout Blaster C	.12	.30
90	Speeder Bike Cannon U	.40	1.00
91	Captain Yutani U	.40	1.00
92	Chewbacca of Kashyyyk R	.75	2.00
93	Chief Chirpa R	1.00	2.50
94	Corporal Beezer U	.40	1.00
95	Corporal Delevar U	.40	1.00
96	Corporal Janse U	.40	1.00
97	Corporal Kensaric R	1.25	3.00
98	Daughter of Skywalker R	10.00	20.00
99	Dresselian Commando C	.12	.30
100	Endor LIGHT U	.40	1.00
101	Ewok Sentry C	.12	.30
102	Ewok Spearman C	.12	.30
103	Ewok Tribesman C	.12	.30
104	General Crix Madine R	1.00	2.50
105	General Solo R	.75	2.00
106	Graak R	.75	2.00
107	Kazak R	1.00	2.50
108	Lieutenant Greeve R	.75	2.00
109	Lieutenant Page R	1.50	4.00
110	Logray R	.75	2.00
111	Lumat U	.40	1.00
112	Mon Mothma R	1.25	3.00
113	Orrimaarko R	.75	2.00
114	Paploo U	.40	1.00
115	Rabin U	.40	1.00
116	Romba R	.75	2.00
117	Sergeant Brooks Carlson R	.75	2.00
118	Sergeant Bruckman R	.75	2.00
119	Sergeant Junkin R	.40	1.00
120	Teebo R	.75	2.00
121	Threepio R	1.25	3.00
122	Wicket R	.75	2.00
123	Wuta U	.40	1.00
124	Aim High R	1.00	2.50
125	Battle Plan U	.40	1.00
126	Commando Training C	.12	.30
127	Count Me In R	.75	2.00
128	I Hope Sheís All Right U	.40	1.00
129	I Wonder Who They Found U	.40	1.00
130	Insurrection U	.40	1.00
131	Thatís One R	.75	2.00
132	Wokling R	6.00	15.00
133	Deactivate The Shield Generator R	1.25	3.00
134	Careful Planning C	.12	.30
135	Covert Landing U	.40	1.00
136	Endor Operations / Imperial Outpost R	2.50	6.00
137	Ewok And Roll C	.12	.30
138	Ewok Log Jam C	.12	.30
139	Ewok Rescue C	.12	.30
140	Firefight C	.12	.30
141	Fly Casual R	.75	2.00
142	Free Ride U	.40	1.00
143	Get Alongside That One U	.40	1.00
144	Here We Go Again R	.75	2.00
145	I Have A Really Bad	.12	.30

Feeling About This C

146	I Know R	1.25	3.00
147	Lost In The Wilderness R	.75	2.00
148	Rapid Deployment R	.75	2.00
149	Sound The Attack C	.12	.30
150	Surprise Counter Assault R	.75	2.00
151	Take The Initiative C	.12	.30
152	This Is Absolutely Right R	.75	2.00
153	Throw Me Another Charge U	.40	1.00
154	Were You Looking For Me? R	4.00	10.00
155	Wookiee Guide C	.12	.30
156	Yub Yub! C	.12	.30
157	Chandrila U	.40	1.00
158	Endor Celebration R	.75	2.00
159	Endor: Back Door DARK U	.40	1.00
160	Endor: Bunker DARK U	.40	1.00
161	Endor: Chief Chirpa's Hut R	3.00	8.00
162	Endor: Dense Forest DARK C	.12	.30
163	Endor: Ewok Village DARK U	.40	1.00
164	Endor: Great Forest DARK C	.12	.30
165	Endor: Hidden Forest Trail U	.40	1.00
166	Endor: Landing Platform	.12	.30

(Docking Bay) DARK C

167	Endor: Rebel Landing Site (Forest) R	2.50	6.00
168	Rebel Strike Team R	1.25	3.00

Garrison Destroyed R

169	Tydirium R	1.25	3.00
170	YT-1300 Transport C	.12	.30
171	Chewie's AT-ST R	3.00	8.00
172	Ewok Glider C	.12	.30
173	Speeder Bike DARK C	.12	.30
174	A280 Sharpshooter Rifle R	2.50	6.00
175	BlasTech E-11B Blaster Rifle C	.12	.30
176	Chewbacca's Bowcaster R	2.50	6.00
177	Ewok Bow C	.12	.30
178	Ewok Catapult U	.40	1.00
179	Ewok Spear C	.12	.30
180	Explosive Charge U	.40	1.00

1999 Star Wars Enhanced Cloud City

COMPLETE SET (12)		12.00	25.00

RELEASED IN 1999

1	4-LOM With Concussion Rifle PM	1.50	4.00
2	Any Methods Necessary PM	2.00	5.00
3	Boba Fett in Slave I PM	1.00	2.50
4	Chewie With Blaster Rifle PM	1.00	2.50
5	Crush The Rebellion PM	1.25	3.00
6	Dengar In Punishing One PM	1.00	2.50
7	IG-88 With Riot Gun PM	3.00	8.00
8	Lando In Millennium Falcon PM	1.00	2.50
9	Lando With Blaster Pistol PM	1.00	2.50
10	Quiet Mining Colony	1.00	2.50

Independent Operation PM

11	This Deal Is Getting Worse All The Time	1.00	2.50

Pray I Don't Alter It Any Further

12	Z-95 Bespin Defense Fighter PM	1.00	2.50

1999 Star Wars Enhanced Jabba's Palace

COMPLETE SET (12)		20.00	40.00

RELEASE IN 1999

1	Bossk With Mortar Gun PM	1.00	2.50
2	Boushh PM	1.25	3.00
3	Court Of The Vile Gangster PM	1.00	2.50

I Shall Enjoy Watching You Die PM

4	Dengar With Blaster Carbine PM	1.00	2.50
5	IG-88 In IG-2000 PM	1.00	2.50
6	Jodo Kast PM	1.50	4.00
7	Mara Jade, The Emperor's Hand PM	10.00	20.00
8	Mara Jade's Lightsaber PM	1.50	4.00
9	Master Luke PM	2.50	6.00
10	See-Threepio PM	1.00	2.50
11	You Can Either Profit By This...	1.00	2.50

Or Be Destroyed PM

12	Zuckuss In Mist Hunter PM	1.25	3.00

2000 Star Wars Death Star II

COMPLETE SET (182)		200.00	300.00
BOOSTER BOX (30 PACKS)		150.00	250.00
BOOSTER PACK (11 CARDS)		5.00	9.00

RELEASED IN JULY 2000

1	Accuser R	1.25	3.00
2	Admiral Ackbar XR	1.25	3.00
3	Admiral Chiraneau R	1.50	4.00
4	Admiral Piett XR	1.00	2.50
5	Anakin Skywalker R	1.00	2.50
6	Aquaris C	.12	.30
7	A-wing C	.12	.30
8	A-wing Cannon C	.12	.30
9	Baron Soontir Fel R	1.50	4.00
10	Battle Deployment R	1.25	3.00
11	Black 11 R	1.00	2.50
12	Blue Squadron 5 U	.40	1.00
13	Blue Squadron B-wing R	1.50	4.00
14	Bring Him Before Me	1.00	2.50

Take Your Father's Place R

15	B-wing Attack Squadron R	1.00	2.50
16	B-wing Bomber C	.12	.30
17	Capital Support R	1.00	2.50
18	Captain Godherdt U	.40	1.00
19	Captain Jonus U	.40	1.00
20	Captain Sarkli R	1.00	2.50
21	Captain Verrack U	.40	1.00
22	Captain Yorr U	.40	1.00
23	Chimaera R	2.50	6.00
24	Close Air Support C	.12	.30
25	Colonel Cracken R	1.00	2.50
26	Colonel Davod Jon U	.40	1.00
27	Colonel Jendon R	1.00	2.50
28	Colonel Salm U	.40	1.00
29	Combat Response C	.12	.30
30	Combined Fleet Action R	1.00	2.50
31	Commander Merrejk R	1.25	3.00
32	Concentrate All Fire R	1.00	2.50
33	Concussion Missiles DARK C	.12	.30
34	Concussion Missiles LIGHT C	.12	.30
35	Corporal Marmor U	.40	1.00
36	Corporal Midge U	.40	1.00
37	Critical Error Revealed C	.12	.30
38	Darth Vader's Lightsaber R	1.00	2.50
39	Death Star II R	1.25	3.00
40	Death Star II: Capacitors C	.12	.30
41	Death Star II: Coolant Shaft C	.12	.30
42	Death Star II: Docking Bay C	.12	.30
43	Death Star II: Reactor Core C	.12	.30
44	Death Star II: Throne Room R	1.00	2.50
45	Defiance R	1.25	3.00
46	Desperate Counter C	.12	.30
47	Dominator R	1.00	2.50
48	DS-181-3 U	.40	1.00
49	DS-181-4 U	.40	1.00
50	Emperor Palpatine UR	30.00	60.00
51	Emperor's Personal Shuttle R	1.00	2.50
52	Emperor's Power U	.40	1.00
53	Endor Shield U	.40	1.00
54	Enhanced Proton Torpedoes C	.12	.30
55	Fighter Cover R	2.00	5.00
56	Fighters Coming In R	1.00	2.50
57	First Officer Thaneespi R	1.00	2.50
58	Flagship Executor R	1.25	3.00
59	Flagship Operations R	1.00	2.50
60	Force Lightning R	2.00	5.00

61	Force Pike C	.12	.30
62	Gall C	.12	.30
63	General Calrissian R	1.00	2.50
64	General Walex Blissex U	.40	1.00
65	Gold Squadron 1 R	1.00	2.50
66	Gray Squadron 1 U	.40	1.00
67	Gray Squadron 2 U	.40	1.00
68	Gray Squadron Y-wing Pilot C	.12	.30
69	Green Leader R	1.00	2.50
70	Green Squadron 1 R	1.00	2.50
71	Green Squadron 3 R	1.00	2.50
72	Green Squadron A-wing R	1.25	3.00
73	Green Squadron Pilot C	.12	.30
74	Head Back To The Surface C	.12	.30
75	Heading For The Medical Frigate C	.12	.30
76	Heavy Turbolaser Battery DARK C	.12	.30
77	Heavy Turbolaser Battery LIGHT C	.12	.30
78	Home One R	4.00	10.00
79	Home One: Docking Bay C	.12	.30
80	Home One: War Room R	1.25	3.00
81	Honor Of The Jedi U	.40	1.00
82	I Feel The Conflict U	.40	1.00
83	I'll Take The Leader R	2.50	6.00
84	I'm With You Too R	1.50	4.00
85	Imperial Command R	4.00	10.00
86	Inconsequential Losses C	.12	.30
87	Independence R	1.25	3.00
88	Insertion Planning C	.12	.30
89	Insignificant Rebellion U	.40	1.00
90	Intensify The Forward Batteries R	1.00	2.50
91	Janus Greejatus R	1.00	2.50
92	Judicator R	1.50	4.00
93	Karie Neth U	.40	1.00
94	Keir Santage U	.40	1.00
95	Kin Kian U	.40	1.00
96	Launching The Assault R	1.00	2.50
97	Leave Them To Me C	.12	.30
98	Let's Keep A Little Optimism Here C	.12	.30
99	Liberty R	1.25	3.00
100	Lieutenant Blount R	1.00	2.50
101	Lieutenant Endicott U	.40	1.00
102	Lieutenant Hebsly U	.40	1.00
103	Lieutenant s'Too Vees U	.40	1.00
104	Lieutenant Telsij U	.40	1.00
105	Lord Vader R	10.00	20.00
106	Luke Skywalker, Jedi Knight UR	30.00	60.00
107	Luke's Lightsaber R	1.50	4.00
108	Luminous U	.40	1.00
109	Major Haashin U	.40	1.00
110	Major Mianda U	.40	1.00
111	Major Olander Brit U	.40	1.00
112	Major Panno U	.40	1.00
113	Major Rhymer U	.40	1.00
114	Major Turr Phennir U	.40	1.00
115	Masanya R	1.50	4.00
116	Menace Fades C	.12	.30
117	Mobilization Points C	.12	.30
118	Moff Jerjerrod R	1.00	2.50
119	Mon Calamari DARK C	.12	.30
120	Mon Calamari LIGHT C	.12	.30
121	Mon Calamari Star Cruiser R	1.25	3.00
122	Myn Kyneugh R	1.00	2.50
123	Nebulon-B Frigate U	.40	1.00
124	Nien Nunb R	1.25	3.00
125	Obsidian 10 U	.40	1.00
126	Onyx 1 R	1.25	3.00
127	Onyx 2 U	.40	1.00
128	Operational As Planned C	.12	.30
129	Orbital Mine C	.12	.30
130	Our Only Hope U	.40	1.00
131	Overseeing It Personally R	1.00	2.50
132	Prepared Defenses C	.12	.30
133	Rebel Leadership R	3.00	8.00
134	Red Squadron 1 R	1.00	2.50
135	Red Squadron 4 U	.40	1.00
136	Red Squadron 7 U	.40	1.00
137	Rise, My Friend R	1.00	2.50
138	Royal Escort C	.12	.30
139	Royal Guard C	.12	.30
140	Saber 1 R	6.00	15.00
141	Saber 2 U	.40	1.00
142	Saber 3 U	.40	1.00
143	Saber 4 U	.40	1.00
144	Scimitar 1 U	.40	1.00
145	Scimitar 2 U	.40	1.00
146	Scimitar Squadron TIE C	.12	.30
147	Scythe 1 U	.40	1.00
148	Scythe 3 U	.40	1.00
149	Scythe Squadron TIE C	.12	.30
150	SFS L-s7.2 TIE Cannon C	.12	.30
151	Sim Aloo R	1.00	2.50

152 Something Special Planned For Them C	.12	.30
153 Squadron Assignments C	.12	.30
154 Staging Areas C	.12	.30
155 Strike Planning R	1.00	2.50
156 Strikeforce C	.12	.30
157 Sullust DARK C	.12	.30
158 Sullust LIGHT C	.12	.30
159 Superficial Damage C	.12	.30
160 Superlaser Mark II U	.40	1.00
161 Taking Them With Us R	1.25	3.00
162 Tala 1 R	1.00	2.50
163 Tala 2 R	1.00	2.50
164 Ten Numb R	1.00	2.50
165 That Thing Is Operational R	1.00	2.50
166 The Emperor's Shield R	1.00	2.50
167 The Emperor's Sword R	1.00	2.50
168 The Time For Our Attack Has Come C	.12	.30
169 The Way Of Things U	.40	1.00
170 There Is Good In Him	1.00	2.50
I Can Save Him R		
171 Thunderflare R	1.00	2.50
172 TIE Interceptor C	.12	.30
173 Twilight Is Upon Me R	1.00	2.50
174 Tycho Celchu R	1.25	3.00
175 Visage R	1.00	2.50
176 We're In Attack Position Now R	2.50	6.00
177 Wedge Antilles, Red Squadron Leader R	1.50	4.00
178 You Cannot Hide Forever U	.40	1.00
179 You Must Confront Vader R	1.50	4.00
180 Young Fool U	1.00	2.50
181 Your Destiny C	.12	.30
182 Your Insight Serves You Well U	.40	1.00

2000 Star Wars Jabba's Palace Sealed Deck

COMPLETE SET (20)	5.00	12.00
RELEASE DATE FALL, 2000		
1 Agents In The Court	.40	1.00
No Love For The Empire PM		
2 Hutt Influence PM	.40	1.00
3 Jabba's Palace: Antechamber PM	.40	1.00
4 Jabba's Palace: Lower Passages PM	.40	1.00
5 Lando With Vibro-Ax PM	.40	1.00
6 Let Them Make The First Move / My Kind Of Scum	.40	1.00
Fearless And Inventive PM		
7 Mercenary Pilot PM	.40	1.00
8 Mighty Jabba PM	.40	1.00
9 No Escape PM	.40	1.00
10 Ounee Ta PM	.40	1.00
11 Palace Raider PM	.40	1.00
12 Power Of The Hutt PM	.40	1.00
13 Racing Skiff DARK PM	.40	1.00
14 Racing Skiff LIGHT PM	.40	1.00
15 Seeking An Audience PM	.40	1.00
16 Stun Blaster DARK PM	.40	1.00
17 Stun Blaster LIGHT PM	.40	1.00
18 Tatooine: Desert Heart PM	.40	1.00
19 Tatooine: Hutt Trade Route (Desert) PM	.40	1.00
20 Underworld Contacts PM	.40	1.00

2000 Star Wars Reflections II

Grand Admiral Thrawn
POWER 2   ABILITY 4   FORCE-SENSITIVE

COMPLETE SET (54)	20.00	50.00
BOOSTER BOX (30 PACKS)	150.00	250.00
BOOSTER PACK (11 CARDS)	5.00	10.00
RELEASED IN DECEMBER 2000		
1 There Is No Try and	.60	1.50
Oppressive Enforcement PM		

2 Abyssin Ornament and	.40	1.00
Wounded Wookiee PM		
3 Agents Of Black Sun	.40	1.00
Vengence Of The Dark Prince PM		
4 Alter and Collateral Damage PM	.60	1.50
5 Alter and Friendly Fire PM	.60	1.50
6 Arica PM	2.00	5.00
7 Artoo and Threepio PM	.60	1.50
8 Black Sun Fleet PM	.40	1.00
9 Captain Gilad Pellaeon PM	.60	1.50
10 Chewbacca, Protector PM	.60	1.50
11 Control and Set For Stun PM	.60	1.50
12 Control and Tunnel Vision PM	1.00	2.50
13 Corran Horn PM	1.50	4.00
14 Dark Maneuvers and Tallon Roll PM	1.00	2.50
15 Dash Rendar PM	1.25	3.00
16 Defensive Fire and Hutt Smooch PM	.40	1.00
17 Do, Or Do Not and Wise Advice PM	.40	1.00
18 Dr Evazan and Ponda Baba PM	.40	1.00
19 Evader and Monnok PM	.60	1.50
20 Ghhhk and Those Rebels	.40	1.00
Won't Escape Us PM		
21 Grand Admiral Thrawn PM	2.50	6.00
22 Guri PM	1.25	3.00
23 Houjix and Out Of Nowhere PM	.60	1.50
24 Jabba's Prize PM	.40	1.00
25 Kir Kanos PM	.40	1.00
26 LE-BO2D9 [Leebo] PM	.40	1.00
27 Luke Skywalker, Rebel Scout PM	1.00	2.50
28 Mercenary Armor PM	.40	1.00
29 Mirax Terrik PM	.60	1.50
30 Nar Shaddaa Wind Chimes	.40	1.00
and Out Of Somewhere PM		
31 No Questions Asked PM	.40	1.00
32 Obi-Wan's Journal PM	.40	1.00
33 Ommni Box and It's Worse PM	.40	1.00
34 Out of Commission and	1.00	2.50
Transmission Terminated PM		
35 Outrider PM	.60	1.50
36 Owen Lars and Beru Lars PM	.40	1.00
37 Path Of Least	.40	1.00
Resistance and Revealed PM		
38 Prince Xizor PM	1.50	4.00
39 Pulsar Skate PM	.40	1.00
40 Sense and Recoil In Fear PM	.60	1.50
41 Sense and Uncertain Is The Future PM	.60	1.50
42 Shocking Information and Grimtaash PM	.40	1.00
43 Sniper and Dark Strike PM	.40	1.00
44 Snoova PM	1.00	2.50
45 Sorry About The Mess	.60	1.50
and Blaster Proficiency PM		
46 Stinger PM	.40	1.00
47 Sunsdown and	.40	1.00
Too Cold For Speeders PM		
48 Talon Karrde PM	.60	1.50
49 The Bith Shuffle and	.40	1.00
Desperate Reach PM		
50 The Emperor PM	1.50	4.00
51 Vigo PM	1.50	4.00
52 Virago PM	.40	1.00
53 Watch Your Step	.40	1.00
This Place Can Be A Little Rough PM		
54 Yoda Stew and You Do Have Your Moments PM	.40	1.00

2000 Star Wars Third Anthology

Artoo-Detoo In Red 5   0 or 7
STARFIGHTER: X-WING
POWER 3   MANEUVER 4   HYPERSPEED 5

COMPLETE SET (6)	4.00	10.00
RELEASED IN 2000		

1 A New Secret Base PM	1.00	2.50
2 Artoo-Detoo In Red 5 PM	1.00	2.50
3 Echo Base Garrison PM	1.00	2.50
4 Massassi Base Operations PM	1.00	2.50
One In A Million PM		
5 Prisoner 2187 PM	1.00	2.50
6 Set Your Course For Alderaan PM	1.00	2.50
The Ultimate Power In The Universe PM		

2001 Star Wars Coruscant

Darth Maul, Young Apprentice
POWER 7   ABILITY 6   DARK JEDI

COMPLETE SET (188)	120.00	250.00
BOOSTER BOX (30 PACKS)	300.00	400.00
BOOSTER PACK (11 CARDS)	12.00	15.00
RELEASED IN AUGUST 2001		
1 A Tragedy Has Occurred U	.40	1.00
2 A Vergence In The Force U	.40	1.00
3 Accepting Trade Federation Control U	.40	1.00
4 Aks Moe R	1.25	3.00
5 All Wings Report In and Darklighter Spin R	6.00	15.00
6 Allegations Of Corruption U	.40	1.00
7 Alter DARK U	.40	1.00
8 Alter LIGHT U	.40	1.00
9 Another Pathetic Lifeform U	.40	1.00
10 Are You Brain Dead?! R	1.50	4.00
11 Ascertaining The Truth U	.40	1.00
12 Baseless Accusations C	.12	.30
13 Baskol Yeesrim U	.40	1.00
14 Battle Droid Blaster Rifle C	.12	.30
15 Battle Order and First Strike R	1.00	2.50
16 Battle Plan and Draw Their Fire R	1.50	4.00
17 Begin Landing Your Troops U	.40	1.00
18 Blockade Flagship: Bridge R	3.00	8.00
19 Captain Madakor R	1.00	2.50
20 Captain Panaka R	1.00	2.50
21 Chokk U	.40	1.00
22 Control DARK U	.40	1.00
23 Control LIGHT U	.40	1.00
24 Coruscant DARK C	.12	.30
25 Coruscant LIGHT C	.12	.30
26 Coruscant Guard DARK C	.12	.30
27 Coruscant Guard LIGHT C	.12	.30
28 Coruscant: Docking Bay DARK C	.12	.30
29 Coruscant: Docking Bay LIGHT C	.12	.30
30 Coruscant: Galactic Senate DARK C	.12	.30
31 Coruscant: Galactic Senate LIGHT C	.12	.30
32 Coruscant: Jedi Council Chamber R	3.00	8.00
33 Credits Will Do Fine C	.12	.30
34 Darth Maul, Young Apprentice R	15.00	30.00
35 Daultay Dofine R	1.25	3.00
36 Depa Billaba R	1.25	3.00
37 Destroyer Droid R	12.00	25.00
38 Dioxis R	1.00	2.50
39 Do They Have A Code Clearance? R	1.00	2.50
40 Droid Starfighter C	.12	.30
41 Drop! U	.40	1.00
42 Edcel Bar Gane C	.12	.30
43 Enter The Bureaucrat U	.40	1.00
44 Establish Control U	.40	1.00
45 Free Ride and Endor Celebration R	1.50	4.00
46 Freon Drevan U	.40	1.00
47 Gardulla The Hutt U	.40	1.00
48 Graxol Kelvyyn U	.40	1.00
49 Grotto Werribee R	1.25	3.00
50 Gungan Warrior C	.12	.30
51 Horox Ryyder C	.12	.30
52 I Will Not Defer U	.40	1.00

#	Card		
53	Iíve Decided To Go Back C	.12	.30
54	Imperial Arrest Order and Secret Plans R	3.00	8.00
55	Imperial Artillery R	3.00	8.00
56	Inconsequential Barriers C	.12	.30
57	Insurrection and Aim High R	2.50	6.00
58	Jawa DARK C	.12	.30
59	Jawa LIGHT C	.12	.30
60	Keder The Black R	1.00	2.50
61	Ki-Adi-Mundi U	.40	1.00
62	Kill Them Immediately C	.12	.30
63	Lana Dobreed U	.40	1.00
64	Laser Cannon Battery U	.40	1.00
65	Liana Merian U	.40	1.00
66	Lieutenant Williams U	.40	1.00
67	Little Real Power C	.12	.30
68	Lott Dod R	1.25	3.00
69	Mace Windu R	10.00	20.00
70	Malastare DARK U	.40	1.00
71	Malastare LIGHT U	.40	1.00
72	Mas Amedda U	.40	1.00
73	Master Qui-Gon R	3.00	8.00
74	Masterful Move and Endor Occupation R	2.00	5.00
75	Maul Strikes R	2.00	5.00
76	Maulís Sith Infiltrator R	3.00	8.00
77	Might Of The Republic R	2.50	6.00
78	Mind Tricks Donít Work On Me U	.40	1.00
79	Mindful Of The Future C	.12	.30
80	Motion Supported U	.40	1.00
81	Murr Danod R	1.00	2.50
82	My Lord, Is That Legal? U	.40	1.00
	I Will Make It Legal U		
83	My Loyal Bodyguard U	.40	1.00
84	Naboo Blaster C	.12	.30
85	Naboo Blaster Rifle DARK C	.12	.30
86	Naboo Blaster Rifle LIGHT C	.12	.30
87	Naboo Defense Fighter C	.12	.30
88	Naboo Fighter Pilot C	.12	.30
89	Naboo Security Officer Blaster C	.12	.30
90	Naboo DARK U	.40	1.00
91	Naboo LIGHT U	.40	1.00
92	Naboo: Battle Plains DARK C	.12	.30
93	Naboo: Battle Plains LIGHT C	.12	.30
94	Naboo: Swamp DARK C	.12	.30
95	Naboo: Swamp LIGHT C	.12	.30
96	Naboo: Theed Palace	.12	.30
	Courtyard DARK C		
97	Naboo: Theed Palace	.12	.30
	Courtyard LIGHT C		
98	Naboo: Theed Palace	.12	.30
	Docking Bay DARK C		
99	Naboo: Theed Palace	.12	.30
	Docking Bay LIGHT C		
100	Naboo: Theed Palace	.12	.30
	Throne Room DARK C		
101	Naboo: Theed Palace	.12	.30
	Throne Room LIGHT C		
102	Neimoidian Advisor U	.40	1.00
103	Neimoidian Pilot C	.12	.30
104	New Leadership Is Needed C	.12	.30
105	No Civility, Only Politics C	.12	.30
106	No Money, No Parts, No Deal! U	.40	1.00
	Youíre A Slave? U		
107	Nute Gunray R	1.00	2.50
108	Odin Nesloor U	.40	1.00
109	On The Payroll Of The Trade Federation C	.12	.30
110	Orn Free Taa C	.12	.30
111	Our Blockade Is Perfectly Legal U	.40	1.00
112	P-59 R	3.00	8.00
113	P-60 R	1.50	4.00
114	Panakaís Blaster R	1.25	3.00
115	Passel Argente C	.12	.30
116	Phylo Gandish R	1.50	4.00
117	Plea To The Court U	.40	1.00
118	Plead My Case To The Senate U	.40	1.00
	Sanity And Compassion U		
119	Plo Koon R	3.00	8.00
120	Queen Amidala, Ruler Of Naboo R	5.00	10.00
121	Queenís Royal Starship R	1.25	3.00
122	Radiant VII R	1.50	4.00
123	Rebel Artillery R	3.00	8.00
124	Republic Cruiser C	.12	.30
125	Reveal Ourselves To The Jedi C	.12	.30
126	Ric Olie R	1.00	2.50
127	Rune Haako R	1.00	2.50
128	Sabe R	1.25	3.00
129	Sache U	.40	1.00
130	Secure Route U	.40	1.00
131	Security Battle Droid C	.12	.30
132	Security Control U	.40	1.00
133	Sei Taria U	.40	1.00

#	Card		
134	Senator Palpatine	3.00	8.00
	(head and shoulders) R		
135	Senator Palpatine (head shot) R	15.00	30.00
136	Sense DARK U	.40	1.00
137	Sense LIGHT U	.40	1.00
138	Short Range Fighters and	2.50	6.00
	Watch Your Back! R		
139	Speak With The Jedi Council R	3.00	8.00
140	Squabbling Delegates R	1.25	3.00
141	Stay Here, Where Itís Safe C	.12	.30
142	Supreme Chancellor Valorum R	1.00	2.50
143	Tatooine DARK U	.40	1.00
144	Tatooine LIGHT U	.40	1.00
145	Tatooine: Marketplace DARK C	.12	.30
146	Tatooine: Marketplace LIGHT C	.12	.30
147	Tatooine: Mos Espa Docking Bay DARK C	.12	.30
148	Tatooine: Mos Espa Docking Bay LIGHT C	.12	.30
149	Tatooine: Wattoís Junkyard DARK C	.12	.30
150	Tatooine: Wattoís Junkyard LIGHT C	.12	.30
151	TC-14 R	1.00	2.50
152	Televan Koreyy R	1.00	2.50
153	Tendau Bendon U	.40	1.00
154	Tey How U	.40	1.00
155	The Gravest Of Circumstances U	.40	1.00
156	The Hyperdrive Generatorís Gone	.40	1.00
	Weíll Need A New One U		
157	The Phantom Menace R	5.00	10.00
158	The Point Is Conceded C	.12	.30
159	They Will Be No Match For You R	1.00	2.50
160	Theyíre Still Coming Through! U	.40	1.00
161	This Is Outrageous! U	.40	1.00
162	Thrown Back C	.12	.30
163	Tikkes C	.12	.30
164	Toonbuck Toora U	.40	1.00
165	Trade Federation Battleship U	.40	1.00
166	Trade Federation Droid Control Ship R	1.25	3.00
167	Tusken Raider C	.12	.30
168	Vote Now! DARK R	1.00	2.50
169	Vote Now! LIGHT R	1.25	3.00
170	We Must Accelerate Our Plans R	10.00	20.00
171	We Wish To Board At Once R	2.00	5.00
172	Weíre Leaving C	.12	.30
173	Wipe Them Out, All Of Them U	.40	1.00
174	Yade Mírak U	.40	1.00
175	YanE U	.40	1.00
176	Yarua U	.40	1.00
177	Yeb Yeb Ademíthorn C	.12	.30
178	Yoda, Senior Council Member R	2.50	6.00
179	You Cannot Hide Forever	2.50	6.00
	and Mobilization Points R		
180	You've Got A Lot Of	1.25	3.00
	Guts Coming Here R		
181	Your Insight Serves You Well	1.00	2.50
	and Staging Areas R		
182	Coruscant Dark Side List 1	.12	.30
183	Coruscant Dark Side List 2	.12	.30
184	Coruscant Light Side List 1	.12	.30
185	Coruscant Light Side List 2	.12	.30
186	Coruscant Rule Card 1	.12	.30
187	Coruscant Rule Card 2	.12	.30
188	Coruscant Rule Card 3	.12	.30

2001 Star Wars Reflections III

COMPLETE SET (96)		80.00	150.00
BOOSTER BOX (30 PACKS)		250.00	350.00
BOOSTER PACK (11 CARDS)		7.50	15.00

RELEASED IN 2001			
1	A Close Race PM	1.00	2.50
2	A Remote Planet PM	1.00	2.50
3	A Tragedy Has Occured PM	1.25	3.00
4	A Useless Gesture PM	1.00	2.50
5	Aim High PM	1.25	3.00
6	Allegations of Coruption PM	1.00	2.50
7	An Unusual Amount Of Fear PM	1.00	2.50
8	Another Pathetic Lifeform PM	1.00	2.50
9	Armarment Dismantled PM	1.00	2.50
10	Battle Order PM	1.00	2.50
11	Battle Plan PM	1.25	3.00
12	Bib Fortuna PM	1.00	2.50
13	Blizzard 4 PM	2.00	5.00
14	Blockade Flagship: Hallway PM	1.00	2.50
15	Blow Parried PM	1.00	2.50
16	Boba Fett, Bounty Hunter PM	6.00	12.00
17	Chewie, Enraged PM	1.50	4.00
18	Clinging To The Edge PM	1.00	2.50
19	Colo Claw Fish DARK PM	1.00	2.50
20	Colo Claw Fish LIGHT PM	1.00	2.50
21	Come Here You Big Coward PM	1.25	3.00
22	Conduct Your Search PM	1.25	3.00
23	Crossfire PM	1.00	2.50
24	Dark Rage PM	1.00	2.50
25	Darth Maulís Demise PM	1.00	2.50
26	Deep Hatred PM	1.00	2.50
27	Desperate Times PM	1.00	2.50
28	Diversionary Tactics PM	1.00	2.50
29	Do They Have A Code Clearance? PM	1.25	3.00
30	Do, Or Do Not PM	1.00	2.50
31	Donít Do That Again PM	1.00	2.50
32	Echo Base Sensors PM	1.25	3.00
33	Energy Walls DARK PM	1.00	2.50
34	Energy Walls LIGHT PM	1.00	2.50
35	Ewok Celebration PM	1.00	2.50
36	Fall Of A Jedi PM	1.00	2.50
37	Fanfare PM	1.00	2.50
38	Fear Is My Ally PM	1.00	2.50
39	Force Push PM	1.25	3.00
40	Han, Chewie, and The Falcon PM	6.00	12.00
41	He Can Go About His Business PM	1.00	2.50
42	Horace Vancil PM	1.00	2.50
43	Inner Strength PM	1.00	2.50
44	Jabba Desilijic Tiure PM	1.00	2.50
45	Jar Jaris Electropole PM	1.00	2.50
46	Jedi Leap PM	1.00	2.50
47	Lando Calrissian, Scoundrel PM	2.00	5.00
48	Landoís Not A System, Heís A Man PM	1.00	2.50
49	Leave them to Me PM	1.00	2.50
50	Leia, Rebel Princess PM	2.50	6.00
51	Letís Keep A Little Optimism Here PM	1.00	2.50
52	Lord Maul PM	7.50	15.00
53	Maulís Double-Bladed Lightsaber PM	2.00	5.00
54	Naboo: Theed Palace	1.00	2.50
	Generator Core DARK PM		
55	Naboo: Theed Palace	1.00	2.50
	Generator Core LIGHT PM		
56	Naboo: Theed Palace	1.00	2.50
	Generator DARK PM		
57	Naboo: Theed Palace	1.00	2.50
	Generator LIGHT PM		
58	No Escape PM	1.00	2.50
59	No Match For A Sith PM	1.00	2.50
60	Obi-Wan Kenobi, Jedi Knight PM	1.50	4.00
61	Obi-Wanís Lightsaber PM	1.00	2.50
62	Only Jedi Carry That Weapon PM	1.00	2.50
63	Opee Sea Killer DARK PM	1.00	2.50
64	Opee Sea Killer LIGHT PM	1.00	2.50
65	Oppressive Enforcement PM	1.00	2.50
66	Ounee Ta PM	1.00	2.50
67	Planetary Defenses PM	1.00	2.50
68	Prepare For A Surface Attack PM	1.00	2.50
69	Qui-Gon Jinn, Jedi Master PM	2.50	6.00
70	Qui-Gonís End PM	1.25	3.00
71	Reistance PM	1.00	2.50
72	Sando Aqua Monster DARK PM	1.00	2.50
73	Sando Aqua Monster LIGHT PM	1.00	2.50
74	Secret Plans PM	1.00	2.50
75	Sio Bibble PM	1.00	2.50
76	Stormtrooper Garrison PM	5.00	10.00
77	Strike Blockaded PM	1.00	2.50
78	The Ebb Of Battle PM	1.00	2.50
79	The Hutts Are Gangsters PM	1.00	2.50
80	There Is No Try PM	1.25	3.00
81	They Must Never Again	1.00	2.50
	Leave This City PM		
82	Thok and Thug PM	1.00	2.50
83	Through The Corridor PM	1.00	2.50

84 Ultimatum PM	1.00	2.50
85 Unsalvageable PM	1.00	2.50
86 Weíll Let Fate-a Decide, Huh? PM	1.00	2.50
87 Weapon Of A Fallen Mentor PM	1.00	2.50
88 Weapon Of A Sith PM	1.00	2.50
89 Where Are Those Droidekas?! PM	1.00	2.50
90 Wipe Them Out, All Of Them PM	1.00	2.50
91 Wise Advice PM	1.00	2.50
92 Yoda, Master Of The Force PM	5.00	10.00
93 You Cannot Hide Forever PM	1.00	2.50
94 Youíve Never Won A Race? PM	1.00	2.50
95 Your Insight Serves You Well PM	1.00	2.50
96 Your Ship? PM	1.25	3.00

2001 Star Wars Tatooine

COMPLETE SET (95)	25.00	60.00
BOOSTER BOX (30 PACKS)	50.00	100.00
BOOSTER PACK (11 CARDS)	2.50	5.00
RELEASED IN MAY 2001		

1 A Jediís Concentration C	.12	.30
2 A Jediís Focus C	.12	.30
3 A Jediís Patience C	.12	.30
4 A Jediís Resilience U	.40	1.00
5 A Million Voices Crying Out R	.75	2.00
6 A Step Backward U	.40	1.00
7 Anakinís Podracer R	.75	2.00
8 Aurra Sing R	1.50	4.00
9 Ben Quadinarosí Podracer C	.12	.30
10 Boonta Eve Podrace DARK R	.75	2.50
11 Boonta Eve Podrace LIGHT R	.75	2.00
12 Brisky Morning Munchen R	.75	2.00
13 Caldera Righim C	.12	.30
14 Changing The Odds C	.12	.30
15 Daroe R	.75	2.00
16 Darth Maul R	1.50	4.00
17 Deneb Both U	.40	1.00
18 Donít Do That Again C	.12	.30
19 Dud Boltís Podracer C	.12	.30
20 Either Way, You Win U	.40	1.00
21 End Of A Reign R	.75	2.00
22 Entering The Arena U	.40	1.00
23 Eopie C	.12	.30
24 Eventually Youíll Lose U	.40	1.00
25 Fanfare C	.12	.30
26 Gamall Wironicc U	.40	1.00
27 Ghana Gleemort U	.40	1.00
28 Gragra U	.40	1.00
29 Great Shot, Kid! R	.75	2.00
30 Grugnak U	.40	1.00
31 His Name Is Anakin C	.12	.30
32 Hit Racer U	.40	1.00
33 I Canít Believe Heís Gone C	.12	.30
34 I Did It! R	.75	2.00
35 I Will Find Them Quickly, Master R	.75	2.00
36 Iím Sorry R	.75	2.00
37 If The Trace Was Correct U	.40	1.00
38 Jar Jar Binks R	.75	2.00
39 Jedi Escape C	.12	.30
40 Join Me! U	.40	1.00
41 Keeping The Empire Out Forever R	.75	2.00
42 Lathe U	.40	1.00
43 Lightsaber Parry C	.12	.30
44 Loci Rosen U	.40	1.00
45 Losing Track C	.12	.30
46 Maulís Electrobinoculars C	.12	.30
47 Maulís Lightsaber R	.75	2.00

48 Neck And Neck U	.40	1.00
49 Ni Chuba Na?? C	.12	.30
50 Obi-Wan Kenobi, Padawan Learner R	1.00	2.50
51 Padme Naberrie R	2.00	5.00
52 Pit Crews U	.40	1.00
53 Pit Droid C	.12	.30
54 Podrace Prep U	.40	1.00
55 Podracer Collision U	.40	1.00
56 Quietly Observing U	.40	1.00
57 Qui-Gon Jinn R	1.50	4.00
58 Qui-Gon Jinnís Lightsaber R	1.00	2.50
59 Rachalt Hyst U	.40	1.00
60 Sebulba R	.75	2.00
61 Sebulbaís Podracer R	.75	2.00
62 Shmi Skywalker R	.75	2.00
63 Sith Fury C	.12	.30
64 Sith Probe Droid R	1.00	2.50
65 Start Your Engines! U	.40	1.00
66 Tatooine: City Outskirts U	.40	1.00
67 Tatooine: Desert Landing Site R	.75	2.00
68 Tatooine: Mos Espa DARK C	.12	.30
69 Tatooine: Mos Espa LIGHT C	.12	.30
70 Tatooine: Podrace Arena DARK C	.12	.30
71 Tatooine: Podrace Arena LIGHT C	.12	.30
72 Tatooine: Podrace Bay C	.12	.30
73 Tatooine: Slave Quarters U	.40	1.00
74 Teemto Pagaliesí Podracer C	.12	.30
75 The Camp C	.12	.30
76 The Shield Is Down! R	.75	2.00
77 There Is No Conflict C	.12	.30
78 Threepio With His Parts Showing R	1.25	3.00
79 Too Close For Comfort U	.40	1.00
80 Vaderís Anger C	.12	.30
81 Watto R	1.25	3.00
82 Wattoís Box C	.12	.30
83 Wattoís Chance Cube U	.40	1.00
84 We Shall Double Our Efforts! R	.75	2.00
85 What Was It U	.40	1.00
86 Yotts Orren U	.40	1.00
87 You May Start Your Landing R	.75	2.00
88 You Swindled Me! U	.40	1.00
89 You Want This, Donít You? C	.12	.30
90 Youíll Find íim Full Of Surprises U	.40	1.00
91 Tatooine Dark Side List	.12	.30
92 Tatooine Light Side List	.12	.30
93 Tatooine Rule Card 1	.12	.30
94 Tatooine Rule Card 2	.12	.30
95 Tatooine Rule Card 3	.12	.30

2001 Star Wars Theed Palace

COMPLETE SET (121)	80.00	150.00
BOOSTER BOX (30 PACKS)	400.00	500.00
BOOSTER PACK (11 CARDS)	15.00	20.00
RELEASED IN DECEMBER 2001		
FINAL EXPANSION PRODUCT BY DECIPHER		

1 3B3-10 U	.30	.75
2 3B3-1204 U	.30	.75
3 3B3-21 U	.30	.75
4 3B3-888 U	.30	.75
5 AAT Assault Leader R	1.00	2.50
6 AAT Laser Cannon U	.30	.75
7 Activate The Droids C	.12	.30
8 After Her! R	.75	2.00
9 Amidalaís Blaster R	.75	2.00
10 Armored Attack Tank U	.30	.75
11 Artoo, Brave Little Droid R	1.50	4.00
12 Ascension Guns U	.30	.75

13 At Last We Are Getting Results C	.12	.30
14 Battle Droid Officer C	.12	.30
15 Battle Droid Pilot C	.12	.30
16 Big Boomers! C	.12	.30
17 Blockade Flaghip R	1.50	4.00
18 Blockade Flagship: Docking Bay DARK U	.30	.75
19 Blockade Flagship: Docking Bay LIGHT U	.30	.75
20 Bok Askol U	.30	.75
21 Booma C	.12	.30
22 Boss Nass R	1.25	3.00
23 Bravo 1 R	.75	2.00
24 Bravo 2 U	.30	.75
25 Bravo 3 U	.30	.75
26 Bravo 4 U	.30	.75
27 Bravo 5 U	.30	.75
28 Bravo Fighter R	.75	2.00
29 Captain Tarpals R	.75	2.00
30 Captain Tarpalsí Electropole C	.12	.30
31 Captian Daultay Dofine R	.75	2.00
32 Cease Fire! C	.12	.30
33 Corporal Rushing U	.30	.75
34 Dams Denna U	.30	.75
35 Darth Maul With Lightsaber R	12.00	25.00
36 Darth Sidious R	25.00	50.00
37 DFS Squadron Starfighter C	.12	.30
38 DFS-1015 U	.30	.75
39 DFS-1308 R	.75	2.00
40 DFS-327 C	.12	.30
41 Droid Racks R	1.25	3.00
42 Droid Starfighter Laser Cannons C	.12	.30
43 Drop Your Weapons C	.12	.30
44 Electropole C	.12	.30
45 Energy Shell Launchers C	.12	.30
46 Fambaa C	.12	.30
47 Fighters Straight Ahead U	.30	.75
48 General Jar Jar R	1.25	3.00
49 Get To Your Ships! C	.12	.30
50 Gian Speeder C	.12	.30
51 Gimme A Lift! R	.75	2.00
52 Gungan Energy Shield C	.12	.30
53 Gungan General C	.12	.30
54 Gungan Guard C	.12	.30
55 Halt! C	.12	.30
56 Iíll Try Spinning R	.75	2.00
57 Infantry Battle Droid C	.12	.30
58 Invasion / In Complete Control U	.30	.75
59 Itís On Automatic Pilot C	.12	.30
60 Jerus Jannick U	.30	.75
61 Kaadu C	.12	.30
62 Letís Go Left R	.75	2.00
63 Lieutenant Arven Wendik U	.30	.75
64 Lieutenant Chamberlyn U	.30	.75
65 Lieutenant Rya Kirsch U	.30	.75
66 Mace Windu, Jedi Master R	7.50	15.00
67 Master, Destroyers! R	1.00	2.50
68 Multi Troop Transport U	.30	.75
69 Naboo Celebration R	.75	2.00
70 Naboo Occupation R	1.00	2.50
71 Naboo: Boss Nassís Chambers U	.30	.75
72 Naboo: Otoh Gunga Entrance U	.30	.75
73 Naboo: Theed Palace Hall U	.30	.75
74 Naboo: Theed Palace Hallway U	.30	.75
75 No Giben Up, General Jar Jar! R	.75	2.00
76 Nothing Can Get Through Are Shield R	1.00	2.50
77 Nute Gunray, Neimoidian Viceroy R	2.00	5.00
78 Officer Dolphe U	.30	.75
79 Officer Ellberger U	.30	.75
80 Officer Perosei U	.30	.75
81 OOM-9 U	.30	.75
82 Open Fire! C	.12	.30
83 OWO-1 With Backup R	1.25	3.00
84 Panaka, Protector Of The Queen R	2.50	6.00
85 Proton Torpedoes C	.12	.30
86 Queen Amidala R	10.00	20.00
87 Qui-Gon Jinn With Lightsaber R	7.50	15.00
88 Rayno Vaca U	.30	.75
89 Rep Been U	.30	.75
90 Ric Olie, Bravo Leader R	.75	2.00
91 Rolling, Rolling, Rolling R	1.00	2.50
92 Royal Naboo Security Officer C	.12	.30
93 Rune Haako, Legal Counsel R	1.25	3.00
94 Senate Hovercam DARK R	1.00	2.50
95 Senate Hovercam LIGHT R	1.00	2.50
96 Sil Unch U	.30	.75
97 Single Trooper Aerial Platform C	.12	.30
98 SSA-1015 U	.30	.75
99 SSA-306 U	.30	.75
100 SSA-719 R	1.25	3.00
101 STAP Blaster Cannons C	.12	.30

102 Steady, Steady C	.12	.30
103 Take Them Away C	.12	.30
104 Take This! C	.12	.30
105 Tank Commander C	.12	.30
106 The Deflector Shield Is Too Strong R	.75	2.00
107 There They Are! U	.30	.75
108 They Win This Round R	.75	2.00
109 This Is Not Good C	.12	.30
110 Trade Federation Landing Craft C	.12	.30
111 TT-6 R	1.00	2.50
112 TT-9 R	.75	2.00
113 We Didnit Hit It C	.12	.30
114 We Donit Have Time For This R	1.00	2.50
115 We Have A Plan	.12	.30
They Will Be Lost And Confused C		
116 Weire Hit Artoo C	.12	.30
117 Wesa Gotta Grand Army C	.12	.30
118 Wesa Ready To Do Our-sa Part C	.12	.30
119 Whoooo! C	.12	.30
120 Theed Palace Dark Side List	.12	.30
121 Theed Palace Light Side List	.12	.30

2002 Star Wars Attack of the Clones

COMPLETE SET (180)	30.00	80.00
BOOSTER BOX (36 PACKS)	20.00	40.00
BOOSTER PACK (11 CARDS)	1.00	1.50
*FOIL: .75X TO 2X BASIC CARDS		
RELEASED IN APRIL 2002		

1 Anakin Skywalker (A) R	.60	1.50
2 Anakin Skywalker (B) R	.60	1.50
3 Assassin Droid ASN-121 (A) R	.60	1.50
4 Bail Organa (A) R	.60	1.50
5 Battle Fatigue R	.60	1.50
6 Boba Fett (A) R	.60	1.50
7 Captain Typho (A) R	.60	1.50
8 Clear the Skies R	.60	1.50
9 Clone Officer R	.60	1.50
10 Dark Rendezvous R	.60	1.50
11 Dark Side's Command R	.60	1.50
12 Dark Side's Compulsion R	.60	1.50
13 Darth Sidious (A) R	.60	1.50
14 Darth Tyranus (A) R	.60	1.50
15 Destruction of Hope R	.60	1.50
16 Dexter Jettster (A) R	.60	1.50
17 Geonosian Sentry R	.60	1.50
18 Hero's Duty R	.60	1.50
19 Hero's Flaw R	.60	1.50
20 Interference in the Senate R	.60	1.50
21 Jango Fett (A) R	.60	1.50
22 Jango Fett (B) R	.60	1.50
23 Jar Jar Binks (A) R	.60	1.50
24 Jedi Call for Help R	.60	1.50
25 Jedi Council Summons R	.60	1.50
26 Jedi Knight's Deflection R	.60	1.50
27 Lama Su (A) R	.60	1.50
28 Luxury Airspeeder U	.20	.50
29 A Moment's Rest R	.60	1.50
30 Naboo Defense Station R	.60	1.50
31 Obi-Wan Kenobi (A) R	.60	1.50
32 Obi-Wan's Starfighter (A) R	.60	1.50
33 Order Here R	.60	1.50
34 PadmÈ Amidala (A) R	.60	1.50
35 PadmÈ Amidala (B) R	.60	1.50
36 PadmÈ's Yacht (A) R	.60	1.50
37 Plo Koon (A) R	.60	1.50
38 Plot the Secession R	.60	1.50
39 Power Dive R	.60	1.50
40 Queen Jamillia (A) R	.60	1.50
41 R2-D2 (A) R	.60	1.50
42 San Hill (A) U	.20	.50
43 Second Effort R	.60	1.50
44 Seek the Council's Wisdom R	.60	1.50
45 Shu Mai (A) U	.20	.50
46 Slave I (A) R	.60	1.50
47 Spirit of the Fallen R	.60	1.50
48 Target the Senator R	.60	1.50
49 Taun We (A) R	.60	1.50
50 Trade Federation Battleship Core R	.60	1.50
51 Tyranus's Edict R	.60	1.50
52 Tyranus's Geonosian Speeder (A) R	.60	1.50
53 Tyranus's Solar Sailer (A) R	.60	1.50
54 Tyranus's Wrath R	.60	1.50
55 War Will Follow R	.60	1.50
56 Ward of the Jedi R	.60	1.50
57 Windu's Solution R	.60	1.50
58 Yoda (A) R	.60	1.50
59 Yoda's Intervention R	.60	1.50
60 Zam Wesell (A) R	.60	1.50
61 Acklay U	.20	.50
62 Anakin Skywalker (C) U	.20	.50
63 Anakin's Inspiration U	.20	.50
64 AT-TE Walker 23X U	.20	.50
65 AT-TE Walker 71E R	.20	1.50
66 Attract Enemy Fire U	.20	.50
67 C-3PO (A) U	.20	.50
68 Capture Obi-Wan U	.20	.50
69 Chancellor Palpatine (A) R	.60	1.50
70 Chase the Villain U	.20	.50
71 Cheat the Game U	.20	.50
72 Cliegg Lars (A) U	.20	.50
73 Clone Warrior 4/163 U	.20	.50
74 Clone Warrior 5/373 U	.20	.50
75 Commerce Guild Droid Platoon U	.20	.50
76 CordÈ (A) U	.20	.50
77 Coruscant Freighter AA-9 (A) U	.20	.50
78 Dark Speed U	.20	.50
79 Darth Tyranus (B) U	.20	.50
80 Departure Time U	.20	.50
81 Destroyer Droid, P Series U	.20	.50
82 Down in Flames U	.20	.50
83 Droid Control Ship U	.20	.50
84 Elan Sleazebaggano (A) R	.60	1.50
85 Geonosian Guard U	.20	.50
86 Geonosian Warrior U	.20	.50
87 Go to the Temple U	.20	.50
88 Infantry Battle Droid, B1 Series U	.20	.50
89 Jango Fett (C) U	.20	.50
90 Jawa Sandcrawler U	.20	.50
91 Jedi Patrol U	.20	.50
92 Kaminoan Guard U	.20	.50
93 Kit Fisto (A) U	.20	.50
94 Master and Apprentice U	.20	.50
95 Naboo Security Guard U	.20	.50
96 Naboo Spaceport U	.20	.50
97 Nexu U	.20	.50
98 Nute Gunray (A) U	.20	.50
99 Obi-Wan Kenobi (B) U	.20	.50
100 PadmÈ Amidala (C) U	.20	.50
101 Poggle the Lesser (A) U	.20	.50
102 Reek U	.20	.50
103 Republic Assault Ship U	.20	.50
104 Republic Cruiser C	.10	.25
105 Shaak Ti (A) U	.20	.50
106 Ship Arrival U	.20	.50
107 Splinter the Republic U	.20	.50
108 Strength of Hate U	.20	.50
109 Subtle Assassination U	.20	.50
110 Super Battle Droid 8EX U	.20	.50
111 Trade Federation Battleship U	.20	.50
112 Trade Federation C-9979 U	.20	.50
113 Tyranus's Gift U	.20	.50
114 Underworld Connections U	.20	.50
115 Wat Tambor (A) U	.20	.50
116 Watto (A) U	.20	.50
117 Weapon Response U	.20	.50
118 Wedding of Destiny U	.20	.50
119 Yoda (B) U	.20	.50
120 Zam's Airspeeder (A) U	.20	.50
121 Anakin Skywalker (D) C	.10	.25
122 Battle Droid Squad C	.10	.25
123 Bravo N-1 Starfighter C	.10	.25
124 Chancellor's Guard Squad C	.10	.25
125 Clone Platoon C	.10	.25
126 Clone Squad C	.10	.25
127 Commerce Guild Droid 81 C	.10	.25
128 Commerce Guild Starship C	.10	.25
129 Corellian Star Shuttle C	.10	.25
130 Darth Tyranus (C) C	.10	.25
131 Destroyer Droid Squad C	.10	.25
132 Droid Starfighter DFS-4CT C	.10	.25
133 Droid Starfighter Squadron C	.10	.25
134 Droid Starfighter Wing C	.10	.25
135 Elite Jedi Squad C	.10	.25
136 Flying Geonosian Squad C	.10	.25
137 Geonosian Defense Platform C	.10	.25
138 Geonosian Fighter C	.10	.25
139 Geonosian Squad C	.10	.25
140 Gozanti Cruiser C	.10	.25
141 Hatch a Clone C	.10	.25
142 Hero's Dodge C	.10	.25
143 High-Force Dodge C	.10	.25
144 Hyperdrive Ring C	.10	.25
145 InterGalactic Banking Clan Starship C	.10	.25
146 Jango Fett (D) C	.10	.25
147 Jedi Starfighter 3R3 C	.10	.25
148 Knockdown C	.10	.25
149 Lost in the Asteroids C	.10	.25
150 Lull in the Fighting C	.10	.25
151 Mending C	.10	.25
152 N-1 Starfighter C	.10	.25
153 Naboo Cruiser C	.10	.25
154 Naboo Royal Starship C	.10	.25
155 Naboo Senatorial Escort C	.10	.25
156 Naboo Starfighter Squadron C	.10	.25
157 Obi-Wan Kenobi (C) C	.10	.25
158 Padawan's Deflection C	.10	.25
159 PadmÈ Amidala (D) C	.10	.25
160 Patrol Speeder C	.10	.25
161 Peace on Naboo C	.10	.25
162 Pilot's Dodge C	.10	.25
163 Recon Speeder C	.10	.25
164 Republic Attack Gunship UH-478 C	.10	.25
165 Repulsorlift Malfunction C	.10	.25
166 Return to Spaceport C	.10	.25
167 Rickshaw C	.10	.25
168 Slumming on Coruscant C	.10	.25
169 Sonic Shockwave C	.10	.25
170 Speeder Bike Squadron C	.10	.25
171 Starship Refit C	.10	.25
172 Surge of Power C	.10	.25
173 Swoop Bike C	.10	.25
174 Take the Initiative C	.10	.25
175 Target Locked C	.10	.25
176 Taylander Shuttle C	.10	.25
177 Techno Union Starship C	.10	.25
178 Trade Federation War Freighter C	.10	.25
179 Walking Droid Fighter C	.10	.25
180 Zam Wesell (A) C	.10	.25

2002 Star Wars A New Hope

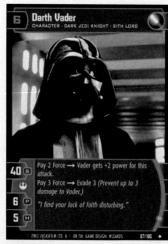

COMPLETE SET (180)	30.00	80.00
BOOSTER BOX (36 PACKS)	25.00	50.00
BOOSTER PACK (11 CARDS)	1.50	3.00
*FOIL: .8X TO 2X BASIC CARDS		
RELEASED IN OCTOBER 2002		

1 Admiral Motti (A) R	.60	1.50
2 Beru Lars (A) R	.60	1.50
3 Blaster Barrage R	.60	1.50
4 Capture the Falcon R	.60	1.50
5 Contingency Plan R	.60	1.50
6 Dannik Jerriko (A) R	.60	1.50
7 Darth Vader (A) R	1.25	3.00
8 Desperate Confrontation R	.75	2.00
9 Destroy Alderaan R	.60	1.50
10 Dianoga (A) R	.60	1.50

11	Disturbance in the Force R	.60	1.50
12	It's Not Over Yet R	.60	1.50
13	EG-6 Power Droid R	.60	1.50
14	Elite Stormtrooper Squad R	.60	1.50
15	Figrin D'an (A) R	.75	2.00
16	Greedo (A) R	.60	1.50
17	Hold 'Em Off R	.60	1.50
18	Imperial Blockade R	.60	1.50
19	Imperial Navy Helmsman R	.60	1.50
20	Imperial Sentry Droid R	.60	1.50
21	IT-0 Interrogator Droid R	.75	2.00
22	Jawa Leader R	.60	1.50
23	Krayt Dragon R	.60	1.50
24	Leia's Kiss R	.60	1.50
25	Luke Skywalker (B) R	.60	1.50
26	Luke Skywalker (A) R	.60	1.50
27	Luke's Speeder (A) R	.60	1.50
28	Luke's X-Wing (A) R	.60	1.50
29	Momaw Nadon (A) R	1.00	2.50
30	Most Desperate Hour R	.60	1.50
31	No Escape R	.60	1.50
32	Obi-Wan Kenobi (E) R	.60	1.50
33	Obi-Wan's Prowess R	.60	1.50
34	Obi-Wan's Task R	.60	1.50
35	Our Only Hope R	.60	1.50
36	Owen Lars (A) R	.60	1.50
37	Plan of Attack R	.60	1.50
38	Princess Leia (A) R	.60	1.50
39	Protection of the Master R	.60	1.50
40	R5-D4 (A) R	.60	1.50
41	Rebel Crew Chief R	.60	1.50
42	Rebel Lieutenant R	.60	1.50
43	Regroup on Yavin R	.60	1.50
44	Sandtrooper R	.60	1.50
45	Starfighter's End R	.60	1.50
46	Stormtrooper TK-421 R	.60	1.50
47	Strategy Session R	.60	1.50
48	Strike Me Down R	.60	1.50
49	Surprise Attack R	.60	1.50
50	Tantive IV (A) R	.60	1.50
51	Tarkin's Stench R	.60	1.50
52	TIE Fighter Elite Pilot U	.20	.50
53	Tiree (A) R	.60	1.50
54	Tractor Beam R	.60	1.50
55	URoRRuR'R'R (A) R	.60	1.50
56	Imperial Manipulation R	.60	1.50
57	Vader's Leadership R	.60	1.50
58	Vader's TIE Fighter (A) R	.60	1.50
59	Wedge Antilles (A) R	.60	1.50
60	Yavin 4 Hangar Base R	.60	1.50
61	Astromech Assistance U	.20	.50
62	Benefits of Training U	.20	.50
63	Biggs Darklighter (A) U	.20	.50
64	C-3PO (C) U	.20	.50
65	Commander Praji (A) U	.20	.50
66	Tatooine Sandcrawler U	.20	.50
67	Darth Vader (B) U	.20	.50
68	Death Star Hangar Bay U	.20	.50
69	Death Star Plans U	.20	.50
70	Death Star Scanning Technician U	.20	.50
71	Death Star Superlaser Gunner U	.20	.50
72	Death Star Turbolaser Gunner U	.20	.50
73	Demonstration of Power U	.20	.50
74	Devastator (A) U	.20	.50
75	Dissolve the Senate U	.20	.50
76	Error in Judgment U	.20	.50
77	Fate of the Dragon U	.20	.50
78	General Dodonna (A) U	.20	.50
79	General Tagge (A) U	.20	.50
80	Han's Courage U	.20	.50
81	Imperial Control Station U	.20	.50
82	Imperial Navy Lieutenant U	.20	.50
83	Insignificant Power U	.20	.50
84	Into the Garbage Chute C	.10	.25
85	Jawa U	.20	.50
86	Jawa Collection Team U	.20	.50
87	Jedi Extinction U	.20	.50
88	Jon Dutch Vander (A) U	.20	.50
89	Learning the Force U	.20	.50
90	Lieutenant Tanbris (A) U	.20	.50
91	LIN Demolitionmech U	.20	.50
92	Luke Skywalker (C) U	.20	.50
93	Luke's Warning U	.20	.50
94	Mounted Stormtrooper U	.20	.50
95	Mouse Droid U	.20	.50
96	Obi-Wan Kenobi (F) U	.20	.50
97	Oil Bath U	.20	.50
98	Princess Leia (B) U	.20	.50
99	R2-D2 (C) U	.20	.50
100	Rebel Blockade Runner U	.20	.50
101	Rebel Control Officer U	.20	.50
102	Rebel Control Post U	.20	.50
103	Rebel Marine U	.20	.50
104	Rebel Surrender U	.20	.50
105	Rebel Trooper U	.20	.50
106	Remote Seeker Droid U	.20	.50
107	Press the Advantage U	.20	.50
108	Stabilize Deflectors U	.20	.50
109	Star Destroyer Commander U	.20	.50
110	Stormtrooper Charge U	.20	.50
111	Stormtrooper DV-692 U	.20	.50
112	Stormtrooper Squad Leader U	.20	.50
113	Stormtrooper TK-119 U	.20	.50
114	Support in the Senate U	.20	.50
115	Disrupt the Power System U	.20	.50
116	Tatooine Speeder U	.20	.50
117	Tusken Sharpshooter U	.20	.50
118	Vader's Interference U	.20	.50
119	Vader's TIE Fighter (B) U	.60	1.50
120	Wuher (A) U	.20	.50
121	Air Cover C	.10	.25
122	Precise Blast C	.10	.25
123	Stay Sharp C	.10	.25
124	Carrack Cruiser C	.10	.25
125	Darth Vader (C) C	.10	.25
126	Death Star Cannon Tower C	.10	.25
127	Death Star Guard Squad C	.10	.25
128	Domesticated Bantha C	.10	.25
129	Flare-S Swoop C	.10	.25
130	Ground Support C	.10	.25
131	Imperial Detention Block C	.10	.25
132	Imperial Star Destroyer C	.10	.25
133	Incom T-16 Skyhopper C	.10	.25
134	Into Hiding C	.10	.25
135	Jawa Squad C	.10	.25
136	Jawa Supply Trip C	.10	.25
137	Jump to Lightspeed C	.10	.25
138	Luke Skywalker (D) C	.10	.25
139	Luke's Repairs C	.10	.25
140	Moisture Farm C	.10	.25
141	Planetary Defense Turret C	.10	.25
142	Nowhere to Run C	.10	.25
143	Obi-Wan Kenobi (G) C	.10	.25
144	Jedi Intervention C	.10	.25
145	Obi-Wan's Plan C	.10	.25
146	Penetrate the Shields C	.10	.25
147	Preemptive Shot C	.10	.25
148	Princess Leia (C) C	.10	.25
149	Rebel Fighter Wing C	.10	.25
150	Rebel Honor Company C	.10	.25
151	Rebel Marine Squad C	.10	.25
152	Rebel Pilot C	.10	.25
153	Rebel Squad C	.10	.25
154	Rescue C	.10	.25
155	Slipping Through C	.10	.25
156	SoruSuub V-35 Courier C	.10	.25
157	Synchronized Assault C	.10	.25
158	Stormtrooper Assault Team C	.10	.25
159	Stormtrooper DV-523 C	.10	.25
160	Stormtrooper Patrol C	.10	.25
161	Stormtrooper Squad C	.10	.25
162	TIE Fighter DS-3-12 C	.10	.25
163	TIE Fighter DS-73-3 C	.10	.25
164	TIE Fighter DS-55-6 C	.10	.25
165	TIE Fighter DS-61-9 C	.10	.25
166	TIE Fighter Pilot C	.10	.25
167	TIE Fighter Squad C	.10	.25
168	Tusken Squad C	.10	.25
169	Vader's Grip U	.10	.25
170	Victory-Class Star Destroyer C	.10	.25
171	Well-Aimed Shot C	.10	.25
172	X-wing Red One C	.10	.25
173	X-wing Red Three C	.10	.25
174	X-wing Red Two C	.10	.25
175	X-wing Attack Formation C	.10	.25
176	Y-wing Gold One C	.10	.25
177	Y-wing Gold Squadron C	.10	.25
178	YT-1300 Transport C	.10	.25
179	YV-664 Light Freighter C	.10	.25
180	Z-95 Headhunter C	.10	.25

2002 Star Wars Sith Rising

COMPLETE SET (90)	15.00	40.00
BOOSTER BOX (36 PACKS)	25.00	50.00
BOOSTER PACK (11 CARDS)	1.00	2.00

*FOIL: .75X TO 2X BASIC CARDS
RELEASED IN JULY 2002

1	Aayla Secura (A) R	.60	1.50
2	Anakin Skywalker (E) R	.60	1.50
3	Aurra Sing (A) R	.60	1.50
4	Chancellor Palpatine (B) R	.60	1.50
5	Clone Captain R	.60	1.50
6	Clone Facility R	.60	1.50
7	Darth Maul (A) R	.60	1.50
8	Darth Maul (C) R	.60	1.50
9	Darth Sidious (B) R	.60	1.50
10	Darth Tyranus (D) R	.60	1.50
11	Geonosian Picadors R	.60	1.50
12	Impossible Victory R	.60	1.50
13	Jango Fett (E) R	.60	1.50
14	Jedi Bravery R	.60	1.50
15	Jedi Starfighter Wing R	.60	1.50
16	Jocasta Nu (A) R	.60	1.50
17	Mace Windu (A) R	.60	1.50
18	Mace Windu (C) R	.60	1.50
19	Massiff R	.60	1.50
20	Nute Gunray (B) R	.60	1.50
21	Republic Drop Ship R	.60	1.50
22	Sio Bibble (A) R	.60	1.50
23	Sith Infiltrator (A) R	.60	1.50
24	Slave I (B) R	.60	1.50
25	Super Battle Droid 5TE R	.60	1.50
26	Trade Federation Control Core R	.60	1.50
27	Tusken Camp R	.60	1.50
28	Twilight of the Republic R	.60	1.50
29	Unfriendly Fire R	.60	1.50
30	Yoda (C) R	.60	1.50
31	Aiwha Rider U	.20	.50
32	C-3PO (B) U	.20	.50
33	Careful Targeting U	.20	.50
34	Clever Escape U	.20	.50
35	Clone Trooper 6/298 U	.20	.50
36	Darth Maul (B) U	.20	.50
37	Darth Tyranus (E) U	.20	.50
38	Destroyer Droid, W Series U	.20	.50
39	Female Tusken Raider U	.20	.50
40	Fog of War U	.20	.50
41	Geonosian Scout U	.20	.50
42	Hailfire Droid U	.20	.50
43	Homing Spider Droid U	.20	.50
44	Infantry Battle Droid U	.20	.50
45	Jedi Heroes U	.20	.50
46	Jedi Starfighter Scout U	.20	.50
47	Mace Windu (B) U	.20	.50
48	Moment of Truth U	.20	.50
49	Obi_Wan Kenobi (D) U	.20	.50
50	Out of His Misery U	.20	.50
51	PadmÈ Amidala (E) U	.20	.50
52	Passel Argente (A) U	.20	.50
53	Price of Failure U	.20	.50
54	R2-D2 (B) U	.20	.50
55	Recognition of Valor U	.20	.50
56	Sun Fac (A) U	.20	.50
57	Techno Union Warship U	.20	.50
58	Trade Federation Offensive U	.20	.50
59	Tusken Raider U	.20	.50
60	Visit the Lake Retreat U	.20	.50

61	Acclamator-Class Assault Ship C	.10	.25
62	Aggressive Negotiations C	.10	.25
63	Anakin Skywalker (F) C	.10	.25
64	AT-TE Troop Transport C	.10	.25
65	Battle Droid Assault Squad C	.10	.25
66	Brutal Assault C	.10	.25
67	Clone Trooper Legion C	.10	.25
68	Commerce Guild Cruiser C	.10	.25
69	Commerce Guild Spider Droid C	.10	.25
70	Concentrated Fire C	.10	.25
71	Corsucant Speeder C	.10	.25
72	Darth Maul (D) C	.10	.25
73	Diplomatic Cruiser C	.10	.25
74	Droid Starfighter DFS-1VR C	.10	.25
75	Geonosian Artillery Battery C	.10	.25
76	Geonosian Defense Fighter C	.10	.25
77	Maul's Strategy C	.10	.25
78	Mobile Assault Cannon C	.10	.25
79	Naboo Starfighter Wing C	.10	.25
80	Nubian Yacht C	.10	.25
81	Padawan and Senator C	.10	.25
82	Reassemble C-3PO C	.10	.25
83	Republic LAAT/i Gunship C	.10	.25
84	Retreat Underground R	.10	.25
85	Run the Gauntlet C	.10	.25
86	Senatorial Cruiser C	.10	.25
87	Shoot Her or Something C	.10	.25
88	Super Battle Droid Squad C	.10	.25
89	Suppressing Fire C	.10	.25
90	Trade Federation Warship C	.10	.25

2003 Star Wars Battle of Yavin

COMPLETE SET (105)		60.00	120.00
BOOSTER BOX (36 PACKS)		30.00	50.00
BOOSTER PACK (11 CARDS)		2.50	5.00

*FOIL: .75X TO 2X BASIC CARDS
RELEASED IN MARCH 2003

1	Artoo's Repairs R	2.00	5.00
2	Blow This Thing R	1.50	4.00
3	Celebrate the Victory R	.75	2.00
4	Chariot Light Assault Vehicle R	.75	2.00
5	Chewbacca (B) R	4.00	10.00
6	Chewbacca (A) R	4.00	10.00
7	Chief Bast (A) R	2.00	5.00
8	Colonel Wulff Yularen (A) R	2.00	5.00
9	Darth Vader (D) R	4.00	10.00
10	Death Star (A) R	3.00	8.00
11	Death Star (C) R	3.00	8.00
12	Garven Dreis (A) R	1.25	3.00
13	Grand Moff Tarkin (A) R	3.00	8.00
14	Han Solo (B) R	5.00	12.00
15	Han Solo (A) R	4.00	10.00
16	Hero's Potential R	.20	.50
17	Jek Porkins (A) R	.60	1.50
18	Lieutenant Shann Childsen (A) R	1.25	3.00
19	Luke Skywalker (E) R	4.00	10.00
20	Luke's Skyhopper (A) R	.20	.50
21	Luke's X-wing (B) R	2.00	5.00
22	Millennium Falcon (A) R	2.00	5.00
23	Millennium Falcon (B) R	2.00	5.00
24	Millennium Falcon (C) R	2.00	5.00
25	Obi-Wan Kenobi (H) R	4.00	10.00
26	Obi-Wan's Guidance R	.75	2.00
27	Princess Leia (D) R	1.25	3.00
28	R2-X2 (A) R	1.25	3.00
29	R2-Q5 (A) R	1.25	3.00
30	Rebel Ground Crew Chief R	.75	2.00

31	Second Wave R	1.25	3.00
32	Stormtrooper Commander R	4.00	10.00
33	Vader's Fury R	2.00	5.00
34	X-wing Squadron R	2.00	5.00
35	Your Powers Are Weak R	1.25	3.00
36	Alien Rage U	.40	1.00
37	C-3PO (D) U	.40	1.00
38	Chewbacca (C) U	.40	1.00
39	Commander Willard (A) U	.40	1.00
40	Countermeasures U	.40	1.00
41	Darth Vader (E) U	.40	1.00
42	Death Star (B) U	.40	1.00
43	Death Star Trooper U	.40	1.00
44	Deflectors Activated U	.40	1.00
45	Grand Moff Tarkin (B) U	.40	1.00
46	Grand Moff Tarkin (C) U	.40	1.00
47	Han Solo (C) U	.40	1.00
48	Heavy Fire Zone U	.40	1.00
49	Imperial Dewback U	.40	1.00
50	Interrogation Droid U	.40	1.00
51	Jawa Crawler U	.40	1.00
52	Jawa Scavenger U	.40	1.00
53	Labria (A) U	.40	1.00
54	Let the Wookiee Win U	.40	1.00
55	Luke Skywalker (F) U	.40	1.00
56	Luke's Speeder (B) U	.40	1.00
57	Mobile Command Base U	.40	1.00
58	Obi-Wan's Handiwork U	.40	1.00
59	Princess Leia (E) U	.40	1.00
60	R2-D2 (D) U	.40	1.00
61	Rebel Armored Freerunner U	.40	1.00
62	Refit on Yavin U	.40	1.00
63	Sabers Locked U	.40	1.00
64	Stormtrooper KE-829 U	.40	1.00
65	Tatooine Hangar U	.40	1.00
66	Tusken Raider Squad U	.40	1.00
67	Tusken War Party U	.40	1.00
68	Untamed Ronto U	.40	1.00
69	WED Treadwell U	.40	1.00
70	Womp Rat U	.40	1.00
71	Accelerate C	.20	.50
72	Blast It! C	.20	.50
73	Chewbacca (D) C	.20	.50
74	Corellian Corvette C	.20	.50
75	Creature Attack C	.20	.50
76	Luke Skywalker (G) C	.20	.50
77	Darth Vader (F) C	.20	.50
78	Death Star Turbolaser Tower C	.20	.50
79	Dewback Patrol C	.20	.50
80	Escape Pod C	.20	.50
81	Greedo's Marksmanship C	.20	.50
82	Han Solo (D) C	.20	.50
83	Han's Evasion C	.20	.50
84	Imperial Landing Craft C	.20	.50
85	Jawa Salvage Team C	.20	.50
86	Juggernaut C	.20	.50
87	Star Destroyer C	.20	.50
88	Malfunction C	.20	.50
89	Outrun C	.20	.50
90	Pilot's Speed C	.20	.50
91	Rebel Defense Team C	.20	.50
92	Sandtrooper Squad C	.20	.50
93	Stormtrooper Assault C	.20	.50
94	Stormtrooper TK-875 C	.20	.50
95	Stormtrooper Platoon C	.20	.50
96	Stormtrooper Regiment C	.20	.50
97	TIE Defense Squadron C	.20	.50
98	TIE Fighter DS-73-5 C	.20	.50
99	TIE Fighter DS-29-4 C	.20	.50
100	TIE Fighter DS-55-2 C	.20	.50
101	Trust Your Feelings C	.20	.50
102	Visit to Mos Eisley C	.20	.50
103	X-wing Red Squadron C	.20	.50
104	X-wing Red Ten C	.20	.50
105	Y-wing Gold Two C	.20	.50

2003 Star Wars The Empire Strikes Back

COMPLETE SET (210)		100.00	200.00
BOOSTER BOX (36 PACKS)		400.00	550.00
BOOSTER PACK (11 CARDS)		1.25	2.50

*FOIL: .75X TO 2X BASIC CARDS
RELEASED IN NOVEMBER 2003

1	2-1B Medical Droid (A) R	1.25	3.00
2	Admiral Firmus Piett (B) R	1.25	3.00
3	AT-AT Assault Group R	1.25	3.00
4	Avenger (A) R	4.00	10.00
5	Blizzard Force Snowtrooper R	1.25	3.00
6	Blizzard One (A) R	1.25	3.00
7	C-3PO (E) R	1.25	3.00
8	Captain Lorth Needa (A) R	1.25	3.00
9	Carbon Freezing Chamber R	5.00	12.00
10	Chewbacca (E) U	1.25	3.00
11	Chewbacca (G) R	1.25	3.00
12	Dack Ralter (A) R	1.25	3.00
13	Dangerous Gamble R	1.25	3.00
14	Dark Cave R	1.25	3.00
15	Darth Vader (H) R	2.00	5.00
16	Darth Vader (I) R	3.00	8.00
17	Decoy Tactics R	1.25	3.00
18	Desperate Times R	1.25	3.00
19	Echo Base R	3.00	8.00
20	Emperor's Bidding R	1.25	3.00
21	Emperor's Prize R	1.25	3.00
22	Executor (A) R	1.25	3.00
23	Failed for the Last Time R	1.25	3.00
24	Future Sight R	1.25	3.00
25	FX-7 Medical Droid (A) R	1.25	3.00
26	General Carlist Rieekan (A) R	1.25	3.00
27	General Maximilian Veers (B) R	1.25	3.00
28	Go for the Legs R	1.25	3.00
29	Han Solo (G) R	2.00	5.00
30	Jedi Test R	1.25	3.00
31	Jedi's Failure R	1.25	3.00
32	K-3PO (A) R	1.25	3.00
33	Kiss From Your Sister R	1.25	3.00
34	Lando Calrissian (A) R	2.50	6.00
35	Lando Calrissian (D) R	2.50	6.00
36	Lieutenant Wes Janson (A) R	2.00	5.00
37	Lobot (A) R	1.25	3.00
38	Luke Skywalker (J) R	6.00	15.00
39	Luke Skywalker (K) R	5.00	12.00
40	Luke's Snowspeeder (A) R	4.00	10.00
41	Luke's Wrath R	1.25	3.00
42	Luke's X-wing (c) R	2.00	5.00
43	Major Bren Derlin (A) R	1.25	3.00
44	Mara Jade (A) R	1.25	3.00
45	Millennium Falcon (E) R	2.00	5.00
46	Millennium Falcon (F) R	2.00	5.00
47	Millennium Falcon (G) R	2.00	5.00
48	Obi-Wan's Spirit (A) R	1.25	3.00
49	Occupation R	1.25	3.00
50	Parting of Heroes R	1.25	3.00
51	Planetary Ion Cannon R	1.25	3.00
52	Princess Leia (G) R	2.00	5.00
53	Quest for Truth R	1.25	3.00
54	R2-D2 (G) R	1.25	3.00
55	R2-D2's Heroism R	1.25	3.00
56	Rally the Defenders R	1.25	3.00
57	Sacrifice R	1.25	3.00
58	Search for the Rebels R	1.25	3.00
59	Stormtrooper Swarm R	1.25	3.00
60	Streets of Cloud City R	1.25	3.00

#	Card	Lo	Hi
61	Toryn Farr (A) R	1.25	3.00
62	Vader's Imperial Shuttle (A) R	2.00	5.00
63	Wampa Cave R	1.25	3.00
64	Wedge Antilles (B) R	4.00	10.00
65	Wedge's Snowspeeder (A) R	4.00	10.00
66	Yoda (F) R	1.25	3.00
67	Yoda (G) R	1.25	3.00
68	Yoda (H) R	1.25	3.00
69	Yoda's Training R	1.25	3.00
70	Zev Senesca (A) R	1.25	3.00
71	3,720 to 1 U	.40	1.00
72	Admiral Firmus Piett (A) U	.40	1.00
73	Admiral Kendal Ozzel (A) U	.40	1.00
74	Outmaneuver Them U	.40	1.00
75	All Terrain Troop Transport U	.40	1.00
76	Anti-Infantry Laser Battery U	.40	1.00
77	Asteroid Field U	.40	1.00
78	AT-AT Driver U	.40	1.00
79	Blizzard Force AT-ST U	.40	1.00
80	Battle the Wampa U	.40	1.00
81	Cloud City Penthouse U	.40	1.00
82	Cloud City Prison U	.40	1.00
83	Bespin Twin-Pod Cloud Car U	.40	1.00
84	Blockade U	.40	1.00
85	Bright Hope (A) U	.40	1.00
86	C-3PO (F) U	.40	1.00
87	Change in Destiny U	.40	1.00
88	Chewbacca (F) R	.40	1.00
89	Darth Vader (G) R	.40	1.00
90	Darth Vader (K) R	.40	1.00
91	Death Mark U	.40	1.00
92	Derek Hobbie Klivian (A) U	.40	1.00
93	Don't Get All Mushy U	.40	1.00
94	Dragonsnake U	.40	1.00
95	Emergency Repairs U	.40	1.00
96	Carbon Freeze U	.40	1.00
97	Executor Bridge U	.40	1.00
98	Executor Hangar U	.40	1.00
99	Quicker Easier More Seductive U	.40	1.00
100	General Maximilian Veers (A) U	.40	1.00
101	Han Enchained U	.40	1.00
102	Han Solo (F) U	.40	1.00
103	Hoth Icefields U	.40	1.00
104	Imperial Fleet U	.40	1.00
105	Imperial Misdirection U	.40	1.00
106	Jungles of Dagobah U	.40	1.00
107	Lambda-Class Shuttle U	.40	1.00
108	Lando Calrissian (C) U	.40	1.00
109	Leia's Warning U	.40	1.00
110	Luke Skywalker (I) U	.40	1.00
111	Medical Center U	.40	1.00
112	Millennium Falcon (D) U	.40	1.00
113	Mynock U	.40	1.00
114	Painful Reckoning U	.40	1.00
115	Princess Leia (H) U	.40	1.00
116	Probe Droid U	.40	1.00
117	Probot U	.40	1.00
118	R2-D2 (F) U	.40	1.00
119	Rebel Fleet U	.40	1.00
120	Rebel Hoth Army U	.40	1.00
121	Rebel Trenches U	.40	1.00
122	Rebel Troop Cart U	.40	1.00
123	Redemption U	.40	1.00
124	See You In Hell U	.40	1.00
125	Self Destruct U	.40	1.00
126	Shield Generator U	.40	1.00
127	Snowspeeder Rogue Ten U	.40	1.00
128	Snowspeeder Squad U	.40	1.00
129	Snowtrooper Elite Squad U	.40	1.00
130	Stormtrooper Sentry U	.40	1.00
131	Surprise Reinforcements U	.40	1.00
132	TIE Bomber Pilot U	.40	1.00
133	TIE Bomber Squad U	.40	1.00
134	TIE Pursuit Pilot U	.40	1.00
135	Torture Room U	.40	1.00
136	Vader's Call U	.40	1.00
137	Vicious Attack U	.40	1.00
138	Wampa U	.40	1.00
139	Yoda's Hut U	.40	1.00
140	725 to 1 C	.20	.50
141	All Terrain Armored Transport C	.20	.50
142	All Terrain Scout Transport C	.20	.50
143	Alter the Deal C	.20	.50
144	Antivehicle Laser Cannon C	.20	.50
145	Armor Plating C	.20	.50
146	Space Slug C	.20	.50
147	Blizzard Force AT-AT C	.20	.50
148	Precise Attack C	.20	.50
149	Belly of the Beast C	.20	.50
150	Cloud City Battleground C	.20	.50
151	Cloud City Dining Hall C	.20	.50

#	Card	Lo	Hi
152	Cloud City Landing Platform C	.20	.50
153	Bespin System C	.20	.50
154	Blizzard C	.20	.50
155	Bogwing C	.20	.50
156	Close the Shield Doors C	.20	.50
157	Darth Vader (J) C	.20	.50
158	Vader's Vengeance C	.20	.50
159	Dagobah System C	.20	.50
160	Explore the Swamps C	.20	.50
161	Float Away C	.20	.50
162	Force Throw C	.20	.50
163	Gallofree Medium Transport C	.20	.50
164	Ground Assault C	.20	.50
165	Han Solo (E) C	.20	.50
166	Han's Attack U	.20	.50
167	Han's Promise C	.20	.50
168	Hanging Around C	.20	.50
169	Hope of Another C	.20	.50
170	Hoth Battle Plains C	.20	.50
171	Hoth System C	.20	.50
172	Imperial II-Class Star Destroyer C	.20	.50
173	Jedi Master's Meditation C	.20	.50
174	Jedi Trap C	.20	.50
175	Kuat Lancer-Class Frigate C	.20	.50
176	Kuat Nebulon-B Frigate C	.20	.50
177	Lando Calrissian (B) C	.20	.50
178	Lando's Repairs C	.20	.50
179	Leap into the Chasm C	.20	.50
180	Luke Skywalker (H) C	.20	.50
181	Meditation Chamber C	.20	.50
182	Navy Trooper C	.20	.50
183	Princess Leia (F) C	.20	.50
184	Probe the Galaxy C	.20	.50
185	Rebel Command Center C	.20	.50
186	Rebel Escape Squad C	.20	.50
187	Rebel Hangar C	.20	.50
188	Rebel Trench Defenders C	.20	.50
189	Rebel Assault Frigate C	.20	.50
190	Dreadnaught Heavy Cruiser C	.20	.50
191	Snowspeeder Rogue Two C	.20	.50
192	Snowstorm C	.20	.50
193	Snowtrooper Heavy Weapons Team C	.20	.50
194	Snowtrooper Squad C	.20	.50
195	Snowtrooper Guard C	.20	.50
196	Imperial II Star Destroyer C	.20	.50
197	Strange Lodgings C	.20	.50
198	Swamps of Dagobah C	.20	.50
199	Tauntaun C	.20	.50
200	Tauntaun Mount C	.20	.50
201	TIE Bomber EX-1-2 C	.20	.50
202	TIE Bomber EX-1-8 C	.20	.50
203	TIE Fighter EX-4-9 C	.20	.50
204	TIE Fighter OS-72-8 C	.20	.50
205	TIE Pursuit Squad C	.20	.50
206	Trust Her Instincts C	.20	.50
207	Visions of the Future C	.20	.50
208	Well-Earned Meal C	.20	.50
209	X-wing Rogue Seven C	.20	.50
210	Y-wing Gold Six C	.20	.50

2003 Star Wars Jedi Guardians

	Lo	Hi
COMPLETE SET (105)	60.00	120.00
BOOSTER BOX (36 PACKS)	120.00	250.00
BOOSTER PACK (11 CARDS)	5.00	7.00

*FOIL: .75X TO 2X BASIC CARDS
RELEASED IN JULY 2003

#	Card	Lo	Hi
1	Adi Gallia (A) R	1.25	3.00
2	Anakin Skywalker (H) R	1.25	3.00
3	Aurra Sing (B) R	1.25	3.00
4	Boba Fett (B) R	1.25	3.00
5	Coup de Grace U	1.25	3.00
6	Dark Dreams R	1.25	3.00
7	Darth Maul (E) R	3.00	8.00
8	Darth Sidious (C) R	1.25	3.00
9	Darth Tyranus (F) R	2.00	5.00
10	Eeth Koth (A) R	1.25	3.00
11	Even Piell (A) R	1.25	3.00
12	Furious Charge C	1.25	3.00
13	Gather the Council R	1.25	3.00
14	Guidance of the Chancellor C	1.25	3.00
15	Homing Missile R	1.25	3.00
16	Jango Fett (G) R	1.25	3.00
17	Jedi Council Quorum R	1.25	3.00
18	Jedi Youngling R	1.25	3.00
19	Ki-Adi-Mundi (A) R	1.25	3.00
20	Kouhun R	1.25	3.00
21	Mace Windu (D) R	2.50	6.00
22	Trade Federation Battle Freighter C	1.25	3.00
23	Obi-Wan Kenobi (I) R	1.25	3.00
24	Obi-Wan's Starfighter (B) R	2.00	5.00
25	Oppo Rancisis (A) R	1.25	3.00
26	Padme Amidala (F) R	2.00	5.00
27	Plo Koon (B) R	1.25	3.00
28	R2-D2 (E) R	1.25	3.00
29	Remember the Prophecy R	1.25	3.00
30	Saesee Tiin (A) R	2.00	5.00
31	Senator Tikkes (A) R	1.25	3.00
32	Shaak Ti (B) R	2.00	5.00
33	Shmi Skywalker (A) R	2.00	5.00
34	Slave I (C) R	1.25	3.00
35	Trade Federation Blockade Ship C	1.25	3.00
36	Rapid Recovery R	1.25	3.00
37	Tipoca Training Ground R	1.25	3.00
38	Trade Federation Core Ship C	1.25	3.00
39	Tyranus's Geonosis Speeder (B) C	1.25	3.00
40	Unified Attack U	1.25	3.00
41	Yoda (D) R	5.00	12.00
42	Zam Wesell (D) R	1.25	3.00
43	Zam's Airspeeder (B) R	1.25	3.00
44	Battle Droid Division U	.40	1.00
45	Battle Protocol Droid (A) U	.40	1.00
46	Call for Reinforcements U	.40	1.00
47	Tyranus's Power C	.40	1.00
48	Clone Cadet U	.40	1.00
49	Coleman Trebor (A) U	.40	1.00
50	Corporate Alliance Tank Droid U	.40	1.00
51	Coruscant Air Bus U	.40	1.00
52	Depa Billaba (A) U	.40	1.00
53	Executioner Cart U	.40	1.00
54	FA-4 (A) U	.40	1.00
55	Jango Fett (F) U	.40	1.00
56	Jedi Arrogance U	.40	1.00
57	Jedi Training Exercise U	.40	1.00
58	Jedi Knight's Survival U	.40	1.00
59	Jedi Superiority U	.40	1.00
60	Lightsaber Gift U	.40	1.00
61	Lightsaber Loss U	.40	1.00
62	Neimoidian Shuttle (A) U	.40	1.00
63	Obi-Wan Kenobi (J) U	.40	1.00
64	Orray U	.40	1.00
65	Padme's Yacht (B) U	.40	1.00
66	Underworld Investigations C	.40	1.00
67	Protocol Battle Droid (A) U	.40	1.00
68	Qui-Gon Jinn (B) U	.40	1.00
69	Republic Communications Tower U	.40	1.00
70	RIC-920 U	.40	1.00
71	Sun-Fac (B) U	.40	1.00
72	Tactical leadership U	.40	1.00
73	Tame the Beast U	.40	1.00
74	Train For War U	.40	1.00
75	Tyranus's Return U	.40	1.00
76	Tyranus's Solar Sailer (B) U	.40	1.00
77	Yoda (E) U	.40	1.00
78	Zam Wesell (C) U	.40	1.00
79	Anakin Skywalker (I) C	.20	.50
80	Mobile Artillery Division C	.20	.50
81	Captured Reek C	.20	.50
82	Clone Fire Team C	.20	.50
83	Close Pursuit C	.20	.50
84	Darth Tyranus (G) C	.20	.50
85	Destroyer Droid Team U	.20	.50
86	Diplomatic Barge C	.20	.50
87	Droid Deactivation C	.20	.50
88	Droid Starfighter Assault Wing C	.20	.50
89	Trade Federation Droid Bomber C	.20	.50
90	Forward Command Center C	.20	.50
91	Geonosian Fighter Escort C	.20	.50
92	Gondola Speeder C	.20	.50

93 Gunship Offensive C	.20	.50
94 Jedi Starfighter Squadron C	.20	.50
95 Obi-Wan's Maneuver C	.20	.50
96 Plan for the Future C	.20	.50
97 Republic Assault Transport C	.20	.50
98 Republic Attack Gunship C	.20	.50
99 Republic Light Assault Cruiser C	.20	.50
100 Republic Hyperdrive Ring C	.20	.50
101 Sabaoth Starfighter C	.20	.50
102 Scurrier C	.20	.50
103 Separatist Battle Droid C	.20	.50
104 Shaak C	.20	.50
105 Synchronized Systems C	.20	.50

2004 Star Wars The Phantom Menace

COMPLETE SET (90)	50.00	100.00
BOOSTER BOX (36 PACKS)	200.00	250.00
BOOSTER PACK (11 CARDS)	1.50	3.00
*FOIL: .75X TO 2X BASIC CARDS		
RELEASED IN JULY 2004		
1 Ann and Tann Gella (A) R	2.00	5.00
2 Aurra Sing (C) R	1.25	3.00
3 Bongo Sub R	1.25	3.00
4 Boss Nass (A) R	1.25	3.00
5 C-9979 R	1.25	3.00
6 Corridors of Power R	1.25	3.00
7 Dark Woman (A) R	2.00	5.00
8 Darth Maul (F) R	2.00	5.00
9 Duel of the Fates R	1.25	3.00
10 Fambaa Shield Beast R	1.25	3.00
11 Fight on All Fronts R	1.25	3.00
12 Gardulla the Hutt (A) R	1.25	3.00
13 Gas Attack R	1.25	3.00
14 Gungan Grand Army R	1.50	4.00
15 Guardian Mantis (A) R	1.25	3.00
16 In Disguise R	1.25	3.00
17 Jar Jar Binks (B) R	1.25	3.00
18 Jedi Temple R	1.25	3.00
19 Ki-Adi-Mundi (B) R	2.00	5.00
20 Marauder-Class Corvette R	1.25	3.00
21 Negotiate the Peace R	1.25	3.00
22 Nute Gunray (C) R	1.25	3.00
23 Orn Free Taa (A) R	1.25	3.00
24 Otoh Gunga R	1.25	3.00
25 Podracing Course R	1.25	3.00
26 Quinlan Vos (A) R	1.25	3.00
27 Sando Aqua Monster R	1.25	3.00
28 Sith Infiltrator (B) R	1.25	3.00
29 Walking Droid Starfighter R	1.25	3.00
30 Watto's Shop R	1.25	3.00
31 A'Sharad Hett (A) U	1.25	3.00
32 Anakin Skywalker (J) U	3.00	8.00
33 Anakin's Podracer (A) U	2.00	5.00
34 Bravo Starfighter U	.40	1.00
35 Captain Panaka (A) U	.40	1.00
36 Captain Tarpals (A) U	.40	1.00
37 Citadel Cruiser U	.40	1.00
38 Colo Claw Fish U	.40	1.00
39 Discuss It in Committee U	.40	1.00
40 Durge (A) U	.40	1.00
41 Falumpaset U	.40	1.00
42 Gungan Battle Wagon U	.40	1.00
43 Gungan Catapult U	.40	1.00
44 Inferno (A) U	.40	1.00
45 Kaadu Scout U	.40	1.00
46 Let the Cube Decide U	.40	1.00
47 Modified YV-330 (A) U	.40	1.00

48 Naboo System U	.40	1.00
49 Qui-Gon Jinn (D) U	.40	1.00
50 Ric OliÈ (A) U	.40	1.00
51 Royal Cruiser U	.40	1.00
52 Rune Haako (A) U	.40	1.00
53 Sebulba (A) U	.40	1.00
54 Sebulba's Podracer (A) U	.40	1.00
55 Streets of Theed U	.40	1.00
56 Trade Federation Hangar U	.40	1.00
57 Trade Federation MTT U	.40	1.00
58 Vilmarh Grahrk (A) U	.40	1.00
59 Watto (B) U	.40	1.00
60 Yaddle (A) U	.40	1.00
61 A Bigger Fish C	.20	.50
62 Aayla Secura (B) C	.20	.50
63 Blockade (TPM) C	.20	.50
64 Blockade Battleship C	.20	.50
65 CloakShape Fighter C	.20	.50
66 Darth Sidious (D) C	.20	.50
67 Delta Six Jedi Starfighter C	.20	.50
68 Eopie C	.20	.50
69 Finis Valorum (B) C	.20	.50
70 Flash Speeder C	.20	.50
71 Gian Speeder C	.20	.50
72 Gungan Kaadu Squad C	.20	.50
73 Jedi Transport C	.20	.50
74 Melt Your Way In C	.20	.50
75 Mos Espa C	.20	.50
76 Naboo Pilot C	.20	.50
77 Obi-Wan Kenobi (K) C	.20	.50
78 Opee Sea Killer C	.20	.50
79 Podrace C	.20	.50
80 Qui-Gon Jinn (C) C	.20	.50
81 Sith Probe Droid C	.20	.50
82 Sneak Attack C	.20	.50
83 Swamps of Naboo C	.20	.50
84 TC-14 (A) C	.20	.50
85 Theed Power Generator C	.20	.50
86 Theed Royal Palace C	.20	.50
87 Trade Federation AAT C	.20	.50
88 Trade Federation STAP C	.20	.50
89 Unconventional Maneuvers C	.20	.50
90 Yinchorri Fighter C	.20	.50

2004 Star Wars Return of the Jedi

COMPLETE SET (109)	50.00	100.00
BOOSTER BOX (36 PACKS)	100.00	200.00
BOOSTER PACK (11 CARDS)	3.00	5.00
*FOIL: .75X TO 2X BASIC CARDS		
RELEASED IN OCTOBER 2004		
1 Admiral Ackbar (A) R	1.25	3.00
2 Anakin Skywalker (K) R	1.25	3.00
3 Anakin's Spirit (A) R	1.25	3.00
4 Bargain with Jabba R	1.25	3.00
5 Bib Fortuna (A) R	1.25	3.00
6 Chewbacca (J) R	1.25	3.00
7 Darth Vader (P) R	1.25	3.00
8 Death Star II (B) R	1.25	3.00
9 Emperor Palpatine (E) R	1.25	3.00
10 Endor Imperial Fleet R	1.25	3.00
11 Endor Rebel Fleet R	1.25	3.00
12 Endor Shield Generator R	1.25	3.00
13 Ephant Mon (A) R	1.25	3.00
14 Endor Regiment R	1.25	3.00
15 Free Tatooine R	1.25	3.00
16 Han Solo (K) R	1.25	3.00
17 Home One (A) R	1.25	3.00

18 Honor the Fallen R	1.25	3.00
19 Jabba the Hutt (A) R	1.25	3.00
20 Jabba's Dancers R	1.25	3.00
21 Jabba's Palace R	1.25	3.00
22 Jabba's Spies R	1.25	3.00
23 Lando Calrissian (H) R	1.25	3.00
24 Luke Skywalker (N) R	1.25	3.00
25 Malakili (A) R	1.25	3.00
26 Max Rebo Band (A) R	1.25	3.00
27 Mixed Battlegroup R	1.25	3.00
28 Mon Mothma (A) R	1.25	3.00
29 Nien Nunb (A) R	1.25	3.00
30 Occupied Tatooine R	1.25	3.00
31 Progress Report R	1.25	3.00
32 Rancor R	1.25	3.00
33 Reactor Core R	1.25	3.00
34 Salacious B. Crumb (A) R	1.25	3.00
35 Sarlacc (A) R	1.25	3.00
36 Scythe Squadron (A) R	1.25	3.00
37 Throne Room R	1.25	3.00
38 Trap Door! R	1.25	3.00
39 Vader's Guile R	1.25	3.00
40 Yoda's Spirit (A) R	1.25	3.00
41 Baited Trap U	.40	1.00
42 Boba Fett (H) U	.40	1.00
43 C-3PO (I) U	.40	1.00
44 Captain Lennox (A) U	.40	1.00
45 Chief Chirpa (A) U	.40	1.00
46 Darth Vader (N) U	.40	1.00
47 Desperate Bluff U	.40	1.00
48 Emperor Palpatine (D) U	.40	1.00
49 Ewok Village U	.40	1.00
50 Free Bespin U	.40	1.00
51 Free Endor U	.40	1.00
52 Han Solo (J) U	.40	1.00
53 Ionization Weapons U	.40	1.00
55 Jabba the Hutt (C) U	.40	1.00
56 Jabba's Sail Barge (A) U	.40	1.00
57 Lando Calrissian (I) U	.40	1.00
58 Luke Skywalker (O) U	.40	1.00
59 Millennium Falcon (J) U	.40	1.00
60 Occupied Bespin U	.40	1.00
61 Occupied Endor U	.40	1.00
62 Princess Leia (J) U	.40	1.00
63 R2-D2 (I) U	.40	1.00
64 Rancor Pit U	.40	1.00
65 Red Squadron X-wing U	.40	1.00
66 Skiff U	.40	1.00
67 Vader's Summons U	.40	1.00
68 Wicket W. Warrick (A) U	.40	1.00
69 Wookiee Hug U	.40	1.00
70 Worrt U	.40	1.00
71 A-wing C	.20	.50
72 B-wing C	.20	.50
73 Cantina Bar Mob C	.20	.50
74 Chewbacca (K) C	.20	.50
75 Close Quarters C	.20	.50
76 Elite Royal Guard C	.20	.50
77 Darth Vader (O) C	.20	.50
78 Death Star Battalion C	.20	.50
79 Death Star II (A) C	.20	.50
80 Decoy C	.20	.50
81 Dune Sea C	.20	.50
82 Elite Squad C	.20	.50
83 Emperor Palpatine (C) C	.20	.50
84 Ewok Artillery C	.20	.50
85 Ewok Glider C	.20	.50
86 Fly Casual C	.20	.50
87 Force Lightning C	.20	.50
88 Forest AT-AT C	.20	.50
89 Forest AT-ST C	.20	.50
90 Endor Attack Squad C	.20	.50
91 Forests of Endor C	.20	.50
92 Free Coruscant C	.20	.50
93 Gray Squadron Y-wing C	.20	.50
94 High-Speed Dodge C	.20	.50
95 Imperial Speeder Bike C	.20	.50
96 Imperial-Class Star Destroyer C	.20	.50
97 Jabba's Guards C	.20	.50
98 Lightsaber Throw C	.20	.50
99 Log Trap C	.20	.50
100 Luke Skywalker (M) C	.20	.50
101 Mon Calamari Cruiser C	.20	.50
102 Occupied Coruscant C	.20	.50
103 Oola (A) C	.20	.50
104 Princess Leia (K) C	.20	.50
105 Rebel Scouts C	.20	.50

106	Royal Guards C	.20	.50
107	Scout Trooper C	.20	.50
108	Surprising Strength C	.20	.50
109	TIE Interceptor C	.20	.50
110	Savage Attack C	.20	.50

2004 Star Wars Rogues and Scoundrels

COMPLETE SET (105)		50.00	100.00
BOOSTER BOX (36 PACKS)		40.00	80.00
BOOSTER PACK (11 CARDS)		1.50	3.00
*FOIL: .75X TO 2X BASIC CARDS			
RELEASED IN APRIL 2004			
1	Admiral Firmus Piett (C) R	1.25	3.00
2	Boba Fett (G) R	1.25	3.00
3	Bossk (A) R	1.25	3.00
4	Call For Hunters R	1.25	3.00
5	Chewbacca (I) R	1.25	3.00
6	Commander Nemet (A) R	1.25	3.00
7	Dantooine System R	1.25	3.00
8	Dark Sacrifice R	1.25	3.00
9	Dengar (A) R	1.25	3.00
10	Doctor Evazan (A) R	1.25	3.00
11	Guri (A) R	1.25	3.00
12	Han Solo (I) R	1.25	3.00
13	Het Nkik (A) R	1.25	3.00
14	Hounds Tooth (A) R	1.25	3.00
15	IG-2000 (A) R	1.25	3.00
16	IG-88 (A) R	1.25	3.00
17	Dune Sea Krayt Dragon R	1.25	3.00
18	Lando Calrissian (F) R	1.25	3.00
19	Lando Calrissian (G) R	1.25	3.00
20	Lando's Influence R	1.25	3.00
21	Lobot (B) R	1.25	3.00
22	Mara Jade (B) R	1.25	3.00
23	Millennium Falcon (I) R	1.25	3.00
24	Mist Hunter (A) R	1.25	3.00
25	Modal Nodes (A) R	1.25	3.00
26	Prince Xizor (A) R	1.25	3.00
27	Princess Leia (I) R	1.25	3.00
28	Slave 1 (F) R	1.25	3.00
29	Stinger (A) R	1.25	3.00
30	Take A Prisoner R	1.25	3.00
31	Trash Compactor R	1.25	3.00
32	Virago (A) R	1.25	3.00
33	Yoda (I) R	1.25	3.00
34	Yoda's Lesson R	1.25	3.00
35	Zuckuss (A) R	1.25	3.00
36	4 Lom (A) U	.40	1.00
37	AT-AT U	.40	1.00
38	Bespin Cloud Car Squad U	.40	1.00
39	Big Asteroid U	.40	1.00
40	Boba Fett (F) U	.40	1.00
41	C 3PO (G) U	.40	1.00
42	Chewbacca (H) U	.40	1.00
43	Cloud City Wing Guard U	.40	1.00
44	Darth Vader (M) U	.40	1.00
45	Death Star Control Room U	.40	1.00
46	Garindan (A) U	.40	1.00
47	Greedo (B) U	.40	1.00
48	Han Solo (H) U	.40	1.00
49	Han's Sacrifice U	.40	1.00
50	Holoprojection Chamber U	.40	1.00
51	Human Shield U	.40	1.00
52	Kessel System U	.40	1.00
53	Lando Calrissian (E) U	.40	1.00
54	Lando's Trickery U	.40	1.00
55	Luke Skywalker (L) U	.40	1.00

56	Luke's X-wing (D) U	.40	1.00
57	Millennium Falcon (H) U	.40	1.00
58	Ponda Baba (A) U	.40	1.00
59	Punishing One (A) U	.40	1.00
60	R2-D2 (H) U	.40	1.00
61	Redoubled Effort U	.40	1.00
62	E-3PO (A) U	.40	1.00
63	Slave 1 (E) U	.40	1.00
64	Slave 1 (D) U	.40	1.00
65	Space Slug {RaS} U	.40	1.00
66	Outrider (A) U	.40	1.00
67	Ugnaught U	.40	1.00
68	Vendetta U	.40	1.00
69	Enraged Wampa U	.40	1.00
70	Lars Homestead U	.40	1.00
71	2-1B's Touch C	.20	.50
72	Bantha Herd C	.20	.50
73	Base Guards C	.20	.50
74	Bespin Patrol Cloud Car C	.20	.50
75	Boba Fett (C) C	.20	.50
76	Boba Fett (D) C	.20	.50
77	Boba Fett (E) C	.20	.50
78	Darth Vader (L) C	.20	.50
79	Dash Rendar (A) C	.20	.50
80	Disrupting Strike C	.20	.50
81	Falcon's Needs C	.20	.50
82	Jabba's Death Mark C	.20	.50
83	Kabe (A) C	.20	.50
84	Kyle Katarn (A) C	.20	.50
85	Lando System? C	.20	.50
86	Leebo (A) C	.20	.50
87	Luke's Garage C	.20	.50
88	Luke's Vow C	.20	.50
89	Medium Asteroid C	.20	.50
90	Mos Eisley C	.20	.50
91	Mos Eisley Cantina C	.20	.50
92	Muftak C	.20	.50
93	No Good To Me Dead C	.20	.50
94	Ord Mantell System C	.20	.50
95	Sleen C	.20	.50
96	Small Asteroid C	.20	.50
97	Zutton (A) C	.20	.50
98	Star Destroyer {RaS} C	.20	.50
99	Stormtrooper Detachment C	.20	.50
100	Streets Of Tatooine C	.20	.50
101	Tatooine Desert C	.20	.50
102	Tie Fighter C	.20	.50
103	Tusken Warrior C	.20	.50
104	Unmodified Snowspeeder C	.20	.50
105	X Wing Escort C	.20	.50

2005 Star Wars Revenge of the Sith

COMPLETE SET (110)		50.00	100.00
BOOSTER BOX (36 PACKS)		30.00	60.00
BOOSTER PACK (11 CARDS)		1.25	2.50
*FOIL: .75X TO 2X BASIC CARDS			
RELEASED IN MAY 2005			
1	Anakin Skywalker (M) R	1.25	3.00
2	Bail Organa (B) R	1.25	3.00
3	Chewbacca (M) R	1.25	3.00
4	Commerce Guild Droid 81-X R	1.25	3.00
5	Commerce Guild Starship (ROTS) R	1.25	3.00
6	Coruscant Shuttle R	1.25	3.00
7	Darth Sidious (G) R	1.25	3.00
8	Darth Tyranus (I) R	1.25	3.00
9	Darth Vader (R) R	1.25	3.00
10	Darth Vader (S) R	1.25	3.00
11	Dismiss R	1.25	3.00
12	Droid Security Escort R	1.25	3.00
13	Engine Upgrade R	1.25	3.00
14	Foil R	1.25	3.00
15	Palpatine's Sanctum R	1.25	3.00
16	Grand Moff Tarkin (D) R	1.25	3.00
17	It Just Might Work R	1.25	3.00
18	Jar Jar Binks (C) R	1.25	3.00
19	Lightsaber Quick Draw R	1.25	3.00
20	Mace Windu (F) R	1.25	3.00
21	Mas Amedda (A) R	1.25	3.00
22	Mustafar Battle Grounds R	1.25	3.00
23	Mustafar System R	1.25	3.00
24	Nos Monster R	1.25	3.00
25	Obi-Wan Kenobi (N) R	1.25	3.00
26	PadmÈ Amidala (G) R	1.25	3.00
27	R4-P17 (A) R	1.25	3.00
28	Rage of Victory R	1.25	3.00
29	Recusant-Class Light Destroyer R	1.25	3.00
30	Republic Fighter Wing R	1.25	3.00
31	Sacrifice the Expendable R	1.25	3.00
32	Separatist Fleet R	1.25	3.00
33	Spinning Slash R	1.25	3.00

34	Strike with Impunity R	1.25	3.00
35	Stubborn Personality R	1.25	3.00
36	Super Battle Droid 7EX R	1.25	3.00
37	Theta-Class Shuttle R	1.25	3.00
38	Unexpected Attack R	1.25	3.00
39	Venator-Class Destroyer R	1.25	3.00
40	Yoda (K) R	1.25	3.00
41	Acclamator II-Class Assault Ship U	.40	1.00
42	AT-AP U	.40	1.00
43	C-3PO (I) U	.40	1.00
44	Chancellor's Office U	.40	1.00
45	Combined Squadron Tactics U	.40	1.00
46	Confusion U	.40	1.00
47	Darth Sidious (F) U	.40	1.00
48	Darth Vader (Q) U	.40	1.00
49	Destroyer Droid, Q Series U	.40	1.00
50	Droid Missiles U	.40	1.00
51	Elite Guardian U	.40	1.00
52	Hardcell-Class Transport U	.40	1.00
53	Jedi Concentration U	.40	1.00
54	Jedi Master's Deflection U	.40	1.00
55	Kashyyyk System U	.40	1.00
56	Naboo Star Skiff U	.40	1.00
57	Nute Gunray (D) U	.40	1.00
58	Obi-Wan Kenobi (L) U	.40	1.00
59	PadmÈ Amidala (H) U	.40	1.00
60	Patrol Mode Vulture Droid U	.40	1.00
61	GH-7 Medical Droid U	.40	1.00
62	R2-D2 (J) U	.40	1.00
63	Thread The Needle U	.40	1.00
64	Thwart U	.40	1.00
65	Treachery U	.40	1.00
66	Techno Union Interceptor U	.40	1.00
67	Utapau System U	.40	1.00
68	Vehicle Shields Package U	.40	1.00
69	Vehicle Weapons Package U	.40	1.00
70	Yoda (J) U	.40	1.00
71	Anakin Skywalker (L) C	.20	.50
72	Anakin's Starfighter (A) C	.20	.50
73	ARC-170 Starfighter C	.20	.50
74	AT-RT C	.20	.50
75	BARC Speeder C	.20	.50
76	Blaster Pistol C	.20	.50
77	Blaster Rifle C	.20	.50
78	Buzz Droid C	.20	.50
79	Chewbacca (L) C	.20	.50
80	Coruscant Emergency Ship C	.20	.50
81	Darth Sidious (E) C	.20	.50
82	Darth Tyranus (H) C	.20	.50
83	DC0052 Intergalactic Airspeeder C	.20	.50
84	Diving Attack C	.20	.50
85	Droid Battlestaff C	.20	.50
86	Droid Tri-Fighter C	.20	.50
87	Force Dodge C	.20	.50
88	HAVw A6 Juggernaut C	.20	.50
89	Homing Missiles Salvo C	.20	.50
90	IBC Hailfire Droid C	.20	.50
91	Instill Doubt C	.20	.50
92	InterGalactic Banking Clan Cruiser C	.20	.50
93	Jedi Lightsaber C	.20	.50
94	Jedi Piloting C	.20	.50
95	Meditate C	.20	.50
96	Obi-Wan Kenobi (M) C	.20	.50
97	Plo Koon's Starfighter (A) C	.20	.50
98	Power Attack C	.20	.50
99	Republic Assault Gunboat C	.20	.50
100	Security Droid C	.20	.50
101	Sith Lightsaber C	.20	.50
102	STAP Squad C	.20	.50
103	Surge of Strength C	.20	.50
104	Tank Droid C	.20	.50
105	TF Battle Droid Army C	.20	.50
106	Trade Federation Cruiser C	.20	.50
107	Unity of the Jedi C	.20	.50
108	Utapau Sinkhole C	.20	.50
109	Vulture Droid Starfighter C	.20	.50
110	V-wing Clone Starfighter C	.20	.50

2013 Star Wars Force Attax Clone Wars Series 5

1 Anakin Skywalker	1.50	4.00
2 Obi-Wan Kenobi	1.50	4.00
3 Ahsoka Tano	1.50	4.00
4 Yoda	1.50	4.00
5 Mace Windu	1.50	4.00
6 Kit Fisto	1.50	4.00
7 Luminara Unduli	1.50	4.00
8 Barriss Offee	1.50	4.00
9 Eeth Koth	1.50	4.00
10 Adi Gallia	1.50	4.00
11 Ima-Gun Di	1.50	4.00
12 Quinlas Vos	1.50	4.00
13 Tera Sinube	1.50	4.00
14 Cin Drallig	1.50	4.00
15 Tiplee	1.50	4.00
16 Tiplar	1.50	4.00
17 Jedi Temple Guard	1.50	4.00
18 R2-D2	1.50	4.00
19 C-3PO	1.50	4.00
20 Huyang	1.50	4.00
21 WAC-47	1.50	4.00
22 AZI-3	1.50	4.00
23 Chancellor Palpatine	1.50	4.00
24 Senator Bail Organa	1.50	4.00
25 Captain Ackbar	1.50	4.00
26 Finis Valorum	1.50	4.00
27 Admiral Wulff Yularen	1.50	4.00
28 Admiral Kilian	1.50	4.00
29 Lieutenant Tan Divo	1.50	4.00
30 Steela Gerrera	1.50	4.00
31 Clone Commander Cody	1.50	4.00
32 Clone Captain Rex	1.50	4.00
33 Clone Commander Wolffe	1.50	4.00
34 Clone Trooper Fives	1.50	4.00
35 Clone Commander Colt	1.50	4.00
36 Clone ARF Trooper (white)	1.50	4.00
37 Clone ARF Trooper (camo)	1.50	4.00
38 Clone Trooper (standing)	1.50	4.00
39 Clone Trooper (aiming)	1.50	4.00
40 Yoda's Jedi Starfighter	1.50	4.00
41 Anakin's Jedi Starfighter (side)	1.50	4.00
42 Ahsoka's Jedi Starfighter (rear)	1.50	4.00
43 Y-Wing Starfighter	1.50	4.00
44 Republic Attack Cruiser	1.50	4.00
45 Republic Frigate	1.50	4.00
46 Twilight	1.50	4.00
47 Republic Attack Gunship	1.50	4.00
48 Republic Medical Base	1.50	4.00
49 Republic Escape Pod	1.50	4.00
50 Republic Assault Ship	1.50	4.00
51 Tantive IV	1.50	4.00
52 Naboo Cruiser	1.50	4.00
53 Coruscant Speeder	1.50	4.00
54 AT-TE Walker	1.50	4.00
55 Naboo Scout Carrier	1.50	4.00
56 Crucible	1.50	4.00
57 Kaminoan Flight Pod	1.50	4.00
58 Darth Sidious	1.50	4.00
59 Count Dooku	1.50	4.00
60 Darth Maul	1.50	4.00
61 Savage Opress	1.50	4.00
62 Asajj Ventress	1.50	4.00
63 General Grievous	1.50	4.00
64 Senator Rush Clovis	1.50	4.00
65 Riff Tamson	1.50	4.00
66 Osi Sobeck	1.50	4.00

67 Bec Lawise	1.50	4.00
68 Nix Card	1.50	4.00
69 Nossor Ri	1.50	4.00
70 Nala Se	1.50	4.00
71 Lama Su	1.50	4.00
72 Mother Talzin	1.50	4.00
73 Battle Droid	1.50	4.00
74 Commando Droid	1.50	4.00
75 Droid Starfighter	1.50	4.00
76 Droid Gunship	1.50	4.00
77 Count Dooku's Solar Sailer	1.50	4.00
78 General Grievous' Speeder	1.50	4.00
79 Trident Drill Ship	1.50	4.00
80 Commerce Guild Destroyer	1.50	4.00
81 Trade Federation Battleship	1.50	4.00
82 Umbaran Starfighter	1.50	4.00
83 STAP	1.50	4.00
84 Pre Vizsla	1.50	4.00
85 Bo-Katan	1.50	4.00
86 Death Watch Torch Trooper	1.50	4.00
87 Ziton Moj	1.50	4.00
88 Cad Bane	1.50	4.00
89 Embo	1.50	4.00
90 Bossk	1.50	4.00
91 Rako Hardeen	1.50	4.00
92 Twazzi	1.50	4.00
93 Derrown	1.50	4.00
94 Seripas	1.50	4.00
95 Lom Pyke	1.50	4.00
96 Garnac	1.50	4.00
97 Ratter	1.50	4.00
98 Jabba The Hutt	1.50	4.00
99 Ziro The Hutt	1.50	4.00
T1 Anakin Skywalker Yoda (LE)	1.50	4.00
100 Slave I	1.50	4.00
101 Trandoshan Speeder	1.50	4.00
102 Jedi Knight #1	1.50	4.00
103 Jedi Knight #2	1.50	4.00
104 Jedi Knight #3	1.50	4.00
105 Jedi Knight #4	1.50	4.00
106 Jedi Knight #5	1.50	4.00
107 Jedi Knight #6	1.50	4.00
108 Jedi Knight #7	1.50	4.00
109 Jedi Knight #8	1.50	4.00
110 Jedi Knight #9	1.50	4.00
111 Sith #1	1.50	4.00
112 Sith #2	1.50	4.00
113 Sith #3	1.50	4.00
114 Sith #4	1.50	4.00
115 Sith #5	1.50	4.00
116 Sith #6	1.50	4.00
117 Sith #7	1.50	4.00
118 Sith #8	1.50	4.00
119 Sith #9	1.50	4.00
120 Bounty Hunter #1	1.50	4.00
121 Bounty Hunter #2	1.50	4.00
122 Bounty Hunter #3	1.50	4.00
123 Bounty Hunter #4	1.50	4.00
124 Bounty Hunter #5	1.50	4.00
125 Bounty Hunter #6	1.50	4.00
126 Bounty Hunter #7	1.50	4.00
127 Bounty Hunter #8	1.50	4.00
128 Bounty Hunter #9	1.50	4.00
129 Anakin Skywalker	1.50	4.00
130 Obi-Wan Kenobi	1.50	4.00
131 Ahsoka Tano	1.50	4.00
132 Yoda	1.50	4.00
133 Mace Windu	1.50	4.00
134 Aalya Secura	1.50	4.00
135 Luminara Unduli	1.50	4.00
136 Barriss Offee	1.50	4.00
137 Adi Gallia	1.50	4.00
138 Shaak Ti	1.50	4.00
139 Ima-Gun Di	1.50	4.00
140 Pong Krell	1.50	4.00
141 Force Priestess	1.50	4.00
142 R2-D2	1.50	4.00
143 C-3PO	1.50	4.00
144 AZI-3	1.50	4.00
145 Clone Commander Cody	1.50	4.00
146 Clone Captain Rex	1.50	4.00
147 Darth Sidious	1.50	4.00
148 Count Dooku	1.50	4.00
149 Darth Maul	1.50	4.00
150 Savage Opress	1.50	4.00
151 General Grievous	1.50	4.00
152 Nala Se	1.50	4.00
153 Pre Vizsla	1.50	4.00
154 Bo-Katan	1.50	4.00
155 Cad Bane	1.50	4.00

156 Pyke	1.50	4.00
157 Black Sun Leader	1.50	4.00
158 Boba Fett	1.50	4.00
159 Bossk	1.50	4.00
160 Embo	1.50	4.00
161 Anakin Skywalker	1.50	4.00
162 Obi-Wan Kenobi	1.50	4.00
163 Ahsoka Tano	1.50	4.00
164 Yoda	1.50	4.00
165 Mace Windu	1.50	4.00
166 Ima-Gun Di	1.50	4.00
167 Shaak Ti	1.50	4.00
168 Luminara Unduli	1.50	4.00
169 Barriss Offee	1.50	4.00
170 Force Priestess	1.50	4.00
171 R2-D2	1.50	4.00
172 Darth Sidious	1.50	4.00
173 Count Dooku	1.50	4.00
174 Darth Maul	1.50	4.00
175 Asajj Ventress	1.50	4.00
176 Mother Talzin	1.50	4.00
LEAS Anakin Skywalker (LEG)	1.50	4.00
LEAT Ahsoka Tano (LEG)	1.50	4.00
LECR Klon-Captain Rex (LEG)	1.50	4.00
LEDM Darth Maul (LEG)	1.50	4.00
LEDS Darth Sidious (LEG)	1.50	4.00
LEFP Macht-Priesterin (LEG)	1.50	4.00
LEOK Obi-Wan Kenobi (LEG)	1.50	4.00
LEPV Pre Vizsla (LEG)	1.50	4.00
LEPV Pre Vizsla (LE)	1.50	4.00
LESO Savage Opress (LEG)	1.50	4.00

2014 Star Wars Force Attax Movie Series 3

1 Luke Skywalker	1.50	4.00
2 Han Solo	1.50	4.00
3 Leia Organa	1.50	4.00
4 Chewbacca	1.50	4.00
5 Obi-Wan Kenobi	1.50	4.00
6 Yoda	1.50	4.00
7 Lando Calrissian	1.50	4.00
8 Admiral Ackbar	1.50	4.00
9 Mon Calamari	1.50	4.00
10 Prune Face	1.50	4.00
11 Nien Nunb	1.50	4.00
12 Rebel Trooper	1.50	4.00
13 Rebel Commando	1.50	4.00
14 Owen Lars	1.50	4.00
15 Beru Lars	1.50	4.00
16 R2-D2	1.50	4.00
17 C-3PO	1.50	4.00
18 2-1B Medical Droid	1.50	4.00
19 Protocol Droid	1.50	4.00
20 R1-G4	1.50	4.00
21 Training Remote	1.50	4.00
22 Momaw Nadon	1.50	4.00
23 Dice Ibegon	1.50	4.00
24 Yoxgit	1.50	4.00
25 Wicket	1.50	4.00
26 Logray	1.50	4.00
27 Paploo	1.50	4.00
28 Teebo	1.50	4.00
29 Romba	1.50	4.00
30 Millennium Falcon	1.50	4.00
31 X-Wing Starfighter	1.50	4.00
32 Y-Wing Starfighter	1.50	4.00
33 B-Wing Starfighter	1.50	4.00
34 A-Wing Starfighter	1.50	4.00

#	Card	Lo	Hi
35	Tantive 4	1.50	4.00
36	Medical Frigate	1.50	4.00
37	Headquarters Frigate	1.50	4.00
38	Rebel Transport	1.50	4.00
39	Snowspeeder	1.50	4.00
40	T-16 Skyhopper	1.50	4.00
41	Landspeeder	1.50	4.00
42	Emperor Palpatine	1.50	4.00
43	Darth Vader	1.50	4.00
44	Grand Moff Tarkin	1.50	4.00
45	Moff Jerjerrod	1.50	4.00
46	General Veers	1.50	4.00
47	Captain Lennox	1.50	4.00
48	Lieutenant Cabbel	1.50	4.00
49	Captain Khurgee	1.50	4.00
50	Stormtrooper	1.50	4.00
51	Snowtrooper	1.50	4.00
52	Sandtrooper	1.50	4.00
53	TIE Fighter Pilot	1.50	4.00
54	Janus Greejatus	1.50	4.00
55	Sim Aloo	1.50	4.00
56	Star Destroyer	1.50	4.00
57	Super Star Destroyer	1.50	4.00
58	TIE Fighter	1.50	4.00
59	TIE Interceptor	1.50	4.00
60	TIE Advanced	1.50	4.00
61	TIE Bomber	1.50	4.00
62	Imperial Shuttle	1.50	4.00
63	AT-ST Walker	1.50	4.00
64	AT-AT Walker	1.50	4.00
65	Speeder Bike	1.50	4.00
66	Probe Droid Capsule	1.50	4.00
67	Probot	1.50	4.00
68	R2-Q5	1.50	4.00
69	Demolition Droid	1.50	4.00
70	Death Star	1.50	4.00
71	Death Star 2	1.50	4.00
72	Jabba the Hutt	1.50	4.00
73	Bib Fortuna	1.50	4.00
74	Salacious Crumb	1.50	4.00
75	Amanaman	1.50	4.00
76	Boba Fett	1.50	4.00
77	Bossk	1.50	4.00
78	IG-88	1.50	4.00
79	Boushh	1.50	4.00
80	Gamorrean Guard	1.50	4.00
81	Umpass-Stay	1.50	4.00
82	Klaatu	1.50	4.00
83	Lathe	1.50	4.00
84	Harc Seff	1.50	4.00
85	Melas	1.50	4.00
86	Brock Starsher	1.50	4.00
87	Muftak	1.50	4.00
88	Tusken Raider	1.50	4.00
89	Jawa	1.50	4.00
90	EV-9D9	1.50	4.00
91	Slave I	1.50	4.00
92	Sandcrawler	1.50	4.00
93	Sailbarge	1.50	4.00
94	Desert Skiff	1.50	4.00
95	Anakin Skywalker	1.50	4.00
96	Obi-Wan Kenobi	1.50	4.00
97	Mace Windu	1.50	4.00
98	Qui-Gon Jinn	1.50	4.00
99	Kit Fisto	1.50	4.00
T1	R2-D2 (LE)	1.50	4.00
100	Ki-Adi-Mundi	1.50	4.00
101	Shaak Ti	1.50	4.00
102	Saesee Tiin	1.50	4.00
103	Plo Koon	1.50	4.00
104	Agen Kolar	1.50	4.00
105	Luminara Unduli	1.50	4.00
106	Stass Allie	1.50	4.00
107	Ma'Kis'Shaalas	1.50	4.00
108	J'oopi She	1.50	4.00
109	Cin Drallig	1.50	4.00
110	Youngling	1.50	4.00
111	Queen Amidala	1.50	4.00
112	Chancellor Palpatine	1.50	4.00
113	Chancellor Valorum	1.50	4.00
114	Bail Organa	1.50	4.00
115	Dorme	1.50	4.00
116	Captain Typho	1.50	4.00
117	Clone Trooper (blue)	1.50	4.00
118	Clone Trooper (orange)	1.50	4.00
119	Clone Trooper (yellow)	1.50	4.00
120	Clone Trooper (red)	1.50	4.00
121	Clone Trooper (white)	1.50	4.00
122	Jar Jar Binks	1.50	4.00
123	Gungan Soldier	1.50	4.00
124	Tion Meddon	1.50	4.00
125	Utapaun Warrior	1.50	4.00
126	Mustafarian	1.50	4.00
127	PK-4 Droid	1.50	4.00
128	Pit Droid	1.50	4.00
129	Otoga 222 Droid	1.50	4.00
130	Forklift Droid	1.50	4.00
131	Bettybot	1.50	4.00
132	Jedi Attack Cruiser	1.50	4.00
133	Jedi Starfighter (red)	1.50	4.00
134	Jedi Starfighter (yellow)	1.50	4.00
135	ARC-170 Starfighter	1.50	4.00
136	Darth Sidious	1.50	4.00
137	Count Dooku	1.50	4.00
138	Darth Maul	1.50	4.00
139	General Grievous	1.50	4.00
140	Destroyer Droid	1.50	4.00
141	Magnaguard	1.50	4.00
142	Crab Droid	1.50	4.00
143	Battle Droid	1.50	4.00
144	Battle Droid Pilot	1.50	4.00
145	TC-14	1.50	4.00
146	Droid Tri-Fighter	1.50	4.00
147	Wheel Bike	1.50	4.00
148	MTT	1.50	4.00
149	Droid Starfighter	1.50	4.00
150	The Invisible Hand	1.50	4.00
151	Droid Control Ship	1.50	4.00
152	Theta-Class Shuttle	1.50	4.00
153	Jango Fett	1.50	4.00
154	Aurra Sing	1.50	4.00
155	Zam Wesell	1.50	4.00
156	Watto	1.50	4.00
157	Alliance Strike Force 1	1.50	4.00
158	Alliance Strike Force 2	1.50	4.00
159	Alliance Strike Force 3	1.50	4.00
160	Alliance Strike Force 4	1.50	4.00
161	Strike Force	1.50	4.00
162	Alliance Strike Force 6	1.50	4.00
163	Alliance Strike Force 7	1.50	4.00
164	Alliance Strike Force 8	1.50	4.00
165	Alliance Strike Force 9	1.50	4.00
166	Empire Strike Force 1	1.50	4.00
167	Empire Strike Force 2	1.50	4.00
168	Empire Strike Force 3	1.50	4.00
169	Empire Strike Force 4	1.50	4.00
170	Strike Force	1.50	4.00
171	Empire Strike Force 6	1.50	4.00
172	Empire Strike Force 7	1.50	4.00
173	Empire Strike Force 8	1.50	4.00
174	Empire Strike Force 9	1.50	4.00
175	Republic Strike Force 1	1.50	4.00
176	Republic Strike Force 2	1.50	4.00
177	Republic Strike Force 3	1.50	4.00
178	Republic Strike Force 4	1.50	4.00
179	Strike Force	1.50	4.00
180	Republic Strike Force 6	1.50	4.00
181	Republic Strike Force 7	1.50	4.00
182	Republic Strike Force 8	1.50	4.00
183	Republic Strike Force 9	1.50	4.00
184	Separatist Strike Force 1	1.50	4.00
185	Separatist Strike Force 2	1.50	4.00
186	Separatist Strike Force 3	1.50	4.00
187	Separatist Strike Force 4	1.50	4.00
188	Strike Force	1.50	4.00
189	Separatist Strike Force 6	1.50	4.00
190	Separatist Strike Force 7	1.50	4.00
191	Separatist Strike Force 8	1.50	4.00
192	Separatist Strike Force 9	1.50	4.00
193	Luke Skywalker / Princess Leia	1.50	4.00
194	Han Solo / Chewbacca	1.50	4.00
195	R2-D2 / C-3PO	1.50	4.00
196	Princess Leia / Wicket	1.50	4.00
197	Obi-Wan Kenobi / Luke Skywalker	1.50	4.00
198	Emperor Palpatine / Darth Vader	1.50	4.00
199	Qui-Gon Jinn / Obi-Wan Kenobi	1.50	4.00
200	Anakin Skywalker / Obi-Wan Kenobi	1.50	4.00
201	Mace Windu / Obi-Wan Kenobi	1.50	4.00
202	Luminara Unduli / Barriss Offee	1.50	4.00
203	Yoda / Chewbacca	1.50	4.00
204	Jango Fett / Boba Fett	1.50	4.00
205	Luke Skywalker	1.50	4.00
206	Han Solo	1.50	4.00
207	Princess Leia	1.50	4.00
208	Chewbacca	1.50	4.00
209	Lando Calrissian	1.50	4.00
210	R2-D2	1.50	4.00
211	C-3PO	1.50	4.00
212	Anakin Skywalker	1.50	4.00
213	Obi-Wan Kenobi	1.50	4.00
214	Yoda	1.50	4.00
215	Mace Windu	1.50	4.00
216	Queen Amidala	1.50	4.00
217	Clone Lieutenant Galle	1.50	4.00
218	Darth Vader	1.50	4.00
219	Count Dooku	1.50	4.00
220	General Grievous	1.50	4.00
221	Darth Vader	1.50	4.00
222	Jabba the Hutt	1.50	4.00
223	Jango Fett	1.50	4.00
224	Boba Fett	1.50	4.00
225	Luke Skywalker	1.50	4.00
226	Han Solo	1.50	4.00
227	Princess Leia	1.50	4.00
228	Chewbacca	1.50	4.00
229	Anakin Skywalker	1.50	4.00
230	Obi-Wan Kenobi	1.50	4.00
231	Yoda	1.50	4.00
232	Mace Windu	1.50	4.00
233	Qui-Gon Jinn	1.50	4.00
234	Queen Amidala	1.50	4.00
235	Boba Fett	1.50	4.00
236	Darth Maul	1.50	4.00
237	Count Dooku	1.50	4.00
238	General Grievous	1.50	4.00
239	Darth Vader	1.50	4.00
240	Emperor Palpatine	1.50	4.00
LE1	Luke Skywalker (LE)	1.50	4.00
LE2	Han Solo (LEG)	1.50	4.00
LE3	Prinzessin Leia (LEG)	1.50	4.00
LE4	Lando Calrissian (LEG)	1.50	4.00
LE5	Darth Vader (LEG)	1.50	4.00
LE6	Anakin Skywalker (LEG)	1.50	4.00
LE7	Yoda (LEG)	1.50	4.00
LE8	C-3PO (LEG)	1.50	4.00
LE9	R2-D2 (LEG)	1.50	4.00
LE10	Chewbacca (LEG)	1.50	4.00
LE11	Boba Fett (LEG)	1.50	4.00

2015 Star Wars Between the Shadows

#	Card	Lo	Hi
12710633	A Hero's Trial	.75	2.00
12720634	Luke Skywalker	.75	2.00
12730635	Speeder Bike	.75	2.00
12740636	Luke's Lightsaber	.75	2.00
12750637	I Am a Jedi	.75	2.00
12760065	Heat of Battle	.75	2.00
12810638	The Master's Domain	.75	2.00
12820639	Yoda	.75	2.00
12830640	Bogwing	.75	2.00
12840641	Yoda's Hut	.75	2.00
12850089	Lightsaber Deflection	.75	2.00
12860642	The Jedi's Resolve	.75	2.00
12910643	Following Fate	.75	2.00
12920644	Obi-Wan Kenobi	.75	2.00
12930106	R2-D2	.75	2.00
12940645	Obi-Wan's Lightsaber	.75	2.00
12950646	Noble Sacrifice	.75	2.00
12960133	Target of Opportunity	.75	2.00
13010647	Journey Through the Swamp	.75	2.00
13020648	Jubba Bird	.75	2.00

13030648	Jubba Bird	.75	2.00
13040649	Knobby White Spider	.75	2.00
13050650	Life Creates It	.75	2.00
13060651	Size Matters Not	.75	2.00
13110652	Sacrifice at Endor	.75	2.00
13120653	Ewok Hunter	.75	2.00
13130653	Ewok Hunter	.75	2.00
13140654	Funeral Pyre	.75	2.00
13150655	Unexpected Assistance	.75	2.00
13160656	Retreat to the Forest	.75	2.00
13210657	Commando Raid	.75	2.00
13220658	Lieutenant Judder Page	.75	2.00
13230659	Pageís Commandos	.75	2.00
13240659	Pageís Commandos	.75	2.00
13250065	Heat of Battle	.75	2.00
13260133	Target of Opportunity	.75	2.00
13310660	Calling In Favors	.75	2.00
13320661	Talon Karrde	.75	2.00
13330662	Skipray Blastboat	.75	2.00
13340662	Skipray Blastboat	.75	2.00
13350663	Dirty Secrets	.75	2.00
13360664	Clever Ruse	.75	2.00
13410665	No Disintegrations	.75	2.00
13420666	Boba Fett	.75	2.00
13430667	Freelance Hunter	.75	2.00
13440668	Flamethrower	.75	2.00
13453378	Prized Possession	.75	2.00
13460669	Entangled	.75	2.00
13510670	Masterful Manipulation	.75	2.00
13520671	Prince Xizor	.75	2.00
13530672	Black Sun Headhunter	.75	2.00
13540673	Debt Collector	.75	2.00
13550674	Shadows of the Empire	.75	2.00
13560675	The Princeís Scheme	.75	2.00
13610676	All Out Brawl	.75	2.00
13620677	Zekka Thyne	.75	2.00
13630673	Debt Collector	.75	2.00
13640678	Armed to the Teeth	.75	2.00
13650669	Entangled	.75	2.00
13660169	Heat of Battle	.75	2.00
13710679	The Best That Credits Can Buy	.75	2.00
13720680	Virago	.75	2.00
13730672	Black Sun Headhunter	.75	2.00
13740681	Rise of the Black Sun	.75	2.00
13750682	Warning Shot	.75	2.00
13760170	Target of Opportunity	.75	2.00
13810683	The Hunters	.75	2.00
13820684	Boushh	.75	2.00
13830685	Snoova	.75	2.00
13840686	A Better Offer	.75	2.00
13850542	Pay Out	.75	2.00
13860687	Show of Force	.75	2.00
13910688	The Investigation	.75	2.00
13920689	Ysanne Isard	.75	2.00
13930690	Imperial Intelligence Officer	.75	2.00
13940690	Imperial Intelligence Officer	.75	2.00
13950691	Confiscation	.75	2.00
13960692	Official Inquiry	.75	2.00
14010693	Family Connections	.75	2.00
14020694	General Tagge	.75	2.00
14030695	Security Task Force	.75	2.00
14040695	Security Task Force	.75	2.00
14050696	Imperial Discipline	.75	2.00
14060697	Precision Fire	.75	

2015 Star Wars Chain of Command

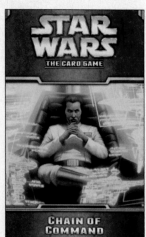

1611	A Heroís Beginning	.75	2.00
1612	Lukeís X-34 Landspeeder	.75	2.00

1613	Owen Lars	.75	2.00
1614	Moisture Vaporator	.75	2.00
1615	Unfinished Business	.75	2.00
1616	Supporting Fire	.75	2.00
1621	Breaking the Blockade	.75	2.00
1622	Smuggling Freighter	.75	2.00
1623	Smuggling Freighter	.75	2.00
1624	Duros Smuggler	.75	2.00
1625	Duros Smuggler	.75	2.00
1626	Surprising Maneuver	.75	2.00
1631	The Imperial Bureaucracy	.75	2.00
1632	Sate Pestage	.75	2.00
1633	Advisor to the Emperor	.75	2.00
1634	Quarren Bureaucrat	.75	2.00
1635	Endless Bureaucracy	.75	2.00
1636	Supporting Fire	.75	2.00
1641	The Last Grand Admiral	.75	2.00
1642	Grand Admiral Thrawn	.75	2.00
1643	Noghri Bodyguard	.75	2.00
1644	Noghri Bodyguard	.75	2.00
1645	Chain of Command	2.00	5.00
1646	Supporting Fire	.75	2.00
1651	Nar Shaddaa Drift	.75	2.00
1652	Race Circut Champion	.75	2.00
1653	Racing Swoop	.75	2.00
1654	Racing Swoop	.75	2.00
1655	Black Market Exchange	.75	2.00
1656	Cut Off	.75	2.00

2015 Star Wars Draw Their Fire

14610722	The Survivors	.75	2.00
14620723	Qu Rahn	.75	2.00
14630724	Sulon Sympathizer	.75	2.00
14640725	Shien Training	.75	2.00
14650061	Force Rejuvenation	.75	2.00
14660256	Protection	.75	2.00
14710726	Called to Arms	.75	2.00
14720727	Gray Squadron Gunner	.75	2.00
14730728	Gray Squadron Y-Wing	.75	2.00
14740729	Advanced Proton Torpedoes	.75	2.00
14750730	Desperation	.75	2.00
14760133	Target of Opportunity	.75	2.00
14810731	The Daring Escape	.75	2.00
14820732	LE-B02D9	.75	2.00
14830733	Outrider	.75	2.00
14840734	Spacer Cantina	.75	2.00
14850735	Punch It	.75	2.00
14860702	Stay on Target	.75	2.00
14910736	The Emperorís Sword	.75	2.00
14920737	Maarek Stele	.75	2.00
14930738	Delta One	.75	2.00
14940739	Advanced Concussion Missiles	.75	2.00
14950740	Hand of the Emperor	.75	2.00
14960169	Heat of Battle	.75	2.00
15010741	Guarding the Wing	.75	2.00
15020742	DS-61-3	.75	2.00
15030743	Black Squadron Fighter	.75	2.00
15040743	Black Squadron Fighter	.75	2.00
15050744	Elite Pilot Training	.75	2.00
15060170	Target of Opportunity	.75	2.00

2015 Star Wars Imperial Entanglement

17110838	House Edge	.75	2.00
17120839	Lando Calrissian	.75	2.00
17130840	Herglic Sabacc Addict	.75	2.00
17140022	Cloud City Casino	.75	2.00
17150841	Sabacc Shift	.75	2.00
17160842	The Gamblerís Trick	.75	2.00
17210843	Debt of Honor	.75	2.00
17220844	Chewbacca	.75	2.00
17230845	Wookiee Defender	.75	2.00
17240846	Kashyyyk Resistance Hideout	.75	2.00
17250847	Wookiee Rage	.75	2.00
17260256	Protection	.75	
17310848	Fortune and Fate	.75	2.00
17320849	Lady Luck	.75	2.00
17330850	Cloud City Technician	.75	2.00
17340850	Cloud City Technician	.75	2.00
17350851	Central Computer	.75	2.00
17360133	Target of Opportunity	.75	2.00
17410852	Honor Among Thieves	.75	2.00
17420853	Mirax Terrik	.75	2.00
17430854	Fringer Captain	.75	2.00
17440854	Fringer Captain	.75	2.00
17450855	Special Discount	.75	2.00
17460856	One Last Trick	.75	2.00
17510857	Renegade Reinforcements	.75	2.00
17520858	Corporal Dansra Beezer	.75	2.00
17530210	Renegade Squadron Operative	.75	2.00
17540859	Hidden Backup	.75	2.00
17550860	Directed Fire	.75	2.00
17560861	Last Minute Reinforcements	.75	2.00
17610862	Mysteries of the Rim	.75	2.00
17620863	Outer Rim Mystic	.75	2.00
17630863	Outer Rim Mystic	.75	2.00
17640864	Niman Training	.75	2.00
17650864	Niman Training	.75	2.00
17660865	Force Illusion	.75	2.00
17710866	Planning the Rescue	.75	2.00
17720867	General Airen Cracken	.75	2.00
17730868	Alliance Infiltrator	.75	2.00
17740869	Superior Intelligence	.75	2.00
17750870	Undercover	.75	2.00
17760117	Rescue Mission	.75	2.00
17810871	The Tarkin Doctrine	.75	2.00
17820872	Grand Moff Tarkin	.75	2.00
17830873	Stormtrooper Assault Team	.75	2.00
17840874	Rule by Fear	.75	2.00
17850875	Moment of Triumph	.75	2.00
17860171	Twist of Fate	.75	2.00
17910876	Might of the Empire	.75	2.00
17920877	Chimaera	.75	2.00
17930878	DP20 Corellian Gunship	.75	2.00
17940879	Fleet Staging Area	.75	2.00
17950392	Tractor Beam	.75	2.00
17960880	The Empire Strikes Back	.75	2.00
18010881	Enforced Loyalty	.75	2.00
18020882	Colonel Yularen	.75	2.00
18030883	Lieutenant Mithel	.75	2.00
18040884	MSE-6 íMouseí Droid	.75	2.00
18050024	Control Room	.75	2.00
18060885	The Imperial Fist	.75	2.00
18110886	Imperial Entanglements	.75	2.00
18120887	Imperial Raider	.75	2.00
18130888	VT-49 Decimator	.75	2.00
18140888	VT-49 Decimator	.75	2.00
18150889	Customs Blockade	.75	2.00
18160890	Ion Cannon	.75	2.00

18210891	Phantoms of Imdaar	.75	2.00
18220892	TIE Phantom	.75	2.00
18230892	TIE Phantom	.75	2.00
18240893	Enhanced Laser Cannon	.75	2.00
18250894	Fighters Coming In!	.75	2.00
18260169	Heat of Battle	.75	2.00
18310895	Brothers of the Sith	.75	2.00
18320896	Gorc	.75	2.00
18330897	Pic	.75	2.00
18340898	Telepathic Connection	.75	2.00
18350062	Force Stasis	.75	2.00
18360899	Force Invisibility	.75	2.00
18410900	The Huttis Menagerie	.75	2.00
18420901	Malakili	.75	2.00
18430902	Jabbais Rancor	.75	2.00
18440903	Bubo	.75	2.00
18450904	Underground Entertainment	.75	2.00
18460905	Jabbais Summons	.75	2.00

2015 Star Wars Jump to Lightspeed

1661	The Forgotten Masters	.75	2.00
1662	Tira Saa	.75	2.00
1663	Lost Master	.75	2.00
1664	Lost Master	.75	2.00
1665	A Gift from the Past	.75	2.00
1666	Echoes of the Force	.75	2.00
1671	Heroes of the Rebellion	.75	2.00
1672	Tycho Celchu	.75	2.00
1673	Wes Janson	.75	2.00
1674	Rogue Six	.75	2.00
1675	Rogue Nine	.75	2.00
1676	Ready for Takeoff	.75	2.00
1681	That Bucket oi Bolts	.75	2.00
1682	Han Solo	.75	2.00
1683	Millennium Falcon	.75	2.00
1684	Well Paid	.75	2.00
1685	Well Paid	.75	2.00
1686	Heat of Battle	.75	2.00
1691	The Reawakening	.75	2.00
1692	Arden Lyn	.75	2.00
1693	Dark Side Apprentice	.75	2.00
1694	Return to Darkness	.75	2.00
1695	Give in to Your Anger	.75	2.00
1696	Give in to Your Anger	.75	2.00
1701	Behind the Black Sun	.75	2.00
1702	Guri	.75	2.00
1703	Freelance Assassin	.75	2.00
1704	Hidden Vibroknife	.75	2.00
1705	Threat Removal	.75	2.00
1706	Heat of Battle	.75	2.00

2015 Star Wars Ready for Takeoff

14110698	Rogue Squadron Assault	.75	2.00
14120699	Derek iHobbiei Klivian	.75	2.00
14130700	Rogue Squadron X-Wing	.75	2.00
14140700	Rogue Squadron X-Wing	.75	2.00
14150701	Pilot Ready Room	.75	2.00
14160702	Stay on Target	.75	2.00
14210703	Memories of Taanab	.75	2.00
14220704	Lando Calrissian	.75	2.00
14230705	System Patrol Craft	.75	2.00
14240705	System Patrol Craft	.75	2.00
14250706	Conner Net	.75	2.00
14260707	A Little Maneuver	.75	2.00
14310708	Black Squadron Formation	.75	2.00
14320709	iMaulerï Mithel	.75	2.00
14330710	Black Two	.75	2.00
14340146	TIE Advanced	.75	2.00
14350711	Death Star Ready Room	.75	2.00
14360712	Stay on Target	.75	2.00
14410713	The Empireis Elite	.75	2.00
14420714	Baron Fel	.75	2.00
14430715	181st TIE Interceptor	.75	2.00
14440715	181st TIE Interceptor	.75	2.00
14450716	Flight Academy	.75	2.00
14460712	Stay on Target	.75	2.00
14510717	The Grand Heist	.75	2.00
14520718	Niles Ferrier	.75	2.00
14530719	Novice Starship Thief	.75	2.00
14540719	Novice Starship Thief	.75	2.00
14550720	Pirate Hideout	.75	2.00
14560721	Salvage Operation	.75	2.00

2016 Star Wars Destiny Awakening

COMPLETE SET (174 CARDS)	450.00	650.00
BOOSTER BOX (36 PACKS)	80.00	120.00
BOOSTER PACK (5 CARDS AND 1 DICE)	4.00	6.00
UNLISTED C	.10	.20
UNLISTED U	.25	.40
UNLISTED R	3.00	5.00
RELEASED IN NOVEMBER, 2016		

1	Captain Phasma L	10.00	15.00
2	First Order Stormtrooper R	3.00	5.00
3	General Grievous R	3.00	5.00
4	General Veers R	3.00	5.00
5	AT ST L	8.00	12.00
6	First Order TIE Fighter R	3.00	5.00
7	Commanding Presence L	10.00	15.00
8	F 11D Rifle S	2.00	3.50
9	Count Dooku R	3.00	5.00
10	Darth Vader L	30.00	35.00
11	Kylo Ren S	1.50	2.50
12	Nightsister R	3.00	5.00
13	Force Choke L	15.00	20.00
14	Immobilize R	3.00	5.00
15	Kylo Rens Lightsaber L	15.00	20.00
16	Sith Holocron R	10.00	13.00
17	Infantry Grenades R	3.00	5.00
18	Speeder Bike Scout R	3.00	5.00
19	Bala Tik R	3.00	5.00
20	Jabba the Hutt L	20.00	25.00
21	Jango Fett R	3.00	5.00
22	Tusken Raider R	3.00	5.00
23	Crime Lord L	10.00	15.00
24	Flame Thrower R	3.00	5.00
25	Gaffi Stick R	3.00	5.00
26	On the Hunt R	3.00	5.00
27	Admiral Ackbar R	3.00	5.00
28	Leia Organa R	3.00	5.00
29	Poe Dameron L	20.00	25.00
30	Rebel Trooper R	3.00	5.00
31	Launch Bay L	7.00	10.00
32	Black One L	5.00	8.00
33	Scout R	3.00	5.00
34	Survival Gear R	3.00	5.00
35	Luke Skywalker L	20.00	25.00
36	Padawan R	3.00	5.00
37	Qui Gon Jinn R	3.00	5.00
38	Rey S	2.00	3.50
39	Force Protection R	3.00	5.00
40	Jedi Robes R	3.00	5.00
41	Luke Skywalkers Lightsaber L	10.00	15.00
42	One With the Force L	20.00	25.00
43	BB 8 R	3.00	5.00
44	Reys Staff R	3.00	5.00
45	Finn S	2.00	3.50
46	Han Solo L	15.00	20.00
47	Hired Gun R	3.00	5.00
48	Padme Amidala R	3.00	5.00
49	Millennium Falcon L	10.00	15.00
50	Diplomatic Immunity R	3.00	5.00
51	DL 44 Heavy Blaster Pistol R	3.00	5.00
52	Infiltrate R	3.00	5.00
53	Outpost R	3.00	5.00
54	DH 17 Blaster Pistol R	3.00	5.00
55	IQA 11 Blaster Rifle R	3.00	5.00
56	Promotion R	3.00	5.00
57	Force Throw S	7.00	10.00
58	Force Training R	3.00	5.00
59	Lightsaber S	2.00	3.50
60	Mind Probe S	5.00	8.00
61	Comlink R	3.00	5.00
62	Datapad R	3.00	5.00
63	Holdout Blaster R	15.00	20.00
64	Black Market R	3.00	5.00
65	Cunning R	3.00	5.00
66	Jetpack R	3.00	5.00
67	Thermal Detonator L	20.00	25.00
68	Cannon Fodder C	.10	.20
69	Closing the Net C	.10	.20
70	Endless Ranks U	1.50	2.00
71	Occupation C	.10	.20
72	Probe C	.10	.20
73	Sweep the Area C	.10	.20
74	Tactical Mastery U	2.00	3.00
75	The Best Defense U	.25	.40
76	Drudge Work C	.10	.20
77	Local Garrison U	.25	.40
78	Personal Escort C	.10	.20
79	Abandon All Hope U	.25	.40
80	Boundless Ambition C	.10	.20
81	Enrage C	.10	.20
82	Feel Your Anger C	.10	.20
83	Force Strike U	.75	1.25
84	Intimidate C	.10	.20
85	Isolation C	.10	.20
86	No Mercy U	2.00	3.00
87	Pulling the Strings C	.10	.20
88	Emperors Favor U	.25	.40
89	Power of the Dark Side S	.40	.60
90	Hidden in Shadow U	.25	.40
91	Nowhere to Run U	.25	.40
92	Ace in the Hole U	.75	1.25
93	Armed to the Teeth C	.10	.20
94	Confiscation U	.25	.40
95	Fight Dirty U	.25	.40
96	Go for the Kill C	.10	.20
97	He Doesnt Like You C	.10	.20
98	Lying in Wait C	.10	.20
99	Backup Muscle C	.10	.20
100	My Kind of Scum C	.10	.20
101	Underworld Connections U	1.00	1.50
102	Prized Possession U	.25	.40
103	Commando Raid U	.25	.40
104	Defensive Position U	.10	.20
105	Field Medic C	.10	.20
106	Hit and Run C	.10	.20
107	Its a Trap U	.75	1.25
108	Natural Talent C	.10	.20
109	Rearm U	.25	.40
110	Retreat U	.25	.40
111	Strategic Planning C	.10	.20

112 Surgical Strike C	.10	.20
113 Resistance HQ U	.25	.40
114 Anticipate U	.25	.40
115 Defensive Stance C	.10	.20
116 Force Misdirection C	.10	.20
117 Heroism C	.10	.20
118 Noble Sacrifice C	.10	.20
119 Patience C	.10	.20
120 Return of the Jedi U	.25	.40
121 Riposte C	.10	.20
122 Willpower U	.40	.60
123 Jedi Council U	.25	.40
124 Awakening S	.60	1.00
125 The Force is Strong C	.10	.20
126 Daring Escape U	.25	.40
127 Dont Get Cocky C	.10	.20
128 Draw Attention C	.10	.20
129 Hyperspace Jump U	.25	.40
130 Let the Wookiee Win U	.25	.40
131 Negotiate C	.10	.20
132 Scavenge C	.10	.20
133 Shoot First U	.25	.40
134 Smuggling C	.10	.20
135 Play the Odds U	.25	.40
136 Street Informants C	.10	.20
137 Second Chance U	1.50	2.50
138 Award Ceremony C	.10	.20
139 Dug In U	2.00	3.00
140 Firepower C	.10	.20
141 Leadership U	.40	.60
142 Logistics C	.10	.20
143 Squad Tactics C	.10	.20
144 Supporting Fire U	.25	.40
145 Deflect C	.10	.20
146 Disturbance in the Force C	.10	.20
147 Mind Trick U	.40	.60
148 The Power of the Force C	.10	.20
149 Use the Force S	.75	1.25
150 It Binds All Things U	1.25	2.00
151 Aim S	.50	.80
152 All In U	1.50	2.00
153 Block C	.10	.20
154 Close Quarters Assault S	1.00	1.50
155 Dodge C	.10	.20
156 Flank U	.25	.40
157 Take Cover C	.10	.20
158 Disarm C	.10	.20
159 Electroshock U	4.00	6.00
160 Reversal U	1.00	1.50
161 Scramble C	.10	.20
162 Unpredictable C	.10	.20
163 Infamous U	1.50	2.50
164 Hunker Down C	.10	.20
165 Command Center U	.25	.40
166 Echo Base U	.25	.40
167 Emperors Throne Room U	.25	.40
168 Frozen Wastes S	.60	1.00
169 Imperial Armory C	.10	.20
170 Jedi Temple C	.10	.20
171 Rebel War Room C	.10	.20
172 Mos Eisley Spaceport C	.10	.20
173 Separatist Base C	.10	.20
174 Starship Graveyard S	1.50	2.50

2016 Star Wars Force Attax The Force Awakens

COMPLETE SET (224 CARDS)
RELEASED IN 2016

1 Luke Skywalker	.20	.35
2 Princess Leia	.20	.35
3 Han Solo	.20	.35
4 Chewbacca	.20	.35
5 Obi Wan Kenobi	.20	.35
6 Yoda	.20	.35
7 Lando Calrissian	.20	.35
8 Mon Mothma	.20	.35
9 General Jan Dodonna	.20	.35
10 General Rieekan	.20	.35
11 Lobot	.20	.35
12 Owen Lars	.20	.35
13 Beru Lars	.20	.35
14 Rebel Trooper	.20	.35
15 Rebel Commando	.20	.35
16 C 3PO	.20	.35
17 R2 D2	.20	.35
18 2 1B Medical Droid	.20	.35
19 K 3PO	.20	.35
20 FX 7 Medical Droid	.20	.35
21 Training Remote	.20	.35
22 Admiral Ackbar	.20	.35
23 Mon Calamari	.20	.35
24 Crix Madine	.20	.35
25 Orrimaarko	.20	.35
26 Wicket	.20	.35
27 Logray	.20	.35
28 Paploo	.20	.35
29 Teebo	.20	.35
30 Tokkat	.20	.35
31 Romba	.20	.35
32 Ten Numb	.20	.35
33 Tauntaun	.20	.35
34 Darth Vader	.20	.35
35 Emperor Palpatine	.20	.35
36 Grand Moff Tarkin	.20	.35
37 Moff Jerjerrod	.20	.35
38 General Veers	.20	.35
39 Captain Lennox	.20	.35
40 Captain Khurgee	.20	.35
41 Lieutenant Cabbel	.20	.35
42 Lieutenant Sheckil	.20	.35
43 Admiral Piett	.20	.35
44 TIE Fighter Pilot	.20	.35
45 Scout Trooper	.20	.35
46 Stormtrooper	.20	.35
47 Sandtrooper	.20	.35
48 Snowtrooper	.20	.35
49 Probot	.20	.35
50 Interrogation Droid	.20	.35
51 Death Star Droid	.20	.35
52 Imperial Astromech Droid	.20	.35
53 R2 Q5	.20	.35
54 Boba Fett	.20	.35
55 Jabba The Hutt	.20	.35
56 Bib Fortuna	.20	.35
57 Salacious B Crumb	.20	.35
58 Oola	.20	.35
59 Yarna D Al Gargan	.20	.35
60 Amanaman	.20	.35
61 Bossk	.20	.35
62 IG 88	.20	.35
63 Boushh	.20	.35
64 Snaggletooth	.20	.35
65 Gamorrean Guard	.20	.35
66 Jawa	.20	.35
67 Tusken Raider	.20	.35
68 Muftak	.20	.35
69 Umpass Stay	.20	.35
70 Klaatu	.20	.35
71 Harc Seff	.20	.35
72 Brock Starsher	.20	.35
73 EV 9D9	.20	.35
74 Millennium Falcon	.20	.35
75 Tantive IV	.20	.35
76 Y Wing Starfighter	.20	.35
77 X Wing Starfighter	.20	.35
78 A Wing Starfighter	.20	.35
79 B Wing Starfighter	.20	.35
80 Home One	.20	.35
81 Nebulon B Frigate	.20	.35
82 Rebel Transport	.20	.35
83 Snowspeeder	.20	.35
84 Landspeeder	.20	.35
85 T 16 Skyhopper	.20	.35
86 Death Star	.20	.35

87 Death Star II	.20	.35
88 Star Destroyer	.20	.35
89 Super Star Destroyer	.20	.35
90 TIE Fighter	.20	.35
91 TIE Interceptor	.20	.35
92 Darth Vader s TIE Advanced	.20	.35
93 TIE Bomber	.20	.35
94 Imperial Shuttle	.20	.35
95 Speeder Bike	.20	.35
96 AT ST Walker	.20	.35
97 AT AT Walker	.20	.35
98 Probe Droid Capsule	.20	.35
99 Slave 1	.20	.35
100 Jabba s Sail Barge	.20	.35
101 Desert Skiff	.20	.35
102 Finn	.20	.35
103 Rey	.20	.35
104 Poe Dameron	.20	.35
105 BB 8	.20	.35
106 Han Solo	.20	.35
107 Chewbacca	.20	.35
108 General Leia Organa	.20	.35
109 C 3PO	.20	.35
110 R2 D2	.20	.35
111 Lor San Tekka	.20	.35
112 Kylo Ren	.20	.35
113 General Hux	.20	.35
114 Captain Phasma	.20	.35
115 Stormtrooper	.20	.35
116 Stormtrooper	.20	.35
117 Snowtrooper	.20	.35
118 TIE Fighter Pilot	.20	.35
119 Rey s Speeder	.20	.35
120 Millennium Falcon	.20	.35
121 X Wing Starfighter	.20	.35
122 Poe s X Wing Starfighter	.20	.35
123 The Finalizer	.20	.35
124 First Order Transporter	.20	.35
125 Rebel Strikeforce 1	.20	.35
126 Rebel Strikeforce 2	.20	.35
127 Rebel Strikeforce 3	.20	.35
128 Rebel Strikeforce 4	.20	.35
129 Rebel Strikeforce 5	.20	.35
130 Rebel Strikeforce 6	.20	.35
131 Rebel Strikeforce 7	.20	.35
132 Rebel Strikeforce 8	.20	.35
133 Rebel Strikeforce 9	.20	.35
134 Empire Strikeforce 1	.20	.35
135 Empire Strikeforce 2	.20	.35
136 Empire Strikeforce 3	.20	.35
137 Empire Strikeforce 4	.20	.35
138 Empire Strikeforce 5	.20	.35
139 Empire Strikeforce 6	.20	.35
140 Empire Strikeforce 7	.20	.35
141 Empire Strikeforce 8	.20	.35
142 Empire Strikeforce 9	.20	.35
143 Rebel Strikeforce 1	.20	.35
144 Rebel Strikeforce 2	.20	.35
145 Rebel Strikeforce 3	.20	.35
146 Rebel Strikeforce 4	.20	.35
147 Rebel Strikeforce 5	.20	.35
148 Rebel Strikeforce 6	.20	.35
149 Rebel Strikeforce 7	.20	.35
150 Rebel Strikeforce 8	.20	.35
151 Rebel Strikeforce 9	.20	.35
152 First Order Strikeforce 1	.20	.35
153 First Order Strikeforce 2	.20	.35
154 First Order Strikeforce 3	.20	.35
155 First Order Strikeforce 4	.20	.35
156 First Order Strikeforce 5	.20	.35
157 First Order Strikeforce 6	.20	.35
158 First Order Strikeforce 7	.20	.35
159 First Order Strikeforce 8	.20	.35
160 First Order Strikeforce 9	.20	.35
161 Luke Skywalker	.20	.35
162 Princess Leia	.20	.35
163 Han Solo	.20	.35
164 Chewbacca	.20	.35
165 Obi Wan Kenobi	.20	.35
166 Yoda	.20	.35
167 Lando Calrissian	.20	.35
168 C 3PO	.20	.35
169 R2 D2	.20	.35
170 Admiral Ackbar	.20	.35
171 Darth Vader	.20	.35
172 Emperor Palpatine	.20	.35

#	Name		
173	Stormtrooper	.20	.35
174	AT AT Pilot	.20	.35
175	AT ST Pilot	.20	.35
176	Jabba The Hutt	.20	.35
177	Boba Fett	.20	.35
178	Dengar	.20	.35
179	Millennium Falcon	.20	.35
180	X Wing Starfighter	.20	.35
181	TIE Interceptor	.20	.35
182	Star Destroyer	.20	.35
183	Finn	.20	.35
184	Rey	.20	.35
185	Poe Dameron	.20	.35
186	BB 8	.20	.35
187	Chewbacca	.20	.35
188	Kylo Ren	.20	.35
189	Captain Phasma	.20	.35
190	Stormtrooper	.20	.35
191	TIE Fighter	.20	.35
192	Millennium Falcon	.20	.35
193	Luke Skywalker	.20	.35
194	Princess Leia	.20	.35
195	Han Solo	.20	.35
196	Chewbacca	.20	.35
197	Obi Wan Kenobi	.20	.35
198	Yoda	.20	.35
199	Lando Calrissian	.20	.35
200	C 3PO	.20	.35
201	R2 D2	.20	.35
202	Darth Vader	.20	.35
203	Emperor Palpatine	.20	.35
204	Boba Fett	.20	.35
205	Finn	.20	.35
206	Poe Dameron	.20	.35
207	Kylo Ren	.20	.35
208	Captain Phasma	.20	.35
209	Finn	.20	.35
210	Rey	.20	.35
211	Poe Dameron	.20	.35
212	BB 8	.20	.35
213	Han Solo	.20	.35
214	Chewbacca	.20	.35
215	C 3PO	.20	.35
216	R2 D2	.20	.35
217	Kylo Ren	.20	.35
218	General Hux	.20	.35
219	Captain Phasma	.20	.35
220	Stormtrooper	.20	.35
221	Stormtrooper	.20	.35
222	Snowtrooper	.20	.35
223	Flametrooper	.20	.35
224	Riot Control Stormtrooper	.20	.35

2016 Star Wars Force Attax Extra The Force Awakens

COMPLETE SET (138 CARDS)		100.00	250.00
1	Finn	.75	2.00
2	Rey	.75	2.00
3	Poe Dameron	.75	2.00
4	BB 8	.75	2.00
5	Han Solo	.75	2.00
6	Chewbacca	.75	2.00
7	General Organa	.75	2.00
8	Admiral Ackbar	.75	2.00
9	Admiral Statura	.75	2.00
10	Major Ematt	.75	2.00
11	Major Brance	.75	2.00
12	Snap Wexley	.75	2.00
13	Jess Testor Pava	.75	2.00
14	Ello Asty	.75	2.00
15	Nien Nunb	.75	2.00
16	Korr Sella	.75	2.00
17	Vober Dand	.75	2.00
18	Pamich Nerro	.75	2.00
19	Kaydel Ko	.75	2.00
20	Goss Toowers	.75	2.00
21	Bollie Prindel	.75	2.00
22	Resistance Soldier	.75	2.00
23	C 3PO	.75	2.00
24	R2 D2	.75	2.00
25	4B EG 6	.75	2.00
26	PZ 4CO	.75	2.00
27	M9 G8	.75	2.00
28	B U4D	.75	2.00
29	GA 97	.75	2.00
30	Kylo Ren	.75	2.00
31	General Hux	.75	2.00
32	Captain Phasma	.75	2.00
33	Lieutenant Mitaka	.75	2.00
34	Colonel Datoo	.75	2.00
35	Chief Petty Officer Unamo	.75	2.00
36	Petty Officer Thanisson	.75	2.00
37	Fleet Engineer	.75	2.00
38	Lieutenant Rodinon	.75	2.00
39	Technician Mandetat	.75	2.00
40	Stormtrooper	.75	2.00
41	Flametrooper	.75	2.00
42	Snowtrooper	.75	2.00
43	Riot Control Stormtrooper	.75	2.00
44	TIE Fighter Pilot	.75	2.00
45	Millennium Falcon	.75	2.00
46	The Erevana	.75	2.00
47	Resistance Transport	.75	2.00
48	X Wing Starfighter	.75	2.00
49	Poe Dameron s X Wing	.75	2.00
50	Rey s Speeder	.75	2.00
51	The Finalizer	.75	2.00
52	Kylo Ren s Command Shuttle	.75	2.00
53	TIE Fighter	.75	2.00
54	Special Forces TIE Fighter	.75	2.00
55	Unkar Plutt	.75	2.00
56	Unkar s Thug	.75	2.00
57	Unkar s Thug	.75	2.00
58	Teedo	.75	2.00
59	Athgar Heece	.75	2.00
60	Bobbajo	.75	2.00
61	Crusher Roodown	.75	2.00
62	Sarco Plank	.75	2.00
63	Constable Zuvio	.75	2.00
64	Bala Tik	.75	2.00
65	Guavian Security Soldier	.75	2.00
66	Guavian Security Soldier	.75	2.00
67	Tasu Leech	.75	2.00
68	Volzang Li Thrull	.75	2.00
69	Crokind Shand	.75	2.00
70	Razoo Qin Fee	.75	2.00
71	Maz Kanata	.75	2.00
72	Captain Ithano	.75	2.00
73	Grummgar	.75	2.00
74	Bazine Netal	.75	2.00
75	Strono Cookie Tuggs	.75	2.00
76	Wollivan	.75	2.00
77	Quiggold	.75	2.00
78	Pru Sweevant	.75	2.00
79	Prashee and Cratinus	.75	2.00
80	Hassk Triplets	.75	2.00
81	Jashco Phurus	.75	2.00
82	Gwellis Bagnoro	.75	2.00
83	Praster Ommlen	.75	2.00
84	Happabore	.75	2.00
85	Luggabeast	.75	2.00
86	Rathtar	.75	2.00
87	FN 2187 and Poe Dameron	.75	2.00
88	Rey and Finn	.75	2.00
89	Han and Chewbacca	.75	2.00
90	Han and Leia	.75	2.00
91	R2 D2 and C 3PO	.75	2.00
92	BB 8 and R2 D2	.75	2.00
93	Rey Finn and BB 8	.75	2.00
94	Han Chewbacca Rey and Finn	.75	2.00
95	Kylo Ren and Captain Phasma	.75	2.00
96	Grummgar and Bazine	.75	2.00
97	Finn	.75	2.00
98	Rey	.75	2.00
99	Poe Dameron	.75	2.00
100	Han Solo	.75	2.00
101	Chewbacca	.75	2.00
102	BB 8	.75	2.00
103	C 3PO	.75	2.00
104	Kylo Ren	.75	2.00
105	General Hux	.75	2.00
106	Captain Phasma	.75	2.00
107	Riot Control Stormtrooper	.75	2.00
108	Stormtrooper	.75	2.00
109	Maz Kanata	.75	2.00
110	Captain Ithano	.75	2.00
111	Tasu Leech	.75	2.00
112	Bala Tik	.75	2.00
113	Starkiller Base	.75	2.00
114	The Finalizer	.75	2.00
115	Kylo Ren s Command Shuttle	.75	2.00
116	TIE Fighter	.75	2.00
117	Millennium Falcon	.75	2.00
118	The Erevana	.75	2.00
119	X Wing Starfighter	.75	2.00
120	Poe Dameron s X Wing	.75	2.00
121	Finn	.75	2.00
122	Rey	.75	2.00
123	Poe Dameron	.75	2.00
124	Han Solo	.75	2.00
125	Luke Skywalker	.75	2.00
126	Kylo Ren	.75	2.00
127	Captain Phasma	.75	2.00
128	Stormtrooper	.75	2.00
129	Finn	.75	2.00
130	Rey	.75	2.00
131	Poe Dameron	.75	2.00
132	Han Solo	.75	2.00
133	Chewbacca	.75	2.00
134	BB 8	.75	2.00
135	Kylo Ren	.75	2.00
136	Captain Phasma	.75	2.00
137	Maz Kanata	.75	2.00
138	Unkar Plutt	.75	2.00

2017 Star Wars Destiny Spirit of Rebellion

COMPLETE SET (160 CARDS)		400.00	550.00
BOOSTER BOX (36 PACKS)		100.00	130.00
BOOSTER PACK (5 CARDS AND 1 DICE)		4.00	6.00
UNLISTED C		.10	.20
UNLISTED U		.25	.40
UNLISTED R		3.00	5.00
RELEASED ON APRIL 28TH, 2017			
1	Death Trooper R	4.00	6.00
2	FN 2199 R	2.50	4.00
3	Director Krennic L	8.00	12.00
4	TIE Pilot R	2.50	4.00
5	E Web Emplacement R	7.00	10.00
6	Imperial Discipline R	2.50	4.00
7	DT 29 Heavy Blaster Pistol R	2.50	4.00

No.	Card	Low	High
8	Z6 Riot Control Baton L	20.00	25.00
9	Asajj Ventress R	2.50	4.00
10	Darth Vader R	2.50	4.00
11	Palpatine L	20.00	25.00
12	Royal Guard R	2.50	4.00
13	Commando Shuttle R	2.50	4.00
14	Force Lightning L	15.00	20.00
15	Lightsaber Pike R	7.00	10.00
16	Lure of Power R	2.50	4.00
17	Interrogation Droid R	2.50	4.00
18	Aurra Sing R	2.50	4.00
19	Guavian Enforcer R	2.50	4.00
20	IG 88 L	8.00	12.00
21	Unkar Plutt R	2.50	4.00
22	Slave I L	8.00	12.00
23	Blackmail L	8.00	12.00
24	Personal Shield R	2.50	4.00
25	Vibroknucklers R	2.50	4.00
26	Baze Malbus L	8.00	12.00
27	Mon Mothma R	2.50	4.00
28	Rebel Commando R	2.50	4.00
29	Temmin "Snap" Wexley R	2.50	4.00
30	C 3PO R	2.50	4.00
31	U Wing L	8.00	12.00
32	A180 Blaster R	2.50	4.00
33	Overkill R	2.50	4.00
34	Jedi Acolyte R	2.50	4.00
35	Chirrut Œmwe R	2.50	4.00
36	Luminara Unduli R	2.50	4.00
37	Obi Wan Kenobi L	8.00	12.00
38	Delta 7 Interceptor R	2.50	4.00
39	Handcrafted Light Bow L	8.00	12.00
40	Force Heal R	2.50	4.00
41	Journals of Ben Kenobi R	2.50	4.00
42	R2 D2 R	2.50	4.00
43	Chewbacca L	8.00	12.00
44	Jyn Erso R	2.50	4.00
45	Maz Kanata R	2.50	4.00
46	Outer Rim Smuggler R	2.50	4.00
47	Smuggling Freighter R	2.50	4.00
48	Bowcaster L	8.00	12.00
49	Lone Operative R	2.50	4.00
50	Mazs Goggles L	8.00	12.00
51	Supply Line R	2.50	4.00
52	Astromech R	2.50	4.00
53	Rocket Launcher L	30.00	35.00
54	Force Push R	2.50	4.00
55	Force Speed L	50.00	65.00
56	Makashi Training R	2.50	4.00
57	Vibroknife R	15.00	20.00
58	Quadjumper L	8.00	12.00
59	Ascension Gun R	7.00	10.00
60	Con Artist R	2.50	4.00
61	Battle Formation C	.10	.20
62	Imperial War Machine U	.25	.40
63	Lockdown C	.10	.20
64	Sustained Fire U	.25	.40
65	Traitor U	.25	.40
66	Trench Warfare C	.10	.20
67	Undying Loyalty C	.10	.20
68	We Have Them Now U	.40	.60
69	Attrition C	.10	.20
70	Imperial Inspection U	.40	.60
71	Anger U	.75	1.25
72	Lightsaber Throw U	.60	1.00
73	Manipulate C	.10	.20
74	No Disintegreations C	.10	.20
75	Now You Will Die C	.10	.20
76	Rise Again U	1.00	1.50
77	The Price of Failure C	.10	.20
78	Dark Presence U	1.00	1.50
79	Now I Am The Master C	.10	.20
80	Doubt C	.10	.20
81	Arms Deal C	.10	.20
82	Bait and Switch C	.10	.20
83	Friends in High Places U	.25	.40
84	Loose Ends U	.25	.40
85	One Quarter Portion C	.10	.20
86	Relentless Pursuit C	.10	.20
87	Scrap Buy U	.25	.40
88	Salvage Stand C	.10	.20
89	Armor Plating U	.60	1.00
90	Emergency Evacuation U	.25	.40
91	Friendly Fire U	.25	.40
92	Guerrilla Warfare C	.10	.20
93	Our Only Hope U	.25	.40
94	Rebel Assault C	.10	.20
95	Sensor Placement U	.25	.40
96	Spirit of Rebellion C	.10	.20
97	Planetary Uprising U	.60	1.00
98	Spy Net C	.10	.20
99	Tactical Aptitude C	.10	.20
100	Caution U	.75	1.25
101	Destiny C	.10	.20
102	Determination C	.10	.20
103	Guard U	.25	.40
104	Krayt Dragon Howl C	.10	.20
105	My Ally Is The Force U	.60	1.00
106	Synchronicity C	.10	.20
107	Your Eyes Can Decive You U	.25	.40
108	Protective Mentor C	.10	.20
109	Confidence U	.25	.40
110	Garbagell Do C	.10	.20
111	Hold On C	.10	.20
112	Rebel U	.25	.40
113	Long Con C	.10	.20
114	Loth Cat and Mouse C	.10	.20
115	Never Tell Me the Odds U	.25	.40
116	Planned Explosion U	.25	.40
117	Double Dealing C	.10	.20
118	Life Debt U	.25	.40
119	Bombing Run U	.25	.40
120	Collateral Damage C	.10	.20
121	Salvo U	.40	.60
122	Suppression C	.10	.20
123	Aftermath C	.10	.20
124	Air Superiority C	.10	.20
125	Training U	2.00	2.50
126	Wingman C	.10	.20
127	Decisive Blow C	.10	.20
128	High Ground C	.10	.20
129	Momentum Shift U	.25	.40
130	Overconfidence C	.10	.20
131	Premonitions U	.25	.40
132	Rejuvenate C	.10	.20
133	Trust Your Instincts U	1.25	2.00
134	Meditate C	.10	.20
135	Force Illusion U	2.00	3.00
136	Evade C	.10	.20
137	New Orders U	.60	1.00
138	Parry C	.10	.20
139	Swiftness C	.10	.20
140	Resolve U	.25	.40
141	Ammo Belt C	.10	.20
142	Bolt Hole C	.10	.20
143	Cheat U	.75	1.25
144	Diversion U	.10	.20
145	Fair Trade U	.25	.40
146	Friends in Low Places C	.10	.20
147	Sabotage U	.25	.40
148	Improvisation C	.10	.20
149	Outmaneuver C	.10	.20
150	Fast Hands U	5.00	7.00
151	Carbon Freezing Chamber U	.25	.40
152	Cargo Hold C	.10	.20
153	Docking Bay C	.10	.20
154	Ewok Village C	.10	.20
155	Mazs Castle U	.25	.40
156	Moisture Farm U	.25	.40
157	Otoh Gunga C	.10	.20
158	Secluded Beach C	.10	.20
159	Secret Facility U	.25	.40
160	War Torn Streets C	.10	.20

2017 Star Wars Destiny Empire at War

	Low	High
COMPLETE SET (160 CARDS)	300.00	550.00
BOOSTER BOX (36 PACKS)	85.00	120.00
BOOSTER PACK (5 CARDS)	3.00	5.00
UNLISTED C	.10	.20
UNLISTED U	.40	.60
UNLISTED R	2.00	5.00

RELEASED IN FALL 2017

No.	Card	Low	High
1	†Ciena Ree† Adept Pilot R	2.00	5.00
2	†General Hux† Aspiring Commander R	2.00	5.00
3	†MagnaGuard R	2.00	5.00
4	†Thrawn†Master Strategist L	15.00	20.00
5	†AT DP R	2.00	5.00
6	†Probe Droid R	2.00	5.00
7	†T 7 Ion Disruptor Rifle L	8.00	15.00
8	†Quinlan Vos† Dark Disciple R	2.00	5.00
9	†Servant of the Dark Side R	2.00	5.00
10	†Seventh Sister† Agile Inquisitor L	8.00	15.00
11	†Grand Inquisitor† Sith Loyalist L	8.00	15.00
12	†Darth Vaders TIE Advanced R	2.00	5.00
13	†ID9 Seeker Droid R	2.00	5.00
14	†Temptation R	2.00	5.00
15	†Grand Inquisitors Lightsaber L	8.00	15.00
16	†Bazine Netal† Master Manipulator R	2.00	5.00
17	†Bosskt† Wookiee Slayer R	2.00	5.00
18	†Cad Bane† Vicious Mercenary L	15.00	20.00
19	†Gamorrean Guard R	2.00	5.00
20	†Hounds Tooth L	8.00	15.00
21	†Cable Launcher R	2.00	5.00
22	†LL 30 Blaster Pistol R	2.00	5.00
23	†Relby V10 Mortar Gun R	2.00	5.00
24	†General Rieekan† Defensive Mastermind R	2.00	5.00
25	†Hera Syndulla† Phoenix Leader R	2.00	5.00
26	†K 2SO† Reprogrammed Droid L	8.00	15.00
27	†Rookie Pilot R	2.00	5.00
28	†Ghost L	8.00	15.00
29	†Y Wing R	2.00	5.00
30	†A280 Blaster Rifle R	2.00	5.00
31	†Ahsoka Tano† Force Operative L	20.00	25.00
32	†Jedi Instructor R	2.00	5.00
33	†Kanan Jarrus† Rebel Jedi R	2.00	5.00
34	†Mace Windu† Jedi Champion L	8.00	15.00
35	†Training Remote R	2.00	5.00
36	†Master of the Council L	8.00	15.00
37	†Coordination R	2.00	5.00
38	†Ezra Bridger† Force sensitive Thief R	2.00	5.00
39	†Lando Calrissian† Galactic Entrepreneur R	2.00	5.00
40	†Sabine Wren† Explosives Expert L	8.00	15.00
41	†Wookiee Warrior R	2.00	5.00
42	†Chopper L	8.00	15.00
43	†Energy Slingshot R	2.00	5.00
44	†Tough Haggler R	2.00	5.00
45	†T 47 Airspeeder R	2.00	5.00
46	†LR1K Sonic Cannon L	8.00	15.00
47	†Electrostaff R	2.00	5.00
48	†Natural Pilot R	2.00	5.00
49	†Ancient Lightsaber L	35.00	45.00
50	†Psychometry R	2.00	5.00
51	†Shoto Lightsaber R	2.00	5.00
52	†Weapons Cache R	2.00	5.00
53	†BD 1 Cutter Vibro AX R	2.00	5.00
54	†Extortion R	2.00	5.00
55	†X 8 Night Sniper L	8.00	15.00
56	†Z 95 Headhunter R	2.00	5.00
57	†Chance Cube R	2.00	5.00
58	†EMP Grenades R	2.00	5.00
59	†Lead by Example R	2.00	5.00
60	†Scatterblaster R	2.00	5.00
61	†Commandeer U	.40	.60
62	†Crossfire C	.10	.20
63	†Drop Your Weapon! U	.40	.60
64	†Imperial Backing U	.40	.60
65	†Prepare for War C	.10	.20
66	†Red Alert C	.10	.20
67	†Ruthless Tactics C	.10	.20
68	†Take Prisoner U	.40	.60
69	†Imperial HQ C	.10	.20
70	†As You Command C	.10	.20
71	†Cornered Prey C	.10	.20
72	†Indomitable C	.10	.20
73	†It Will All Be Mine U	.40	.60
74	†Kill Them All C	.10	.20
75	†Unyielding U	.40	.60
76	†Insidious C	.10	.20
77	†Hate U	.40	.60
78	†Anarchy U	.40	.60
79	†Bounty Postings C	.10	.20
80	†Buy Out U	.40	.60
81	†Coercion U	.40	.60
82	†Only Business Matters C	.10	.20

83 †Pilfered Goods U	.40	.60
84 †Twin Shadows U	.40	.60
85 †Hutt Ties C	.10	.20
86 †Deadly U	.40	.60
87 †No Survivors C	.10	.20
88 †Detention Center U	.40	.60
89 †All Quiet On The Front U	.40	.60
90 †Entrenched U	.40	.60
91 †Fortuitous Strike C	.10	.20
92 †Rearguard C	.10	.20
93 †Reckless Reentry U	.40	.60
94 †Strike Briefing C	.10	.20
95 †Swift Strike C	.10	.20
96 †Rally Aid U	.40	.60
97 †Shield Generator C	.10	.20
98 †At Peace C	.10	.20
99 †Bestow C	.10	.20
100 †Bring Balance U	.40	.60
101 †Reaping The Crystal U	.40	.60
102 †Secret Mission C	.10	.20
103 †Trust The Force C	.10	.20
104 †Funeral Pyre C	.10	.20
105 †Yodas Quarters U	.40	.60
106 †Fearless U	.40	.60
107 †Against The Odds C	.10	.20
108 †Appraise C	.10	.20
109 †Bad Feeling C	.10	.20
110 †Double Cross U	.40	.60
111 †Impersonate U	.40	.60
112 †Local Patrol C	.10	.20
113 †Quick Escape U	.40	.60
114 †Tenacity C	.10	.20
115 †Running Interference U	.40	.60
116 †Thermal Paint C	.10	.20
117 †Defiance C	.10	.20
118 †Covering Fire C	.10	.20
119 †Deploy Squadron C	.10	.20
120 †Fall Back U	.40	.60
121 †Feint U	.40	.60
122 †Flanking Maneuver U	.40	.60
123 †Heat Of Battle C	.10	.20
124 †Pinned Down C	.10	.20
125 †The Day is Ours C	.10	.20
126 †Drop Zone U	.40	.60
127 †Tech Team C	.10	.20
128 †Battle of Wills U	.40	.60
129 †Force Vision C	.10	.20
130 †Lightsaber Pull C	.10	.20
131 †Lightsaber Training C	.10	.20
132 †No Surrender C	.10	.20
133 †Something familiar U	.40	.60
134 †Voices Cry Out C	.10	.20
135 †Keen Instincts U	.40	.60
136 †Battle Rage C	.10	.20
137 †Disable C	.10	.20
138 †Persuade C	.10	.20
139 †Pickpocket C	.10	.20
140 †Threaten U	.40	.60
141 †Trickery U	.40	.60
142 †Truce U	.10	.20
143 †Stolen Cache C	.10	.20
144 †Hidden Agenda U	.40	.60
145 †Mandalorian Armor C	.10	.20
146 †Dangerous Mission C	.10	.20
147 †Endurance U	.40	.60
148 †Partnership C	.10	.20
149 †Recycle C	.10	.20
150 †Rend C	.10	.20
151 †Roll On C	.10	.20
152 †Plastoid Armor C	.10	.20
153 †BOmarr Monastery† Teth C	.10	.20
154 †Fort Anaxes† Anaxes U	.40	.60
155 †Garel Spaceport† Garel U	.40	.60
156 †Imperial Academy† Lothal U	.40	.60
157 †Main Plaza† Vashka C	.10	.20
158 †Medical Center† Kaliida Shoals U	.40	.60
159 †Port District† Bespin U	.40	.60
160 †Weapons Factory Alpha† Cymoon 1 U	.40	.60

2017 Star Wars Force Attax Universe

COMPLETE SET (272 CARDS)	70.00	110.00
BOOSTER BOX (36 PACKS)	50.00	80.00
BOOSTER PACK (5 CARDS)	2.00	3.50
RELEASED IN FEBRUARY, 2017		

1 Anakin Skywalker	.25	.40
2 Boss Nass	.25	.40
3 C 3PO	.25	.40
4 Captain Panaka	.25	.40
5 Jar Jar Binks	.25	.40
6 Naboo Pilot	.25	.40
7 Obi Wan Kenobi	.25	.40
8 Padme Amidala	.25	.40
9 Qui Gon Jinn	.25	.40
10 R2 D2	.25	.40
11 Senator Palpatine	.25	.40
12 Shmi Skywalker	.25	.40
13 Sio Bibble	.25	.40
14 Battle Droid	.25	.40
15 Darth Maul	.25	.40
16 Darth Sidious	.25	.40
17 Destroyer Droid	.25	.40
18 Nute Gunray	.25	.40
19 Sebulba	.25	.40
20 Watto	.25	.40
21 Droid Control Ship	.25	.40
22 N 1 Starfighter	.25	.40
23 Naboo Royal Starship	.25	.40
24 Sith Infiltrator	.25	.40
25 Anakin Skywalker	.25	.40
26 C 3PO	.25	.40
27 Captain Typho	.25	.40
28 Chancellor Palpatine	.25	.40
29 Clone Trooper	.25	.40
30 Dexter Jettster	.25	.40
31 Ki Adi Mundi	.25	.40
32 Lama Su	.25	.40
33 Mace Windu	.25	.40
34 Obi Wan Kenobi	.25	.40
35 Padme Amidala	.25	.40
36 R2 D2	.25	.40
37 Yoda	.25	.40
38 Count Dooku	.25	.40
39 Geonosian Warrior	.25	.40
40 Jango Fett	.25	.40
41 Poggle The Lesser	.25	.40
42 Shu Mai	.25	.40
43 Super Battle Droid	.25	.40
44 Wat Tambor	.25	.40
45 Zam Wesell	.25	.40
46 Jedi Starfighter	.25	.40
47 Republic Gunship	.25	.40
48 Slave 1	.25	.40
49 Aayla Secura	.25	.40
50 Anakin Skywalker	.25	.40
51 Bail Organa	.25	.40
52 C 3PO	.25	.40
53 Clone Trooper	.25	.40
54 Commander Cody	.25	.40
55 Kit Fisto	.25	.40
56 Mace Windu	.25	.40
57 Obi Wan Kenobi	.25	.40
58 Padme Amidala	.25	.40
59 Plo Koon	.25	.40
60 R2 D2	.25	.40
61 Yoda	.25	.40

62 Count Dooku	.25	.40
63 Darth Sidious	.25	.40
64 General Grievous	.25	.40
65 San Hill	.25	.40
66 Magnaguard	.25	.40
67 Muckraker Crab Droid	.25	.40
68 ARC 170 Starfighter	.25	.40
69 The Invisible Hand	.25	.40
70 Jedi Attack Cruiser	.25	.40
71 Jedi Starfighter	.25	.40
72 Soulless One Belbullab 22 Starfighter	.25	.40
73 Admiral Raddus	.25	.40
74 Baze Malbus	.25	.40
75 Bistan	.25	.40
76 Bodhi Rook	.25	.40
77 Cassian Andor	.25	.40
78 Chirrut Imwe	.25	.40
79 Edrio Two Tubes	.25	.40
80 General Draven	.25	.40
81 Jyn Erso	.25	.40
82 K 2SO	.25	.40
83 Mon Mothma	.25	.40
84 Moroff	.25	.40
85 Pao	.25	.40
86 Saw Gerrera	.25	.40
87 Darth Vader	.25	.40
88 Death Trooper	.25	.40
89 Director Krennic	.25	.40
90 Galen Erso	.25	.40
91 Shoretrooper	.25	.40
92 Stormtrooper	.25	.40
93 AT ACT	.25	.40
94 Death Star	.25	.40
95 Rebel U Wing Fighter	.25	.40
96 TIE Striker	.25	.40
97 Beru Lars	.25	.40
98 C 3PO	.25	.40
99 Chewbacca	.25	.40
100 General Dodonna	.25	.40
101 Han Solo	.25	.40
102 Jawa	.25	.40
103 Luke Skywalker	.25	.40
104 Obi Wan Kenobi	.25	.40
105 Owen Lars	.25	.40
106 Princess Leia	.25	.40
107 R2 D2	.25	.40
108 Darth Vader	.25	.40
109 Grand Moff Tarkin	.25	.40
110 Imperial Gunner	.25	.40
111 Sandtrooper	.25	.40
112 Stormtrooper	.25	.40
113 TIE Fighter Pilot	.25	.40
114 Tusken Raider	.25	.40
115 Death Star	.25	.40
116 Millennium Falcon	.25	.40
117 Tantive IV	.25	.40
118 TIE Fighter	.25	.40
119 X Wing Starfighter	.25	.40
120 Y Wing Starfighter	.25	.40
121 C 3PO	.25	.40
122 Chewbacca	.25	.40
123 General Rieekan	.25	.40
124 Lando Calrissian	.25	.40
125 Leia Organa	.25	.40
126 Lobot	.25	.40
127 Luke Skywalker	.25	.40
128 R2 D2	.25	.40
129 Rebel Trooper	.25	.40
130 Yoda	.25	.40
131 Admiral Ozzel	.25	.40
132 Admiral Piett	.25	.40
133 Boba Fett	.25	.40
134 Bossk	.25	.40
135 Darth Vader	.25	.40
136 General Veers	.25	.40
137 IG 88	.25	.40
138 Snowtrooper	.25	.40
139 AT AT	.25	.40
140 The Executor	.25	.40
141 Medical Frigate	.25	.40
142 Slave 1	.25	.40
143 Snowspeeder	.25	.40
144 Star Destroyer	.25	.40
145 Admiral Ackbar	.25	.40
146 C 3PO	.25	.40
147 Chewbacca	.25	.40
148 Han Solo	.25	.40

149	Lando Calrissian	.25	.40
150	Leia Organa	.25	.40
151	Luke Skywalker	.25	.40
152	Mon Mothma	.25	.40
153	Nien Nunb	.25	.40
154	R2 D2	.25	.40
155	Wicket	.25	.40
156	Bib Fortuna	.25	.40
157	Boba Fett	.25	.40
158	Darth Vader	.25	.40
159	Emperor Palpatine	.25	.40
160	Gamorrean Guard	.25	.40
161	Jabba The Hutt	.25	.40
162	Scout Trooper	.25	.40
163	AT ST	.25	.40
164	A Wing Starfighter	.25	.40
165	Death Star II	.25	.40
166	Millennium Falcon	.25	.40
167	Speeder Bike	.25	.40
168	TIE Interceptor	.25	.40
169	Admiral Statura	.25	.40
170	BB 8	.25	.40
171	C 3PO	.25	.40
172	Chewbacca	.25	.40
173	Finn	.25	.40
174	General Leia Organa	.25	.40
175	Han Solo	.25	.40
176	Lor San Tekka	.25	.40
177	Luke Skywalker	.25	.40
178	Maz Kanata	.25	.40
179	Poe Dameron	.25	.40
180	R2 D2	.25	.40
181	Rey	.25	.40
182	Captain Phasma	.25	.40
183	Flametrooper	.25	.40
184	General Hux	.25	.40
185	Kylo Ren	.25	.40
186	Stormtrooper	.25	.40
187	Tasu Leech	.25	.40
188	Unkar Plutt	.25	.40
189	The Finalizer	.25	.40
190	Millennium Falcon	.25	.40
191	Poe Dameron s X Wing	.25	.40
192	Starkiller Base	.25	.40
193	Star Wars The Phantom Menace	.25	.40
194	Star Wars Attack of The Clones	.25	.40
195	Star Wars Revenge of The Sith	.25	.40
196	Star Wars Rogue One	.25	.40
197	Star Wars A New Hope	.25	.40
198	Star Wars The Empire Strikes Back	.25	.40
199	Star Wars Return of The Jedi	.25	.40
200	Star Wars The Force Awakens	.25	.40
201	Star Wars The Phantom Menace	.25	.40
202	Star Wars The Phantom Menace	.25	.40
203	Star Wars The Phantom Menace	.25	.40
204	Star Wars Attack of The Clones	.25	.40
205	Star Wars Attack of The Clones	.25	.40
206	Star Wars Attack of The Clones	.25	.40
207	Star Wars Revenge of The Sith	.25	.40
208	Star Wars Revenge of The Sith	.25	.40
209	Star Wars Revenge of The Sith	.25	.40
210	Star Wars Rogue One	.25	.40
211	Star Wars Rogue One	.25	.40
212	Star Wars Rogue One	.25	.40
213	Star Wars A New Hope	.25	.40
214	Star Wars A New Hope	.25	.40
215	Star Wars A New Hope	.25	.40
216	Star Wars The Empire Strikes Back	.25	.40
217	Star Wars The Empire Strikes Back	.25	.40
218	Star Wars The Empire Strikes Back	.25	.40
219	Star Wars Return of The Jedi	.25	.40
220	Star Wars Return of The Jedi	.25	.40
221	Star Wars Return of The Jedi	.25	.40
222	Star Wars The Force Awakens	.25	.40
223	Star Wars The Force Awakens	.25	.40
224	Star Wars The Force Awakens	.25	.40
225	Aurra Sing	.25	.40
226	Jar Jar Binks	.25	.40
227	Yaddle	.25	.40
228	Podracer	.25	.40
229	Boba Fett	.25	.40
230	Jocasta Nu	.25	.40
231	Mas Amedda	.25	.40
232	Geonosian Starfighter	.25	.40
233	Commander Bly	.25	.40
234	Darth Vader	.25	.40
235	Tarful	.25	.40
236	Droid Tri Fighter	.25	.40
237	Death Trooper	.25	.40
238	K 2SO	.25	.40
239	Saw Gerrera	.25	.40
240	Death Star	.25	.40
241	Barquin D an	.25	.40
242	Captain Khurgee	.25	.40
243	R5 D4	.25	.40
244	TIE Advanced	.25	.40
245	Dengar	.25	.40
246	Ugnaught	.25	.40
247	TIE Bomber	.25	.40
248	X Wing	.25	.40
249	General Madine	.25	.40
250	Max Rebo	.25	.40
251	Royal Guard	.25	.40
252	Imperial Shuttle	.25	.40
253	Bala Tik	.25	.40
254	Riot Control Stormtrooper	.25	.40
255	Sidon Ithano	.25	.40
256	Kylo Ren s Command Shuttle	.25	.40
257	Qui-Gon Jinn	.25	.40
258	Darth Maul	.25	.40
259	Yoda	.25	.40
260	Count Dooku	.25	.40
261	Anakin Skywalker	.25	.40
262	Obi Wan Kenobi	.25	.40
263	Jyn Erso	.25	.40
264	Director Krennic	.25	.40
265	Princess Leia	.25	.40
266	Han Solo	.25	.40
267	Darth Vader	.25	.40
268	Boba Fett	.25	.40
269	Luke Skywalker	.25	.40
270	Emperor Palpatine	.25	.40
271	Rey	.25	.40
272	Kylo Ren	.25	.40

1999 Young Jedi Menace of Darth Maul

Darth Maul
Sith Assassin
6
POWER
6
5
DAMAGE
Subtracts 2 from his DAMAGE when he is using **Darth Maul's Lightsaber**.

COMPLETE SET (140)		10.00	25.00
BOOSTER BOX (30 PACKS)		30.00	50.00
BOOSTER PACK (11 CARDS)		1.00	2.00
RELEASED ON MAY 12, 1999			
1	Obi-Wan Kenobi, Young Jedi R	2.00	5.00
2	Qui-Gon Jinn, Jedi Master R	1.50	4.00
3	Jar Jar Binks, Gungan Chuba Thief R	1.00	2.50
4	Anakin Skywalker, Podracer Pilot R	.75	2.00
5	Padme Naberrie, Handmaiden R	1.25	3.00
6	Captain Panaka, Protector of the Queen R	.75	2.00
7	Mace Windu, Jedi Master R	1.00	2.50
8	Queen Amidala, Ruler of Naboo R	1.25	3.00
9	Queen Amidala, Royal Leader R	1.25	3.00
10	Yoda, Jedi Master R	1.25	3.00
11	R2-D2, Astromech Droid R	1.00	2.50
12	C-3PO, Anakin's Creation R	1.00	2.50
13	Boss Nass, Leader of the Gungans U	.30	.75
14	Ric Olie, Ace Pilot U	.30	.75
15	Captain Tarpals, Gungan Guard U	.30	.75
16	Rabe, Handmaiden U	.30	.75
17	Rep Been, Gungan U	.30	.75
18	Mas Amedda, Vice Chancellor U	.30	.75
19	Naboo Officer, Battle Planner U	.30	.75
20	Naboo Security, Guard C	.10	.25
21	Bravo Pilot, Veteran Flyer C	.10	.25
22	Gungan Official, Bureaucrat C	.10	.25
23	Gungan Soldier, Scout C	.10	.25
24	Gungan Guard C	.10	.25
25	Gungan Warrior, Infantry C	.10	.25
26	Gungan Soldier, Veteran C	.10	.25
27	Ishi Tib, Warrior C	.10	.25
28	Ithorian, Merchant C	.10	.25
29	Jawa, Thief C	.10	.25
30	Jawa, Bargainer S	.10	.25
31	Royal Guard, Leader C	.10	.25
32	Royal Guard, Veteran C	.10	.25
33	Obi-Wan Kenobi, Jedi Padawan S	.10	.25
34	Obi-Wan Kenobi's Lightsaber R	1.00	2.50
35	Jedi Lightsaber	.30	.75
	Constructed by Ki-Adi-Mundi U		
36	Anakin Skywalker's Podracer R	.75	2.00
37	Captain Panaka's Blaster C	.10	.25
38	Jar Jar Binks' Electropole U	.30	.75
39	Electropole C	.10	.25
40	Eopie C	.10	.25
41	Kaadu C	.10	.25
42	Flash Speeder C	.10	.25
43	Jawa Ion Blaster C	.10	.25
44	Naboo Blaster C	.10	.25
45	Blaster C	.10	.25
46	Blaster Rifle C	.10	.25
47	Anakin Skywalker	.30	.75
	Meet Obi-Wan Kenobi U		
48	Are You An Angel? U	.30	.75
49	Cha Skrunee Da Pat, Sleemo C	.10	.25
50	Counterparts U	.30	.75
51	Da Beings Hereabouts Cawazy C	.10	.25
52	Enough Of This Pretense U	.30	.75
53	Fear Attracts The Fearful U	.30	.75
54	Gungan Curiosity C	.10	.25
55	He Was Meant To Help You U	.30	.75
56	I Have A Bad Feeling About This U	.30	.75
57	I've Been Trained In Defense U	.30	.75
58	Security Volunteers C	.10	.25
59	Shmi's Pride U	.30	.75
60	The Federation Has Gone Too Far C	.10	.25
61	The Negotiations Were Short C	.10	.25
62	The Queen's Plan C	.10	.25
63	We're Not In Trouble Yet U	.30	.75
64	Yousa Guys Bombad! R	.60	1.50
65	Tatooine Podrace Arena S	.10	.25
66	Coruscant Capital City S	.10	.25
67	Naboo Theed Palace S	.10	.25
68	Bravo 1, Naboo Starfighter U	.30	.75
69	Naboo Starfighter C	.10	.25
70	Republic Cruiser, Transport C	.10	.25
71	Darth Maul, Sith Apprentice R	2.50	6.00
72	Darth Sidious, Sith Master R	1.50	4.00
73	Sebulba, Bad-Tempered Dug R	1.00	2.50
74	Watto, Slave Owner R	.75	2.00
75	Aurra Sing, Bounty Hunter R	1.25	3.00
76	Jabba the Hutt, Vile Crime Lord R	1.00	2.50
77	Gardulla the Hutt, Crime Lord U	.30	.75
78	Destroyer Droid Squad	.60	1.50
	Security Division R		
79	Battle Droid Squad, Assault Unit R	.75	2.00
80	Ben Quadinaros, Podracer Pilot U	.30	.75
81	Gasgano, Podracer Pilot U	.30	.75
82	Mawhonic, Podracer Pilot U	.30	.75
83	Teemto Pagalies, Podracer Pilot U	.30	.75
84	Bib Fortuna, Twi'lek Advisor U	.30	.75
85	Ann and Tann Gella	.30	.75
	Sebulba's Attendants U		
86	Gragra, Chuba Peddler C	.10	.25
87	Passel Argente, Senator C	.10	.25
88	Trade Federation Tank	.75	2.00
	Armored Division R		
89	Destroyer Droid, Wheel Droid C	.10	.25
90	Destroyer Droid, Defense Droid C	.10	.25
91	Sith Probe Droid, Spy Drone C	.10	.25
92	Pit Droid, Engineer C	.10	.25
93	Pit Droid, Heavy Lifter C	.10	.25
94	Pit Droid, Mechanic C	.10	.25
95	Tusken Raider, Nomad C	.10	.25
96	Tusken Raider, Marksman C	.10	.25
97	Battle Droid: Pilot, MTT Division C	.10	.25
98	Battle Droid: Security, MTT Division C	.10	.25
99	Battle Droid: Infantry, MTT Division C	.10	.25
100	Battle Droid: Officer, MTT Division C	.10	.25
101	Battle Droid: Pilot, AAT Division C	.10	.25
102	Battle Droid: Security, AAT Division C	.10	.25
103	Battle Droid: Infantry, AAT Division C	.10	.25
104	Battle Droid: Officer, AAT Division C	.10	.25
105	Neimoidian, Trade Federation Pilot S	.10	.25
106	Darth Maul, Sith Lord S	.40	1.00
107	Sith Lightsaber R	.75	2.00
108	Aurra Sing's Blaster Rifle R	.60	1.50
109	Sebulba's Podracer R	.60	1.50
110	Ben Quadinaros' Podracer U	.30	.75
111	Gasgano's Podracer U	.30	.75
112	Mawhonic's Podracer U	.30	.75
113	Teemto Pagalies' Podracer U	.30	.75
114	Trade Federation Tank Laser Cannon U	.30	.75
115	Multi Troop Transport U	.30	.75
116	STAP U	.30	.75

117 Tatooine Thunder Rifle C	.10	.25
118 Battle Droid Blaster Rifle C	.10	.25
119 Blaster C	.10	.25
120 Blaster Rifle C	.10	.25
121 At Last We Will Have Revenge R	.60	1.50
122 Begin Landing Your Troops C	.10	.25
123 Boonta Eve Podrace U	.30	.75
124 Grueling Contest U	.30	.75
125 In Complete Control C	.10	.25
126 Kaa Bazza Kundee Hodrudda! U	.30	.75
127 Opee Sea Killer C	.10	.25
128 Podrace Preparation U	.30	.75
129 Sandstorm C	.10	.25
130 Sniper C	.10	.25
131 The Invasion Is On Schedule U	.10	.25
132 Vile Gangsters U	.30	.75
133 Watto's Wager U	.30	.75
134 You Have Been Well Trained R	.60	1.50
135 Tatooine Desert Landing Site S	.10	.25
136 Coruscant Jedi Council Chamber S	.10	.25
137 Naboo Gungan Swamp S	.10	.25
138 Darth Maul's Starfighter Sith Infiltrator R	1.00	2.50
139 Droid Starfighter C	.10	.25
140 Battleship Trade Federation Transport C	.10	.25

1999 Young Jedi Menace of Darth Maul Foil

COMPLETE SET (18)	6.00	15.00
RELEASED ON MAY 12, 1999		
F1 Obi-Wan Kenobi, Young Jedi R	2.50	6.00
F2 Jar-Jar Binks, Gungan Chuba Thief R	1.25	3.00
F3 Mace Windu, Jedi Master U	1.25	3.00
F4 Queen Amidala, Ruler of Naboo U	2.00	5.00
F5 C-3PO, Anakin's Creation U	1.25	3.00
F6 Obi-Wan Kenobi's Lightsaber C	1.00	2.50
F7 Anakin Skywalker's Podracer C	.75	2.00
F8 Bravo 1, Naboo Starfighter C	.40	1.00
F9 Republic Cruiser, Transport C	.40	1.00
F10 Darth Maul, Sith Apprentice R	3.00	8.00
F11 Darth Sidious, Sith Master R	2.00	5.00
F12 Destroyer Droid Squad Security Division U	.60	1.50
F13 Battle Droid Squad, Assault Unit U	.60	1.50
F14 Sebulba's Podracer U	.60	1.50
F15 Ben Quadinaros' Podracer C	.40	1.00
F16 Gasgano's Podracer C	.40	1.00
F17 Mawhonic's Podracer C	.40	1.00
F18 Teemto Pagalies' Podracer C	.40	1.00

1999 Young Jedi The Jedi Council

Queen Amidala
Voice of Her People

"I was not elected to watch my people suffer and die..." – Queen Amidala

COMPLETE SET (140)	8.00	20.00
BOOSTER BOX (30 PACKS)	20.00	30.00
BOOSTER BOX (11 CARDS)	.75	1.25
RELEASED ON OCTOBER 27, 1999		
1 Obi-Wan Kenobi, Jedi Apprentice R	1.50	4.00
2 Qui-Gon Jinn, Jedi Protector R	1.25	3.00
3 Jar Jar Binks, Gungan Outcast R	.75	2.00
4 Anakin Skywalker, Child of Prophecy R	.75	2.00
5 Padme Naberrie, Queen's Handmaiden R	1.00	2.50
6 Captain Panaka, Amidala's Bodyguard R	.60	1.50
7 Mace Windu Senior Jedi Council Member R	.75	2.00
8 Queen Amidala, Representative of Naboo R	1.00	2.50
9 Queen Amidala, Voice of Her People R	1.00	2.50
10 Yoda, Jedi Council Member R	1.00	2.50
11 R2-D2, Loyal Droid R	.75	2.00

12 Ki-Adi-Mundi, Cerean Jedi Knight R	.75	2.00
13 Adi Gallia, Corellian Jedi Master U	.30	.75
14 Depa Billaba, Jedi Master U	.30	.75
15 Eeth Koth, Zabrak Jedi Master U	.30	.75
16 Even Piell, Lannik Jedi Master U	.30	.75
17 Oppo Rancisis, Jedi Master U	.30	.75
18 Plo Koon, Jedi Master U	.30	.75
19 Saesee Tiin, Iktotchi Jedi Master U	.30	.75
20 Yaddle, Jedi Master U	.30	.75
21 Yarael Poof, Quermian Jedi Master U	.30	.75
22 Boss Nass, Gungan Leader U	.30	.75
23 Ric Olié, Chief Pilot U	.30	.75
24 Captain Tarpals, Gungan Battle Leader U	.30	.75
25 Eirtae, Handmaiden U	.30	.75
26 Valorum, Supreme Chancellor C	.10	.25
27 Sci Taria, Chancellor's Aide C	.10	.25
28 Naboo Officer, Liberator C	.10	.25
29 Bravo Pilot, Naboo Volunteer C	.10	.25
30 Naboo Security, Amidala's Guard C	.10	.25
31 Republic Captain, Officer C	.10	.25
32 Republic Pilot, Veteran C	.10	.25
33 Coruscant Guard Coruscant Detachment C	.10	.25
34 Coruscant Guard, Peacekeeper C	.10	.25
35 Coruscant Guard, Officer C	.10	.25
36 Coruscant Guard, Chancellor's Guard C	.10	.25
37 Wookiee Senator, Representative C	.10	.25
38 Galactic Senator, Delegate S	.10	.25
39 Obi-Wan Kenobi, Jedi Warrior S	.10	.25
40 Qui-Gon Jinn's Lightsaber R	.60	1.50
41 Amidala's Blaster R	.60	1.50
42 Adi Gallia's Lightsaber U	.30	.75
43 Coruscant Guard Blaster Rifle U	.30	.75
44 Ascension Gun C	.10	.25
45 Electropole C	.10	.25
46 Kaadu C	.10	.25
47 Flash Speeder C	.10	.25
48 Gian Speeder C	.10	.25
49 Naboo Blaster C	.10	.25
50 Blaster C	.10	.25
51 Blaster Rifle C	.10	.25
52 Balance To The Force U	.30	.75
53 Brave Little Droid U	.30	.75
54 Dos Mackineeks No Comen Here! C	.10	.25
55 Galactic Chancellor C	.10	.25
56 Hate Leads To Suffering U	.30	.75
57 I Will Not Cooperate U	.30	.75
58 Invasion! C	.10	.25
59 May The Force Be With You C	.10	.25
60 Senator Palpatine C	.10	.25
61 The Might Of The Republic C	.10	.25
62 We Don't Have Time For This C	.10	.25
63 We Wish To Board At Once C	.10	.25
64 Wisdom Of The Council R	.60	1.50
65 Tatooine Mos Espa S	.10	.25
66 Coruscant Jedi Council Chamber S	.10	.25
67 Naboo Gungan Swamp S	.10	.25
68 Bravo 2, Naboo Starfighter U	.30	.75
69 Naboo Starfighter C	.10	.25
70 Radiant VII, Republic Cruiser Transport C	.10	.25
71 Darth Maul, Master of Evil R	2.00	5.00
72 Darth Sidious, Lord of the Sith R	1.25	3.00
73 Sebulba, Podracer Pilot R	.75	2.00
74 Watto, Junk Merchant R	.60	1.50
75 Jabba the Hutt, Gangster R	.75	2.00
76 Nute Gunray, Neimoidian Viceroy R	.60	1.50
77 Rune Haako, Neimoidian Advisor R	.60	1.50
78 Destroyer Droid Squad, Defense Division R	.60	1.50
79 Battle Droid Squad, Escort Unit R	.60	1.50
80 Trade Federation Tank, Assault Division R	.60	1.50
81 Lott Dod, Neimoidian Senator R	.60	1.50
82 Fode and Beed, Podrace Announcer R	.60	1.50
83 Clegg Holdfast, Podracer Pilot U	.30	.75
84 Dud Bolt, Podracer Pilot U	.30	.75
85 Mars Guo, Podracer Pilot U	.30	.75
86 Ody Mandrell, Podracer Pilot U	.30	.75
87 Ratts Tyerell, Podracer Pilot U	.30	.75
88 Aks Moe, Senator C	.10	.25
89 Horox Ryyder, Senator C	.10	.25
90 Edcel Bar Gane, Roona Senator C	.10	.25
91 Galactic Delegate, Representative C	.10	.25
92 Destroyer Droid, Assault Droid C	.10	.25
93 Destroyer Droid, Battleship Security C	.10	.25
94 Sith Probe Droid, Hunter Droid C	.10	.25
95 Rodian, Mercenary C	.10	.25
96 Battle Droid: Pilot, Assault Division C	.10	.25
97 Battle Droid: Security, Assault Division C	.10	.25
98 Battle Droid: Infantry, Assault Division C	.10	.25
99 Battle Droid: Officer, Assault Division C	.10	.25
100 Battle Droid: Pilot, Guard Division C	.10	.25
101 Battle Droid: Security, Guard Division C	.10	.25
102 Battle Droid: Infantry, Guard Division C	.10	.25
103 Battle Droid: Officer, Guard Division C	.10	.25

104 Neimoidian Aide Trade Federation Delegate S	.10	.25
105 Darth Maul, Sith Warrior S	.10	.25
106 Darth Maul's Lightsaber R	.60	1.50
107 Darth Maul's Sith Speeder R	.60	1.50
108 Clegg Holdfast's Podracer U	.30	.75
109 Dud Bolt's Podracer U	.30	.75
110 Mars Guo's Podracer U	.30	.75
111 Ody Mandrell's Podracer U	.30	.75
112 Ratts Tyerell's Podracer U	.30	.75
113 Trade Federation Tank Laser Cannon U	.30	.75
114 Multi Troop Transport U	.30	.75
115 STAP U	.30	.75
116 Thermal Detonator U	.30	.75
117 Battle Droid Blaster Rifle C	.10	.25
118 Blaster C	.10	.25
119 Blaster Rifle C	.10	.25
120 I Object! C	.10	.25
121 I Will Deal With Them Myself C	.10	.25
122 Let Them Make The First Move R	.60	1.50
123 Move Against The Jedi First C	.10	.25
124 Open Fire! U	.30	.75
125 Seal Off The Bridge U	.30	.75
126 Start Your Engines! U	.30	.75
127 Switch To Bio C	.10	.25
128 Take Them To Camp Four C	.10	.25
129 Very Unusual C	.10	.25
130 Vote Of No Confidence C	.10	.25
131 We Are Meeting No Resistance C	.10	.25
132 We Have Them On The Run U	.30	.75
133 Yoka To Bantha Poodoo C	.10	.25
134 Your Little Insurrection Is At An End U	.30	.75
135 Tatooine Podrace Arena S	.10	.25
136 Coruscant Galactic Senate S	.10	.25
137 Naboo Battle Plains S	.10	.25
138 Sith Infiltrator, Starfighter U	.30	.75
139 Droid Starfighter C	.10	.25
140 Battleship, Trade Federation Transport C	.10	.25

1999 Young Jedi The Jedi Council Foil

COMPLETE SET (18)	4.00	10.00
RELEASED ON OCTOBER 27, 1999		
F1 Obi-Wan Kenobi, Jedi Apprentice UR	2.00	5.00
F2 Qui-Gon Jinn, Jedi Protector SR	.75	2.00
F3 PadmE Naberrie Queen's Handmaiden SR	.75	2.00
F4 Captain Panaka Amidala's Bodyguard SR	.60	1.50
F5 Mace Windu Senior Jedi Council Member SR	1.00	2.50
F6 Queen Amidala Representative of Naboo VR	1.25	3.00
F7 R2-D2, Loyal Droid VR	1.25	3.00
F8 Qui-Gon Jinn's Lightsaber VR	.40	1.00
F9 Amidala's Blaster VR	.40	1.00
F10 Darth Maul, Master of Evil UR	2.00	5.00
F11 Darth Sidious, Lord of the Sith UR	1.25	3.00
F12 Watto, Junk Merchant SR	.60	1.50
F13 Jabba the Hutt, Gangster SR	.60	1.50
F14 Nute Gunray, Neimoidian Viceroy SR	.60	1.50
F15 Rune Haako, Neimoidian Advisor VR	.40	1.00
F16 Lott Dod, Neimoidian Senator VR	.40	1.00
F17 Darth Maul's Lightsaber VR	.40	1.00
F18 Darth Maul's Sith Speeder VR	.40	1.00

2000 Young Jedi Battle of Naboo

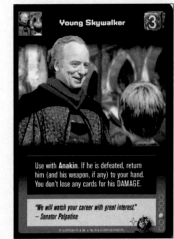

Young Skywalker

Use with Anakin. If he is defeated, return him (and his weapon, if any) to your hand. You don't lose any cards for his DAMAGE.

"We will watch your career with great interest."
– Senator Palpatine

COMPLETE SET (140)	8.00	20.00
BOOSTER BOX (30 PACKS)	15.00	30.00

BOOSTER PACK (11 CARDS)	.75	1.25
RELEASED ON APRIL 5, 2000		
1 Obi-Wan Kenobi, Jedi Knight R	1.50	4.00
2 Qui-Gon Jinn, Jedi Ambassador R	1.25	3.00
3 Jar Jar Binks, Bombad Gungan General R	.75	2.00
4 Anakin Skywalker, Padawan R	.75	2.00
5 Padme Naberrie, Amidala's Handmaiden R	1.00	2.50
6 Captain Panaka, Veteran Leader R	.60	1.50
7 Mace Windu, Jedi Speaker R	.75	2.00
8 Queen Amidala, Resolute Negotiator R	1.00	2.50
9 Queen Amidala, Keeper of the Peace R	1.00	2.50
10 Yoda, Jedi Elder R	1.00	2.50
11 R2-D2, The Queen's Hero R	.75	2.00
12 Boss Nass, Gungan Chief U	.30	.75
13 Ric Olie, Bravo Leader U	.30	.75
14 Captain Tarpals, Gungan Officer U	.30	.75
15 Sio Bibble, Governor of Naboo U	.30	.75
16 Sabe, Handmaiden Decoy Queen U	.30	.75
17 Sache, Handmaiden U	.30	.75
18 Yane, Handmaiden U	.30	.75
19 Naboo Officer, Squad Leader U	.30	.75
20 Naboo Officer, Commander C	.10	.25
21 Naboo Bureaucrat, Official C	.10	.25
22 Naboo Security, Trooper C	.10	.25
23 Naboo Security, Defender C	.10	.25
24 Bravo Pilot, Ace Flyer C	.10	.25
25 Coruscant Guard, Chancellor's Escort C	.10	.25
26 Alderaan Diplomat, Senator C	.10	.25
27 Council Member, Naboo Governor C	.10	.25
28 Gungan Warrior, Veteran C	.10	.25
29 Gungan Guard, Lookout C	.10	.25
30 Gungan General, Army Leader C	.10	.25
31 Gungan Soldier, Infantry C	.10	.25
32 Rep Officer, Gungan Diplomat S	.10	.25
33 Obi-Wan Kenobi, Jedi Negotiator S	.10	.25
34 Mace Windu's Lightsaber R	.60	1.50
35 Eeth Koth's Lightsaber U	.30	.75
36 Captain Tarpals' Electropole U	.30	.75
37 Planetary Shuttle C	.10	.25
38 Fambaa C	.10	.25
39 Electropole C	.10	.25
40 Kaadu C	.10	.25
41 Flash Speeder C	.10	.25
42 Blaster C	.10	.25
43 Heavy Blaster C	.10	.25
44 Capture The Viceroy C	.10	.25
45 Celebration C	.10	.25
46 Guardians Of The Queen U	.30	.75
47 Gunga City C	.10	.25
48 Gungan Battle Cry U	.30	.75
49 How Wude! U	.30	.75
50 I Will Take Back What Is Ours C	.10	.25
51 Jedi Force Push U	.30	.75
52 Meeeesa Lika Dis! C	.10	.25
53 NOOOOOOOOOO! R	.60	1.50
54 Thanks, Artoo! U	.30	.75
55 The Chancellor's Ambassador U	.30	.75
56 The Will Of The Force R	.60	1.50
57 Young Skywalker U	.30	.75
58 Your Occupation Here Has Ended C	.10	.25
59 Bombad General U	.30	.75
60 Kiss Your Trade Franchise Goodbye U	.30	.75
61 There's Always A Bigger Fish C	.10	.25
62 Uh-Oh! C	.10	.25
63 We Wish To Form An Alliance C	.10	.25
64 Tatooine Desert Landing Site S	.10	.25
65 Coruscant Galactic Senate S	.10	.25
66 Naboo Battle Plains S	.10	.25
67 Amidala's Starship, Royal Transport R	.60	1.50
68 Bravo 3, Naboo Starfighter U	.30	.75
69 Naboo Starfighter C	.10	.25
70 Republic Cruiser, Transport C	.10	.25
71 Darth Maul, Dark Lord of the Sith R	2.00	5.00
72 Darth Sidious, Sith Manipulator R	1.25	3.00
73 Sebulba, Dangerous Podracer Pilot R	.60	1.50
74 Watto, Toydarian Gambler R	.60	1.50
75 Aurra Sing, Mercenary R	.75	2.00
76 Jabba The Hutt, Crime Lord R	.60	1.50
77 Nute Gunray, Neimoidian Despot R	.60	1.50
78 Rune Haako, Neimoidian Deputy R	.60	1.50
79 Destroyer Droid Squad, Guard Division R	.60	1.50
80 Battle Droid Squad, Guard Unit R	.60	1.50
81 Trade Federation Tank, Guard Division R	.60	1.50
82 Trade Federation Tank, Patrol Division R	.60	1.50
83 P-59, Destroyer Droid Commander U	.30	.75
84 OOM-9, Battle Droid Commander U	.30	.75
85 Daultay Dofine, Neimoidian Attendant U	.30	.75
86 Diva Shaliqua, Singer U	.30	.75
87 Diva Funquita, Dancer U	.30	.75

88 Bith, Musician U	.30	.75
89 Quarren, Smuggler U	.30	.75
90 Toonbuck Toora, Senator U	.30	.75
91 Aqualish, Galactic Senator C	.10	.25
92 Twi'lek Diplomat, Senator C	.10	.25
93 Weequay, Enforcer C	.10	.25
94 Nikto, Slave C	.10	.25
95 Pacithhip, Prospector C	.10	.25
96 Destroyer Droid, Vanguard Droid C	.10	.25
97 Destroyer Droid, MTT Droid C	.10	.25
98 Sith Probe Droid, Remote Tracker C	.10	.25
99 Battle Droid: Pilot, Patrol Division C	.10	.25
100 Battle Droid: Security, Patrol Division C	.10	.25
101 Battle Droid: Infantry, Patrol Division C	.10	.25
102 Battle Droid: Officer, Patrol Division C	.10	.25
103 Battle Droid: Pilot, Defense Division C	.10	.25
104 Battle Droid: Security, Defense Division C	.10	.25
105 Battle Droid: Infantry, Defense Division C	.10	.25
106 Battle Droid: Officer, Defense Division C	.10	.25
107 Neimoidian Advisor, Bureaucrat S	.10	.25
108 Darth Maul, Evil Sith Lord S	.10	.25
109 Darth Maul's Lightsaber R	.75	2.00
110 Sith Lightsaber R	.60	1.50
111 Darth Maul's Electrobinoculars U	.30	.75
112 Trade Federation Tank Laser Cannon U	.30	.75
113 Multi Troop Transport U	.30	.75
114 STAP U	.30	.75
115 Battle Droid Blaster Rifle C	.10	.25
116 Blaster C	.10	.25
117 Blaster Rifle C	.10	.25
118 A Thousand Terrible Things C	.10	.25
119 Armored Assault C	.10	.25
120 Death From Above C	.10	.25
121 Don't Spect A Werm Welcome C	.10	.25
122 I Will Make It Legal C	.10	.25
123 Not For A Sith R	.60	1.50
124 Now There Are Two Of Them U	.30	.75
125 Sith Force Push U	.30	.75
126 The Phantom Menace U	.30	.75
127 They Win This Round C	.10	.25
128 We Are Sending All Troops C	.10	.25
129 After Her! U	.30	.75
130 Da Dug Chaaa! U	.30	.75
131 Sando Aqua Monster C	.10	.25
132 They Will Not Stay Hidden For Long C	.10	.25
133 This Is Too Close! U	.30	.75
134 Tatooine Mos Espa S	.10	.25
135 Coruscant Capital City S	.10	.25
136 Naboo Theed Palace S	.10	.25
137 Droid Control Ship	.30	.75
Trade Federation Transport U		
138 Sith Infiltrator, Starfighter U	.30	.75
139 Droid Starfighter C	.10	.25
140 Battleship, Trade Federation Transport C	.10	.25

2000 Young Jedi Battle of Naboo Foil

COMPLETE SET (18)	4.00	10.00
F1 Obi-Wan Kenobi, Jedi Knight UR	1.50	4.00
F2 Qui-Gon Jinn, Jedi Ambassador UR	.75	2.00
F3 Queen Amidala, Keeper of the Peace SR	.75	2.00
F4 Yoda, Jedi Elder SR	.75	2.00
F5 R2-D2, The Queen's Hero SR	.75	2.00
F6 Queen Amidala, Resolute Negotiator VR	.60	1.50
F7 Mace Windu's Lightsaber VR	.40	1.00
F8 The Will Of The Force VR	.40	1.00
F9 Amidala's Starship, Royal Transport VR	.40	1.00
F10 Darth Maul, Dark Lord of the Sith UR	1.50	4.00
F11 Aurra Sing, Mercenary UR	.60	1.50
F12 Nute Gunray	.60	1.50
Neimoidian Despot SR		
F13 Destroyer Droid Squad	.60	1.50
Guard Division SR		
F14 Trade Federation Tank	.60	1.50
Guard Division SR		
F15 Battle Droid Squad, Guard Unit VR	.40	1.00
F16 Trade Federation Tank	.40	1.00
Patrol Division VR		
F17 Darth Maul's Lightsaber VR	.40	1.00
F18 Not For A Sith VR	.40	1.00

2000 Young Jedi Duel of the Fates

COMPLETE SET (60)	5.00	12.00
BOOSTER BOX (30 PACKS)	30.00	40.00
BOOSTER PACK (11 CARDS)	1.00	1.50
RELEASED ON NOVEMBER 8, 2000		
1 Obi-Wan Kenobi, Jedi Student R	1.50	4.00
2 Qui-Gon Jinn, Jedi Mentor UR	1.25	3.00
3 Anakin Skywalker, Rookie Pilot R	.75	2.00
4 Captain Panaka, Security Commander R	.60	1.50
5 Mace Windu, Jedi Councilor R	.75	2.00
6 Queen Amidala, Young Leader R	1.00	2.50
7 Yoda, Jedi Philosopher R	1.00	2.50

8 R2-D2, Repair Droid R	.75	2.00
9 Ric Olie, Starship Pilot R	.60	1.50
10 Bravo Pilot, Flyer C	.10	.25
11 Valorum, Leader of the Senate C	.10	.25
12 Qui-Gon Jinn's Lightsaber	.60	1.50
Wielded by Obi-Wan Kenobi R		
13 Booma U	.30	.75
14 A Powerful Opponent C	.10	.25
15 Come On, Move! U	.30	.75
16 Critical Confrontation C	.10	.25
17 Gungan Mounted Troops U	.30	.75
18 Naboo Fighter Attack C	.10	.25
19 Qui-Gon's Final Stand C	.10	.25
20 Run The Blockade C	.10	.25
21 Twist Of Fate C	.10	.25
22 You Are Strong With The Force U	.30	.75
23 Gungan Energy Shield U	.30	.75
24 He Can See Things Before They Happen U	.30	.75
25 Jedi Meditation U	.30	.75
26 Jedi Training U	.30	.75
27 Naboo Royal Security Forces U	.30	.75
28 Pounded Unto Death C	.10	.25
29 Senate Guard C	.10	.25
30 Naboo Starfighter C	.10	.25
31 Darth Maul, Student of the Dark Side UR	1.50	4.00
32 Darth Sidious, Master of the Dark Side R	1.00	2.50
33 Aurra Sing, Trophy Collector R	.75	2.00
34 Tey How, Neimoidian Command Officer R	.60	1.50
35 OWO-1, Battle Droid Command Officer R	.60	1.50
36 Rayno Vaca, Taxi Driver R	.60	1.50
37 Baskol Yeesrim, Gran Senator R	.60	1.50
38 Starfighter Droid, DFS-327 R	.60	1.50
39 Starfighter Droid, DFS-1104 R	.60	1.50
40 Starfighter Droid, DFS-1138 R	.60	1.50
41 Jedi Lightsaber, Stolen by Aurra Sing U	.30	.75
42 Coruscant Taxi U	.30	.75
43 Neimoidian Viewscreen C	.10	.25
44 Battle Droid Patrol U	.30	.75
45 Change In Tactics C	.10	.25
46 Dangerous Encounter C	.10	.25
47 Darth Maul Defiant C	.10	.25
48 Impossible! C	.10	.25
49 It's A Standoff! U	.30	.75
50 Mobile Assassin U	.30	.75
51 Power Of The Sith C	.10	.25
52 Starfighter Screen C	.10	.25
53 To The Death C	.10	.25
54 Use Caution U	.30	.75
55 Blockade U	.30	.75
56 End This Pointless Debate U	.30	.75
57 The Duel Begins U	.30	.75
58 The Jedi Are Involved U	.30	.75
59 Where Are Those Droidekas? U	.30	.75
60 Droid Starfighter C	.10	.25

2000 Young Jedi Enhanced Menace of Darth Maul

P1 Qui-Gon Jinn, Jedi Protector	2.00	5.00
P2 Mace Windu, Jedi Warrior	1.25	3.00
P3 Queen Amidala, Cunning Warrior	4.00	10.00
P4 Darth Maul, Sith Assassin	2.00	5.00
P5 Sebulba, Champion Podracer Pilot	4.00	10.00
P6 Trade Federation Tank, Assault Leader	2.50	6.00

2001 Young Jedi Boonta Eve Podrace

COMPLETE SET (63)	4.00	10.00
BOOSTER BOX (30 PACKS)	30.00	40.00
BOOSTER PACK (11 CARDS)	1.00	1.50
RELEASED ON SEPTEMBER 5, 2001		

1	Anakin Skywalker, Boonta Eve Podracer Pilot UR	.75	2.00
2	Yoda, Jedi Instructor R	1.00	2.50
3	C-3PO, Human-Cyborg Relations Droid R	.75	2.00
4	Jira, Pallie Vendor R	.60	1.50
5	Kitster, Anakin's Friend R	.60	1.50
6	Wald, Anakin's Friend R	.60	1.50
7	Seek, Anakin's Friend U	.30	.75
8	Amee, Anakin's Friend U	.30	.75
9	Melee, Anakin's Friend U	.30	.75
10	Captain Tarpals, Gungan Leader R	.60	1.50
11	Boles Roor, Podracer Pilot U	.30	.75
12	Elan Mak, Podracer Pilot U	.30	.75
13	Neva Kee, Podracer Pilot U	.30	.75
14	Wan Sandage, Podracer Pilot U	.30	.75
15	Shmi Skywalker, Anakin's Mother R	.60	1.50
16	Boles Roor's Podracer U	.30	.75
17	Elan Mak's Podracer U	.30	.75
18	Neva Kee's Podracer U	.30	.75
19	Wan Sandage's Podracer U	.30	.75
20	Comlink C	.10	.25
21	Hold-Out Blaster C	.10	.25
22	Dis Is Nutsen C	.10	.25
23	Masquerade C	.10	.25
24	No Giben Up, General Jar Jar C	.10	.25
25	What Does Your Heart Tell You? C	.10	.25
26	All-Out Defense U	.30	.75
27	Bravo Squadron C	.10	.25
28	Hologram Projector C	.10	.25
29	Boonta Eve Classic R	.60	1.50
30	Amidala's Starship R	.60	1.50
31	Sebulba, Dug Podracer Pilot UR	.60	1.50
32	Watto, Podrace Sponsor R	.60	1.50
33	Aurra Sing, Formidable Adversary R	.75	2.00
34	Jabba The Hutt, O Grandio Lust R	.60	1.50
35	TC-14, Protocol Droid R	.60	1.50
36	Orr'UrRuuR'R, Tusken Raider Leader Rare R	.60	1.50
37	UrrOr'RuuR, Tusken Raider Warrior U	.30	.75
38	RuuR'Ur, Tusken Raider Sniper C	.10	.25
39	Sil Unch, Neimoidian Comm Officer U	.30	.75
40	Graxol Kelvyyn and Shakka U	.30	.75
41	Corix Venne, Bith Musician C	.10	.25
42	Reike Th'san, Arms Smuggler R	.60	1.50
43	Meddun, Nikto Mercenary U	.30	.75
44	Rum Sleg, Bounty Hunter R	.60	1.50
45	Aehrrley Rue, Freelance Pilot U	.30	.75
46	Jedwar Seelah, Explorer Scout U	.30	.75
47	Chokk, Klatooinian Explosives Expert C	.10	.25
48	Tatooine Backpack C	.10	.25
49	Gaderffii Stick C	.10	.25
50	Hold-Out Blaster C	.10	.25
51	Watto's Datapad U	.30	.75
52	Colo Claw Fish C	.10	.25
53	He Always Wins! C	.10	.25
54	Bounty Hunter C	.10	.25
55	Two-Pronged Attack C	.10	.25
56	All-Out Attack U	.30	.75
57	Eventually You'll Lose U	.30	.75
58	Gangster's Paradise U	.30	.75
59	Boonta Eve Classic R	.60	1.50
60	Viceroy's Battleship R	.60	1.50
R1	Rule Card 1	.08	.20
R2	Rule Card 2	.08	.20
R3	Rule Card 3	.08	.20

2001 Young Jedi Enhanced Battle of Naboo

Obi-Wan Kenobi
Jedi Avenger

5 POWER

5 DAMAGE

Adds 2 to the DAMAGE of each character he defeats.

	COMPLETE SET (12)	30.00	80.00
	RELEASED IN 2001		
P8	Obi-Wan Kenobi, Jedi Avenger	4.00	10.00
P9	Anakin Skywalker, Tested By the Jedi Council	10.00	25.00
P10	PadmÈ Naberrie, Loyal Handmaiden	12.00	30.00
P11	Captain Panaka, Royal Defender	2.00	5.00
P12	Yoda, Wise Jedi	4.00	10.00
P13	R2-D2, Starship Maintenance Droid	5.00	12.00
P14	Darth Sidious, The Phantom Menace	2.00	5.00
P15	Watto, Risk Taker	4.00	10.00
P16	Aurra Sing, Scoundrel	4.00	10.00
P17	Jabba The Hutt	4.00	10.00
P18	Nute Gunray, Neimoidean Bureaucrat	2.50	6.00
P19	Rune Haako, Neimoidean Lieutenant	5.00	12.00

2001 Young Jedi Reflections

	COMPLETE SET (106)	200.00	350.00
	RELEASED ON JULY 18, 2001		
A1	Jar Jar Binks, Bombad Gungan General	1.25	3.00
	Jar Jar Binks' Electropole		
A2	Boss Nass, Gungan Chief	2.00	5.00
	Fambaa		
A3	Adi Gallia, Corellian Jedi Master	1.50	4.00
	Adi Gallia's Lightsaber		
A4	Eeth Koth, Zabrak Jedi Master	2.00	5.00
	Eeth Koth's Lightsaber		
A5	Ki-Adi-Mundi, Cerean Jedi Knight	2.00	5.00
	Jedi Lightsaber, Constructed by Ki-Adi-Mundi		
A6	Valorum, Supreme Chancellor	1.25	3.00
	Planetary Shuttle		
A7	Aurra Sing, Trophy Collector	2.00	5.00
	Jedi Lightsaber, Stolen by Aurra Sing		
A8	Nute Gunray, Neimoidian Viceroy	1.50	4.00
	Neimoidian Viewscreen		
A9	OOM-9, Battle Droid Commander	1.50	4.00
	Battle Droid Blaster Rifle		
A10	OWO-1, Battle Droid Command Officer	2.00	5.00
	STAP		
A11	P-59, Destroyer Droid Commander	1.50	4.00
	Multi Troop Transport		
A12	Toonbuck Toora, Senator	2.00	5.00
	Coruscant Taxi		
C1	Are You An Angel?	.75	2.00
	I've Been Trained In Defense		
C2	Brave Little Droid	.60	1.50
	Counterparts		
C3	Celebration	.75	2.00
	Gungan Mounted Trooops		
C4	Enough Of This Pretense	.60	1.50
	I Will Not Cooperate		
C5	Fear Attracts The Fearful	.75	2.00
	How Wude!		
C6	I Have A Bad Feeling About This	.75	2.00
	NOOOOOOOOOOO!		
C7	Jedi Force Push	.75	2.00
	We're Not In Trouble Yet		
C8	Dos Mackineeks No Comen Here!	.75	2.00
	Bombad General		
C9	At last we will have revenge	.40	1.00
	Sith force push		
C10	The Queen's Plan	.75	2.00
	Naboo Royal Security Forces		
C11	The Might Of The Republic	.75	2.00
	Senate Guard		
C12	The Negotiations Were Short	.75	2.00
	Qui-Gon's Final Stand		
C13	Wisdom Of The Council	.75	2.00
	Jedi Training		
C14	Yousa Guys Bombad!	.75	2.00
	Uh-Oh!		
C15	A Thousand Terrible Things & We Are Sending All Troops	.60	1.50
C16	Battle Droid Patrol & In Complete Control	.60	1.50
C17	Boonta Eve Podrace & Kaa Bazza Kundee Hodrudda!	.60	1.50
C18	Podrace Preparation & Yoka To Bantha Poodoo	.75	2.00
C19	Switch To Bio & Your Little Insurrection Is At An End	.40	1.00
C20	The Phantom Menace & Use Caution	.75	2.00
D1	Dos Mackineeks No Comen Here!	.75	2.00
	Bombad General		
D2	Gunga City	.75	2.00
	Gungan Energy Shield		
D3	The Queen's Plan	.75	2.00
	Naboo Royal Security Forces		
D4	The Might Of The Republic	.75	2.00

	Senate Guard		
D5	The Negotiations Were Short	.75	2.00
	Qui-Gon's Final Stand		
D6	Wisdom Of The Council	.75	2.00
	Jedi Training		
D7	Yousa Guys Bombad!	.75	2.00
	Uh-Oh!		
D8	Grueling Contest	.75	2.00
	Da Dug Chaaa!		
D9	Let Them Make The First Move	.40	1.00
	Very Unusual		
D10	Now There Are Two Of Them	.60	1.50
	The Duel Begins		
D11	Opee Sea Killer	.75	2.00
	To The Death		
D12	Starfighter Screen	.75	2.00
	Blockade		
D13	We Have Them On The Run	.75	2.00
	Where Are Those Droidekas?		
D14	You Have Been Well Trained	.44	1.00
	After Her!		
2BEP	Yoda, Jedi Instructor (foil)	2.50	6.00
2MDM	Qui-Gon Jinn, Jedi Master (foil)	10.00	25.00
3BEP	C-3PO, Human-Cyborg Relations Droid (foil)	2.50	6.00
4BEP	Jira, Pallie Vendor (foil)	1.25	3.00
4BON	Anakin Skywalker, Padawan (foil)	3.00	8.00
4TJC	Anakin Skywalker, Child of Prophecy (foil)	6.00	15.00
5BEP	Kitster, Anakin's Friend (foil)	2.00	5.00
6BEP	Wald, Anakin's Friend (foil)	1.50	4.00
7BON	Mace Windu, Jedi Speaker (foil)	10.00	25.00
9MDM	Queen Amidala, Royal Leader (foil)	3.00	8.00
9TJC	Queen Amidala, Voice of Her People (foil)	4.00	10.00
10MDM	Yoda, Jedi Master (foil)	2.00	5.00
1DOTF	Obi-Wan Kenobi, Jedi Student (foil)	6.00	15.00
2DOTF	Qui-Gon Jinn, Jedi Mentor (foil)	3.00	8.00
30BEP	Amidala's Starship, Queen's Transport (foil)	2.00	5.00
32BEP	Watto, Podrace Sponsor (foil)	2.00	5.00
33BEP	Aurra Sing, Formidable Adversary (foil)	4.00	10.00
34BEP	Jabba The Hutt, O Grandio Lust (foil)	2.00	5.00
35BEP	TC-14, Protocol Droid (foil)	2.00	5.00
36BEP	Orr'UrRuuR'R, Tusken Raider Leader (foil)	2.00	5.00
3DOTF	Anakin Skywalker, Rookie Pilot (foil)	3.00	8.00
4DOTF	Captain Panaka, Security Commander (foil)	2.00	5.00
5DOTF	Mace Windu, Jedi Councilor (foil)	2.50	6.00
60BEP	Viceroy's Battleship, Trade Federation Transport (foil)	1.50	4.00
6DOTF	Queen Amidala, Young Leader (foil)	3.00	8.00
72BON	Darth Sidious, Sith Manipulator (foil)	3.00	8.00
73BON	Sebulba, Dangerous Podracer Pilot (foil)	8.00	20.00
73TJC	Sebulba, Podracer Pilot (foil)	1.50	4.00
74BON	Watto, Toydarian Gambler (foil)	1.00	2.50
74MDM	Watto, Slave Owner (foil)	2.00	5.00
75MDM	Aurra Sing, Bounty Hunter (foil)	4.00	10.00
76BON	Jabba The Hutt, Crime Lord (foil)	2.00	5.00
78BON	Rune Haako, Neimoidian Deputy (foil)	2.00	5.00
78TJC	Destroyer Droid Squad, Defense Division (foil)	3.00	8.00
79TJC	Battle Droid Squad, Escort Unit (foil)	2.00	5.00
7DOTF	Yoda, Jedi Philosopher (foil)	4.00	10.00
80TJC	Trade Federation Tank, Assault Division (foil)	6.00	15.00
88MDM	Trade Federation Tank, Armored Division (foil)	2.00	5.00
31DOTF	Darth Maul, Student of the Dark Side (foil)	3.00	8.00
32DOTF	Darth Sidious, Master of the Dark Side (foil)	10.00	25.00
33DOTF	Aurra Sing, Trophy Collector (foil)	1.50	4.00
P1EMDM	Qui-Gon Jinn, Jedi Protector (foil)	4.00	10.00
P2EMDM	Mace Windu, Jedi Warrior (foil)	4.00	10.00
P3EMDM	Queen Amidala, Cunning Warrior (foil)	8.00	20.00
P4EMDM	Darth Maul, Sith Assassin (foil)	8.00	20.00
P5EMDM	Sebulba, Champion Podracer Pilot (foil)	2.00	5.00
P6EMDM	Trade Federation Tank, Assault Leader (foil)	1.50	4.00
P7PREM	Shmi Skywalker, Anakin's Mother (foil)	1.50	4.00
P8EBON	Obi-Wan Kenobi, Jedi Avenger (foil)	3.00	8.00
P9EBON	Anakin Skywalker, Tested by the Jedi Council (foil)	3.00	8.00
P10EBON	PadmÈ Naberrie, Loyal Handmaiden (foil)	3.00	8.00
P11EBON	Captain Panaka, Royal Defender (foil)	2.00	5.00
P12EBON	Yoda, Wise Jedi (foil)	4.00	10.00
P13EBON	R2-D2, Starship Maintenance Droid (foil)	3.00	8.00
P14EBON	Darth Sidious, The Phantom Menace (foil)	3.00	8.00
P15EBON	Watto, Risk Taker (foil)	2.00	5.00
P16EBON	Aurra Sing, Scoundrel (foil)	1.50	4.00
P17EBON	Jabba The Hutt, Tatooine Tyrant (foil)	2.00	5.00
P18EBON	Nute Gunray, Neimoidian Bureaucrat (foil)	1.50	4.00
P19EBON	Rune Haako, Neimoidian Lieutenant (foil)	2.00	5.00

MINIATURES

2004 Star Wars Rebel Storm Miniatures

COMPLETE SET (60)		120.00	250.00
RELEASED ON SEPTEMBER 3, 2004			
1 4-LOM R		5.00	10.00
2 Bespin Guard C		.30	.75
3 Boba Fett VR		15.00	40.00
4 Bossk R		5.00	10.00
5 Bothan Spy U		.60	1.50
6 C-3PO R		5.00	10.00
7 Chewbacca R		6.00	12.00
8 Commando on Speeder Bike VR		15.00	25.00
9 Darth Vader, Dark Jedi R		6.00	12.00
10 Darth Vader, Sith Lord VR		12.50	25.00
11 Dengar R		5.00	10.00
12 Duros Mercenary U		.60	1.50
13 Elite Hoth Trooper U		.60	1.50
14 Elite Rebel Trooper C		.30	.75
15 Elite Snowtrooper U		.60	1.50
16 Elite Stormtrooper U		.60	1.50
17 Emperor Palpatine VR		15.00	30.00
18 Ewok C		.30	.75
19 Gamorrean Guard U		.60	1.50
20 General Veers R		5.00	10.00
21 Grand Moff Tarkin R		5.00	10.00
22 Greedo R		5.00	10.00
23 Han Solo R		5.00	10.00
24 Heavy Stormtrooper U		.60	1.50
25 Hoth Trooper C		.30	.75
26 IG-88 R		5.00	10.00
27 Imperial Officer U		.60	1.50
28 Ithorian Scout U		.60	1.50
29 Jabba the Hutt VR		12.50	25.00
30 Jawa C		.30	.75
31 Lando Calrissian R		5.00	10.00
32 Luke Skywalker, Jedi Knight VR		18.00	30.00
33 Luke Skywalker, Rebel R		6.00	12.00
34 Mara Jade Emperor's Hand R		5.00	10.00
35 Mon Calamari Mercenary C		.30	.75
36 Obi-Wan Kenobi VR		12.50	25.00
37 Princess Leia, Captive VR		12.50	25.00
38 Princess Leia, Senator R		6.00	12.00
39 Probe Droid VR		10.00	20.00
40 Quarren Assassin U		.60	1.50
41 R2-D2 R		6.00	12.00

42 Rebel Commando U		.60	1.50
43 Rebel Officer U		.60	1.50
44 Rebel Pilot C		.30	.75
45 Rebel Trooper C		.30	.75
46 Rebel Trooper C		.30	.75y
47 Royal Guard U		.60	1.50
48 Sandtrooper on Dewback VR		10.00	20.00
49 Scout Trooper on Bike VR		10.00	20.00
50 Scout Trooper U		.60	1.50
51 Snowtrooper C		.30	.75
52 Stormtrooper C		.30	.75
53 Stormtrooper C		.30	.75
54 Stormtrooper C		.30	.75
55 Stormtrooper Officer U		.60	1.50
56 Tusken Raider C		.30	.75
57 Twi'lek Bodyguard U		.60	1.50
58 Twi'lek Scoundrel C		.30	.75
59 Wampa VR		10.00	20.00
60 Wookiee Soldier C		.30	.75

2004 Star Wars Clone Strike Miniatures

COMPLETE SET (60)		150.00	300.00
RELEASED ON DECEMBER 13, 2004			
1 48 Super Battle Droid U		.60	1.50
2 Aayla Secura VR		12.00	20.00
3 Aerial Clone Trooper Captain R		6.00	12.00
4 Agen Kolar R		6.00	12.00
5 Anakin Skywalker VR		15.00	25.00
6 Aqualish Spy C		.30	.75
7 ARC Trooper U		.60	1.50
8 Asajj Ventress R		6.00	12.00
9 Aurra Sing VR		20.00	35.00
10 Battle Droid C		.30	.75
11 Battle Droid C		.30	.75
12 Battle Droid C		.30	.75
13 Battle Droid Officer U		.60	1.50
14 Battle Droid on STAP R		6.00	12.00
15 Captain Typho R		6.00	12.00
16 Clone Trooper C		.30	.75
17 Clone Trooper C		.30	.75
18 Clone Trooper Commander U		.60	1.50
19 Clone Trooper Grenadier C		.30	.75
20 Clone Trooper Sergeant C		.30	.75
21 Count Dooku VR		15.00	25.00
22 Dark Side Acolyte U		.60	1.50
23 Darth Maul VR		18.00	30.00
24 Darth Sidious VR		15.00	25.00
25 Destroyer Droid R		6.00	12.00
26 Devaronian Bounty Hunter C		.30	.75
27 Durge R		6.00	12.00
28 Dwarf Spider Droid R		6.00	12.00
29 General Grievous VR		18.00	30.00
30 General Kenobi R		6.00	12.00
31 Geonosian Drone C		.30	.75
32 Geonosian Overseer U		.60	1.50
33 Geonosian Picador on Orray R		6.00	12.00
34 Geonosian Soldier U		.60	1.50
35 Gran Raider C		.30	.75
36 Gungan Cavalry on Kaadu R		6.00	12.00
37 Gungan Infantry C		.30	.75
38 Ishi Tib Scout U		.60	1.50
39 Jango Fett R		6.00	12.00
40 Jedi Guardian U		.60	1.50
41 Ki-Adi-Mundi R		6.00	12.00
42 Kit Fisto R		6.00	12.00
43 Klatooinian Enforcer C		.30	.75
44 Luminara Unduli R		6.00	12.00

45 Mace Windu VR		15.00	25.00
46 Naboo Soldier U		.60	1.50
47 Nikto Soldier C		.30	.75
48 Padme Amidala VR		12.00	20.00
49 Plo Koon R		6.00	12.00
50 Quarren Raider U		.60	1.50
51 Qui-Gon Jinn VR		12.00	20.00
52 Quinlan Vos VR		12.00	20.00
53 Rodian Mercenary U		.60	1.50
54 Saesee Tiin R		6.00	12.00
55 Security Battle Droid C		.30	.75
56 Super Battle Droid U		.60	1.50
57 Weequay Mercenary C		.30	.75
58 Wookiee Commando U		.60	1.50
59 Yoda VR		18.00	30.00
60 Zam Wesell R		6.00	12.00

2005 Star Wars Revenge of the Sith Miniatures

COMPLETE SET (61)		120.00	250.00
RELEASED ON APRIL 2, 2005			
1 49 Nautolan Soldier C		.30	.75
2 Agen Kolar, Jedi Master R		6.00	12.00
3 Alderaan Trooper U		.75	1.50
4 Anakin Skywalker, Jedi Knight R		6.00	12.00
5 Anakin Skywalker Sith Apprentice VR		15.00	25.00
6 AT-RT VR		15.00	25.00
7 Bail Organa VR		10.00	20.00
8 Battle Droid C		.30	.75
9 Battle Droid C		.30	.75
10 Boba Fett, Young Mercenary R		6.00	12.00
11 Bodyguard Droid U		.75	1.50
12 Bodyguard Droid U		.75	1.50
13 Captain Antilles R		6.00	12.00
14 Chagrian Mercenary Commander U		.75	1.50
15 Chewbacca of Kashyyk VR		15.00	25.00
16 Clone Trooper C		.30	.75
17 Clone Trooper C		.30	.75
18 Clone Trooper Commander U		.75	1.50
19 Clone Trooper Gunner C		.30	.75
20 Dark Side Adept U		.75	1.50
21 Darth Tyranus R		6.00	12.00
22 Darth Vader VR		18.00	30.00
23 Destroyer Droid R		6.00	12.00
24 Devaronian Soldier C		.30	.75
25 Emperor Palpatine, Sith Lord VR		18.00	30.00
26 General Grievous VR		18.00	30.00
27 General Grievous, Supreme Commander R		6.00	12.00
28 Gotal Fringer U		.75	1.50
29 Grievous Wheel Bike VR		15.00	25.00
30 Human Mercenary U		.75	1.50
31 Iktotchi Tech Specialist U		.75	1.50
32 Jedi Knight U		.75	1.50

33 Mace Windu, Jedi Master VR	18.00	30.00
34 Medical Droid R	6.00	12.00
35 Mon Mothma VR	10.00	20.00
36 Muun Guard U	.75	1.50
37 Neimoidian Soldier U	.75	1.50
38 Neimoidian Soldier U	.75	1.50
39 Obi-Wan Kenobi, Jedi Master R	6.00	12.00
40 Polis Massa Medic C	.30	.75
41 R2-D2, Astromech Droid VR	15.00	25.00
42 Royal Guard U	.75	1.50
43 San Hill R	6.00	12.00
44 Senate Guard U	.75	1.50
45 Separatist Commando C	.30	.75
46 Shaak Ti R	6.00	12.00
47 Sly Moore R	6.00	12.00
48 Stass Allie R	6.00	12.00
49 Super Battle Droid C	.30	.75
50 Super Battle Droid C	.30	.75
51 Tarfful R	6.00	12.00
52 Tion Medon R	6.00	12.00
53 Utapaun Soldier C	.30	.75
54 Utapaun Soldier C	.30	.75
55 Utapaun Soldier C	.30	.75
56 Wat Tambor R	6.00	12.00
57 Wookiee Berserker C	.30	.75
58 Wookiee Scout U	.75	1.50
59 Yoda, Jedi Master R	7.50	15.00
60 Yuzzem C	.30	.75
61 Zabrak Fringer C	.30	.75

2005 Star Wars Universe Miniatures

COMPLETE SET (61)	150.00	300.00
RELEASED ON AUGUST 19, 2005		
1 Abyssin Black Sun Thug C	.30	.75
2 Acklay U	.75	1.50
3 Admiral Ackbar VR	10.00	20.00
4 ASP-7 U	.75	1.50
5 AT-ST R	7.50	15.00
6 B'omarr Monk R	7.50	15.00
7 Baron Fel VR	18.00	30.00
8 Battle Droid U	.75	1.50
9 Battle Droid U	.75	1.50
10 Bith Rebel C	.30	.75
11 Chewbacca, Rebel Hero R	7.50	15.00
12 Clone Trooper C	.30	.75
13 Clone Trooper on BARC Speeder R	10.00	20.00
14 Dark Side Marauder U	.75	1.50
15 Dark Trooper Phase III U	.75	1.50
16 Darth Maul on Speeder VR	12.50	25.00
17 Darth Vader, Jedi Hunter R	7.50	15.00
18 Dash Rendar R	7.50	15.00
19 Dr. Evazan VR	10.00	20.00
20 Dressellian Commando C	.30	.75
21 Elite Clone Trooper U	.75	1.50
22 Flash Speeder U	.75	1.50
23 Gonk Power Droid C	.30	.75
24 Grand Admiral Thrawn VR	18.00	30.00
25 Guri R	7.50	15.00
26 Hailfire Droid U	.75	1.50

27 Han Solo, Rebel Hero R	7.50	15.00
28 Kaminoan Ascetic C	.30	.75
29 Kyle Katarn VR	10.00	20.00
30 Lando Calrissian, Hero of Taanab R	7.50	15.00
31 Lobot R	6.00	12.00
32 Luke Skywalker on Tauntaun R	10.00	20.00
33 Luke Skywalker, Jedi Master VR	18.00	30.00
34 New Republic Commander U	.75	1.50
35 New Republic Trooper C	.30	.75
36 Nexu U	.75	1.50
37 Nien Nunb R	6.00	12.00
38 Nightsister Sith Witch U	.75	1.50
39 Noghri U	.75	1.50
40 Nom Anor R	7.50	15.00
41 Nute Gunray R	6.00	12.00
42 Obi-Wan on Boga VR	12.50	25.00
43 Ponda Baba R	6.00	12.00
44 Prince Xizor VR	10.00	20.00
45 Princess Leia, Rebel Hero VR	10.00	20.00
46 Rancor VR	20.00	35.00
47 Reek U	.75	1.50
48 Rodian Black Sun Vigo U	.75	1.50
49 Shistavanen Pilot U	.75	1.50
50 Stormtrooper C	.30	.75
51 Stormtrooper Commander U	.75	1.50
52 Super Battle Droid C	.30	.75
53 Super Battle Droid Commander U	.75	1.50
54 Tusken Raider on Bantha U	.75	1.50
55 Vornskr C	.30	.75
56 Warmaster Tsavong Lah VR	15.00	25.00
57 Wedge Antilles R	7.50	15.00
58 X-1 Viper Droid U	.75	1.50
59 Young Jedi Knight C	.30	.75
60 Yuuzhan Vong Subaltern U	.75	1.50
61 Yuuzhan Vong Warrior C	.30	.75

2006 Star Wars Champions of the Force Miniatures

COMPLETE SET (61)	120.00	250.00
RELEASED ON JUNE 6, 2006		
1 Arcona Smuggler C	.30	.75
2 Barriss Offee R	6.00	12.00
3 Bastila Shan VR	10.00	20.00
5 Clone Commander Bacara R	6.00	12.00
6 Clone Commander Cody R	7.50	15.00
7 Clone Commander Gree R	6.00	12.00
8 Corran Horn R	6.00	12.00
9 Coruscant Guard C	.30	.75
10 Crab Droid U	.60	1.50
11 Dark Jedi U	.60	1.50
12 Dark Jedi Master U	.60	1.50
13 Dark Side Enforcer U	.60	1.50
14 Dark Trooper Phase I C	.30	.75
15 Dark Trooper Phase II U	.60	1.50
16 Dark Trooper Phase II VR	10.00	20.00

17 Darth Bane VR	12.50	25.00
18 Darth Malak VR	12.50	25.00
19 Darth Maul, Champion of the Sith R	7.50	15.00
20 Darth Nihilus VR	10.00	20.00
21 Darth Sidious, Dark Lord of the Sith R	6.00	12.00
22 Depa Billaba R	6.00	12.00
23 Even Piell R	6.00	12.00
24 Exar Kun VR	12.50	25.00
25 General Windu R	6.00	12.00
26 Gundark Fringe U	.60	1.50
27 HK-47 VR	10.00	20.00
28 Hoth Trooper with Atgar Cannon R	6.00	12.00
29 Jacen Solo VR	10.00	20.00
30 Jaina Solo VR	10.00	20.00
31 Jedi Consular U	.60	1.50
32 Jedi Guardian U	.60	1.50
33 Jedi Padawan U	.60	1.50
34 Jedi Sentinel U	.60	1.50
35 Jedi Weapon Master C	.30	.75
36 Kashyyyk Trooper C	.30	.75
37 Luke Skywalker, Young Jedi VR	12.50	25.00
38 Mas Amedda R	7.50	15.00
39 Massassi Sith Mutant U	.60	1.50
41 Octuparra Droid R	6.00	12.00
42 Old Republic Commander U	.60	1.50
43 Old Republic Trooper U	.60	1.50
44 Old Republic Trooper C	.30	.75
45 Queen Amidala R	6.00	12.00
46 Qui-Gon Jinn, Jedi Master R	7.50	15.00
47 R5 Astromech Droid C	.30	.75
48 Republic Commando Boss U	.60	1.50
49 Republic Commando Fixer C	.30	.75
50 Republic Commando Scorch C	.30	.75
51 Republic Commando Sev C	.30	.75
52 Saleucami Trooper C	.30	.75
53 Sandtrooper C	.30	.75
54 Sith Assault Droid U	.60	1.50
55 Sith Trooper C	.30	.75
56 Sith Trooper C	.30	.75
57 Sith Trooper Commander U	.60	1.50
58 Snowtrooper with E-Web Blaster R	6.00	12.00
59 Ugnaught Demolitionist C	.30	.75
60 Ulic Qel-Droma VR	7.50	15.00
61 Utapau Trooper C	.30	.75
62 Varactyl Wrangler C	.30	.75
63 Yoda of Dagobah VR	12.50	25.00

2006 Star Wars Bounty Hunters Miniatures

COMPLETE SET (60)	150.00	300.00
RELEASED ON SEPTEMBER 23, 2006		
1 4-LOM, Bounty Hunter R	6.00	12.00
2 Aqualish Assassin C	.30	.75
3 Ayy Vida R	6.00	12.00
4 Basilisk War Droid U	.60	1.50
5 Bib Fortuna R	6.00	12.00
6 Bith Black Sun Vigo U	.60	1.50
7 Boba Fett, Bounty Hunter VR	15.00	40.00
8 BoShek R	6.00	12.00
9 Bossk, Bounty Hunter R	7.50	15.00
10 Boushh R	6.00	12.00
11 Calo Nord†R	6.00	12.00

12 Chewbacca w/C-3PO VR	10.00	18.00
13 Commerce Guild Homing Spider Droid U	.60	1.50
14 Corellian Pirate U	.60	1.50
15 Corporate Alliance Tank Droid U	.60	1.50
16 Dannik Jerriko VR	7.50	15.00
17 Dark Hellion Marauder on Swoop Bike U	.60	1.50
18 Dark Hellion Swoop Gang Member C	.30	.75
19 Defel Spy C	.30	.75
20 Dengar, Bounty Hunter R	7.50	15.00
21 Djas Puhr R	6.00	12.00
22 Droid Starfighter in Walking Mode R	7.50	15.00
23 E522 Assassin Droid U	.60	1.50
24 Gamorrean Thug C	.30	.75
25 Garindan R	6.00	12.00
26 Han Solo, Scoundrel VR	7.50	15.00
27 Huge Crab Droid U	.60	1.50
28 Human Blaster-for-Hire C	.30	.75
29 IG-88, Bounty Hunter VR	15.00	25.00
30 ISP Speeder R	6.00	12.00
31 Jango Fett, Bounty Hunter VR	15.00	30.00
32 Klatooinian Hunter C	.30	.75
33 Komari Vosa R	7.50	15.00
34 Lord Vader VR	10.00	20.00
35 Luke Skywalker of Dagobah R	7.50	15.00
36 Mandalore the Indomitable VR	12.50	25.00
37 Mandalorian Blademaster U	.60	1.50
38 Mandalorian Commander U	.60	1.50
39 Mandalorian Soldier C	.30	.75
40 Mandalorian Supercommando C	.30	.75
41 Mandalorian Warrior C	.30	.75
42 Mistryl Shadow Guard U	.60	1.50
43 Mustafarian Flea Rider R	6.00	12.00
44 Mustafarian Soldier C	.30	.75
45 Nikto Gunner on Desert Skiff VR	10.00	20.00
46 Nym VR	7.50	15.00
47 Princess Leia, Hoth Commander R	7.50	15.00
48 Quarren Bounty Hunter C	.30	.75
49 Rebel Captain U	.60	1.50
50 Rebel Heavy Trooper U	.60	1.50
51 Rebel Snowspeeder U	.60	1.50
52 Rodian Hunt Master U	.60	1.50
53 Talon Karrde VR	7.50	15.00
54 Tamtel Skreej VR	7.50	15.00
55 Tusken Raider Sniper C	.30	.75
56 Utapaun on Dactillion VR	7.50	15.00
57 Weequay Leader U	.60	1.50
58 Weequay Thug C	.30	.75
59 Young Krayt Dragon VR	10.00	20.00
60 Zuckuss R	7.50	15.00

2007 Star Wars Alliance and Empire Miniatures

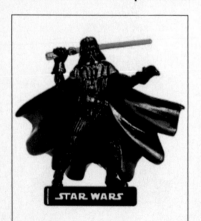

COMPLETE SET (60)	100.00	200.00
RELEASED IN MAY 2007		
1 Admiral Piett R	5.00	10.00
2 Advance Agent, Officer U	.60	1.50
3 Advance Scout C	.30	.75
4 Aurra Sing, Jedi Hunter VR	10.00	20.00
5 Biggs Darklighter VR	7.50	15.00
6 Boba Fett, Enforcer VR	12.50	25.00
7 C-3PO and R2-D2 R	5.00	10.00
8 Chadra-Fan Pickpocket U	.60	1.50
9 Chewbacca, Enraged Wookiee R	5.00	10.00

10 Darth Vader, Imperial Commander VR	12.50	25.00
11 Death Star Gunner U	.60	1.50
12 Death Star Trooper C	.30	.75
13 Duros Explorer C	.30	.75
14 Elite Hoth Trooper C	.30	.75
15 Ephant Mon VR	7.50	15.00
16 Ewok Hang Glider R	5.00	10.00
17 Ewok Warrior C	.30	.75
18 Gamorrean Guard C	.30	.75
19 Han Solo in Stormtrooper Armor R	5.00	10.00
20 Han Solo on Tauntaun VR	10.00	20.00
21 Han Solo Rogue R	5.00	10.00
22 Heavy Stormtrooper U	.60	1.50
23 Human Force Adept C	.30	.75
24 Imperial Governor Tarkin R	5.00	10.00
25 Imperial Officer U	.60	1.50
26 Ithorian Commander U	.60	1.50
27 Jabba, Crime Lord VR	7.50	15.00
28 Jawa on Ronto VR	7.50	15.00
29 Jawa Trader U	.60	1.50
30 Lando Calrissian, Dashing Scoundrel R	5.00	10.00
31 Luke Skywalker, Champion of the Force VR	12.50	25.00
32 Luke Skywalker, Hero of Yavin R	5.00	10.00
33 Luke's Landspeeder VR	7.50	15.00
34 Mara Jade, Jedi R	5.00	10.00
35 Mon Calamari Tech Specialist C	.30	.75
36 Nikto Soldier C	.30	.75
37 Obi-Wan Kenobi, Force Spirit VR	7.50	15.00
38 Princess Leia R	5.00	10.00
39 Quinlan Vos, Infiltrator VR	10.00	20.00
40 Rampaging Wampa VR	7.50	15.00
41 Rebel Commando C	.30	.75
42 Rebel Commando Strike Leader U	.60	1.50
43 Rebel Leader U	.60	1.50
44 Rebel Pilot C	.30	.75
45 Rebel Trooper U	.60	1.50
46 Rodian Scoundrel U	.60	1.50
47 Scout Trooper U	.60	1.50
48 Snivvian Fringer C	.30	.75
49 Snowtrooper C	.30	.75
50 Storm Commando R	5.00	10.00
51 Stormtrooper C	.30	.75
52 Stormtrooper Officer U	.60	1.50
53 Stormtrooper on Repulsor Sled VR	10.00	20.00
54 Talz Spy Fringe U	.60	1.50
55 Trandoshan Mercenary U	.60	1.50
56 Tusken Raider C	.30	.75
57 Twi'lek Rebel Agent U	.60	1.50
58 Wicket R	5.00	10.00
59 Wookiee Freedom Fighter C	.30	.75
60 Yomin Carr R	6.00	12.00

2007 Star Wars The Force Unleashed Miniatures

COMPLETE SET (60)	350.00	800.00
RELEASED IN 2007		
1 Darth Revan VR	50.00	80.00
2 Kazdan Paratus R	4.00	10.00
3 Shaak Ti, Jedi Master VR	8.00	20.00
4 Chewbacca of Hoth VR	4.00	10.00
5 Elite Hoth Trooper C	4.00	10.00
6 Golan Arms DF.9 Anti-Infantry Battery UC	4.00	10.00

7 Han Solo in Carbonite VR	4.00	10.00
8 Han Solo of Hoth VR	4.00	10.00
9 Hoth Trooper Officer UC	4.00	10.00
10 Hoth Trooper with Repeating Blaster Cannon UC	4.00	10.00
11 Juno Eclipse R	4.00	10.00
12 K-3PO R	4.00	10.00
13 Luke Skywalker, Hoth Pilot Unleashed R	4.00	10.00
14 Luke Skywalker and Yoda VR	6.00	15.00
15 Luke's Snowspeeder VR	6.00	15.00
16 Master Kota R	6.00	15.00
17 Mon Calamari Medic C	4.00	10.00
18 Obi-Wan Kenobi, Unleashed R	4.00	10.00
19 Princess Leia of Cloud City R	4.00	10.00
20 Rebel Marksman UC	4.00	10.00
21 Rebel Troop Cart UC	4.00	10.00
22 Rebel Trooper on Tauntaun R	4.00	10.00
23 Rebel Vanguard UC	4.00	10.00
24 2-1B R	4.00	10.00
25 Vader's Secret Apprentice, Redeemed R	8.00	20.00
26 Verpine Tech Rebel C	4.00	10.00
27 Wedge Antilles, Red Two Rebel R	4.00	10.00
28 Wookiee Warrior Rebel C	4.00	10.00
29 Admiral Ozzel R	4.00	10.00
30 AT-AT Driver UC	4.00	10.00
31 Dark trooper UC	4.00	10.00
32 Darth Vader, Unleashed VR	4.00	10.00
33 Emperor's Shadow Guard UC	4.00	10.00
34 Evo Trooper UC	4.00	10.00
35 Felucian Stormtrooper Officer UC	4.00	10.00
36 Gotal Imperial Assassin C	4.00	10.00
37 Imperial Navy trooper C	4.00	10.00
38 Raxus Prime Trooper C	4.00	10.00
39 Snowtrooper C	4.00	10.00
40 Star Destroyer Officer UC	4.00	10.00
41 Stormtrooper UC	4.00	10.00
42 TIE Crawler UC	4.00	10.00
43 Vader's Apprentice, Unleashed VR	4.00	10.00
44 Wookiee Hunter AT-ST R	6.00	15.00
45 Garm Bel Iblis R	4.00	10.00
46 Amanin Scout UC	4.00	10.00
47 Boba Fett, Mercenary VR	30.00	50.00
48 Caamasi Noble C	4.00	10.00
49 Cloud Car Pilot C	4.00	10.00
50 Felucian Warrior on Rancor VR	20.00	40.00
51 Junk golem UC	4.00	10.00
52 Knobby white spider UC	4.00	10.00
53 Maris Brood VR	6.00	15.00
54 Muun Tactics Broker C	4.00	10.00
55 Mynock UC	4.00	10.00
56 PROXY R	4.00	10.00
57 Telosian Tank Droid UC	4.00	10.00
58 Uggernaught R	4.00	10.00
59 Ugnaught Boss UC	4.00	10.00
60 Ugnaught Tech UC	4.00	10.00

2008 Star Wars Legacy of the Force Miniatures

COMPLETE SET (60)	300.00	700.00
RELEASED MARCH 28, 2008		
1 Nomi Sunrider VR	6.00	15.00
2 Old Republic Recruit C	4.00	10.00
3 Old Republic Scout C	4.00	10.00
4 Darth Caedus VR	15.00	30.00

5 Darth Krayt VR	15.00	30.00
6 Darth Nihl VR	4.00	10.00
7 Darth Talon VR	30.00	50.00
8 Lumiya, the Dark Lady R	4.00	10.00
9 Republic Commando Training Sergeant U	4.00	10.00
10 Darth Tyranus, Legacy of the dark side R	4.00	10.00
11 Bothan Noble U	4.00	10.00
12 Deena Shan R	4.00	10.00
13 Elite Rebel Commando U	4.00	10.00
14 General Dodonna R	4.00	10.00
15 Luke Skywalker, Legacy of the Light Side R	4.00	10.00
16 Rebel Honor Guard C	4.00	10.00
17 Twi'lek Scout C	4.00	10.00
18 Antares Draco R	5.00	12.00
19 Emperor Roan Fel VR	4.00	10.00
20 Imperial Knight U	4.00	10.00
21 Imperial Knight U	4.00	10.00
22 Imperial Pilot C	4.00	10.00
23 Imperial Security Officer U	4.00	10.00
24 Jagged Fel R	4.00	10.00
25 Marasiah Fel R	4.00	10.00
26 Moff Morlish Veed VR	4.00	10.00
27 Moff Nyna Calixte R	4.00	10.00
28 Noghri Commando U	4.00	10.00
29 Shadow Stormtrooper U	4.00	10.00
30 Corellian Security Officer U	4.00	10.00
31 Galactic Alliance Scout C	4.00	10.00
32 Galactic Alliance Trooper C	4.00	10.00
33 Han Solo, Galactic Hero R	4.00	10.00
34 Kyle Katarn, Jedi Battlemaster VR	4.00	10.00
35 Leia Organa Solo, Jedi Knight VR	4.00	10.00
36 Luke Skywalker, Force Spirit VR	4.00	10.00
37 Mara Jade Skywalker VR	6.00	15.00
38 Shado Vao R	4.00	10.00
39 Wolf Sazen VR	4.00	10.00
40 Cade Skywalker, Bounty Hunter VR	4.00	10.00
41 Deliah Blue R	4.00	10.00
42 Dug Fringer U	4.00	10.00
43 Duros Scoundrel C	4.00	10.00
44 Gotal Mercenary C	4.00	10.00
45 Guard Droid C	4.00	10.00
46 Human Bodyguard C	4.00	10.00
47 Human Scoundrel C	4.00	10.00
48 Human Scout C	4.00	10.00
49 Jariah Syn R	4.00	10.00
50 Kel Dor Bounty Hunter C	4.00	10.00
51 Rodian Blaster for Hire U	4.00	10.00
52 Trandoshan Mercenary C	4.00	10.00
53 Boba Fett, Mercenary Commander VR	4.00	10.00
54 Canderous Ordo R	4.00	10.00
55 Mandalorian Gunslinger U	4.00	10.00
56 Mandalorian Trooper U	4.00	10.00
57 Yuuzhan Vong Elite Warrior U	4.00	10.00
58 Yuuzhan Vong Jedi Hunter U	4.00	10.00
59 Yuuzhan Vong Shaper U	4.00	10.00
60 Yuuzhan Vong Warrior C	4.00	10.00

2008 Star Wars The Clone Wars Miniatures

COMPLETE SET (40)	200.00	400.00
RELEASED ON NOVEMBER 4, 2008		
1 Darth Sidious Hologram VR	4.00	10.00
2 Ahsoka Tano VR	10.00	25.00
3 Anakin Skywalker Champion of Nelvaan R	4.00	10.00
4 Anakin Skywalker on STAP VR	4.00	10.00
5 ARC Trooper Sniper U	4.00	10.00
6 Barriss Offee, Jedi Knight R	4.00	10.00
7 Captain Rex VR	4.00	10.00
8 Clone Trooper on Gelagrub R	4.00	10.00
9 Commander Gree R	4.00	10.00
10 Elite Clone Trooper Commander U	4.00	10.00
11 Elite Clone Trooper Grenadier C	4.00	10.00
12 Galactic Marine U	4.00	10.00
13 General Aayla Secura R	6.00	15.00
14 Heavy Clone Trooper C	4.00	10.00
15 Mon Calamari Knight U	4.00	10.00
16 Odd Ball R	4.00	10.00
17 Padmè Amidala Senator VR	5.00	12.00
18 Star Corps Trooper U	4.00	10.00
19 Wookiee Scoundrel C	4.00	10.00
20 Yoda on Kybuck VR	4.00	10.00
21 Battle Droid C	4.00	10.00
22 Battle Droid C	4.00	10.00
23 Battle Droid Sniper U	4.00	10.00
24 Chameleon Droid R	4.00	10.00
25 Durge, Jedi Hunter VR	10.00	25.00
26 General Grievous, Droid Army Commander VR	4.00	10.00
27 Heavy Super Battle Droid C	4.00	10.00
28 IG-100 MagnaGuard U	4.00	10.00
29 Neimoidian Warrior C	4.00	10.00
30 Quarren Isolationist U	4.00	10.00
31 Rocket Battle Droid U	4.00	10.00
32 Super Battle Droid C	4.00	10.00
33 Techno Union Warrior C	4.00	10.00
34 Aqualish Warrior C	4.00	10.00
35 Gha Nachkt R	4.00	10.00
36 Human Soldier of Fortune C	4.00	10.00
37 IG-86 Assassin Droid U	4.00	10.00
38 Nelvaanian Warrior U	4.00	10.00
39 Trandoshan Scavenger U	4.00	10.00
40 Utapaun Warrior C	4.00	10.00

2008 Star Wars The Clone Wars Miniatures Starter

COMPLETE SET (6)	20.00	50.00
RELEASED ON NOVEMBER 4, 2008		
1 General Obi-Wan Kenobi	3.00	8.00
2 Clone Trooper	3.00	8.00
3 Clone Trooper Commander	3.00	8.00
4 Count Dooku of Serenno	3.00	8.00
5 Security Battle Droid	3.00	8.00
6 Super Battle Droid Commander	3.00	8.00

2009 Star Wars Galaxy at War Miniatures

COMPLETE SET (40)	60.00	160.00
RELEASED ON OCTOBER 27, 2009		
1 501st Clone Trooper C	1.50	4.00
2 A4-Series Lab Droid U	1.50	4.00

3 Admiral Yularen VR	1.50	4.00
4 Aqualish Technician C	1.50	4.00
5 ARF Trooper C	1.50	4.00
6 Asajj Ventress, Strike Leader R	1.50	4.00
7 AT-TE Driver C	1.50	4.00
8 B3 Ultra Battle Droid U	1.50	4.00
9 Battle Droid C	1.50	4.00
10 Battle Droid Sergeant U	1.50	4.00
11 Cad Bane VR	1.50	4.00
12 Captain Argyus VR	1.50	4.00
13 Captain Mar Tuuk VR	1.50	4.00
14 Captain Rex, 501st Commander R	1.50	4.00
15 Clone Trooper Pilot C	1.50	4.00
16 Clone Trooper Sergeant U	1.50	4.00
17 Clone Trooper with Night Vision C	1.50	4.00
18 Clone Trooper with Repeating Blaster U	1.50	4.00
19 Commander Ahsoka R	1.50	4.00
20 Commander Cody R	1.50	4.00
21 Commando Droid C	1.50	4.00
22 Commando Droid C	1.50	4.00
23 Commando Droid Captain U	1.50	4.00
24 Elite Senate Guard U	1.50	4.00
25 General Grievous, Scourge of the Jedi R	1.50	4.00
26 General Skywalker R	1.50	4.00
27 General Whorm Loathsom VR	1.50	4.00
28 Hondo Ohnaka VR	1.50	4.00
29 IG-100 MagnaGuard Artillerist U	1.50	4.00
30 IG-100 MagnaGuard U	1.50	4.00
31 Jedi Master Kit Fisto R	1.50	4.00
32 LR-57 Combat Droid U	1.50	4.00
33 Nahdar Vebb VR	1.50	4.00
34 Obi-Wan Kenobi, Jedi General R	1.50	4.00
35 R7 Astromech Droid U	1.50	4.00
36 Rodian Trader C	1.50	4.00
37 Senate Commando C	1.50	4.00
38 Treadwell Droid U	1.50	4.00
39 Wat Tambor, Techno Union Foreman VR	1.50	4.00
40 Weequay Pirate C	1.50	4.00

2009 Star Wars Imperial Entanglements Miniatures

COMPLETE SET (40)	180.00	450.00
RELEASED ON MARCH 17, 2009		
1 Bothan Commando C	4.00	10.00
2 C-3PO, Ewok Deity VR	4.00	10.00
3 General Crix Madine R	4.00	10.00
4 General Rieekan VR	5.00	12.00
5 Leia, Bounty Hunter VR	4.00	10.00
6 Luke Skywalker, Rebel Commando VR	8.00	20.00
7 Rebel Commando Pathfinder U	4.00	10.00
8 Rebel Trooper C	4.00	10.00
9 R2-D2 with Extended Sensor R	4.00	10.00

10	Veteran Rebel Commando C	4.00	10.00
11	Arica R	4.00	10.00
12	Darth Vader, Legacy of the Force VR	8.00	20.00
13	Emperor Palpatine on Throne VR	10.00	25.00
14	Imperial Dignitary U	4.00	10.00
15	Moff Tiaan Jerjerrod R	4.00	10.00
16	181st Imperial Pilot U	4.00	10.00
17	Sandtrooper C	4.00	10.00
18	Sandtrooper Officer U	4.00	10.00
19	Scout Trooper C	4.00	10.00
20	Shock Trooper U	4.00	10.00
21	Snowtrooper C	4.00	10.00
22	Snowtrooper Commander U	4.00	10.00
23	Stormtrooper C	4.00	10.00
24	Thrawn Mitth'raw'nuruodo R	4.00	10.00
25	Kyp Durron R	4.00	10.00
26	Bacta Tank U	4.00	10.00
27	Bespin Guard C	4.00	10.00
28	Chiss Mercenary C	4.00	10.00
29	Dash Rendar, Renegade Smuggler VR	6.00	15.00
30	Duros Scout C	4.00	10.00
31	Ewok Scout C	4.00	10.00
32	Jawa Scavenger C	4.00	10.00
33	Lobot, Computer Liaison Officer R	4.00	10.00
34	Logray, Ewok Shaman R	4.00	10.00
35	Mercenary Commander U - resembling Airen Cracken	4.00	10.00
36	Mouse Droid U	4.00	10.00
37	Twi'lek Black Sun Vigo U	4.00	10.00
38	Ugnaught Droid Destroyer U	4.00	10.00
39	Whiphid Tracker U	4.00	10.00
40	Xizor VR	8.00	20.00

2009 Star Wars Jedi Academy Miniatures

| COMPLETE SET (40) | | 200.00 | 450.00 |
| RELEASED ON JUNE 30, 2009 | | | |

1	Anakin Solo R	4.00	10.00
2	Antarian Ranger C	4.00	10.00
3	Cade Skywalker, Padawan R	4.00	10.00
4	Crimson Nova Bounty Hunter UC	4.00	10.00
5	Darth Maul, Sith apprentice VR	10.00	25.00
6	Darth Plagueis VR	10.00	25.00
7	Darth Sidious, Sith Master R	4.00	10.00
8	Death Watch Raider C	4.00	10.00
9	Disciples of Ragnos C	4.00	10.00
10	Exceptional Jedi Apprentice UC	4.00	10.00
11	Felucian UC	4.00	10.00
12	Grand Master Luke Skywalker R	6.00	15.00
13	Grand Master Yoda R	5.00	12.00
14	Heavy Clone Trooper C	4.00	10.00
15	HK-50 Series Assassin Droid UC	4.00	10.00
16	Imperial Sentinel U	4.00	10.00
17	Jedi Battlemaster UC	4.00	10.00
18	Jedi Crusader UC	4.00	10.00
19	Jensaarai Defender UC	4.00	10.00
20	Kol Skywalker VR	4.00	10.00

21	Krath War Droid C	4.00	10.00
22	Kyle Katarn, Combat Instructor R	4.00	10.00
23	Leia Skywalker, Jedi Knight R	4.00	10.00
24	Master K'Kruhk VR	4.00	10.00
25	Naga Sadow VR	6.00	15.00
26	Peace Brigade Thug C	4.00	10.00
27	Praetorite Vong Priest UC	4.00	10.00
28	Praetorite Vong Warrior C	4.00	10.00
29	Qui-Gon Jinn, Jedi Trainer R	4.00	10.00
30	R4 Astromech Droid C	4.00	10.00
31	Reborn C	4.00	10.00
32	Rocket Battle Droid C	4.00	10.00
33	Sith apprentice UC - resembling Darth Bandon	4.00	10.00
34	Sith Lord U	4.00	10.00
35	Stormtrooper C	4.00	10.00
36	The Dark Woman VR	8.00	20.00
37	The Jedi Exile VR	10.00	25.00
38	Vodo-Siosk Baas VR	6.00	15.00
39	Youngling C	4.00	10.00
40	Yuuzhan Vong Ossus Guardian UC	4.00	10.00

2010 Star Wars Dark Times Miniatures

| COMPLETE SET (40) | | 75.00 | 200.00 |
| RELEASED ON JANUARY 26, 2010 | | | |

1	4-LOM, Droid Mercenary R	1.50	4.00
2	501st Legion Clone Commander UC	1.50	4.00
3	501st Legion Clone Trooper C	1.50	4.00
4	501st Legion Stormtrooper C	1.50	4.00
5	ARF Trooper UC	1.50	4.00
6	A'Sharad Hett VR	6.00	15.00
7	Bomo Greenbark VR	1.50	4.00
8	Bossk, Trandoshan Hunter R	1.50	4.00
9	Boushh, Ubese Hunter R	1.50	4.00
10	Chewbacca, Fearless Scout VR	1.50	4.00
11	Dass Jennir VR	4.00	10.00
12	Dengar, Hired Killer R	1.50	4.00
13	EG-5 Jedi Hunter Droid UC	3.00	8.00
14	Elite Sith Assassin UC	1.50	4.00
15	Emperor's Hand UC	1.50	4.00
16	Ferus Olin VR	1.50	4.00
17	Gungan Bounty Hunter C	1.50	4.00
18	Human Engineer C	1.50	4.00
19	IG-88, Assassin Droid R	3.00	8.00
20	Imperial Engineer C	1.50	4.00
21	Imperial Inquisitor UC	1.50	4.00
22	Imperial Sovereign Protector UC	1.50	4.00
23	Jax Pavan VR	1.50	4.00
24	Jedi Watchman C	1.50	4.00
25	Kir Kanos VR	4.00	10.00
26	K'Kruhk VR	1.50	4.00
27	Kota's Elite Militia UC	1.50	4.00
28	Kota's Militia C	1.50	4.00

29	Major Maximilian Veers R	1.50	4.00
30	Mandalorian Jedi Hunter UC	1.50	4.00
31	Merumeru R	1.50	4.00
32	Rodian Brute C	1.50	4.00
33	Rodian Raider C	1.50	4.00
34	Talz Chieftain UC	1.50	4.00
35	Talz Warrior C	1.50	4.00
36	Togorian Soldier UC	1.50	4.00
37	Trandoshan Elite Mercenary UC	4.00	10.00
38	Trianii Scout UC	1.50	4.00
39	T'Surr C	1.50	4.00
40	Zuckuss, Bounty Hunter C	5.00	12.00

2010 Star Wars Masters of the Force Miniatures

| COMPLETE SET (40) | | 115.00 | 280.00 |
| RELEASED APRIL 6, 2010 | | | |

1	Cay Qel-Droma VR	6.00	15.00
2	Jedi Healer UC	2.50	6.00
3	Jedi Instructor - resembling Coleman Trebor UC	2.50	6.00
4	Jedi Sith Hunter UC	2.50	6.00
5	Lord Hoth VR	2.50	6.00
6	Freedon Nadd VR	2.50	6.00
7	Kit Fisto, Jedi Master R	2.50	6.00
8	Master Windu R	2.50	6.00
9	Plo Koon, Jedi Master R	4.00	10.00
10	Rodian Diplomat UC	2.50	6.00
11	Saesee Tiin, Jedi Master R	6.00	15.00
12	Voolvif Monn VR	10.00	25.00
13	Battle Droid Officer C	2.50	6.00
14	Anakin Skywalker, Force Spirit R	2.50	6.00
15	General Han Solo R	2.50	6.00
16	Lando Calrissian, Rebel Leader R	2.50	6.00
17	Rebel Soldier C	2.50	6.00
18	Red Hand Trooper UC	2.50	6.00
19	Yoda, Force Spirit VR	2.50	6.00
20	Arden Lyn VR	2.50	6.00
21	Darth Vader, Sith apprentice R	2.50	6.00
22	Ganner Rhysode VR	2.50	6.00
23	Blood Carver Assassin C	2.50	6.00
24	Chiss Trooper UC	2.50	6.00
25	Ewok Warrior C	2.50	6.00
26	Gamorrean Bodyguard C	2.50	6.00
27	Ghhhk UC	3.00	8.00
28	Grievous, Kaleesh Warlord VR	2.50	6.00
29	Houjix C	2.50	6.00
30	K'lor'slug UC	3.00	8.00
31	Kaminoan Medic UC	2.50	6.00
32	Kintan Strider C	2.50	6.00
33	Mantellian Savrip C	2.50	6.00
34	Molator UC	2.50	6.00
35	Monnok UC	2.50	6.00
36	Ng'ok UC	3.00	8.00
37	Sullustan Scout C	2.50	6.00
38	Toydarian Soldier C	2.50	6.00
39	Far-Outsider C	2.50	6.00
40	Taung Warrior C	2.50	6.00

HOT WHEELS

2014 Hot Wheels Star Wars Character Cars Black Cards 1:64

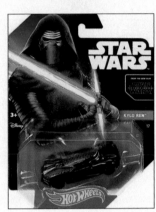

1	Darth Vader	10.00	20.00
2	R2-D2	5.00	10.00
3	Luke Skywalker	5.00	10.00
4	Chewbacca	4.00	8.00
5	Yoda	4.00	8.00
6	Tusken Raider	5.00	10.00
7	501st Clone Trooper	8.00	15.00
8	Stormtrooper	4.00	8.00
9	Darth Maul	4.00	8.00
10	Boba Fett	6.00	12.00
11	Chopper (Star Wars Rebels)	5.00	10.00
12	The Inquisitor (Star Wars Rebels)	4.00	8.00
13	C-3PO	8.00	15.00
14	Wicket the Ewok	5.00	10.00
15	Kanan Jarrus (Star Wars Rebels)	4.00	8.00
16	Zeb (Star Wars Rebels)	4.00	8.00
17	Kylo Ren	5.00	10.00
18	BB-8	8.00	15.00
19	General Grievous	6.00	12.00
20	Han Solo (The Force Awakens)	8.00	15.00
21	First Order Stormtrooper	6.00	12.00
22	Obi-Wan Kenobi	12.00	25.00
23	Rey	8.00	15.00
24	Jabba the Hutt	5.00	10.00
25	Admiral Ackbar	5.00	10.00
26	First Order Flametrooper	6.00	12.00
27	Battle Droid	6.00	12.00
28	Sabine Wren (Star Wars Rebels)	12.50	25.00
29	Clone Shock Trooper/(UER #27)		
30	C-3PO (The Force Awakens)	8.00	15.00
31	Sidon Ithano (The Force Awakens)	8.00	15.00
32	Jango Fett	6.00	12.00

2014 Hot Wheels Star Wars Character Cars Blue Cards 1:64

1	Darth Vader	4.00	8.00
2	R2-D2	4.00	8.00
3	Luke Skywalker	4.00	8.00
4	Chewbacca	6.00	12.00
5	Yoda	7.50	15.00
6	Tusken Raider	4.00	8.00
7	501st Clone Trooper	4.00	8.00
8	Stormtrooper	4.00	8.00
9	Darth Maul	5.00	10.00
10	Boba Fett	4.00	8.00
11	Chopper (Star Wars Rebels)	4.00	8.00
12	The Inquisitor (Star Wars Rebels)	3.00	6.00
13	C-3PO	6.00	12.00
14	Wicket the Ewok	4.00	8.00
15	Kanan Jarrus (Star Wars Rebels)	5.00	10.00
16	Zeb (Star Wars Rebels)		
17	Kylo Ren		
18	BB-8		
19	General Grievous		
20	Han Solo (The Force Awakens)		
21	First Order Stormtrooper	6.00	12.00
22	Obi-Wan Kenobi		
23	Rey		
24	Jabba the Hutt		
25	Admiral Ackbar		
26	First Order Flametrooper		
27	Battle Droid		
28	Sabine Wren (Star Wars Rebels)		
29	Clone Shock Trooper/(UER #27)		
30	C-3PO (The Force Awakens)		
31	Sidon Ithano (The Force Awakens)		
32	Jango Fett		

2014 Hot Wheels Star Wars Saga Walmart Exclusives 1:64

1	Gearonimo (The Phantom Menace)	5.00	10.00
2	Nitro Scorcher (Attack of the Clones)	6.00	12.00
3	Duel Fueler (Revenge of the Sith)	8.00	15.00
4	Motoblade (A New Hope)		
5	Spectyte (Empire Strikes Back)	10.00	20.00
6	Ballistik (Return of the Jedi)	4.00	8.00
7	Brutalistic (The Clone Wars)	4.00	8.00
8	Jet Threat 3.0 (Star Wars Rebels)	12.00	25.00

2014-16 Hot Wheels Star Wars Exclusives 1:64

1	Darth Vader (w/lightsaber box)/(2014 SDCC Exclusive)	80.00	150.00
2	R2-KT/(2015 Star Wars Celebration Make-a-Wish Foundation Exclusive)	40.00	80.00
3	First Order Stormtrooper/(2015 SDCC Exclusive)	25.00	50.00
4	Carships Trench Run Set/(2016 SDCC Exclusive)	50.00	100.00
5	Boba Fett Prototype Armor/(2016 Star Wars Celebration Exclusive)	25.00	50.00

2014-16 Hot Wheels Star Wars Target Exclusive 5-Packs 1:64

1 Character Cars (Battle-Damaged Stormtrooper Luke Skywalker/Darth Vader/Yoda/Chewbacca)	25.00	50.00
2 Light Side vs. Dark Side (Luke Skywalker/Obi-Wan Kenobi Anakin Skywalker/Emperor Palpatine/Kylo Ren)	15.00	30.00
3 Heroes of the Resistance (Chewbacca/Han Solo/Rey Poe Dameron/Maz Kanata)	20.00	40.00

2015 Hot Wheels Star Wars Walmart Exclusives 1:64

1 Obi-Wan Kenobi/(Jedi Order Scorcher)	4.00	8.00
2 Darth Maul/(Sith Scoopa di Fuego)	5.00	10.00
3 Clone Trooper/(Galactic Republic Impavido 1)	4.00	8.00
4 General Grievous/(Separatists Sinistra)	4.00	8.00
5 Luke Skywalker/(Rebel Alliance Enforcer)	4.00	8.00
6 Darth Vader/(Galactic Empire Prototype H-24)	5.00	10.00
7 Poe Dameron/(Resistance Fast Felion)	4.00	8.00
8 Kylo Ren/(First Order Ettorium)	4.00	8.00

2015-16 Hot Wheels Star Wars Character Cars Black Carded 2-Packs 1:64

1 Chewbacca & Han Solo	5.00	10.00
2 R2-D2 & C-3PO (weathered)	4.00	8.00
3 Obi-Wan Kenobi & Darth Vader	20.00	40.00
4 501st Clone Trooper & Battle Droid	4.00	8.00
5 Emperor Palpatine vs. Yoda	8.00	15.00
6 Darth Vader & Princess Leia	10.00	20.00
7 Captain Phasma & First Order Stormtrooper	5.00	10.00
8 Rey vs. First Order Flametrooper	8.00	15.00
9 BB-8 & Poe Dameron	10.00	20.00
10 Han Solo vs. Greedo	12.00	25.00
11 Boba Fett & Bossk		
12 Luke Skywalker vs. Rancor		
13 Stormtrooper & Death Trooper (Rogue One)	8.00	15.00

2015-16 Hot Wheels Star Wars Character Cars Blue Carded 2-Packs 1:64

1 Chewbacca & Han Solo	6.00	12.00
2 R2-D2 & C-3PO (weathered)	6.00	12.00
3 Obi-Wan Kenobi & Darth Vader	6.00	12.00
4 501st Clone Trooper & Battle Droid	8.00	15.00
5 Emperor Palpatine vs. Yoda		
6 Darth Vader & Princess Leia	6.00	12.00
7 Captain Phasma & First Order Stormtrooper		
8 Rey vs. First Order Flametrooper		
9 BB-8 & Poe Dameron		
10 Han Solo vs. Greedo	8.00	15.00
11 Boba Fett & Bossk		
12 Luke Skywalker vs. Rancor		
13 Stormtrooper & Death Trooper (Rogue One)	10.00	20.00

2015-16 Hot Wheels Star Wars Tracksets 1:64

1 TIE Factory Takedown (w/Ezra Bridger car)	12.00	25.00
2 Throne Room Raceway (w/Luke Skywalker car)	12.00	25.00
3 Death Star Battle Blast (w/X-Wing inspired vehicle)	10.00	20.00
4 Blast & Battle Lightsaber Launcher (w/Darth Vader car)	8.00	15.00
5 Starkiller Base Battle (w/Finn car)		
6 Rancor Rumble set (w/Gamorrean Guard car)	15.00	30.00

2017 Hot Wheels Star Wars 40th Anniversary Carships 1:64

NNO Millennium Falcon	6.00	12.00
NNO TIE Advanced XI Prototype	6.00	12.00
NNO TIE Fighter	5.00	10.00
NNO X-Wing Fighter	5.00	10.00
NNO Y-Wing Fighter	8.00	15.00

2017 Hot Wheels Star Wars 40th Anniversary Character Cars 1:64

NNO Biggs Darklighter/(Celebration Exclusive)	12.00	25.00
NNO Chewbacca	5.00	10.00
NNO Darth Vader	6.00	12.00
NNO Luke Skywalker	4.00	8.00
NNO Princess Leia	5.00	10.00
NNO R2-D2	4.00	8.00
NNO Stormtrooper	4.00	8.00

2017 Hot Wheels Star Wars 40th Anniversary Starships 1:64

NNO Millennium Falcon	8.00	15.00
NNO Star Destroyer	10.00	20.00
NNO TIE Advanced X1 Prototype	6.00	12.00
NNO TIE Fighter	6.00	12.00
NNO X-Wing Fighter	6.00	12.00
NNO Y-Wing Fighter	8.00	15.00

2017 Hot Wheels Star Wars The Last Jedi 2-Packs 1:64

NNO BB-8 & Poe Dameron	8.00	15.00
NNO Boba Fett & Bossk	6.00	12.00
NNO Jabba the Hutt & Han Solo in Carbonite	12.00	25.00
NNO Kylo Ren & Snoke	15.00	30.00
NNO R2-D2 & C-3PO	8.00	15.00
NNO Rey (Jedi Training) & Luke Skywalker	15.00	30.00

2017 Hot Wheels Star Wars The Last Jedi Carships 1:64

NNO First Order TIE Fighter	6.00	12.00
NNO Kylo Ren's TIE Silencer		
NNO Millennium Falcon		
NNO Poe's X-Wing Fighter		
NNO Resistance Ski Speeder		
NNO Y-Wing Fighter		

2017 Hot Wheels Star Wars The Last Jedi Character Cars 1:64

NNO	BB-8	7.50	15.00
NNO	BB-9E	6.00	12.00
NNO	C-3PO	4.00	8.00
NNO	Captain Phasma	4.00	8.00
NNO	Chewbacca	4.00	8.00
NNO	Darth Vader	5.00	10.00
NNO	Elite Praetorian Guard	10.00	20.00
NNO	Finn	7.50	15.00
NNO	First Order Executioner	5.00	10.00
NNO	First Order Stormtrooper		
NNO	Kylo Ren	6.00	12.00
NNO	Luke Skywalker	5.00	10.00
NNO	R2-D2	4.00	8.00
NNO	Rey (Jedi Training)	6.00	12.00

2017 Hot Wheels Star Wars The Last Jedi Character Cars All-Terrain 1:64

NNO	BB-8	10.00	20.00
NNO	Darth Vader		

NNO	Luke Skywalker		
NNO	Stormtrooper		

2017 Hot Wheels Star Wars The Last Jedi Starships 1:64

NNO	First Order Heavy Assault Walker		
NNO	First Order Special Forces TIE Fighter		
NNO	First Order Star Destroyer		
NNO	Kylo Ren's TIE Silencer		
NNO	Kylo Ren's TIE Silencer (boxed)/(SDCC Exclusive)		
NNO	Millennium Falcon		
NNO	Poe's Ski Speeder		
NNO	Resistance Bomber		
NNO	Resistance X-Wing Fighter		

LEGO

1999 LEGO Star Wars Episode I

7101	Lightsaber Duel	25.00	50.00
7111	Droid Fighter	15.00	30.00
7121	Naboo Swamp	20.00	40.00
7131	Anakin's Podracer	25.00	50.00
7141	Naboo Fighter	40.00	80.00
7151	Sith Infiltrator	30.00	60.00
7161	Gungan Sub	60.00	120.00
7171	Mos Espa Podrace	80.00	150.00

1999 LEGO Star Wars Episode IV

7110	Landspeeder	20.00	40.00
7140	X-wing Fighter	60.00	120.00
7150	TIE Fighter & Y-wing	80.00	150.00

1999 LEGO Star Wars Episode V

7130	Snowspeeder	40.00	80.00

1999 LEGO Star Wars Episode VI

7128	Speeder Bikes	25.00	50.00

2000 LEGO Star Wars Episode I

7115	Gungan Patrol	25.00	50.00
7124	Flash Speeder	15.00	30.00
7155	Trade Federation AAT	40.00	80.00
7159	Star Wars Bucket	30.00	75.00
7184	Trade Federation MTT	30.00	75.00

2000 LEGO Star Wars Episode IV

7190	Millennium Falcon	150.00	300.00

2000 LEGO Star Wars Episode V

7144	Slave I	50.00	100.00

2000 LEGO Star Wars Episode VI

7104	Desert Skiff	20.00	40.00
7134	A-wing Fighter	25.00	50.00
7180	B-wing at Rebel Control Center	30.00	60.00

2000 LEGO Star Wars Minifigure Pack

3340	Emperor Palpatine, Darth Maul and Darth Vader Minifig Pack - Star Wars #1	40.00	80.00
3341	Luke Skywalker, Han Solo and Boba Fett Minifig Pack - Star Wars #2	40.00	80.00
3342	Chewbacca and 2 Biker Scouts Minifig Pack - Star Wars #3	12.00	25.00
3343	2 Battle Droids and Command Officer Minifig Pack - Star Wars #4	12.00	25.00

2000 LEGO Star Wars Technic

8000	Pit Droid	20.00	40.00
8001	Battle Droid	25.00	50.00
8002	Destroyer Droid	120.00	200.00

2000 LEGO Star Wars Ultimate Collector Series

7181	TIE Interceptor	300.00	600.00
7191	X-wing Fighter	450.00	900.00

2001 LEGO Star Wars Episode I

7126 Battle Droid Carrier	20.00	40.00
7186 Watto's Junkyard	50.00	100.00

2001 LEGO Star Wars Episode IV

7106 Droid Escape	15.00	30.00
7146 TIE Fighter	60.00	120.00

2001 LEGO Star Wars Episode VI

7127 Imperial AT-ST	20.00	40.00
7166 Imperial Shuttle	40.00	80.00

2001 LEGO Star Wars Technic

8007 C-3PO	50.00	100.00
8008 Stormtrooper	20.00	50.00

2001 LEGO Star Wars Ultimate Collector Series

10018 Darth Maul	200.00	400.00
10019 Rebel Blockade Runner	700.00	1,400.00

2002 LEGO Star Wars Episode I

7203 Jedi Defense I	15.00	30.00
7204 Jedi Defense II	20.00	40.00

2002 LEGO Star Wars Episode II

7103 Jedi Duel	15.00	30.00
7113 Tusken Raider Encounter	20.00	40.00
7133 Bounty Hunter Pursuit	30.00	60.00

7143 Jedi Starfighter	30.00	60.00
7153 Jango Fett's Slave I	125.00	250.00
7163 Republic Gunship	125.00	250.00

2002 LEGO Star Wars Episode IV

7142 X-wing Fighter	100.00	200.00
7152 TIE Fighter & Y-wing	.00	.00

2002 LEGO Star Wars Episode V

7119 Twin-Pod Cloud Car	25.00	50.00

2002 LEGO Star Wars Episode VI

7139 Ewok Attack	40.00	80.00
7200 Final Duel I	30.00	60.00
7201 Final Duel II	20.00	40.00

2002 LEGO Star Wars Miniature Building Set

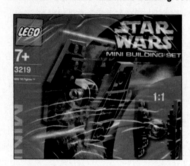

3219 Mini TIE Fighter	15.00	30.00

2002 LEGO Star Wars Product Collection

65081 R2-D2 & C-3PO Droid Collectors Set	50.00	100.00
65145 X-wing Fighter TIE Fighter & Y-wing Fighter Collectors Set	.00	.00
65153 Jango Fett's Slave I with Bonus Cargo Case	.00	.00

2002 LEGO Star Wars Technic

8009 R2-D2	30.00	60.00
8010 Darth Vader	60.00	120.00
8011 Jango Fett	40.00	80.00
8012 Super Battle Droid	20.00	40.00

2002 LEGO Star Wars Ultimate Collector Series

7194 Yoda	300.00	600.00
10026 Naboo Starfighter Special Edition	300.00	600.00
10030 Imperial Star Destroyer	1,200.00	2,000.00

2003 LEGO Star Wars Episode II

4482 AT-TE	120.00	250.00
4478 Geonosian Fighter	90.00	150.00
4481 Hailfire Droid	60.00	120.00

2003 LEGO Star Wars Episode IV

4477 T-16 Skyhopper	20.00	40.00

2003 LEGO Star Wars Episode V

4483 AT-AT	250.00	500.00
4479 TIE Bomber	100.00	200.00
10123 Cloud City	600.00	1,000.00

2003 LEGO Star Wars Episode VI

4475 Jabba's Message	25.00	50.00
4476 Jabba's Prize	80.00	150.00
4480 Jabba's Palace	100.00	200.00

2003 LEGO Star Wars Miniature Building Set

4484 X-Wing Fighter & TIE Advanced	20.00	40.00
4485 Sebulba's Podracer & Anakin's Podracer	10.00	20.00
4486 AT-ST & Snowspeeder	20.00	40.00
4487 Jedi Starfighter & Slave I	12.00	25.00
4488 Millennium Falcon	25.00	50.00
4489 AT-AT	12.00	25.00
4490 Republic Gunship	8.00	15.00
4491 MTT	10.00	20.00

2003 LEGO Star Wars Product Collection

4207901 Star Wars MINI Bonus Pack	.00	.00

2003 LEGO Star Wars Ultimate Collector Series

10129	Rebel Snowspeeder	600.00	1,200.00

2004 LEGO Star Wars Episode IV

4501	Mos Eisley Cantina	100.00	200.00
7262	TIE Fighter and Y-Wing	30.00	60.00

2004 LEGO Star Wars Episode V

4500	Rebel Snowspeeder	25.00	50.00
4502	X-wing Fighter	100.00	200.00
4504	Millennium Falcon	120.00	250.00

2004 LEGO Star Wars Legends

10131	TIE Fighter Collection	150.00	300.00

2004 LEGO Star Wars Miniature Building Set

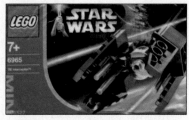

4492	Star Destroyer	20.00	40.00
4493	Sith Infiltrator	8.00	15.00
4494	Imperial Shuttle	15.00	30.00
4495	AT-TE	12.00	25.00
6963	X-wing Fighter	15.00	30.00
6964	Boba Fett's Slave I	12.00	25.00
6965	TIE Interceptor	12.00	25.00

2004 LEGO Star Wars Product Collection

65707	Bonus/Value Pack	.00	.00

2004 LEGO Star Wars Ultimate Collector Series

10134	Y-wing Attack Starfighter	600.00	1,000.00

2005 LEGO Star Wars Episode III

6966	Jedi Starfighter	8.00	15.00
6967	ARC Fighter	8.00	15.00
6968	Wookiee Attack	.00	.00
7250	Clone Scout Walker	30.00	60.00
7251	Darth Vader Transformation	50.00	100.00
7252	Droid Tri-Fighter	20.00	40.00
7255	General Grievous Chase	60.00	120.00
7256	Jedi Starfighter and Vulture Droid	40.00	80.00
7257	Ultimate Lightsaber Duel	100.00	200.00
7258	Wookiee Attack	60.00	120.00
7259	ARC-170 Fighter	60.00	120.00
7260	Wookiee Catamaran	50.00	100.00
7261	Clone Turbo Tank	120.00	250.00
7283	Ultimate Space Battle	150.00	300.00

2005 LEGO Star Wars Episode IV

7263	TIE Fighter	50.00	100.00
10144	Sandcrawler	200.00	400.00

2005 LEGO Star Wars Episode VI

7264	Imperial Inspection	100.00	200.00

2005 LEGO Star Wars Product Collection

65771	Episode III Collectors' Set	100.00	200.00
65828	Bonus/Value Pack	.00	.00
65844	Bonus/Value Pack	.00	.00
65845	Bonus/Value Pack	.00	.00

2005 LEGO Star Wars Exclusives

PROMOSW002	Anakin Skywalker/(2005 International Toy Fair Exclusive)	.00	.00
PROMOSW003	Luminara Unduli (2005 International Toy Fair Exclusive)	.00	.00
SW117PROMO	Darth Vader (2005 Nurnberg Toy Fair Exclusive)	.00	.00
TF05	Star Wars V.I.P. Gala Set/(2005 International Toy Fair Exclusive)	.00	.00

2005 LEGO Star Wars Ultimate Collector Series

10143	Death Star II	400.00	800.00

2006 LEGO Star Wars Episode III

6205	V-wing Fighter	25.00	50.00
72612	Clone Turbo Tank (non-light-up edition)	150.00	300.00

2006 LEGO Star Wars Episode IV

6211	Imperial Star Destroyer	150.00	300.00

2006 LEGO Star Wars Episode V

6209	Slave I	80.00	150.00
6212	X-wing Fighter	80.00	150.00

2006 LEGO Star Wars Episode VI

6206	TIE Interceptor	50.00	100.00
6207	A-wing Fighter	30.00	60.00
6208	B-wing Fighter	30.00	60.00
6210	Jabba's Sail Barge	200.00	350.00

2006 LEGO Star Wars Product Collection

66142	Bonus/Value Pack	.00	.00
66150	Bonus/Value Pack	.00	.00
66221	Bonus/Value Pack	.00	.00

2006 LEGO Star Wars Ultimate Collector Series

10174	Imperial AT-ST	275.00	550.00
10175	Vader's TIE Advanced	350.00	700.00

2007 LEGO Star Wars Episode I

7660	Naboo N-1 Starfighter with Vulture Droid	20.00	40.00
7662	Trade Federation MTT	150.00	300.00
7663	Sith Infiltrator	25.00	50.00
7665	Republic Cruiser	100.00	200.00

2007 LEGO Star Wars Episode III

7654	Droids Battle Pack	25.00	50.00
7655	Clone Troopers Battle Pack	25.00	50.00
7656	General Grievous Starfighter	40.00	80.00
7661	Jedi Starfighter with Hyperdrive Booster Ring	60.00	120.00

2007 LEGO Star Wars Episode IV

7658	Y-wing Fighter	50.00	100.00
7659	Imperial Landing Craft	50.00	100.00

2007 LEGO Star Wars Episode V

7666	Hoth Rebel Base	100.00	200.00
10178	Motorised Walking AT-AT	300.00	600.00

2007 LEGO Star Wars Episode VI

7657	AT-ST	80.00	150.00

2007 LEGO Star Wars Legends

7664	TIE Crawler	50.00	100.00

2007 LEGO Star Wars Minifigure Pack

4521221	Gold chrome plated C-3PO	250.00	500.00
PROMOSW004	Star Wars Celebration IV Exclusive/500*	600.00	1,000.00

2007 LEGO Star Wars Ultimate Collector Series

10179	Ultimate Collector's Millennium Falcon	3,000.00	5,000.00

2008 LEGO Star Wars The Clone Wars

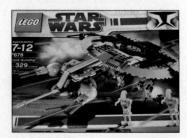

7669	Anakin's Jedi Starfighter	40.00	80.00
7670	Hailfire Droid & Spider Droid	30.00	60.00
7673	MagnaGuard Starfighter	30.00	80.00
7674	V-19 Torrent	80.00	150.00

7675	AT-TE Walker	120.00	250.00
7676	Republic Attack Gunship	175.00	350.00
7678	Droid Gunship	30.00	60.00
7679	Republic Fighter Tank	80.00	150.00
7680	The Twilight	80.00	150.00
7681	Separatist Spider Droid	50.00	100.00
8031	V-19 Torrent	10.00	20.00
20006	Clone Turbo Tank	20.00	40.00

2008 LEGO Star Wars Episode III

7671	AT-AP Walker	40.00	80.00

2008 LEGO Star Wars Episode V

8029	Mini Snowspeeder	6.00	12.00

2008 LEGO Star Wars Legends

7667	Imperial Dropship	30.00	60.00
7668	Rebel Scout Speeder	25.00	50.00
7672	Rogue Shadow	120.00	250.00

2008 LEGO Star Wars Miniature Building Set

8028	TIE Fighter	6.00	15.00

2008 LEGO Star Wars Miscellaneous

COMCON001	Clone Wars/(2008 SDCC Exclusive)	.00	.00

2008 LEGO Star Wars Ultimate Collector Series

10186	General Grievous	120.00	200.00
10188	Death Star	225.00	450.00

2009 LEGO Star Wars The Clone Wars

7748	Corporate Alliance Tank Droid	25.00	50.00
7751	Ahsoka's Starfighter and Droids	80.00	150.00
7752	Count Dooku's Solar Sailer	40.00	80.00
7753	Pirate Tank	50.00	100.00
8014	Clone Walker Battle Pack	30.00	60.00
8015	Assassin Droids Battle Pack	12.00	25.00
8016	Hyena Droid Bomber	25.00	50.00
8018	Armored Assault Tank (AAT)	100.00	200.00
8019	Republic Attack Shuttle	60.00	120.00
8033	General Grievous' Starfighter	8.00	15.00
8036	Separatist Shuttle	30.00	60.00
8037	Anakin's Y-wing Starfighter	80.00	150.00
8039	Venator-Class Republic Attack Cruiser	175.00	350.00
10195	Republic Dropship with AT-OT Walker	300.00	600.00
20007	Republic Attack Cruiser	12.00	25.00
20009	AT-TE Walker	10.00	20.00
20010	Republic Gunship	15.00	30.00
30004	Battle Droid on STAP	10.00	20.00
30006	Clone Walker	10.00	20.00
COMCON010	Mini Republic Dropship Mini	.00	.00
	AT-TE Brickmaster Pack/(SDCC 2009 Exclusive)		

2009 LEGO Star Wars Episode IV

7778	Midi-scale Millennium Falcon	60.00	120.00
8017	Darth Vader's TIE Fighter	60.00	120.00
10198	Tantive IV	150.00	300.00

2009 LEGO Star Wars Episode V

7749	Echo Base	40.00	80.00

2009 LEGO Star Wars Episode VI

7754	Home One Mon Calamari Star Cruiser	100.00	200.00
8038	The Battle of Endor	100.00	200.00
30005	Imperial Speeder Bike	12.00	25.00

2009 LEGO Star Wars Minifigure Pack

4547551	Chrome Darth Vader	120.00	250.00

2009 LEGO Star Wars SDCC Exclusives

COMCON004	Collectible Display Set 1	.00	.00
COMCON005	Collectible Display Set 2	.00	.00
COMCON006	Collectible Display Set 4	.00	.00
COMCON007	Collectible Display Set 5	.00	.00

COMCON008 Collectible Display Set 3	.00	.00
COMCON009 Collectible Display Set 6	.00	.00
COMCON011 Holo-Brick Archives	.00	.00

2009 LEGO Star Wars Product Collection

66308 3 in 1 Superpack	.00	.00

2010 LEGO Star Wars The Clone Wars

8085 Freeco Speeder	20.00	40.00
8086 Droid Tri-Fighter	25.00	50.00
8093 Plo Koon's Jedi Starfighter	25.00	50.00
8095 General Grievous' Starfighter	40.00	80.00
8098 Clone Turbo Tank	120.00	250.00
8128 Cad Bane's Speeder	25.00	50.00
30050 Republic Attack Shuttle	10.00	20.00

2010 LEGO Star Wars Episode III

8088 ARC-170 Starfighter	80.00	150.00
8091 Republic Swamp Speeder	30.00	60.00
8096 Emperor Palpatine's Shuttle	60.00	120.00

2010 LEGO Star Wars Episode IV

8092 Luke's Landspeeder	50.00	100.00
8099 Midi-Scale Imperial Star Destroyer	60.00	120.00

2010 LEGO Star Wars Episode V

8083 Rebel Trooper Battle Pack	12.00	25.00
8084 Snowtrooper Battle Pack	12.00	25.00
8089 Hoth Wampa Cave	50.00	100.00
8097 Slave I	100.00	200.00
8129 AT-AT Walker	150.00	300.00
20018 AT-AT Walker	12.00	25.00

2010 LEGO Star Wars Legends

8087 TIE Defender	80.00	150.00

2010 LEGO Star Wars Miniature Building Set

20016 Imperial Shuttle	10.00	20.00

2010 LEGO Star Wars Minifigure Pack

2853590 Chrome Stormtrooper	40.00	80.00
2853835 White Boba Fett Figure	60.00	120.00

2010 LEGO Star Wars Miscellaneous

BOBAFETT1 White Boba Fett minifig and Star Wars Book	.00	.00

2010 LEGO Star Wars Product Collection

66341 Star Wars Super Pack 3 in 1	.00	.00
66364 Star Wars Super Pack 3 in 1	.00	.00
66366 Star Wars Super Pack 3 in 1	.00	.00
66368 Star Wars Super Pack 3 in 1	.00	.00

2010 LEGO Star Wars Ultimate Collector Series

10212 Imperial Shuttle	350.00	700.00
10215 Obi-Wan's Jedi Starfighter	100.00	200.00

2011 LEGO Star Wars The Clone Wars

7868 Mace Windu's Jedi Starfighter	60.00	120.00
7869 Battle for Geonosis	40.00	80.00
7913 Clone Trooper Battle Pack	25.00	50.00
7914 Mandalorian Battle Pack	15.00	30.00
7930 Bounty Hunter Assault Gunship	50.00	100.00

7931 T-6 Jedi Shuttle	40.00	80.00
7957 Sith Nightspeeder	25.00	50.00
7959 Geonosian Starfighter	40.00	80.00
7964 Republic Frigate	120.00	250.00
20021 Bounty Hunter Assault Gunship	10.00	20.00
30053 Republic Attack Cruiser	8.00	15.00

2011 LEGO Star Wars Episode I

7877 Naboo Starfighter	25.00	50.00
7929 The Battle of Naboo	20.00	40.00
7961 Darth Maul's Sith Infiltrator	50.00	100.00
7962 Anakin Skywalker and Sebulba's Podracers	60.00	120.00
30052 AAT	8.00	15.00

2011 LEGO Star Wars Episode IV

7965 Millennium Falcon	200.00	400.00

2011 LEGO Star Wars Episode V

7879 Hoth Echo Base	150.00	300.00
20019 Slave I	15.00	30.00

2011 LEGO Star Wars Episode VI

7956 Ewok Attack	20.00	40.00
30054 AT-ST	10.00	20.00

2011 LEGO Star Wars Legends

7915 Imperial V-wing Starfighter	20.00	50.00

2011 LEGO Star Wars Miniature Building Set

30051 Mini X-wing	8.00	15.00
30055 Vulture Droid	8.00	15.00

2011 LEGO Star Wars Minifigure Pack

2856197 Shadow ARF Trooper	40.00	80.00

2011 LEGO Star Wars Exclusive

PROMOSW007 Star Wars Miniland Figures	.00	.00
(2011 Toy Fair Collector's Party Exclusive)		

2011 LEGO Star Wars Product Collection

66377	Star Wars Super Pack 3 in 1	60.00	120.00
66378	Star Wars Super Pack 3 in 1	.00	.00
66395	Star Wars Super Pack 3 in 1	60.00	120.00
66396	Star Wars Super Pack 3 in 1	.00	.00

2011 LEGO Star Wars Seasonal Set

COMCON015	Advent calendar/(2011 SDCC Exclusive)	60.00	120.00
7958	Star Wars Advent Calendar	30.00	60.00

2011 LEGO Star Wars Ultimate Collector Series

10221	Super Star Destroyer	600.00	1,100.00

2012 LEGO Star Wars The Clone Wars

9488	Elite Clone Trooper & Commando Droid Battle Pack	15.00	30.00
9491	Geonosian Cannon	25.00	50.00
9498	Saesee Tiin's Jedi Starfighter	30.00	60.00
9515	Malevolence	120.00	250.00
9525	Pre Vizsla's Mandalorian Fighter	60.00	120.00
30059	MTT	8.00	15.00

2012 LEGO Star Wars Episode I

9499	Gungan Sub	80.00	150.00
30057	Anakin's Pod Racer	6.00	12.00
30058	STAP	8.00	15.00
5000063	Chrome TC-14	25.00	50.00
COMCON019	Sith Infiltrator/(2012 SDCC Exclusive)	80.00	150.00

2012 LEGO Star Wars Episode III

9494	Anakin's Jedi Interceptor	60.00	120.00
9526	Palpatine's Arrest	80.00	150.00

2012 LEGO Star Wars Episode IV

9490	Droid Escape	30.00	60.00
9492	TIE Fighter	100.00	200.00
9493	X-wing Starfighter	100.00	200.00
9495	Gold Leader's Y-wing Starfighter	80.00	150.00
COMCON024	Luke Skywalker's Landspeeder Mini	120.00	250.00
	(2012 NYCC Exclusive)		

2012 LEGO Star Wars Episode V

CELEBVI	Mini Slave I/(2012 Star Wars Celebration VI Exclusive)	100.00	200.00

2012 LEGO Star Wars Episode VI

9489	Endor Rebel Trooper & Imperial Trooper Battle Pack	25.00	50.00
9496	Desert Skiff	50.00	100.00
9516	Jabba's Palace	100.00	200.00

2012 LEGO Star Wars Miniature Building Set

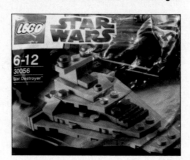

30056	Star Destroyer	8.00	15.00

2012 LEGO Star Wars Minifigure Pack

5000062	Darth Maul	15.00	30.00

2012 LEGO Star Wars The Old Republic

9497	Republic Striker-class Starfighter	40.00	80.00
9500	Sith Fury-class Interceptor	100.00	200.00

2012 LEGO Star Wars Planet Set

9674	Naboo Starfighter & Naboo	10.00	20.00
9675	Sebulba's Podracer & Tatooine	8.00	15.00
9676	TIE Interceptor & Death Star	15.00	30.00
9677	X-wing Starfighter & Yavin 4	10.00	20.00
9678	Twin-Pod Cloud Car & Bespin	10.00	20.00
9679	AT-ST & Endor	8.00	15.00

2012 LEGO Star Wars Product Collection

66411	Super Pack 3-in-1	.00	.00
66431	Super Pack 3-in-1	.00	.00
66432	Super Pack 3-in-1	.00	.00

2012 LEGO Star Wars Seasonal Set

9509	Star Wars Advent Calendar	30.00	60.00

2012 LEGO Star Wars Ultimate Collector Series

10225	R2-D2	200.00	400.00
10227	B-Wing Starfighter	175.00	350.00

2013 LEGO Star Wars The Clone Wars

11905	Brickmaster Star Wars: Battle for the Stolen Crystals parts	.00	.00
30240	Z-95 Headhunter	8.00	15.00
30241	Mandalorian Fighter	8.00	15.00
30242	Republic Frigate	8.00	15.00
30243	Umbaran MHC	8.00	15.00
75002	AT-RT	25.00	50.00
75004	Z-95 Headhunter	40.00	80.00
75012	BARC Speeder with Sidecar	60.00	120.00
75013	Umbaran MHC (Mobile Heavy Cannon)	40.00	80.00
75022	Mandalorian Speeder	40.00	80.00
75024	HH-87 Starhopper	50.00	100.00

2013 LEGO Star Wars Episode II

75000	Clone Troopers vs. Droidekas	20.00	40.00
75015	Corporate Alliance Tank Droid	30.00	60.00
75016	Homing Spider Droid	25.00	50.00
75017	Duel on Geonosis	50.00	100.00
75019	AT-TE	100.00	200.00
75021	Republic Gunship	150.00	300.00
5001709	Clone Trooper Lieutenant	8.00	15.00

2013 LEGO Star Wars Episode V

75014	Battle of Hoth	80.00	150.00
5001621	Han Solo (Hoth)	8.00	15.00

2013 LEGO Star Wars Episode VI

75003	A-wing Starfighter	30.00	60.00
75005	Rancor Pit	100.00	200.00
75020	Jabba's Sail Barge	120.00	250.00

2013 LEGO Star Wars The Old Republic

75001	Republic Troopers vs. Sith Troopers	20.00	40.00
75025	Jedi Defender-class Cruiser	60.00	120.00

2013 LEGO Star Wars Originals

75018 JEK-14's Stealth Starfighter	80.00	150.00
COMCON032 Jek-14 Mini Stealth Starfighter/(2013 SDCC Exclusive)	120.00	250.00
MAY2013 Holocron Droid	12.00	25.00
TRU03 Mini Jek-14 Stealth Fighter/(2013 Toys R Us Exclusive)	12.00	25.00
YODACHRON Yoda Chronicles Promotional Set	.00	.00

2013 LEGO Star Wars Planet Set

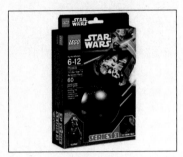

75006 Jedi Starfighter & Planet Kamino	12.00	25.00
75007 Republic Assault Ship & Planet Coruscant	8.00	15.00
75008 TIE Bomber & Asteroid Field	12.00	25.00
75009 Snowspeeder & Hoth	25.00	50.00
75010 B-Wing Starfighter & Planet Endor	20.00	40.00
75011 Tantive IV & Planet Alderaan	25.00	50.00

2013 LEGO Star Wars Product Collection

66449 Super Pack 3-in-1	80.00	150.00
66456 Star Wars Value Pack	100.00	200.00
66473 LEGO Star Wars Super Pack	120.00	250.00

2013 LEGO Star Wars Promotional Set

NYCC2013 Yoda display box/(2013 NYCC Exclusive)	.00	.00
YODA Yoda minifig, NY I Heart Torso	120.00	250.00

2013 LEGO Star Wars Seasonal Set

75023 Star Wars Advent Calendar	.00	.00

2013 LEGO Star Wars Ultimate Collector Series

10236 Ewok Village	175.00	350.00
10240 Red Five X-wing Starfighter	150.00	300.00

2014 LEGO Star Wars The Clone Wars

75045 Republic AV-7 Anti-Vehicle Cannon	50.00	100.00
75046 Coruscant Police Gunship	50.00	100.00

2014 LEGO Star Wars Episode I

75058 MTT	80.00	150.00

2014 LEGO Star Wars Episode III

30244 Anakin's Jedi Interceptor	8.00	15.00
30247 ARC-170 Starfighter	8.00	15.00
75035 Kashyyyk Troopers	20.00	40.00
75036 Utapau Troopers	20.00	40.00
75037 Battle on Saleucami	25.00	50.00
75038 Jedi Interceptor	50.00	100.00
75039 V-Wing Starfighter	30.00	60.00
75040 General Grievous' Wheel Bike	40.00	80.00
75041 Vulture Droid	40.00	80.00
75042 Droid Gunship	60.00	120.00
75043 AT-AP	100.00	200.00
75044 Droid Tri-Fighter	25.00	50.00

2014 LEGO Star Wars Episode IV

75034 Death Star Troopers	25.00	50.00
75052 Mos Eisley Cantina	60.00	120.00
75055 Imperial Star Destroyer	200.00	400.00

2014 LEGO Star Wars Episode V

75049 Snowspeeder	50.00	100.00
75054 AT-AT	150.00	300.00

2014 LEGO Star Wars Episode VI

30246 Imperial Shuttle	12.00	25.00
75050 B-Wing	40.00	80.00

2014 LEGO Star Wars MicroFighters

75029 AAT	15.00	30.00
75028 Clone Turbo Tank	20.00	40.00
75030 Millennium Falcon	25.00	50.00
75031 TIE Interceptor	15.00	30.00
75032 X-Wing Fighter	15.00	30.00
75033 Star Destroyer	12.00	25.00

2014 LEGO Star Wars Minifigure Pack

5002122 TC-4	15.00	30.00

2014 LEGO Star Wars The Old Republic

5002123 Darth Revan	25.00	50.00

2014 LEGO Star Wars Original Content

75051 Jedi Scout Fighter	60.00	120.00

2014 LEGO Star Wars Product Collection

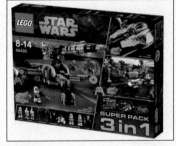

66479 Value Pack	.00	.00
66495 Star Wars Value Pack	.00	.00
66512 Rebels Co-Pack	.00	.00
66514 Microfighter Super Pack 3 in 1	.00	.00
66515 Microfighter Super Pack 3 in 1	.00	.00

2014 LEGO Star Wars Toys R Us Exclusives

TRUGHOST The Ghost micro-model	10.00	20.00
TRUTIE TIE Fighter	.00	.00
TRUXWING X-wing	.00	.00

2014 LEGO Star Wars Rebels

75048 The Phantom	80.00	150.00

75053 The Ghost	100.00	200.00
COMCON039 The Ghost Starship/(2014 SDCC Exclusive)	80.00	150.00
FANEXPO0001 The Ghost Starship/(2014 Fan Expo Exclusive)	60.00	120.00

2014 LEGO Star Wars Seasonal Set

75056 Star Wars Advent Calendar	.00	.00

2014 LEGO Star Wars Ultimate Collector Series

75059 Sandcrawler	175.00	350.00

2015 LEGO Star Wars Buildable Figures

75107 Jango Fett	20.00	40.00
75108 Clone Commander Cody	12.00	25.00
75109 Obi-Wan Kenobi	20.00	40.00
75110 Luke Skywalker	25.00	50.00
75111 Darth Vader	25.00	50.00
75112 General Grievous	40.00	80.00

2015 LEGO Star Wars The Clone Wars

75087 Anakin's Custom Jedi Starfighter	25.00	50.00

2015 LEGO Star Wars Episode I

75080 AAT	20.00	40.00
75086 Battle Droid Troop Carrier	30.00	60.00
75091 Flash Speeder	20.00	40.00
75092 Naboo Starfighter	30.00	60.00
75096 Sith Infiltrator	50.00	100.00

2015 LEGO Star Wars Episode II

75085 Hailfire Droid	25.00	50.00

2015 LEGO Star Wars Episode IV

75081 T-16 Skyhopper	25.00	50.00
5002947 Admiral Yularen	10.00	20.00

2015 LEGO Star Wars Episode VI

30272 A-Wing Starfighter	10.00	20.00
75093 Death Star Final Duel	50.00	100.00
75094 Imperial Shuttle Tydirium	60.00	120.00

2015 LEGO Star Wars The Force Awakens

30276 First Order Special Forces TIE Fighter	6.00	12.00
75099 Rey's Speeder	12.00	30.00
75100 First Order Snowspeeder	25.00	50.00
75101 First Order Special Forces TIE Fighter	40.00	80.00
75102 Poe's X-wing Fighter	50.00	100.00
75103 First Order Transporter	60.00	120.00
75104 Kylo Ren's Command Shuttle	60.00	120.00
75105 Millennium Falcon	100.00	200.00
5002948 C-3PO	10.00	20.00
30UNIQUE15 Force Friday Commemorative Brick	.00	.00

2015 LEGO Star Wars Legends

75079 Shadow Troopers	15.00	30.00
75088 Senate Commando Troopers	10.00	20.00
75089 Geonosis Troopers	20.00	40.00

2015 LEGO Star Wars Magazine Gift

SW911506 Snowspeeder	8.00	15.00
SW911508 Mini Slave I	.00	.00
SW911509 Imperial Shooter	8.00	15.00
SW911510 Micro Star Destroyer and TIE Fighter	.00	.00
SW911511 Jedi Weapon Stand	.00	.00
SWCOMIC1 Mini X-Wing Starfighter	15.00	30.00

2015 LEGO Star Wars MicroFighters

75072 ARC-170 Starfighter	15.00	30.00
75073 Vulture Droid	12.00	25.00
75074 Snowspeeder	12.00	25.00
75075 AT-AT	20.00	40.00
75076 Republic Gunship	12.00	25.00
75077 Homing Spider Droid	15.00	30.00

2015 LEGO Star Wars Product Collection

66533 Microfighter 3 in 1 Super Pack	25.00	50.00
66534 Microfighter 3 in 1 Super Pack	25.00	50.00
66535 Battle Pack 2 in 1	50.00	100.00
66536 Luke Skywalker and Darth Vader	50.00	100.00

2015 LEGO Star Wars Exclusives

CELEB2015 Tatooine Mini-build/(2015 Star Wars Celebration Exclusive)	50.00	100.00

FANEXPO2015 Tatooine Mini Build/(2015 Fan Expo Exclusive)	80.00	150.00
SDCC2015 Dagobah Mini Build/(2015 SDCC Exclusive)	100.00	200.00
TRUWOOKIEE Wookiee Gunship/(2015 Toys R Us Exclusive)	8.00	15.00
TRUXWING Poe's X-wing Fighter/(2015 Toys R Us Exclusive)	10.00	20.00

2015 LEGO Star Wars Rebels

30274 AT-DP	8.00	15.00
30275 TIE Advanced Prototype	8.00	15.00
75078 Imperial Troop Transport	12.00	25.00
75082 TIE Advanced Prototype	20.00	40.00
75083 AT-DP	50.00	100.00
75084 Wookiee Gunship	50.00	100.00
75090 Ezra's Speeder Bike	15.00	30.00
75106 Imperial Assault Carrier	80.00	150.00
5002938 Stormtrooper Sergeant	8.00	15.00
5002939 The Phantom	8.00	15.00

2015 LEGO Star Wars Seasonal Set

75097 Star Wars Advent Calendar	.00	.00

2015 LEGO Star Wars Ultimate Collector Series

75060 Slave I	120.00	250.00
75095 TIE Fighter	100.00	200.00

2016 LEGO Star Wars Battlefront

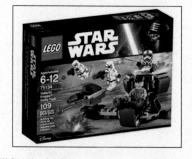

75133 Rebel Alliance Battle Pack	20.00	40.00
75134 Galactic Empire Battle Pack	15.00	30.00

2016 LEGO Star Wars Buildable Figures

75113 Rey	12.00	25.00
75114 First Order Stormtrooper	12.00	25.00
75115 Poe Dameron	12.00	25.00
75116 Finn	10.00	20.00

MISCELLANEOUS

75117 Kylo Ren	12.00	25.00
75118 Captain Phasma	15.00	30.00
75119 Sergeant Jyn Erso	15.00	30.00
75120 K-2SO	15.00	30.00
75121 Imperial Death Trooper	12.00	25.00

2016 LEGO Star Wars Episode III

75135 Obi-Wan's Jedi Interceptor	30.00	75.00
75142 Homing Spider Droid	25.00	50.00
75151 Clone Turbo Tank	50.00	100.00

2016 LEGO Star Wars Episode IV

75136 Droid Escape Pod	20.00	40.00

2016 LEGO Star Wars Episode V

75137 Carbon-Freezing Chamber	20.00	40.00
75138 Hoth Attack	25.00	50.00

2016 LEGO Star Wars The Force Awakens

30277 First Order Star Destroyer	8.00	15.00
30278 Poe's X-wing Fighter	6.00	12.00
30279 Kylo Ren's Command Shuttle	6.00	12.00
30602 First Order Stormtrooper	10.00	20.00
30605 Finn (FN-2187)	6.00	12.00
75131 Resistance Trooper Battle Pack	10.00	20.00
75132 First Order Battle Pack	10.00	20.00
75139 Battle on Takodana	25.00	50.00
75140 Resistance Troop Transporter	30.00	75.00
75148 Encounter on Jakku	25.00	50.00
75149 Resistance X-wing Fighter	60.00	120.00
5004406 First Order General	8.00	15.00

2016 LEGO Star Wars Magazine Gift

SW911607 Millennium Falcon	6.00	12.00
SW911608 Landspeeder	6.00	12.00
SW911609 Naboo Starfighter	6.00	12.00
SW911610 Probe Droid	6.00	12.00
SW911611 AAT	6.00	12.00
SW911612 Acklay	6.00	12.00
SW911613 TIE Bomber	6.00	12.00
SW911614 Yoda's Hut	6.00	12.00
SW911615 AT-AT	6.00	12.00

SW911616 MTT	6.00	12.00
SW911617 Palpatine's Shuttle	6.00	12.00

2016 LEGO Star Wars MicroFighters

75125 Resistance X-wing Fighter	12.00	25.00
75126 First Order Snowspeeder	10.00	20.00
75127 The Ghost	12.00	25.00
75128 TIE Advanced Prototype	12.00	25.00
75129 Wookiee Gunship	8.00	15.00
75130 AT-DP	12.00	25.00

2016 LEGO Star Wars Miscellaneous

11912 Star Wars: Build Your Own Adventure parts	

2016 LEGO Star Wars Originals

75145 Eclipse Fighter	20.00	40.00
75147 StarScavenger	20.00	40.00

2016 LEGO Star Wars Product Collection

66542 Microfighters Super Pack 3 in 1	12.00	25.00
66543 Microfighters Super Pack 3 in 1	15.00	30.00
5005217 Death Star Ultimate Kit		

2016 LEGO Star Wars Promotional Set

6176782 Escape the Space Slug	75.00	150.00
TRUFALCON Millennium Falcon/(2016 Toys R Us Exclusive)		

2016 LEGO Star Wars Rebels

75141 Kanan's Speeder Bike	25.00	50.00
75150 Vader's TIE Advanced vs. A-wing Starfighter	50.00	100.00
75157 Captain Rex's AT-TE	50.00	100.00
75158 Rebel Combat Frigate	60.00	120.00
5004408 Rebel A-wing Pilot	6.00	12.00

2016 LEGO Star Wars Rogue One

75152 Imperial Assault Hovertank	25.00	50.00
75153 AT-ST Walker	30.00	60.00
75154 TIE Striker	25.00	50.00
75155 Rebel U-wing Fighter	30.00	75.00
75156 Krennic's Imperial Shuttle	60.00	120.00

2016 LEGO Star Wars Seasonal Set

75146 Star Wars Advent Calendar	30.00	75.00

2016 LEGO Star Wars Ultimate Collector Series

75098 Assault on Hoth	200.00	400.00
75159 Death Star	250.00	500.00

2017 LEGO Star Wars BrickHeadz

41498 Boba Fett & Han Solo in Carbonite/NYCC Exclusive	

2017 LEGO Star Wars Buildable Figures

75523 Scarif Stormtrooper	12.00	25.00
75524 Chirrut Imwe	15.00	30.00
75525 Baze Malbus	12.00	25.00
75526 Elite TIE Fighter Pilot	15.00	30.00
75528 Rey	15.00	30.00
75529 Elite Praetorian Guard	20.00	40.00
75530 Chewbacca	25.00	50.00
75531 Stormtrooper Commander	12.00	25.00
75532 Scout Trooper & Speeder Bike	20.00	40.00

2017 LEGO Star Wars The Clone Wars

75168 Yoda's Jedi Starfighter	20.00	40.00

2017 LEGO Star Wars Episode I

75169 Duel on Naboo	12.00	25.00

2017 LEGO Star Wars Episode II

75191 Jedi Starfighter (w/hyperdrive)	60.00	120.00

2017 LEGO Star Wars Episode III

75183	Darth Vader Transformation	20.00	40.00

2017 LEGO Star Wars Episode IV

75173	Luke's Landspeeder	25.00	50.00

2017 LEGO Star Wars Episode VI

75174	Desert Skiff Escape	20.00	40.00
75175	A-Wing Starfighter	30.00	60.00

2017 LEGO Star Wars The Force Awakens

75166	First Order Transport Speeder Battle Pack	15.00	30.00
75178	Jakku Quadjumper	25.00	50.00
75180	Rathtar Escape	50.00	100.00

2017 LEGO Star Wars The Last Jedi

30497	First Order Heavy Assault Walker	8.00	15.00
75176	Resistance Transport Pod	20.00	40.00
75177	First Order Heavy Scout Walker	30.00	75.00
75179	Kylo Ren's TIE Fighter	50.00	100.00
75187	BB-8	100.00	200.00
75188	Resistance Bomber	75.00	150.00
75189	First Order Heavy Assault Walker	150.00	300.00
75190	First Order Star Destroyer	150.00	300.00

2017 LEGO Star Wars Legends

75182	Republic Fighter Tank	15.00	30.00

2017 LEGO Star Wars Magazine Gift

SW911618	Flash Speeder
SW911719	Kanan Jarrus
SW911720	The Ghost
SW911721	Imperial Combat Driver
SW911722	TIE Advanced
SW911723	Vulture Droid
SW911724	A-Wing
SW911725	Sandcrawler
SW911726	Imperial Snowtrooper
SW911727	Rey's Speeder
SW911728	First Order Snowspeeder
SW911729	Droid Gunship
SW911730	Y-Wing

2017 LEGO Star Wars MicroFighters

75160	U-Wing	7.50	15.00
75161	TIE Striker	7.50	15.00
75162	Y-Wing	7.50	15.00
75163	Krennic's Imperial Shuttle	7.50	15.00

2017 LEGO Star Wars Originals

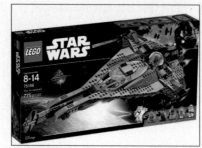

75167	Bounty Hunter Speeder Bike Battle Pack	12.00	25.00
75185	Tracker I	30.00	75.00
75186	The Arrowhead	60.00	120.00

2017 LEGO Star Wars Promotional

30611	R2-D2	12.00	25.00
CELEB2017	Detention Block Rescue	120.00	250.00
SWMF	Millennium Falcon	7.50	15.00
TRUBB8	BB-8		
TRULEIA	Princess Leia		

2017 LEGO Star Wars Rebels

75170	The Phantom	20.00	40.00

2017 LEGO Star Wars Rogue One

30496	U-Wing Fighter	6.00	12.00
40176	Scarif Stormtrooper	12.00	25.00
40268	R3-M2	7.50	15.00
75164	Rebel Trooper Battle Pack	15.00	30.00
75165	Imperial Trooper Battle Pack	15.00	30.00
75171	Battle on Scarif	30.00	75.00
75172	Y-Wing Starfighter	30.00	75.00

2017 LEGO Star Wars Seasonal

75184	Star Wars Advent Calendar	30.00	60.00

2017 LEGO Star Wars Ultimate Collector Series

75144	Snowspeeder	120.00	250.00
75192	Millennium Falcon	500.00	1,000.00

2018 LEGO Star Wars Buildable Figures

75533	Boba Fett	30.00	60.00
75534	Darth Vader	30.00	60.00
75535	Han Solo	15.00	30.00
75536	Range Trooper	12.50	25.00
75537	Darth Maul	20.00	40.00
75538	Super Battle Droid		
75539	501st Legion Clone Trooper & AT-RT Walker		

2018 LEGO Star Wars The Clone Wars

75199	General Grievous' Combat Speeder	15.00	30.00
75214	Anakin's Jedi Starfighter	25.00	50.00

2018 LEGO Star Wars Episode II

75206	Jedi and Clone Troopers Battle Pack

2018 LEGO Star Wars Episode IV

75198	Tatooine Battle Pack	25.00	50.00
75205	Mos Eisley Cantina	30.00	60.00
75218	X-Wing Starfighter	75.00	150.00
75220	Sandcrawler	75.00	150.00
75221	Imperial Landing Craft	60.00	120.00

2018 LEGO Star Wars Episode V

75203	Hoth Medical Chamber	30.00	75.00
75208	Yoda's Hut	30.00	60.00

2018 LEGO Star Wars The Last Jedi

30380	Kylo Ren's Shuttle	7.50	15.00
40298	DJ	15.00	30.00
75197	First Order Specialists Battle Pack	12.50	25.00
75200	Ahch-To Island Training	15.00	30.00
75201	First Order AT-ST	15.00	30.00
75202	Defense of Crait	30.00	60.00
75216	Snoke's Throne Room	60.00	120.00
75230	Porg	60.00	120.00

2018 LEGO Star Wars Legends

75204	Sandspeeder	15.00	30.00

2018 LEGO Star Wars Magazine Gift

SW911831	Kylo Ren's Shuttle	
SW911832	Imperial Shuttle Pilot	
SW911833	Imperial Shuttle	
SW911834	Finn	
SW911835	Dwarf Spider Droid	
SW911836	Quadjumper	
SW911837	AT-ST	
SW911838	Probe Droid	
SW911839	Obi-Wan Kenobi	
SW911840	Droideka	

2018 LEGO Star Wars Master Builder

75222	Betrayal at Cloud City	200.00	400.00

2018 LEGO Star Wars Microfighters

75193	Millennium Falcon Microfighter	12.50	25.00
75194	First Order TIE Fighter Microfighter	10.00	20.00
75195	Ski Speeder vs. First Order Walker Microfighters	15.00	30.00
75196	A-Wing vs. TIE Silencer Microfighters	15.00	30.00

2018 LEGO Star Wars Promotional

40288	BB-8	12.50	25.00
75512	Millennium Falcon Cockpit (SDCC Exclusive)	90.00	175.00
5005376	Star Wars Anniversary Pod	10.00	20.00
PORG	Porg		

2018 LEGO Star Wars Seasonal

75213	Star Wars Advent Calendar	12.50	25.00

2018 LEGO Star Wars Solo

30381	Imperial TIE Fighter	7.50	15.00
30498	Imperial AT-Hauler	10.00	20.00
40299	Kessel Mine Worker	12.50	25.00
40300	Han Solo Mudtrooper		
75207	Imperial Patrol Battle Pack	10.00	20.00
75209	Han Solo's Landspeeder	20.00	40.00
75210	Moloch's Landspeeder	20.00	40.00
75211	Imperial TIE Fighter	30.00	75.00
75212	Kessel Run Millennium Falcon	125.00	250.00
75215	Cloud-Rider Swoop Bikes	25.00	50.00
75217	Imperial Conveyex Transport	45.00	90.00
75219	Imperial AT-Hauler	60.00	120.00

2018 LEGO Star Wars Ultimate Collector Series

75181	Y-wing Starfighter	150.00	300.00

MICRO MACHINES

1993-97 Micro Machines Star Wars Planet Playsets

65872	Ice Planet Hoth	15.00	40.00
65995	Cloud City (w/Twin-Pod Cloud Car)	8.00	20.00
65858A	Planet Tatooine (1994)	10.00	25.00
65858B	Planet Tatooine (1996)	8.00	20.00
65859A	Planet Dagobah (1994)	10.00	25.00
65859B	Planet Dagobah (1996)		
65871A	Death Star from A New Hope (1994)	10.00	25.00
65871B	Death Star from A New Hope (1996)	5.00	12.00
65873A	Planet Endor (w/Imperial AT-ST)(1993)	8.00	20.00
65873B	Planet Endor (w/Imperial AT-ST)(1997)	6.00	15.00

1993-98 Micro Machines Star Wars Vehicle 3-Packs

65123	Imperial Landing Craft/Death Star/S-Swoop	8.00	20.00
65124	Outrider Tibanna/Gas Refinery/V-35 Landspeeder	6.00	15.00
65886	Star Wars A New Hope (silver)		
65886	Star Wars A New Hope #1	6.00	15.00

65887	Star Wars Empire Strikes Back #2		
65887	Star Wars Empire Strikes Back (silver)	5.00	12.00
65888	Star Wars Return of the Jedi (silver)		
65888	Star Wars Return of the Jedi #3		
65897	Star Wars A New Hope #4		
65898	Star Wars Empire Strikes Back #5	5.00	12.00
65899	Star Wars Return of the Jedi #6		
66111	TIE Interceptor/Imperial Star Destroyer/Rebel Blockade Runner	5.00	12.00
66112	Landspeeder/Millennium Falcon/Jawa Sandcrawler	8.00	20.00
66113	Darth Vader's TIE Fighter/Y-Wing Starfighter/X-Wing Starfighter	5.00	12.00
66114	Snowspeeder/Imperial AT-AT/Imperial Probot	15.00	40.00
66115	Rebel Transport/TIE Bomber/Imperial AT-ST	6.00	15.00
66116	Escort Frigate/Slave I/Twin-Pod Cloud Car	5.00	12.00
66117	Desert Sail Barge/Mon Calamari Star Cruiser/Speeder Bike and Rebel Pilot		
66118	Speeder Bike and Imperial Pilot/Imperial Shuttle Tydirium/TIE Starfighter		
66119	Super Star Destroyer Executor	10.00	25.00
	A-Wing Starfighter/B-Wing Starfighter		
66137	Lars Family Landspeeder/Death Star II/T-16 Skyhopper	8.00	20.00
66138	Bespin Cloud City/Mon Calamari Rebel Cruiser/Escape Pod	6.00	15.00
66139	A-Wing Starfighter/Y-Wing Starfighter/TIE Starfighter	10.00	25.00
66155	2 Red Squad X-Wings/Green Squad X-Wing		

1994 Micro Machines Star Wars Fan Club Pieces

18279	Han Solo and the Millennium Falcon	6.00	15.00
28450	Darth Vader and Imperial Star Destroyer	6.00	15.00

1994-96 Micro Machines Star Wars Gift Sets

64624	Bronze Finish Collector's Gift Set	12.00	30.00
65836	Rebel Force Gift Set	6.00	15.00
65837	Imperial Force Gift Set	5.00	12.00
65847	11-Piece Collector's Gift Set	10.00	25.00
65851	A New Hope	5.00	12.00
65852	Empire Strikes Back		
65853	Return of the Jedi	8.00	20.00
65856	Rebel Force Gift Set 2nd Edition	6.00	15.00
65857	Imperial Force Gift Set 2nd Edition		
67079	Star Wars Trilogy Gift Set	15.00	40.00
68042	Rebel vs. Imperial Forces		

1994-97 Micro Machines Star Wars Collector's Sets

64598	Galaxy Battle Collector's Set 2nd Edition	8.00	20.00
64601	Master Collector's Edition (19 Items)	15.00	40.00
64602	Galaxy Battle Collector's Set	10.00	25.00
66090	Droids	10.00	25.00
68048	Master Collector's Edition (40 Items)	8.00	20.00

1994-99 Micro Machines Star Wars Transforming Action Sets

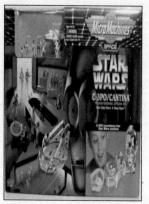

65694	TIE Fighter Pilot/Academy	10.00	25.00
65695	Royal Guard/Death Star II	15.00	40.00
65811	C-3PO/Cantina	10.00	25.00
65812	Darth Vader/Bespin	10.00	25.00
65813	R2-D2/Jabba's Palace	12.00	30.00
65814	Stormtrooper/Death Star	12.00	30.00
65815	Chewbacca/Endor	10.00	25.00
65816	Boba Fett/Cloud City	15.00	40.00
65817	Luke Skywalker/Hoth	10.00	25.00
66551	Jar Jar Binks/Naboo	6.00	15.00
66552	Battle Droid/Trade Federation Droid Control Ship		
66553	Darth Maul/Theed Generator	30.00	80.00
66554	Gungan Sub/Otoh Gunga		
67094	Star Destroyer/Space Fortress	15.00	40.00
67095	Slave I/Tatooine	10.00	25.00
68063	Yoda/Dagobah	12.00	30.00
68064	Jabba/Mos Eisley Spaceport	15.00	40.00

1995 Micro Machines Star Wars Action Fleet Playsets

67091	Ice Planet Hoth (w/Battle-Damaged Snow Speeder	10.00	25.00
	Luke Skywalker on Tauntaun		
	Wampa Ice Creature/Rebel Pilot/Princess Leia/2-1B Droid)		
67092	The Death Star (w/Darth Vader's Battle-Damaged TIE Fighter	10.00	25.00
	Imperial Pilot		
	Imperial Gunner/Darth Vader/Stormtrooper/Imperial Royal Guard/Emperor Palpatine)		
67093	Yavin Rebel Base (w/Battle-Damaged X-Wing	12.00	30.00
	Wedge Antilles/R2 Unit		
	Luke Skywalker/Han Solo/Princess Leia/Rebel Sentry)		
68177	Naboo Hangar Final Combat (w/Obi-Wan Kenobi	20.00	50.00
	Darth Maul/Qui-Gon Jinn)		

1995 Micro Machines Star Wars Gold Classic

67085	X-Wing Fighter and Slave I	12.00	30.00
67086	Imperial Shuttle		
67088	Millennium Falcon and TIE Fighter	30.00	80.00

1995-03 Micro Machines Star Wars Action Fleet Vehicles

46846	AT-TE		
46848	Solar Sailer		
46849	Millennium Falcon	12.00	30.00
46850	X-Wingfighter		
47045	Luke Skywalker's Snowspeeder		
47224	Imperial AT-AT	8.00	20.00
47287	Republic Gunship		
47305	Slave I	5.00	12.00
47356	TIE Advance X1		
47414	Naboo N-1 Starfighter		
47425	Republic Assault Ship	30.00	80.00
47766	Anakin's Speeder		
47767	Zam Wessel Speeder		
47768	Homing Spider Droid	4.00	10.00
47994	Jedi Starfighter	8.00	20.00
47995	Star Destroyer		
47997	Mon Calamari Cruiser	8.00	20.00
66989	Rancor (w/Gamorrean Guard and Luke Skywalker)	10.00	25.00
66990	Virago (w/Prince Xizor and Guri)	10.00	25.00
66991	X-Wing Starfighter (w/Wedge and R2 Unit)		
66992	Y-Wing Starfighter (red)(w/Gold Leader and R2 Unit)		
66993	A-Wing Starfighter (green)(w/Rebel pilot and Mon Mothma)	8.00	20.00
66994	B-Wing Starfighter (w/Rebel pilot and Admiral Ackbar)	10.00	25.00
66995	TIE Fighter (w/Imperial pilot and Grand Moff Tarkin)		
66996	Bespin Twin-Pod Cloud Car (w/Cloud Car pilot and Lobot)		
66997	Y-Wing Starfighter (blue)(w/Blue Leader and R2 Unit)	10.00	25.00
66998	X-Wing Starfighter (w/Jek Porkins and R2 Unit)		
67014	Jabba's Sail Barge (w/Jabba the Hutt/Saelt Marae and R2-D2	12.00	30.00
67031	Luke's X-Wing Starfighter (w/Luke and R2-D2)	15.00	40.00
67032	Darth Vader's TIE Fighter (w/Darth Vader and Imperial pilot)		
67033	Imperial AT-AT (w/Imperial drive and snowtrooper)	10.00	25.00
67034	A-Wing Starfighter (w/C-3PO and Rebel pilot)	6.00	15.00
67035	Imperial Shuttle Tydirium (w/Han Solo and Chewbacca)		
67036	Rebel Snowspeeder (w/Luke Skywalker and Rebel gunner)		
67039	Jawa Sandcrawler (w/Jawa and scavenger droid)	8.00	20.00

67040	Y-Wing Starfighter (w/Gold Leader and R2 Unit)	8.00	20.00
67041	Slave I (w/Boba Fett and Han Solo)	12.00	30.00
67058	TIE Interceptor (w/2 Imperial pilots)	8.00	20.00
67059	TIE Bomber (w/Imperial pilot and Imperial Naval pilot)	10.00	25.00
67077	Landspeeder and Imperial AT-ST 2-Pack	10.00	25.00
	(w/Luke Skywalker/Obi-Wan Kenobi/Imperial Driver/Stormtrooper)		
67098	Luke's X-Wing from Dagobah (w/Luke Skywalker and R2-D2)	8.00	20.00
	(1998 Toy Fair Magazine Exclusive)		
67100	Millennium Falcon (w/Han Solo and Chewbacca)		
67101	Rebel Blockade Runner (w/Princess Leia and Rebel trooper)	8.00	20.00
67102	Incom T-16 Skyhopper (w/Luke Skywalker and Biggs Darklighter)	6.00	15.00
67103	Imperial Landing Craft (w/Sandtrooper and Imperial Officer)	15.00	40.00
67105	TIE Defender (w/Imperial pilot and Moff Jerjerrod)	30.00	80.00
67106	E-Wing Starfighter (w/Rebel pilot and R7 Unit)		
68131	Naboo Starfighter (w/Anakin)		
68132	Trade Federation MTT (w/Battle Droid)	25.00	60.00
68133	Sebulba's Pod Racer (w/Sebulba)		
68134	Republic Cruiser (w/Qui-Gon Jinn)	12.00	30.00
68135	Droid Fighter (w/Daultry Dofine)		
68136	Gungan Sub (w/Qui-Gon Jinn)	4.00	10.00
68137	Flash Speeder (w/Naboo Royal Guard)		
68138	Trade Federation Landing Ship (w/Battle Droid)		
68140	Mars Guo's Pod Racer (w/Mars Guo)		
68180	Gian Speeder and Theed Palace (w/Captain Panaka/Naboo Foot Soldier/2 Battle Droids)		
79050	Anakin's Pod Racer (w/Anakin)		
79967	Royal Starship (w/Rick Olie)	25.00	60.00
79968	Droid Control Ship (w/Neimoidian Commander)		
79971	Trade Federation Tank (w/Battle Droid)	12.00	30.00
79972	Sith Infiltrator (w/Darth Maul)	30.00	80.00
1327CM6	Darth Vader's TIE Fighter (w/Darth Vader and Imperial pilot)		

1996 Micro Machines Star Wars Adventure Gear

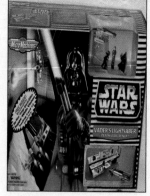

68031	Vader's Lightsaber (w/Death Star Trench/X-Wing	8.00	20.00
	Imperial Gunner/Grand Moff Tarkin/Darth Vader		
68032	Luke's Binoculars (w/Yavin Rebel Base/Y-Wing	8.00	20.00
	Luke Skywalker/R5 Droid/Wedge Antilles		

1996 Micro Machines Star Wars Epic Collections

66281	Heir to the Empire	8.00	20.00
66282	Jedi Search	6.00	15.00
66283	The Truce at Bakura	8.00	20.00

1996 Micro Machines Star Wars Exclusives

66091 Balance of Power (Special Offer)		
68060 Star Wars Trilogy (Special Giveaway)	20.00	50.00

1996 Micro Machines Star Wars Shadows of the Empire

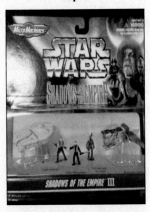

66194 Stinger/IG-2000/Guri/Darth Vader/Asp	5.00	12.00
66195 Virago/Swoop with Rider/Prince Xizor/Emperor Palpatine	6.00	15.00
66196 Outrider/Hound's Tooth/Dash Rendar/LE-B02D9	10.00	25.00

1996 Micro Machines Star Wars X-Ray Fleet

67071 Darth Vader's TIE Fighter/A-Wing Starfighter		
67072 X-Wing Starfighter/Imperial AT-AT		
67073 Millennium Falcon/Jawa Sandcrawler	6.00	15.00
67074 Boba Fett's Slave I/Y-Wing Starfighter		

1996-97 Micro Machines Star Wars Action Sets

65878 Millennium Falcon (w/Y-Wing/Mynock/Han Solo/Chewbacca	20.00	50.00
Lando Calrissian/Nien Nunb/Leia		
65996 Rebel Transport (w/X-Wing/Rebel mechanic/General Rieekan/Major Derlin		

1996-98 Micro Machines Star Wars Character Sets

66081 Imperial Stormtroopers	10.00	25.00
66082 Ewoks	10.00	25.00
66083 Rebel Pilots	6.00	15.00
66084 Imperial Pilots	6.00	15.00
66096 Jawas	5.00	12.00
66097 Imperial Officers	6.00	15.00
66098 Echo Base Troops	5.00	12.00
66099 Imperial Naval Troops	8.00	20.00

66108 Rebel Fleet Troops	8.00	20.00
66109 Tusken Raiders	6.00	15.00
66158 Classic Characters	8.00	20.00
67112 Endor Rebel Strike Force	10.00	25.00
67113 Imperial Scout Troopers	5.00	12.00
67114 Bounty Hunters	10.00	25.00

1996-98 Micro Machines Star Wars Mini Heads

68021 Boba Fett/Admiral Ackbar/Gamorrean Guard	5.00	12.00
68022 Greedo/Nien Nunb/Tusken Raider	5.00	12.00
68023 Jawa/Yoda/Leia	5.00	12.00
68024 Bib Fortuna/Figrin D'an/Scout Trooper	4.00	10.00
68038 Darth Vader Set	5.00	10.00
68046 C-3PO Set		
NNO Pizza Hut Set		

1996-99 Micro Machines Star Wars Battle Packs

68011 Rebel Alliance	6.00	15.00
68012 Galactic Empire	6.00	15.00
68013 Aliens and Creatures	6.00	15.00
68014 Galactic Hunters	6.00	15.00
68015 Shadow of the Empire	6.00	15.00
68016 Dune Sea	6.00	15.00
68017 Droid Escape	6.00	15.00
68018 Desert Palace	6.00	15.00
68035 Endor Adventure	8.00	20.00
68036 Mos Eisley Spaceport	12.00	30.00
68037 Cantina Encounter	6.00	15.00
68090 Cantina Smugglers and Spies	8.00	20.00
68091 Hoth Attack	10.00	25.00
68092 Death Star Escape	6.00	15.00
68093 Endor Victory	12.00	30.00
68094 Lars Family Homestead	8.00	20.00
68095 Imperial Troops	15.00	40.00
68096 Rebel Troops	10.00	25.00

1996-99 Micro Machines Star Wars Die-Cast Vehicles

66267 Death Star	10.00	25.00
66268 A-Wing Starfighter		
66269 Snowspeeder		
66270 TIE Bomber	8.00	20.00
66271 Landspeeder		
66272 Executor (w/Star Destroyer)	6.00	15.00
66273 Slave I		

66520 Royal Starship	5.00	12.00
66523 Gian Speeder		
66524 Trade Federation Battleship	6.00	15.00
66525 Sith Infiltrator	4.00	10.00
66526 Republic Cruiser		
66527 Trade Federation Tank	6.00	15.00
66528 Sebulba's Pod Racer		
79021 Trade Federation Droid Starfighter		
66261A X-Wing Starfighter (bubble)		
66261B X-Wing Starfighter (stripe)		
66262A Millennium Falcon (bubble)	5.00	12.00
66262B Millennium Falcon (stripe)	8.00	20.00
66263A Imperial Star Destroyer (bubble)	4.00	10.00
66263B Imperial Star Destroyer (stripe)	4.00	10.00
66264A TIE Fighter (bubble)		
66264B TIE Fighter (stripe)		
66265A Y-Wing Starfighter (bubble)		
66265B Y-Wing Starfighter (stripe)		
66266A Jawa Sandcrawler (bubble)	6.00	15.00
66266B Jawa Sandcrawler (stripe)	4.00	10.00

1996-99 Micro Machines Star Wars Electronic Action Fleet Vehicles

73419 AT-AT (w/Snowtrooper and Imperial Driver)	15.00	40.00
79072 FAMBAA		
79073 Trade Federation Tank		

1996-99 Micro Machines Star Wars Series Alpha

73421 X-Wing Starfighter	8.00	20.00
73422 Imperial Shuttle	10.00	25.00
73423 Rebel Snowspeeder	6.00	15.00
73424 Imperial AT-AT	8.00	20.00
73430 Twin-Pod Cloud Car		
73431 Y-Wing Starfighter		
73432 B-Wing Starfighter		
97033 Naboo Fighter		
97034 Droid Fighter		
97035 Sith Infiltrator	25.00	60.00
97036 Royal Starship		

1997 Micro Machines Star Wars Classic Duels

68301 TIE Fighter vs. X-Wing Starfighter		
68302 TIE Interceptor vs. Millennium Falcon		

1997 Micro Machines Star Wars Double Takes

75118 Death Star (w/Millennium Falcon/Obi-Wan Kenobi/Owen Lars	30.00	80.00

Ronto and Jawas/Beru Lars/2 Scurriers

1997-98 Micro Machines Star Wars Flight Controllers

73417 Luke Skywalker's X-Wing Starfighter		
73418 Darth Vader's TIE Fighter	10.00	25.00
73440 Y-Wing Starfighter	8.00	20.00
73441 TIE Interceptor	8.00	20.00

1998-99 Micro Machines Star Wars Action Fleet Mini Scenes

68121 STAP Invasion (w/STAP/Jar Jar Binks/Battle Droid)	5.00	12.00
68122 Destroyer Droid Ambush (w/Destroyer Droid	4.00	10.00
Obi-Wan Kenobi/TC-14)		
68123 Gungan Assault (w/Gungan/Kaadu/Battle Droid)	4.00	10.00
68124 Sith Pursuit (w/Sith speeder/Darth Maul/Qui-Gon Jinn)		
79025 Trade Federation Raid (w/Trade Federation MTT	5.00	12.00
Ikopi/Jar Jar Binks/Qui-Gon Jinn)		
79026 Throne Room Reception (w/Throne Room	6.00	15.00
Sio Bibble/Nute Gunray)		
79027 Watto's Deal (w/Watto's Shop/Anakin/Pit droid)		
79028 Generator Core Duel (w/generator core	8.00	20.00
Darth Maul/Obi-Wan Kenobi		

1998-99 Micro Machines Star Wars Platform Action Sets

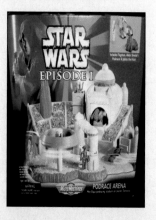

66541 Pod Race Arena	8.00	20.00
66542 Naboo Temple Ruins	6.00	15.00
66543 Galactic Senate	6.00	15.00
66544 Galactic Dogfight	10.00	25.00
66545 Theed Palace		
66546 Tatooine Desert		

1999 Micro Machines Star Wars Deluxe Platform Action Sets

66561 Royal Starship Repair	30.00	80.00
66562 Theed Palace Assault	100.00	200.00

1999 Micro Machines Star Wars Deluxe Action Sets

68156 Pod Racer Hangar Bay (w/pit droid and pit mechanic)		
68157 Mos Espa Market (w/Anakin Skywalker and C-3PO)	8.00	20.00
68158 Otoh Gunga (w/Obi-Wan Kenobi and Jar Jar Binks)		
68159 Theed Palace		

1999 Micro Machines Star Wars Mega Platform Set

66566 Trade Federation MTT/Naboo Battlefield	25.00	60.00

1999 Micro Machines Star Wars Pod Racer

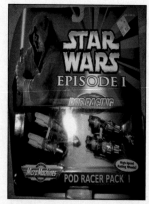

66531 Pack 1 (w/Anakin and Ratts Tyrell)	5.00	12.00
66532 Pack 2 (w/Sebulba and Clegg Holdfast)	5.00	12.00
66533 Pack 3 (w/Dud Bolt and Mars Guo)	5.00	12.00
66534 Pack 4 (w/Boles Roor and Neva Kee)	5.00	12.00
66548A Build Your Own Pod Racer Green (Galoob)	5.00	12.00
66548B Build Your Own Pod Racer Yellow (Galoob)	5.00	12.00
97023A Build Your Own Pod Racer Black (Hasbro)	5.00	12.00
97023B Build Your Own Pod Racer Blue (Hasbro)	5.00	12.00

1999 Micro Machines Star Wars Pod Racing Gravity Track

66566 Beggar's Canyon Challenge		
66570 Boonta Eve Challenge	15.00	40.00
66577 Arch Canyon Adventure		

1999 Micro Machines Star Wars Turbo Pod Racers

68148 Gasgano		
68149 Ody Mandrell		

2002 Micro Machines Star Wars Action Fleet Movie Scenes

32549 Dune Sea Ambush (w/Tusken Raider/Bantha/Luke's Landspeeder)	5.00	12.00
32553 Tatooine Droid Hunter (w/Dewback/Sandtrooper/Escape Pod)	6.00	15.00
32554 Imperial Endor Pursuit (w/Luke Skywalker	6.00	15.00
Scout Trooper/2 speeder bikes/AT-ST)		
32557 Mos Eisley Encounter (w/Ranto/Jawa/Black Landspeeder)	5.00	12.00

2015 Micro Machines Star Wars The Force Awakens Playsets

1 First Order Stormtrooper (w/Poe Dameron and transport)	6.00	15.00
2 Millennium Falcon (w/smaller Millennium Falcon and stormtrooper)	8.00	20.00
3 R2-D2 (w/Chewbacca/2 snowtroopers and transport)	5.00	12.00
4 Star Destroyer (w/Kylo Ren/Finn/X-Wing/TIE Fighter)	12.00	30.00

2015 Micro Machines Star Wars The Force Awakens Vehicles

1 Battle of Hoth (ESB)	5.00	12.00
2 Clone Army Raid (AOTC)	4.00	10.00
3 Desert Invasion	4.00	10.00
4 Droid Army (ROTS)	5.00	12.00
5 Endor Forest Battle (ROTJ)	6.00	15.00
6 First Order Attacks	4.00	10.00
7 First Order TIE Fighter Attack	4.00	10.00
8 Galactic Showdown	5.00	12.00
9 Imperial Pursuit (ANH)	4.00	10.00
10 Inquisitor's Hunt (Rebels)	4.00	10.00
11 Speeder Chase	5.00	12.00
12 Trench Run (ANH)	6.00	15.00

Comics
PRICE GUIDE

Marvel STAR WARS (1977-1986)

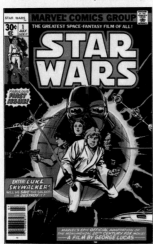

1	July 1977/"Star Wars: A New Hope" adaptation Part 1	75.00	200.00
1	July 1977/Star Wars 35-cent price variant	3,000.00	6,000.00
2	August 1977/"Star Wars: A New Hope" adaptation Part 2	20.00	50.00
2	August 1977/Star Wars 35-cent price variant	1,000.00	3,000.00
3	September 1977/"Star Wars: A New Hope" adaptation Part 3	15.00	40.00
3	September 1977/Star Wars 35-cent price variant	1,000.00	3,000.00
4	October 1977/"Star Wars: A New Hope" adaptation Part 4	15.00	40.00
4	October 1977/Star Wars 35-cent price variant	1,000.00	3,000.00
5	November 1977/"Star Wars: A New Hope" adaptation Part 5	15.00	40.00
6	December 1977/"Star Wars: A New Hope" adaptation Part 6	15.00	40.00
7	January 1978	8.00	20.00
8	February 1978	8.00	20.00
9	March 1978	8.00	20.00
10	April 1978	8.00	20.00
11	May 1978	8.00	20.00
12	June 1978/1st appearance of Governor Quarg	8.00	20.00
13	July 1978/John Byrne & Terry Austin cover	10.00	25.00
14	August 1978	8.00	20.00
15	September 1978	8.00	20.00
16	October 1978/1st appearance of Valance	6.00	15.00
17	November 1978	6.00	15.00
18	December 1978	6.00	15.00
19	January 1979	6.00	15.00
20	February 1979	6.00	15.00
21	March 1979	6.00	15.00
22	April 1979	6.00	15.00
23	May 1979/Darth Vader appearance	6.00	15.00
24	June 1979	6.00	15.00
25	July 1979	6.00	15.00
26	August 1979	6.00	15.00
27	September 1979	6.00	15.00
28	October 1979	6.00	15.00
29	November 1979/1st appearance of Tyler Lucian	6.00	15.00
30	December 1979	5.00	12.00
31	January 1980	5.00	12.00
32	February 1980	5.00	12.00
33	March 1980	5.00	12.00
34	April 1980	5.00	12.00
35	May 1980/Darth Vader cover	6.00	15.00
36	June 1980	5.00	12.00
37	July 1980	5.00	12.00
38	August 1980	5.00	12.00
39	September 1980/"The Empire Strikes Back" adaptation - Part 1	8.00	20.00
40	October 1980/"The Empire Strikes Back" adaptation - Part 2	8.00	20.00
41	November 1980/"The Empire Strikes Back" adaptation - Part 3	8.00	20.00
42	December 1980/"The Empire Strikes Back" adaptation - Part 4, "Bounty Hunters" cover w/Boba Fett	30.00	80.00
43	January 1981/"The Empire Strikes Back" adaptation - Part 5	8.00	20.00
44	February 1981/"The Empire Strikes Back" adaptation - Part 6	8.00	20.00
45	March 1981	5.00	12.00
46	April 1981	5.00	12.00
47	May 1981/1st appearance Captain Kligson	5.00	12.00
48	June 1981/Princess Leia vs. Darth Vader	8.00	20.00
49	July 1981/"The Last Jedi" story title on cover	12.00	30.00
50	August 1981/Giant-Size issue	6.00	15.00
51	September 1981	5.00	12.00
52	October 1981/Darth Vader cover	6.00	15.00
53	November 1981	5.00	12.00
54	December 1981	5.00	12.00
55	January 1982/1st appearance Plif	5.00	12.00
56	February 1982	5.00	12.00
57	March 1982	5.00	12.00
58	April 1982	5.00	12.00
59	May 1982	5.00	12.00
60	June 1982	5.00	12.00
61	July 1982	5.00	12.00
62	August 1982	5.00	12.00
63	September 1982	5.00	12.00
64	October 1982	5.00	12.00
65	November 1982	5.00	12.00
66	December 1982	5.00	12.00
67	January 1983	5.00	12.00
68	February 1983/Boba Fett cover	30.00	80.00
69	March 1983	5.00	12.00
70	April 1983	5.00	12.00
71	May 1983	5.00	12.00
72	June 1983	5.00	12.00
73	July 1983	5.00	12.00
74	August 1983	5.00	12.00
75	September 1983	5.00	12.00
76	October 1983	5.00	12.00
77	November 1983	5.00	12.00
78	December 1983	5.00	12.00
79	January 1984	5.00	12.00
80	February 1984	5.00	12.00
81	March 1984/Boba Fett appearance	12.00	30.00
82	April 1984	5.00	12.00
83	May 1984	5.00	12.00
84	June 1984	5.00	12.00
85	July 1984	5.00	12.00
86	August 1984	5.00	12.00
87	September 1984	5.00	12.00
88	October 1984/1st appearance of Lumiya	6.00	15.00
89	November 1984	5.00	12.00
90	December 1984	5.00	12.00
91	January 1985	6.00	15.00
92	February 1985/Giant-Size issue	8.00	20.00
93	March 1985	6.00	15.00
94	April 1985	6.00	15.00
95	May 1985	6.00	15.00
96	June 1985	6.00	15.00
97	July 1985	6.00	15.00
98	August 1985	6.00	15.00
99	September 1985	6.00	15.00
100	October 1985/Giant-Size issue	10.00	25.00
101	November 1985	8.00	20.00
102	December 1985	8.00	20.00
103	January 1986	8.00	20.00
104	March 1986	8.00	20.00
105	May 1986	8.00	20.00
106	July 1986	10.00	25.00
107	September 1986/Final issue	30.00	80.00

Marvel STAR WARS Annual

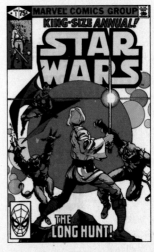

1	Star Wars Annual 1979	6.00	15.00
2	Star Wars Annual 1982	6.00	15.00
3	Star Wars Annual 1983	6.00	15.00

STAR WARS: RETURN OF THE JEDI MINI-SERIES (1983-1984)

1	October 1983/"Return of the Jedi" adaptation Part 1	4.00	10.00
2	November 1983/"Return of the Jedi" adaptation Part 2	3.00	8.00
3	December 1983/"Return of the Jedi" adaptation Part 3	3.00	8.00
4	January 1984/"Return of the Jedi" adaptation Part 4	3.00	8.00

JOURNEY TO STAR WARS: THE FORCE AWAKENS - SHATTERED EMPIRE (2015)

1	November 2015	1.50	4.00
1	November 2015/Blank Cover Variant	3.00	8.00
1	November 2015/1:20 Hyperspace Variant	3.00	8.00
1	November 2015/1:25 Movie Photo Variant	3.00	8.00
1	November 2015/1:25 Marco Chechetto Variant	5.00	12.00
2	December 2015	1.50	4.00
2	December 2015/1:25 Movie Photo Variant	4.00	10.00
2	December 2015/1:25 Kris Anka Variant	4.00	10.00
3	December 2015	1.50	4.00
3	December 2015/1:25 Movie Photo Variant	4.00	10.00
3	December 2015/1:25 Mike Deodato Jr. Variant	4.00	10.00
4	December 2015	1.50	4.00
4	December 2015/1:25 Movie Photo Variant	4.00	10.00
4	December 2015/1:25 Sara Pichelli Variant	4.00	10.00

Marvel STAR WARS (2015-)

1	March 2015	3.00	8.00
1	March 2015/Blank Cover Variant	4.00	10.00
1	March 2015/Skottie Young "Baby" Variant	3.00	8.00
1	March 2015/Luke Skywalker Action Figure Variant	6.00	15.00
1	March 2015/1:15 Movie Photo Variant	4.00	10.00
1	March 2015/1:20 Sara Pichelli Variant	4.00	10.00
1	March 2015/1:25 "Two Suns" Variant	3.00	8.00
1	March 2015/1:25 Bob McLeod Variant	4.00	10.00
1	March 2015/1:50 Alex Ross Variant	20.00	50.00
1	March 2015/1:50 J. Scott Campbell Variant	15.00	40.00
1	March 2015/1:100 Joe Quesada Variant	15.00	40.00
1	March 2015/1:200 Alex Ross Sketch Variant	30.00	80.00
1	March 2015/1:500 Joe Quesada Sketch Variant	75.00	200.00
1	April 2015/2nd printing	4.00	10.00
1	April 2015/3rd printing	4.00	10.00
1	June 2015/4th printing	4.00	10.00
1	July 2015/5th printing	4.00	10.00
1	September 2015/6th printing (double cover)	6.00	15.00
1	7th printing	4.00	10.00
2	April 2015	4.00	10.00
2	April 2015/Han Solo Action Figure Variant	30.00	80.00
2	April 2015/Sergio Aragones Variant	3.00	8.00
2	April 2015/1:25 Leinil Francis Yu Variant	6.00	15.00
2	April 2015/1:25 Howard Chaykin Variant	6.00	15.00
2	April 2015/1:100 John Cassaday Sketch Variant	20.00	50.00
2	May 2015/2nd printing	4.00	10.00
2	June 2015/3rd printing	3.00	8.00
2	July 2015/4th printing	3.00	8.00
2	August 2015/5th printing	3.00	8.00
2	6th printing	3.00	8.00
3	May 2015	2.50	6.00
3	May 2015/Obi-Wan Kenobi Action Figure Variant	2.50	6.00
3	May 2015/1:25 Leinil Francis Yu Variant	6.00	15.00
3	May 2015/1:100 John Cassaday Sketch Variant	15.00	40.00
3	July 2015/2nd printing	2.00	5.00
3	July 2015/3rd printing	2.00	5.00
3	4th printing	2.00	5.00
4	June 2015	2.50	6.00
4	June 2015/Chewbacca Action Figure Variant	2.50	6.00
4	June 2015/1:25 Giuseppe Camuncoli Variant	5.00	12.00
4	June 2015/1:100 John Cassaday Sketch Variant	15.00	40.00
4	2nd printing	2.00	5.00
5	July 2015	2.00	5.00
5	July 2015/C-3PO Action Figure Variant	2.50	6.00
5	July 2015/1:100 John Cassaday Sketch Variant	15.00	40.00
5	2nd printing	2.00	5.00
6	August 2015	2.00	5.00
6	August 2015/R2-D2 Action Figure Variant	3.00	8.00
6	2nd printing	2.00	5.00
6	3rd printing	2.00	5.00
7	September 2015	2.00	5.00
7	September 2015/Stormtrooper Action Figure Variant	2.50	6.00
7	September 2015/1:25 Simone Bianchi Variant Cover	3.00	8.00
7	September 2015/1:25 Tony Moore Variant Cover	3.00	8.00
7	September 2015/1:100 John Cassaday Sketch Variant	15.00	40.00
8	October 2015	2.00	5.00
8	October 2015/Tusken Raider Action Figure Variant	2.50	6.00
8	October 2015/1:50 John Cassaday Variant	6.00	15.00
8	October 2015/1:100 Stuart Immonen Sketch Variant	15.00	40.00
9	November 2015	2.00	5.00
9	November 2015/Star Destroyer Commander Action Figure Variant	2.50	6.00
9	November 2015/1:100 Stuart Immonen Sketch Variant	15.00	40.00
10	December 2015	2.00	5.00
10	December 2015/Jawa Action Figure Variant	2.50	6.00
10	December 2015/1:100 Stuart Immonen Sketch Variant	15.00	40.00
11	January 2016	2.00	5.00
11	January 2016/Luke Skywalker: X-Wing Pilot Action Figure Variant	2.50	6.00
11	January 2016/1:100 Stuart Immonen Sketch Variant	15.00	40.00
12	January 2016	2.00	5.00
12	January 2016/Greedo Action Figure Variant	2.50	6.00
12	January 2016/1:100 Stuart Immonen Sketch Variant	15.00	40.00
13	February 2016	2.00	5.00
13	February 2016/R5-D4 Action Figure Variant	2.50	6.00
13	February 2016/Clay Mann Variant	2.50	6.00
13	March 2016/2nd printing	2.00	5.00
14	March 2016	2.00	5.00
14	March 2016/Hammerhead Action Figure Variant	2.50	6.00
14	March 2016/Clay Mann Variant	2.50	6.00
14	April 2016/2nd printing	2.00	5.00
15	March 2016	2.00	5.00
15	March 2016/Snaggletooth Action Figure Variant	2.50	6.00
15	March 2016/1:100 Mike Mayhew Sketch Variant	15.00	40.00
15	May 2016/2nd printing	2.00	5.00
16	April 2016	2.00	5.00
16	April 2016/Death Star Droid Action Figure Variant	2.50	6.00
16	April 2016/1:25 Stuart Immonen Variant	4.00	10.00
16	April 2016/1:25 Leinil Francis Yu Variant	4.00	10.00
16	April 2016/1:100 Terry Dodson Sketch Variant	15.00	40.00
17	May 2016	2.00	5.00
17	May 2016/Walrus Man Action Figure Variant	2.50	6.00
17	May 2016/1:25 Leinil Francis Yu Variant	4.00	10.00
17	May 2016/1:100 Terry Dodson Sketch Variant	15.00	40.00

18 June 2016	2.00	5.00
18 June 2016/Power Droid Action Figure Variant	2.50	6.00
18 June 2016/1:100 Leinil Francis Yu Sketch Variant	20.00	50.00
19 July 2016	2.00	5.00
19 July 2016/Leia Organa: Bespin Gown Action Figure Variant	3.00	8.00
19 July 2016/1:100 Leinil Francis Yu Sketch Variant	15.00	40.00
20 August 2016	2.00	5.00
20 August 2016/Yoda Action Figure Variant	4.00	10.00
20 August 2016/1:100 Mike Mayhew Sketch Variant	15.00	40.00
21 September 2016	2.00	5.00
21 September 2016/Stormtrooper: Hoth Battle Gear Action Figure Variant	3.00	8.00
21 September 2016/1:100 David Aja Sketch Variant	20.00	50.00
22 October 2016	2.00	5.00
22 October 2016/Dengar Action Figure Variant	2.50	6.00
22 October 2016/1:100 Mike Deodato Sketch Variant	20.00	50.00
23 November 2016	2.00	5.00
23 November 2016/Rebel Soldier: Hoth Battle Gear Action Figure Variant	2.50	6.00
23 November 2016/1:25 Jorge Molina Variant	5.00	12.00
23 November 2016/1:100 Mike Deodato Sketch Variant	20.00	50.00
24 December 2016	2.00	5.00
24 December 2016/Lobot Action Figure Variant	2.50	6.00
24 December 2016/1:100 Mike Deodato Sketch Variant	20.00	50.00
25 January 2017	2.00	5.00
25 January 2017/IG-88 Action Figure Variant	2.50	6.00
25 January 2017/1:100 Mike Deodato Sketch Variant	20.00	50.00
26 February 2017	2.00	5.00
26 February 2017/2-1B Action Figure Variant	2.50	6.00
26 February 2017/Qui-Gon Jinn Action Figure Variant	20.00	50.00
26 February 2017/1:100 Mike Deodato Sketch Variant	20.00	50.00
27 March 2017	2.00	5.00
27 March 2017/R2-D2 with Sensorscope Action Figure Variant	2.50	6.00
27 March 2017/Star Wars 40th Anniversary Variant	4.00	10.00
28 April 2017	2.00	5.00
28 April 2017/C-3PO Removable Limbs Action Figure Variant	2.50	6.00
28 April 2017/Star Wars 40th Anniversary Variant	4.00	10.00
29 May 2017	2.00	5.00
29 May 2017/Luke Skywalker: Hoth Battle Gear Action Figure Variant	2.50	6.00
29 May 2017/Star Wars 40th Anniversary Variant	3.00	8.00
30 June 2017	2.00	5.00
30 June 2017/AT-AT Commander Action Figure Variant	2.50	6.00
30 June 2017/Star Wars 40th Anniversary Variant	3.00	8.00
31 July 2017	2.00	5.00
31 July 2017/Luke Skywalker: Bespin Fatigues Action Figure Variant	2.50	6.00
31 July 2017/Star Wars 40th Anniversary Variant	3.00	8.00
32 August 2017	2.00	5.00
32 August 2017/FX-7 Medical Droid Action Figure Variant	2.50	6.00
32 August 2017/Star Wars 40th Anniversary Variant	3.00	8.00
33 September 2017	2.00	5.00
33 September 2017/Bespin Security Guard Action Figure Variant	2.50	6.00
33 September 2017/Star Wars 40th Anniversary Variant	3.00	8.00
34 October 2017	2.00	5.00
34 October 2017/Han Solo: Hoth Outfit Action Figure Variant	2.50	6.00
34 October 2017/Star Wars 40th Anniversary Variant	3.00	8.00
35 October 2017	2.00	5.00
35 October 2017/Ugnaught Action Figure Variant	2.50	6.00
35 October 2017/Star Wars 40th Anniversary Variant	3.00	8.00
36 November 2017	2.00	5.00
36 November 2017/Leia Organa: Hoth Outfit Action Figure Variant	3.00	8.00
36 November 2017/Star Wars 40th Anniversary Variant	3.00	8.00
37 December 2017	2.00	5.00
37 December 2017/Rebel Commander Action Figure Variant	2.50	6.00
37 December 2017/Star Wars 40th Anniversary Variant	3.00	8.00
38 January 2018	2.00	5.00
38 January 2018/Michael Walsh Variant	2.00	5.00
38 January 2018/AT-AT Driver Action Figure Variant	3.00	8.00
38 January 2018/1:25 Pepe Larraz Variant	5.00	12.00
38 January 2018/1:50 Terry Dodson Variant	12.00	30.00
38 January 2018/Star Wars 40th Anniversary Variant	3.00	8.00
39 January 2018	2.00	5.00
39 January 2018/Imperial Commander Action Figure Variant	3.00	8.00
40 February 2018	2.00	5.00
40 February 2018/Star Wars 40th Anniversary Variant	3.00	8.00
40 February 2018/Luke Skywalker: Yavin Fatigues Action Figure Variant	20.00	50.00
41 March 2018	2.00	5.00
41 March 2018/Zuckuss Action Figure Variant	3.00	8.00
41 March 2018/Rey Galactic Icons Variant	6.00	15.00
42 March 2018	2.00	5.00
42 March 2018/4-LOM Action Figure Variant	3.00	8.00
43 April 2018	2.00	5.00
43 April 2018/Imperial TIE Fighter Pilot Action Figure Variant	3.00	8.00
43 April 2018/Poe Dameron Galactic Icons Variant	2.50	6.00
44 May 2018	2.00	5.00
44 May 2018/(Twin Pod) Cloud Car Pilot Action Figure Variant	3.00	8.00
44 May 2018/Captain Phasma Galactic Icons Variant	2.50	6.00
45 May 2018	2.00	5.00
45 May 2018/Bib Fortune Action Figure Variant	3.00	8.00
46 June 2018	2.00	5.00
46 June 2018/Ree-Yees Action Figure Variant	3.00	8.00
46 June 2018/Han Solo Galactic Icons Variant	2.50	6.00
47 July 2018	2.00	5.00
47 July 2018/Weequay Action Figure Variant	3.00	8.00
47 July 2018/Qi'ra Galactic Icons Variant	2.50	6.00
48 July 2018	2.00	5.00
48 July 2018/Bespin Security Guard Action Figure Variant	3.00	8.00
49 August 2018	2.00	5.00
49 August 2018/Emperor's Royal Guard Action Figure Variant	3.00	8.00
49 August 2018/Sheev Palpatine Galactic Icons Variant	2.50	6.00
50 September 2018	2.50	6.00
50 September 2018/David Marquez Variant	2.50	6.00
50 September 2018/The Emperor Action Figure Variant	4.00	10.00
50 September 2018/Thrawn Galactic Icons Variant	4.00	10.00
50 September 2018/1:25 Phil Noto Variant	5.00	12.00
50 September 2018/1:50 Terry Dodson Variant	12.00	30.00
50 September 2018/1:100 Terry Dodson Virgin Variant	30.00	80.00
50 October 2018/2nd printing	2.50	6.00
51 September 2018	2.00	5.00
51 September 2018/Chief Chirpa Action Figure Variant	3.00	8.00
51 September 2018/Jabba the Hutt Action Figure Variant	20.00	50.00
52 October 2018	2.00	5.00
52 October 2018/Lando Calrissian: Skiff Guard Disguise Action Figure Variant	3.00	8.00
52 October 2018/Ben Kenobi Galactic Icons Variant	2.50	6.00
53 November 2018	2.00	5.00
53 November 2018/Logray (Ewok Shaman) Action Figure Variant	3.00	8.00
54 November 2018	2.00	5.00
54 November 2018/Squid Head Action Figure Variant	3.00	8.00
55 December 2018	2.00	5.00
55 December 2018/Klaatu Action Figure Variant	3.00	8.00
55 December 2018/Cad Bane Galactic Icons Variant	2.50	6.00

Marvel STAR WARS ANNUAL (2015-)

1 February 2016	2.00	5.00
1 February 2016/Blank Cover Variant	3.00	8.00
2 January 2017	2.00	5.00
2 January 2017/Elsa Charretier Variant	2.00	5.00
3 November 2017	2.00	5.00
3 November 2017/Rod Reis Variant	2.00	5.00
4 July 2018	2.50	6.00
4 July 2018/1:25 John Tyler Christopher Variant	15.00	40.00

Marvel DARTH VADER (2015-2016)

1 April 2015	4.00	10.00
1 April 2015/Blank Cover Variant	3.00	8.00
1 April 2015/Skottie Young "Baby" Variant	2.50	6.00
1 April 2015/Darth Vader Action Figure Variant	3.00	8.00
1 April 2015/1:15 Movie Photo Variant	4.00	10.00
1 April 2015/1:25 John Cassaday Variant	5.00	12.00
1 April 2015/1:25 Whilce Portacio Variant	6.00	15.00
1 April 2015/1:25 Mike Del Mundo Variant	8.00	20.00
1 April 2015/1:50 J. Scott Campbell Variant	15.00	40.00
1 April 2015/1:50 Alex Ross Variant	20.00	50.00
1 April 2015/1:200 Alex Ross Sketch Variant	75.00	200.00
1 2nd printing	2.00	5.00
1 3rd printing	2.00	5.00
1 4th printing	2.00	5.00
1 5th printing	2.00	5.00
2 April 2015	4.00	10.00
2 April 2015/1:25 Dave Dorman Variant	5.00	12.00
2 April 2015/1:25 Salvador Larroca Variant	5.00	12.00
2 2nd printing	4.00	10.00
2 3rd printing	4.00	10.00
2 4th printing	3.00	8.00
2 5th printing	3.00	8.00
3 May 2015/1st appearance of Dr. Aphra, 0-0-0 & BT-1	10.00	25.00
3 May 2015/1:25 Salvador Larroca Variant	40.00	100.00
3 2nd printing	4.00	10.00
3 3rd printing	4.00	10.00
3 4th printing	4.00	10.00
4 June 2015	2.50	6.00
4 June 2015/1:25 Salvador Larroca Variant	6.00	15.00
4 2nd printing	2.00	5.00
4 3rd printing	2.00	5.00
4 4th printing	2.00	5.00
5 July 2015	2.50	6.00
5 July 2015/1:25 Salvador Larroca Variant	4.00	10.00
5 2nd printing	2.00	5.00
6 August 2015	2.50	6.00
6 2nd printing	2.00	5.00
7 September 2015	2.50	6.00
8 October 2015	2.50	6.00
9 November 2015	2.50	6.00
9 November 2015/1:25 Adi Granov Variant	6.00	15.00
10 December 2015	2.50	6.00
11 December 2015	2.50	6.00
12 January 2016	2.50	6.00
13 January 2016	2.50	6.00
13 January 2016/Clay Mann Variant	2.50	6.00
13 2nd printing	2.50	6.00
14 February 2016	2.50	6.00
14 February 2016/Clay Mann Variant	2.50	6.00
14 2nd printing	2.50	6.00
15 March 2016	2.50	6.00

15 April 2016/Clay Mann Variant	2.50	6.00
15 May 2016/1:25 Francesco Francavilla Variant	6.00	15.00
15 June 2016/1:100 Mark Brooks Sketch Variant	20.00	50.00
15 2nd printing	2.50	6.00
16 April 2016	2.50	6.00
16 2nd printing	2.00	5.00
17 May 2016	2.50	6.00
18 May 2016	2.50	6.00
19 June 2016	2.50	6.00
20 July 2016	2.50	6.00
20 July 2016/Inspector Thanoth Action Figure Variant	2.50	6.00
20 July 2016/"The Story Thus Far" Reilly Brown Variant	2.50	6.00
20 2nd printing	2.00	5.00
21 August 2016	2.50	6.00
21 August 2016/Tulon Action Figure Variant	2.50	6.00
21 2nd printing	2.00	5.00
22 August 2016	2.50	6.00
22 August 2016/Cylo Action Figure Variant	2.50	6.00
22 2nd printing	2.00	5.00
23 September 2016	2.50	6.00
23 September 2016/BT-1 Action Figure Variant	2.50	6.00
23 2nd printing	2.00	5.00
24 October 2016	2.50	6.00
24 0-0-0 (Triple-Zero) Action Figure Variant	2.50	6.00
25 December 2016/final issue	2.50	6.00
25 December 2016/Doctor Aphra Action Figure Variant	4.00	10.00
25 December 2016/Adi Granov Variant	2.50	6.00
25 December 2016/Jamie McKelvie Variant	3.00	8.00
25 December 2016/Karmome Shirahama Variant	3.00	8.00
25 December 2016/Salvador Larroca Variant	2.50	6.00
25 December 2016/1:25 Chris Samnee Variant	6.00	15.00
25 December 2016/1:25 Sara Pichelli Variant	6.00	15.00
25 December 2016/1:25 Cliff Chiang Variant	8.00	20.00
25 December 2016/1:50 Michael Cho Variant	20.00	50.00
25 December 2016/1:100 Joe Quesada Variant	40.00	100.00
25 December 2016/1:200 Joe Quesada Sketch Variant	75.00	200.00

Marvel DARTH VADER ANNUAL (2015-2016)

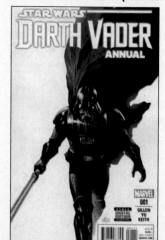

1 February 2015	3.00	8.00
1 February 2015/Blank Cover Variant	3.00	8.00

Marvel STAR WARS: THE FORCE AWAKENS (2016-)

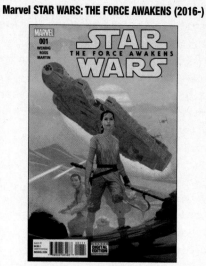

1 August 2016/"Star Wars: The Force Awakens " adaptation Part 1	2.00	5.00
1 August 2016/Blank Cover Variant	4.00	10.00
1 August 2016/1:15 Movie Photo Variant	5.00	12.00
1 August 2016/1:25 Phil Noto Variant	10.00	25.00
1 August 2016/1:50 John Cassaday Variant	12.00	30.00
1 August 2016/1:75 Esad Ribic Sketch Variant	20.00	50.00
1 August 2016/1:100 Joe Quesada Variant	150.00	400.00
1 August 2016/1:200 John Cassaday Sketch Variant	20.00	50.00
1 August 2016/1:300 Joe Quesada Sketch Variant	300.00	600.00
2 September 2016/"Star Wars: The Force Awakens " adaptation Part 2	1.50	4.00
2 September 2016/1:15 Movie Photo Variant	4.00	10.00
2 September 2016/1:25 Chris Samnee Variant	6.00	15.00
2 September 2016/1:75 Mike Mayhew Sketch Variant	30.00	80.00
3 October 2016/"Star Wars: The Force Awakens" adaptation Part 3	1.50	4.00
3 October 2016/1:15 Movie Photo Variant	4.00	10.00
3 October 2016/1:75 Mike Deodato Jr. Sketch Variant	30.00	80.00
4 November 2016/"Star Wars: The Force Awakens" adaptation Part 4	1.50	4.00
4 November 2016/1:15 Movie Photo Variant	4.00	10.00
4 November 2016/1:75 Mike Del Mundo Sketch Variant	30.00	80.00
5 December 2016/"Star Wars: The Force Awakens" adaptation Part 5	1.50	4.00
5 December 2016/1:15 Movie Photo Variant	6.00	15.00
5 December 2016/1:75 Rafael Albuquerque Sketch Variant	50.00	120.00
6 January 2017/"Star Wars: The Force Awakens" adaptation Part 6	1.50	4.00
6 January 2017/1:15 Movie Photo Variant	6.00	15.00
6 January 2017/1:25 Esad Ribic Variant	10.00	25.00
6 January 2017/1:75 Paolo Rivera Variant	30.00	80.00